LLOYD N. FERGUSON CHAIRMAN, DEPARTMENT OF CHEMISTRY, HOWARD UNIVERSITY

THE MODERN STRUCTURAL THEORY OF ORGANIC CHEMISTRY

PRENTICE-HALL, INC. ENGLEWOODS CLIFFS, NEW JERSEY

PRENTICE-HALL INTERNATIONAL, INC., *London*
PRENTICE-HALL OF AUSTRALIA, PTY., LTD., *Sydney*
PRENTICE-HALL OF CANADA, LTD., *Toronto*
PRENTICE-HALL OF JAPAN, INC., *Tokyo*

Prentice-Hall Chemistry Series

Current printing (last digit):

12 11 10 9 8 7 6 5 4

THE MODERN STRUCTURAL THEORY OF ORGANIC CHEMISTRY
by LLOYD N. FERGUSON

Portions of this book appeared in *Electron Structures of
Organic Molecules* by Lloyd N. Ferguson, copyright 1952,
by Prentice-Hall, Inc., Englewood Cliffs, New Jersey.

PREFACE

Organic chemistry made its first surge forward as an organized science about one hundred years ago when Kekulé and others devised a method of describing organic molecules in terms of structural formulas. This was called the *structural theory of organic chemistry*, and it greatly facilitated the interpretation and prediction of properties of organic compounds. The inadequacies of this theory were recognized gradually, and in time it was supplemented with the ideas of resonance, steric hindrance, induction, hydrogen bonding, atomic and molecular orbitals, and hybridization. For simplicity, we shall call this multi-effect approach the *modern structural theory of organic chemistry*.

The second period of rapid advancement of organic chemistry occurred during the second quarter of this century. During this time, the organic chemist gave increasingly more attention to the mechanisms of organic reactions, and now the trend is to classify reactions on a basis of types rather than in terms of functional groups or molecular structure. This has led to a clearer understanding of the behavior of reaction intermediates and of their roles in the course of chemical reactions. As a result, organic chemists have provided us with a synthetic kingdom which is comparable to the familiar mineral, vegetable, and animal kingdoms. That is, the organic chemist has given us many valuable synthetic substances which are as good or better than natural materials. For. instance, there are the plastics, the drugs, rubbers, insecticides, textiles, high temperature lubricants, paints, dyes, fertilizers, and others. These commodities have been important factors in raising man's standard of living and in bringing about the miraculous revolution in public health.

Overlapping the development of the modern structural theory of organic chemistry is another moderately successful method of describing organic molecules. It is a mathematical approach through the use of wave mechanics and adopting quantum concepts. Each of these theories, the modern structural theory and the wave mechanical theory aids the development of the other. However, most chemists are unable to use the latter method with dexterity, and until a better scheme is devised for describing molecules, the present-day structural theory will have to carry the load. Therefore, this book is an attempt to provide a unified up-to-date discussion of the applications of the modern structural theory of organic chemistry. It must be remembered, nevertheless, that this theory is only a qualitative approach. Quantum mechanical treatments, when applicable, are essentially quantitative and therein offer this distinct advantage. An additional benefit to be derived from this book, however, is a familiarity with the physical methods used for solving certain chemical problems such as structure determination, conformational analysis, and equilibria and kinetics study. It is not necessary that all students be experts in the theory and operation of even most of the physical tools, but each student should know which methods, i.e., infrared spectroscopy, X-ray diffraction, etc., should best provide an answer to his problem, and be familiar with the unique offerings of each. The various methods provide data which supplement one another in most cases but occasionally one method will be successful where others will not.

The second year of study of organic chemistry is normally along one of two lines. One is commonly called *physical organic chemistry* and the second, which is concerned with the determination of structure and synthesis of complex compounds resembling those of natural origin, is usually referred to as *natural products*. This book falls in the first category. Many excellent books on various phases of physical organic chemistry have appeared recently. This one differs by being written along the style of a textbook, and by placing its emphasis on the structure and dynamic charge distributions of molecules in the normal state rather than on reaction mechanisms. This latter topic is rarely discussed herein and the reader is referred to modern texts covering the subject.

This will be a descriptive discussion without quantum mechanical or molecular orbital treatments. Nevertheless, frequent advantage will be taken of the results of such works by other authors. Most of the topics discussed herein have been given more rigorous treatments elsewhere. However, essentially all advanced students study most of the topics found in this book, for which a single textbook should be quite useful. Furthermore, it discusses in depth many concepts taken for granted in more advanced books. Also, many practicing chemists might wish to review this subject, in which case the book could serve as an outline or starting point. Numerous references are given so that the reader, if he wishes, may read more detailed discussions on the topics taken up. Study questions appear at the end of certain sections to help the student become familiar with the concepts and principles presented in the text. In a very few instances, interpretations are sought for observed phenomena although no clear-cut explanations are readily apparent in terms of the Modern Structural Theory. This is done purposely to reveal some of the limitations of the theory and to allow the reader to apply his original thoughts to the field.

A single-authored book nowadays cannot help but omit some topics which others feel should be included. Therefore, the contents are to be regarded as illustrative rather than exhaustive or definitive. Furthermore, the discussion of some points may be overly long or too short. It is hoped that these weaknesses will not prevent the book from being useful to its intended readers—primarily seniors and first-year graduate students.

The accumulation of new data during the past decade, through the use of new and more sensitive instruments, has brought about a refinement of some earlier views and concepts. Also, there are sometimes two or more schools of thought in explaining certain phenomena. Such unsettled topics are pointed out to the student, for they reveal the very nature of progress in science.

The author does not presume to be a pioneering contributor to the field of physical organic chemistry. Rather, he has attempted here to weave together the work of many investigators into a unified treatment for presentation to students in textbook style. Thus, he has taken the role of a *historian* and not of a *history maker.* Accordingly, he acknowledges his indebtedness to the many superbly executed and almost divinely conceived explorations in the field made by those whose works have been cited herein.

LLOYD N. FERGUSON

CONTENTS

CHAPTER ONE: CHEMICAL BONDS

1.1 Historical development of structural and electronic theories of organic chemistry, 2.

1.2 Covalent bonds, 6.

1.2.1 Atomic orbitals, 6. 1.2.2 Shapes of atomic orbitals, 6. 1.2.3 Relative energies of atomic orbitals, 10. 1.2.4 Molecular orbitals and covalent bond formation, 19. 1.2.5 Covalent bond angles, 20. 1.2.6 Hybridization of bond orbitals, 21. 1.2.7 Multiple covalent bonds, 26. 1.2.8 Polycentric molecular orbitals, 28. 1.2.9 Covalent bond distances and covalent radii, 31. 1.2.10 Covalent bond energies, 39. 1.2.11 Bond length-bond energy relationships, 48. 1.2.12 Molecular absorption of energy, 49. 1.2.13 Magnetic susceptibility, 53.

1.3 Polar bonds, 57.

1.3.1 Ionic bonds, 57. 1.3.2 Ion-dipole bonds, 57.

1.4 Coordinate covalent bonds, 60.

1.4.1 Chelates, 62. 1.4.2 Methods of studying chelates, 64. 1.4.3 Bonding in chelates, 67. 1.4.4 Structural parameters, 78.

1.5 Molecular bonds, 88.

1.5.1 Metallocenes, 88. 1.5.2 Charge-transfer and sigma complexes, 103.

1.6 Hydrogen bonds, 125.

1.6.1 The nature of the H bond force, 127. 1.6.2 Effects of H bonding on physical properties, 136. 1.6.3 Effects of H bonds on chemical properties, 153. 1.6.4 Bonding in biological systems, 155.

1.7 Nonbonding intermolecular forces, 158.

1.7.1 van der Waals attraction, 158. 1.7.2 Dipole association, 159. 1.7.3 Inclusion compounds, 160.

CHAPTER TWO: ELECTRONEGATIVITY AND ELECTRIC DIPOLE MOMENTS

2.1 Relative atomic electronegativities, 172.

2.2 Relative group electronegativities, 182.

2.3 Ionic character of covalent molecules, 191.

> 2.3.1 Permanent and induced dipole moments, 196. 2.3.2 Vector addition of dipole moments, 199. 2.3.3 Applications of dipole moment data, 208.

CHAPTER THREE: INTRAMOLECULAR FORCES

3.1 van der Waals radii, 212.

3.2 Stereochemistry, 215.

3.3 Steric hindrance to internal rotations, 217.

> 3.3.1 Conformational analysis, 217. 3.3.2 Alicyclic systems, 230. 3.3.3 Isomerism and hindered rotations, 274.

3.4 Steric effects and chemical equilibria, 284.

3.5 Chemical properties and steric requirements, 294.

> 3.5.1 Esterifications, 294. 3.5.2 Additions to multiple bonds, 296. 3.5.3 Aromatic substitution, 297. 3.5.4 2,6-Di-t-butylphenols, 299.

CHAPTER FOUR: CHARGE DISTRIBUTIONS AND MOLECULAR PROPERTIES

4.1 The modern structural theory of organic chemistry, 306.

4.2 The concept of resonance, 308.

4.3 Resonance structures, 310.

4.4 Resonance energies, 317.

4.5 Hyperconjugation, 320.

4.6 Resonance and spatial configuration, 330.

4.7 Resonance and ionic character of molecules, 336.

> 4.7.1 Resonance and dipole moments, 336. 4.7.2 Dipole moments as criteria for resonance structures, 341. 4.7.3 Induction and resonance moments, 343. 4.7.4 Interaction resonance, 344. 4.7.5 Steric inhibition of resonance, 345.

4.8 Resonance and chemical equilibria, 349.

> 4.8.1 Dissociation of acids and bases, 350. 4.8.2 Dissociations into free radicals, 355. 4.8.3 Additions to multiple bonds, 366. 4.8.4 1,3-tautomerism, 368.

4.9 Aromatic character of cyclic compounds, 379.

4.9.1 Six-π-electron rings, 380. 4.9.2 Two-π-electron rings, 386. 4.9.3 Ten-π-electron rings, 387. 4.9.4 Eighteen-π-electron rings, 390. 4.9.5 The cyclobutadiene ring, 391. 4.9.6 Alternant and nonalternant molecules, 392.

4.10 Bonding in halobenzenes and alkylbenzenes, 393.

4.10.1 Halobenzenes, 393. 4.10.2 Alkylbenzenes, 401.

4.11 Electrical effects in substituted benzenes, 411.

4.11.1 The Hammet equation, 412. 4.11.2 Electrophilic and nucleophilic substituent constants, 416. 4.11.3 Inductive and resonance substituent constants, 418. 4.11.4 Polar substituent constants, 423. 4.11.5 Applications of Hammett-type relations, 424. 4.11.6 Correlations of physical properties with substituent constants, 428. 4.11.7 Conclusion, 433.

4.12 Homoconjugation and nonclassical resonance, 434.

4.13 Charge densities by theoretical methods, 443.

4.13.1 Bond order and free valence by the valence bond method, 443. 4.13.2 Bond order and free valence by the M.O. method, 445. 4.13.3 Molecular diagrams and chemical reactivity, 447.

CHAPTER FIVE: ABSORPTION SPECTRA

5.1 Spectroscopy as a tool, 460.

5.2 The electromagnetic spectrum and spectrophotometry, 462.

5.3 The origin of spectra, 464.

5.3.1 Infrared spectra, 464. 5.3.2 Raman spectra, 474. 5.3.3 Ultraviolet-visible spectra, 477. 5.3.4 Nuclear magnetic resonance spectra, 486.

5.4 Spectra-structure relationships, 493.

5.4.1 Resonance and spectra, 493. 5.4.2 Intramolecular environment and spectra, 510. 5.4.3 H bonding and spectra, 527. 5.4.4 Electronegativity and spectra, 541. 5.4.5 Polarizability and spectra, 545.

5.5 Applications of spectroscopy, 547.

5.5.1 Qualitative and quantitative analysis, 547. 5.5.2 Structure assignment, 554. 5.5.3 Identity confirmation, 564. 5.5.4 Study of complexes, 564. 5.5.5 Detection of transient products and study of reaction kinetics, 567. 5.5.6 Study of isomerism and confirmational analysis, 569. 5.5.7 Data for calculation of thermodynamic functions, bond distances, and dipole moments, 570. 5.5.8 Molecular weight determinations, 572. 5.5.9 Process control, 572.

AUTHOR INDEX, 581.

SUBJECT INDEX, 592.

TO MY WIFE

1.1 Historical development of structural and electronic theories of organic chemistry[1]

The first published distinction between organic and inorganic substances was made by Bergmann in 1780. Lavoisier showed four years later that all compounds examined from vegetable and animal sources contain carbon and hydrogen and frequently nitrogen and phosphorus. The complexity of constitution of organic compounds, their combustibility, and the fact that most such compounds stemmed from animals, led Berzelius, one of the most influential chemists at the beginning of the nineteenth century, to postulate that organic compounds contain a "vital force" which puts them beyond mortal synthesis from the elements. Wöhler's classic experiment in

---

[1] For more complete, interesting accounts of the history of chemistry, see H. M. Leicester, *The Historical Background of Chemistry* (New York: Wiley, 1956); J. R. Partington, *A Short History of Chemistry* (3rd ed.; New York: Macmillan, 1957); E. J. Holmyard, *Makers of Chemistry* (Oxford: Clarendon Press, 1945).

CHEMICAL BONDS

1828, in which he produced the recognized organic compound urea from the supposedly inorganic ammonium cyanate, started the downfall of this vitalistic theory.[2] After Kolbe prepared the naturally occurring acetic acid from its elements in 1845, Gmelin redefined organic chemistry as the chemistry of carbon-containing substances. This is the usual definition of organic chemistry accepted today.

One of the earliest theories on chemical bonding in organic compounds was Berzelius' *dualistic theory* in which he held that electronegative substances (oxygen or an acid) were united with electropositive substances (a metal or a base). Liebig and Wöhler recognized later (1832) that certain atomic groupings could be traced unchanged through a series of reactions, so these men described compounds in terms of organic radicals. Dumas showed, about this same period (1834), that the electronegative element

---

[2] Several articles have appeared debating the effect that Wöhler's experiment had on the downfall of the vital-force theory. Cf. D. McKie, *Nature,* **153,** 608 (1944); E. Campaigne, *J. Chem. Educ.,* **32,** 403 (1955); L. Hartman, *J. Chem. Educ.,* **34,** 141 (1957).

chlorine could replace in wax the electropositive element hydrogen, which led him to propose the *theory of types.* According to this theory, organic compounds were derived from certain basic inorganic types by substitution of organic radicals. For illustration, there were the four types, hydrogen, hydrogen chloride, water, and ammonia.

Hydrogen type	*Hydrogen chloride type*	*Water type*	*Ammonia type*
$\left.\begin{array}{c} H \\ \\ H \end{array}\right\}$	$\left.\begin{array}{c} H \\ \\ Cl \end{array}\right\}$	$\left.\begin{array}{c} H \\ \\ H \end{array}\right\}O$	$\left.\begin{array}{c} H \\ H \\ H \end{array}\right\}N$

and William's 1850 preparation of ethyl ether could be written:

Water type		*HCl type*		*Water type*		*HCl type*
$\left.\begin{array}{c} C_2H_5 \\ \\ K \end{array}\right\}O$	$+$	$\left.\begin{array}{c} C_2H_5 \\ \\ I \end{array}\right\}$	$\longrightarrow$	$\left.\begin{array}{c} C_2H_5 \\ \\ C_2H_5 \end{array}\right\}O$	$+$	$\left.\begin{array}{c} K \\ \\ I \end{array}\right\}$

Frankland first expressed in 1852 the concept of what is now called *valence,* and in 1858 Kekulé published his famous definitive paper on the chemical bonding of carbon. His thesis was (1) that carbon is tetravalent, (2) that a carbon atom can form bonds with other carbon atoms, thereby losing part of its capacity to unite with other elements, (3) that a carbon atom may form multiple-type bonds with another atom, and (4) that carbon atoms may form closed rings as well as open chains. In that same year, Kekulé and Couper independently introduced the use of valence bonds and the pictorial representation of molecules as connected atoms.[3] Couper's scheme is simpler than Kekulé's. Kekulé made what has been considered his greatest contribution to organic chemistry a few years later (1865): his proposal for the structure of benzene.[4] Our present-day concept is somewhat different; however, Kekulé's novel idea served as a nucleus for the crystallization of many unrelated ideas and facts of that period and initiated a strong development of organic chemistry.

Butlerov was the first to use the term *chemical structure,* and he emphasized that each organic compound has a fixed structure which determines its properties. Thus, the work of Kekulé, Couper, and Butlerov laid the

---

[3] William Higgins, in 1789, was the first to publish graphic formulas, but his intent was somewhat different from the intent today.

[4] Kekulé's contribution as a teacher was perhaps of equal significance. Among those who studied under him were Jacobus Van't Hoff (1852–1911), first Nobel Award winner in chemistry, Emil Fischer (1852–1919), second Nobel Award winner in chemistry, Adolf von Baeyer (1835–1917), fifth Nobel Award winner in chemistry, and Victor Meyer (1848–1897), a prominent organic chemist of the nineteenth century.

Kekulé's structural formula for
acetic acid (1861)

$$C \begin{cases} O & OH \\ O_2 \end{cases}$$
$$C-CH_3$$

Couper's structural
formula for acetic acid
(1858). He used 8
instead of 16 as the
atomic weight for
oxygen

foundations for the present-day practice of employing graphic structural formulas to represent molecules and interpreting molecular properties in terms of these formulas.

In the last half of the nineteenth century, tautomerism and geometric isomerism were attributed eventually to differences in spatial arrangements of atoms within molecules. Then, LeBel in 1874 and Van't Hoff in 1875 independently resolved the problem of optical isomerism on the basis that the four valences of carbon are directed towards the four corners of a tetrahedron. In 1888, Kehrmann advanced the notion of a mechanical obstruction of atoms to chemical reactions to which Victor Meyer gave the term *steric hindrance.* Werner presented evidence for the existence of *coordination valences* in 1891, and just after the turn of the century Oddu and Puxeddu introduced the notion of hydrogen bonds (1906).

Following Thompson's discovery of the electron (1897) and Lord Rutherford's description of a planetary, particle structure of atoms (1911), Kossel and Lewis independently proposed their electronic theories of valence (1916). Lewis also suggested the occurence of electron-pair bonds. Bohr announced his quantum theory of the atom in this same period. This led to the description of electrons in terms of the Schrödinger wave equation, and a new type of physics evolved: quantum and wave mechanics. Simple molecules could be described in terms of atomic orbitals from the work of Burrau, Hund, Pauli, Mulliken, Leonard-Jones, Hartree, Heisenberg, Heitler, and London. Then followed the ideas of the valence bond and resonance theories developed largely by Pauling and Wheland. Soon molecular orbital theory, including hybridization, made rapid advances through the early contributions of Condon, Coulson, Mulliken, and Moffitt. Over the past decade, the wide occurrence of molecular and charge-transfer bonds has attracted the attention of many workers, and a semitheoretical description has been given by Mulliken. Finally, the ligand field theory shows promise of extending the applicability of molecular orbital theory and furthering our understanding of chemical bonding.

Many persons have made significant contributions to the various stages of development of the structural and electronic theories of chemical bonding, and only a few of the major contributors who introduced new concepts have been mentioned here. Now we shall consider covalent bonding more fully in terms of present-day concepts.

1.2 Covalent bonds.   *1.2.1 ATOMIC ORBITALS*

In order to account for certain observed properties of the elements, such as their ionization potentials, magnetic susceptibilities, valences, redox potentials, complex-forming abilities, and chemical properties, the view has been developed that electrons move around atomic nuclei in discrete, successive, concentric volumes called *shells.* Each shell will accommodate a definite number of electrons, and the electrons are most likely to be found in certain regions within each shell, called *orbitals.* These orbitals are of four types,[5] distinguished by their geometric shapes and by the angular momentum which an electron exhibits when within one. The orbital types are referred to as *s, p, d,* and *f* orbitals, and in a given shell there are one *s,* three *p,* five *d,* and seven *f* orbitals. The successive shells, starting nearest the nucleus, are designated K, L, M, N, O, P, and Q, with corresponding principal quantum or energy reference numbers of 1, 2, 3, 4, 5, 6, and 7, respectively. Hence, the orbitals in the L shell are the $2s$ and the $2p$ orbitals (it will only hold 8 electrons, which can be accommodated by two s-and p-type orbitals), and the orbitals of the N shell are the $4s$, $4p$, $4d$, and $4f$ orbitals. The term $3d$,[8] for example, refers to 8 electrons in the d orbitals of the third or M shell. The family of orbitals of one type in a given shell make up what is called a *subshell.* Thus, the five $4d$ orbitals are in the same *subshell* of the N *shell.*

1.2.2 SHAPES OF ATOMIC ORBITALS[6]

The atomic s orbitals are spherically symmetrical about the nucleus as shown in Fig. 1.1. An orbital is an electron cloud and may be thought of as a specifically shaped *space* or volume within which electrons are most likely to be found. All s orbitals are spherical and concentric about the nucleus. Thus, the $2s$ orbital surrounds the $1s$ orbital, although the latter is now shrunken owing to the greater nuclear charge (see Fig. 1.2). In these figures, the populations of dots represent electron densities or electron clouds. They are only schematic and are not drawn in accordance with quantum mechanical calculations of wave function probabilities. Strictly speaking, one should refer to the probability density, but the electron-cloud density is a direct measure of the probability density. One supposes that

[5] Others are possible and would be used were the number of chemical elements at least 121.
[6] H. E. White, *Introduction to Atomic Spectra* (New York: McGraw-Hill, 1934), p. 63.

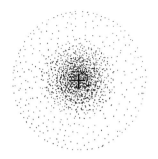

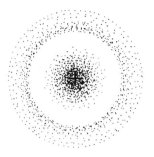

Fig. 1.1. Cross section representation of an atomic 1s orbital. The nucleus is designated by +.

Fig. 1.2. Cross section representation of a 2s atomic orbital.

at a given instant he could determine exactly where an electron is and indicate it by a dot. Then, if this observation were repeated many times, the resulting drawing would reveal the places where the electron is most likely to be found at any certain moment. Another useful interpretation is to replace the electron-cloud by a cloud of water vapor. The fog–density would then give a picture of the charge distribution.

A p orbital consists of two spheres not quite touching at the nucleus.[7] The three p orbitals in any given shell are mutually perpendicular, like the Cartesian coordinates, and are referred to as p_x, p_y, and p_z orbitals. Although distinct, they correspond to the same energy, i.e., they are *degenerate*. The d orbitals consist of four "almonds" around the origin and a fifth aligned on an axis [see Figs. 1.4(a) and (b)]. The d_{xy}, d_{yz}, and d_{xz} orbitals are directed towards points midway between the three axes. The other axial orbitals may be aligned along any of the three axes, but ordinarily the $d_{x^2-y^2}$ and the d_{z^2} are used.

It should be pointed out here that E. Schrödinger set up his well-known wave equation because he believed that one could describe the "position probabilities" of orbital electrons in a way similar to that by which one describes the motion of a point on a vibrating string. Schrödinger's equa-

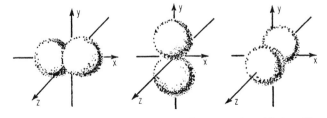

Fig. 1.3. Representation of p_x, p_y, and p_z, atomic orbitals. The nucleus is at the origin.

[7] I. Cohen, *J. Chem. Educ.*, **38**, 21 (1961).

d_{z^2}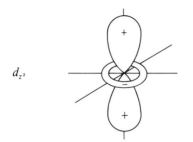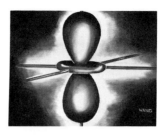

$d_{x^2-y^2}$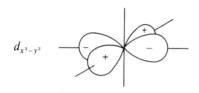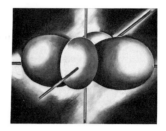

d_{xz}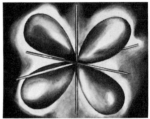

d_{yz}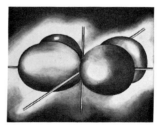

d_{xy}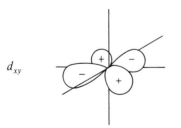

Fig. 1.4. (a) Shapes of d orbitals.   (b) Models of the five d atomic orbitals.[8]

[8] Redrawn from R. G. Pearson, *Chem. Eng. News*, June 29, 1959. Copyright 1959 by the American Chemical Society. Reprinted by permission of the copyright owner.

tion is a simple differential equation and has many mathematical solutions. However, most of these have no physical significance. We might compare them with a string vibrating in space: it has no usefulness. But, if the ends are fixed to stationary objects–that is, if boundary conditions are established–the string becomes a harmonic oscillator whose point-by-point positions can be described relative to a reference point. Similarly, in order to get meaningful solutions to the Schrödinger equation–solutions that predict energies, bond distances, etc., consistent with observed properties–certain conditions must be imposed. From this procedure there evolve four parameters called *quantum numbers.*

n = the principal quantum number, and is an approximate measure of the *size* of the electron cloud, i.e., the order of magnitude of the potential energy. It has the values 1, 2, 3, 4, 5, 6, or 7, corresponding to the K, L, M, N, O, P, or Q shell.

l = the azumuthal quantum number, and is related to the *shape* of the electron cloud, indicating whether it is that of a sphere or dumbbell or one more complex such as shown in Fig. 1.4. It may have values of $0, 1, 2, \ldots, (n - 1)$, corresponding to s, p, d, f orbitals. A $5p$ electron, for example, would have an n value of 5 and an l value of 1.

m = the magnetic quantum number, and is related to the *orientation* of the electron cloud in space. It may have values of $0, \pm 1, \pm 2, \ldots, \pm l$. For a spherical cloud there is only one orientation, of course, since all degrees of rotation look the same from a given point in space. However, the dumbbell-shaped orbital, for example, could be oriented at various inclinations to a set of Cartesian coordinates in space. Normally the direction of an externally applied magnetic field is used as the reference axis in space.

s = the spin quantum number, and indicates the *direction* of spin of the electron spinning on its own axis as a top. It can spin clockwise or counterclockwise, and therefore may have one of two values, set at $+\frac{1}{2}$ or $-\frac{1}{2}$.

These quantum numbers serve as characteristics in describing a given electron bound to the nucleus of an atom. One of the basic principles that applies here is *Pauli's exclusion principle,* which states in effect that no two electrons in the same atom may have an identical set of four quantum numbers. This is analogous to the principle in classical physics that no two bodies can be in the same place at the same time. For illustration, the two electrons of a helium atom, being in the $1s$ subshell, will have the lowest value of n and l, namely $n = 1$ and $l = 0$. Since m may not be larger than l, it too is zero. The s quantum number for one electron will be $+\frac{1}{2}$, and $-\frac{1}{2}$ for the other. Thus, the set of four quantum numbers for the two electrons are as shown in the following table.

n	l	m	s
1	0	0	$+1/2$
1	0	0	$-1/2$

Lithium, atomic number (Z) 3, has the electron structure $1s^2 2s^1$. The set of quantum numbers for the third electron is

n	l	m	s
2	0	0	$+1/2$

Actually the s quantum number could be plus or minus since the two spin states have the same energy. Going on to the next eight elements, the quantum numbers for the last electron in each element would be as follows:

		Orbital	Quantum numbers			
Symbol	Z	designation	n	l	m	s
Be	4	$2s^2$	2	0	0	$-1/2$
B	5	$2p^1$	2	1	$+1$	$+1/2$
C	6	$2p^2$	2	1	0	$+1/2$
N	7	$2p^3$	2	1	-1	$+1/2$
O	8	$2p^4$	2	1	$+1$	$-1/2$
F	9	$2p^5$	2	1	0	$-1/2$
Ne	10	$2p^6$	2	1	-1	$-1/2$
Na	11	$3s^1$	3	0	0	$+1/2$

Notice that the electrons take all possible values of m before two take the same value, i.e., before two "pair up." Two electrons having the same $n, l,$ and m values would occupy the same orbital and therefore repel each other more strongly than would two electrons having the same n and l values but different m values. In other words, electrons in the same subshell occupy different orbitals until all orbitals have least one electron.

1.2.3 RELATIVE ENERGIES OF ATOMIC ORBITALS

There is an electrostatic attraction between the electrons and the nucleus, so that the electrons will occupy orbitals as close to the nucleus as possible. The decreasing order of attraction of the nucleus for orbital electrons is $s, p, d,$ and f. Hence, there is a greater tendency for an electron to occupy a $2s$ than a $2p$ orbital, and a $2p$ rather than a $3s$ orbital. An electron in a given orbital represents a definite amount of energy. The situation has been explained[9] by means of an analogy to a stone on a series of shelves at different heights. The gravitational energy (potential) of the stone is greater the higher is the shelf, and it is released in the form of mechanical, heat, or other forms of energy when the stone falls to a lower-level shelf. We diagram on paper the stone on a shelf, or electron in an orbital, by placing

[9]D. DeVault, *J. Chem. Educ.,* **21,** 526, 575 (1944).

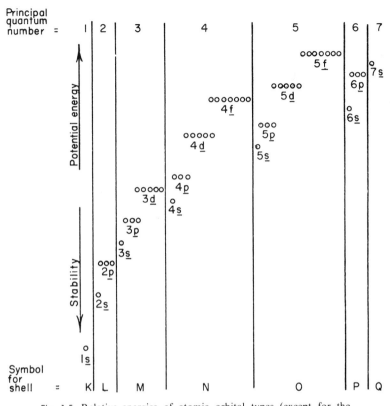

Fig. 1.5. Relative energies of atomic orbital types (except for the hydrogen atom). The circles represent orbitals which may be occupied either by one electron or by two of opposite spin.

horizontal lines at different heights. These lines may be called, interchangeably, *energy levels* or *orbitals*.

From experimental data, mostly spectroscopic and magnetic, and from theoretical considerations, the relative energies of the atomic orbitals are approximately as diagrammed in Fig. 1.5. Thus, the order of decreasing energy of attraction is $1s, 2s, 2p, 3s, 3p, 4s, 3d, 4p, \ldots$. Several empirical rules[10] have been developed to help the student reproduce this sequence without having to memorize it. The Wiswesser rule,[10(e)] referred to as the $(n + l)$ rule, has the closest relationship to theory and states[10(a)] that *in the successive building up of the electron structures of the elements as the atomic numbers increase, the electrons will enter the orbitals in order of the lowest*

[10] (a) B. Carroll and A. Lehrman, *J. Chem. Educ.*, **25**, 662 (1948); (b) L. M. Simmons, *J. Chem. Educ.*, **25**, 698 (1948); (c) R. W. Hakala, *J. Chem. Educ.*, **25**, 229 (1948); (d) P. Yi, *J. Chem. Educ.*, **24**, 567 (1947); (e) W. J. Wiswesser, *J. Chem. Educ.*, **22**, 319 (1945); (f) Y. Ta, *Ann. Phys.*, **1**, (12) 93 (1946).

(n + l) value, and when two levels have the same (n + l) value, the electrons will go into that orbital of lowest n value. The energy difference between states with different *l* and equal *n* values is, as a rule, smaller than that between states with different *n* values.

According to the *(n + l)* rule, to which there are very few exceptions, the order of increasing energy of orbitals is 1*s*, 2*s*, 2*p*, 3*s*, 3*p*, 4*s*, 3*d*, 4*p*, 5*s*, 4*d*, 5*p*, 6*s*, 4*f*, 5*d*, 6*p*, 7*s*, 5*f*, 6*d*, 7*p*, 8*s*, ... Notice that the 4*f*, 5*d*, 6*p*, and 7*s* orbitals each have an *(n + l)* value of seven, and accordingly are in order of increasing *n* values. The schemes of Hakala[10(c)] and Simmons[10(b)] to determine this same sequence are easy to remember and apply. The order of orbitals is obtained by following the nonintersecting dotted lines. Since *(n + l)* must always be positive, the smallest *n* value for *s*-type orbitals (for which *l* = 0) is 1; for *p*-type orbitals it is 2; for *d*-type, 3; and for *f*-type, 4. Accordingly, there are no 2*d* or 3*f* orbitals.

Table 1.1. GROUND-STATE ELECTRON CONFIGURATION OF THE ELEMENTS

KERNEL STRUCTURE	s^1	s^2	p^1	p^2	p^3	p^4	p^5	p^6	d^1	d^2	d^3	d^4	d^5	d^6	d^7
	1 H $1s^1$	2 He $1s^2$													
$1s^2$	3 Li $2s^1$	4 Be $2s^2$	5 B $2s^22p^1$	6 C $2s^22p^2$	7 N $2s^22p^3$	8 O $2s^22p^4$	9 F $2s^22p^5$	10 Ne $2s^22p^6$							
$1s^22s^22p^6$	11 Na $3s^1$	12 Mg $3s^2$	13 Al $3s^23p^1$	14 Si $3s^23p^2$	15 P $3s^23p^3$	16 S $3s^23p^4$	17 Cl $3s^23p^5$	18 A $3s^23p^6$							
$1s^22s^22p^63s^23p^6$	19 K $4s^1$	20 Ca $4s^2$							21 Sc $4s^23d^1$	22 Ti $4s^23d^2$	23 V $4s^23d^3$	24 Cr $4s^13d^5$	25 Mn $4s^23d^5$	26 Fe $4s^23d^6$	27 Co $4s^23d^7$
$1s^22s^22p^63s^2$ $3p^63d^{10}4s^2$			31 Ga $4p^1$	32 Ge $4p^2$	33 As $4p^3$	34 Se $4p^4$	35 Br $4p^5$	36 Kr $4p^6$							
$1s^22s^22p^63s^2$ $3p^63d^{10}4s^24p^6$	37 Rb $5s^1$	38 Sr $5s^2$							39 Y $5s^24d^1$	40 Zr $5s^24d^2$	41 Nb $5s^14d^4$	42 Mo $5s^14d^5$	43 Tc $5s^24d^5$	44 Ru $5s^14d^7$	45 Rh $5s^14d^8$
$1s^22s^22p^63s^23p^6$ $3d^{10}4s^24p^64d^{10}5s^2$			49 In $5p^1$	50 Sn $5p^2$	51 Sb $5p^3$	52 Te $5p^4$	53 I $5p^5$	54 Xe $5p^6$							
$1s^22s^22p^63s^23p^6$ $3d^{10}4s^24p^64d^{10}$ $5s^25p^6$	55 Cs $6s^1$	56 Ba $6s^2$							57 La $6s^25d^1$						
$1s^22s^22p^63s^23p^6$ $3d^{10}4s^24p^64d^{10}$ $4f^{14}5s^25p^6$										72 Hf $6s^25d^2$	73 Ta $6s^25d^3$	74 W $6s^25d^4$	75 Re $6s^25d^5$	76 Os $6s^25d^6$	77 Ir $6s^25d^7$
$1s^22s^22p^63s^23p^6$ $3d^{10}4s^24p^64d^{10}$ $4f^{14}5s^25p^65d^{10}6s^2$			81 Tl $6p^1$	82 Pb $6p^2$	83 Bi $6p^3$	84 Po $6p^4$	85 At $6p^5$	86 Rn $6p^6$							
$1s^22s^22p^63s^23p^63d^{10}$ $4s^24p^64d^{10}4f^{14}5s^2$ $5p^65d^{10}6s^26p^6$	87 Fr $7s^1$	88 Ra $7s^2$							89 Ac $7s^26d^1$						

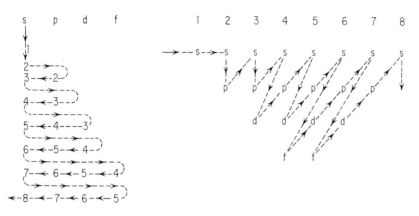

Hakala's array [10(c)]   *Simmons' array* [10(b)]

Table 1.1 (Cont.)

d^8	d^9	d^{10}	f^1	f^2	f^3	f^4	f^5	f^6	f^7	f^8	f^9	f^{10}	f^{11}	f^{12}	f^{13}	f^{14}
28 Ni $4s^23d^8$	29 Cu $4s^13d^{10}$	30 Zn $4s^23d^{10}$														
46 Pd $4d^{10}$	47 Ag $5s^14d^{10}$	48 Cd $5s^24d^{10}$														
			58 Ce $6s^24f^2$	59 Pr $6s^24f^3$	60 Nd $6s^24f^4$	61 Pm $6s^24f^5$	62 Sm $6s^24f^6$	63 Eu $6s^24f^7$	64 Gd $6s^25d^1$ $4f^7$	65 Tb $6s^24f^9$	66 Dy $6s^24f^{10}$	67 Ho $6s^24f^{11}$	68 Er $6s^24f^{12}$	69 Tm $6s^24f^{13}$	70 Yb $6s^24f^{14}$	71 Lu $6s^25d^1$ $4f^{14}$
78 Pt $6s^15d^9$	79 Au $6s^15d^{10}$	80 Hg $6s^25d^{10}$														
			90 Th $7s^26d^2$	91 Pa $7s^26d^1$ $5f^2$	92 U $7s^26d^1$ $5f^3$	93 Nr $7s^26d^1$ $5f^4$	94 Pu $7s^26d^1$ $5f^5$	95 Am $7s^26d^1$ $5f^6$	96 Cm $7s^26d^1$ $5f^7$	97 Bk $7s^26d^1$ $5f^8$	98 Cf $7s^26d^1$ $5f^9$	99 Es $7s^25f^{11}$	100 Fm $7s^25f^{12}$	101 Md $7s^25f^{13}$	102 No $7s^25f^{14}$	

The electron distributions for all the elements are given in Table 1.1. These distributions are consistent with the following five principles:

1. Each shell will hold up to $2n^2$ electrons, where n is the shell number or principal quantum number. There may be one s, three p, five d, and seven f orbitals in each shell, depending on how many are needed to accommodate $2n^2$ electrons.
2. The electrons will enter the available orbital of lowest energy.
3. In any one subshell, the electrons will tend to occupy separate orbitals (Hund's rule or the *principle of maximum multiplicity*).
4. Provided their spins are antiparallel, up to two electrons can be in the same orbital (Pauli's principle).
5. Subshells tend to become completely full or exactly half full of electrons.

The student will have numerous occasions throughout this book to see how these electron distributions permit an interpretation of molecular properties. Here we shall consider a single example, that of ionization potentials. As the electron structures predict [see Table 1.2 and Fig 1.6], it is more difficult to ionize helium (i.e., remove an electron completely by

Table 1.2. ELECTRON DISTRIBUTION AND IONIZATION POTENTIALS
FOR THE FIRST 18 ELEMENTS

Element	Number and type of electrons	$1s$	$2s$	$2p$	$3s$	$3p$	I.P. (volts)
H	$1s^1$						13.6
He	$1s^2$						24.6
Li	$1s^2 2s^1$						5.4
Be	$1s^2 2s^2$						9.3
B	$1s^2 2s^2 2p^1$						8.3
C	$1s^2 2s^2 2p^2$						11.3
N	$1s^2 2s^2 2p^3$						14.5
O	$1s^2 2s^2 2p^4$						13.6
F	$1s^2 2s^2 2p^5$						17.4
Ne	$1s^2 2s^2 2p^6$						21.6
Na	$1s^2 2s^2 2p^6 3s^1$						5.2
Mg	$1s^2 2s^2 2p^6 3s^2$						7.6
Al	$1s^2 2s^2 2p^6 3s^2 3p^1$						6.0
Si	$1s^2 2s^2 2p^6 3s^2 3p^2$						8.1
P	$1s^2 2s^2 2p^6 3s^2 3p^3$						11.0
S	$1s^2 2s^2 2p^6 3s^2 3p^4$						10.4
Cl	$1s^2 2s^2 2p^6 3s^2 3p^5$						13.0
A	$1s^2 2s^2 2p^6 3s^2 3p^6$						15.8

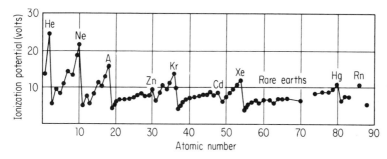

Fig. 1.6. Ionization potentials of the elements.

heat, bombardment, or electric discharge) than hydrogen although their electrons are approximately equally distant from the nuclei, because the electrons of helium are held more firmly by the larger positive nuclear charge. The same order is found for lithium and beryllium whose outer electrons are in a 2*s* orbital, but because of the greater distance from the nuclei and in spite of the larger nuclear charges, the electrons are more easily removed from the 2*s* orbitals than from the 1*s* orbitals of hydrogen and helium. The ionization potential of the next element, boron, is a little smaller than that of beryllium owing to the greater distance of the 2*p* orbital from the nucleus. The potentials of carbon and nitrogen increase over that of boron because of the greater nuclear charges. However, the 2*p* orbitals of nitrogen are half-filled, whereas those of oxygen are more than half-filled. In spite of the greater nuclear charge of oxygen, it is easier to remove an electron from oxygen than nitrogen because by removing one of the paired 2*p* electrons of oxygen, there results the favored arrangement of a completely half-filled subshell. This observation supports principle 5 on p. 14. Similarly, chromium has the valence shell distribution of $3d^5\ 4s^1$ rather than $3d^4\ 4s^2$ as would be expected on the basis of the distribution of the preceding element vanadium ($3d^3\ 4s^2$). However, in accordance with principle 5 above, greater stabilization results when the two subshells are each half-filled than when one is completely filled and the other neither completely filled nor half-filled. This principle also accounts for the electron distribution of other elements, e.g., copper, silver, gold, palladium, etc. Generally, a filled *d* subshell takes preference over a filled *s* subshell.

Note that the sequence of relative stabilities of orbitals given in Fig. 1.5 refers only to the last electron added to each element. Thus, the 4*s* orbital is more stable than the 3*d* for the atoms with nuclear charge less than 20 (calcium), but for all larger nuclear charges the 3*d* orbitals are more stable than the 4*s*. Beginning with element 21, the shielding by inner electrons and other forces make the more distant 4*s* orbitals less stable than the 3*d*. Consequently, for atoms of elements 21 to 30, for example, a 4*s* electron is the easiest to pull away from the atom. Similarly, 5*s* orbitals are more stable than $4d$ orbitals up to elements 38, but beginning with element 39 the reverse is true.

An atom becomes temporarily "excited" when by the influence of heat or an electric discharge one of its electrons is moved from the normal condition (the ground state) to a higher energy state, e.g., $2s$ to $3p$, or $3p$ to $4s$. It is analogous to raising the stone from a lower to a higher shelf. When eventually the electron falls back to the orbital of lower energy, its loss in energy appears as light. This is the basis for determining the relative energy levels of the various orbitals. The characteristic spectral lines for an element result from the discrete amounts of energy released when the electrons of the excited atoms undergo transitions from various energy states to lower energy states. For example, the familiar yellow-orange light of sodium vapor lamps results when the outermost electrons in the excited atoms drop from the $3p$ to the $3s$ level (wavelength in angstroms = 12,395/energy in electron-volts).

The actual situation is not as simple as implied in the preceding paragraph. Because of the different possibilities for relative orbital and spin orientations among the valence electrons, atoms or monatomic ions in the same energy level may have slightly different energy contents, i.e., exist in different spectroscopic states. The various spectroscopic states are designated by term symbols based on the total angular momentum of each.[11] The angular momentum of an electron is a measure of its revolution about some axis through the nucleus. Often one studies effects in a magnetic field, and it is then convenient to choose an axis parallel to the magnetic field. A *magnetic* angular momentum of zero, then, would mean the axis of rotation is at right angles to the magnetic field.

The *orbital* angular momentum of an electron, m_l, indicates its angular momentum arising from its motion about the orbital. Obviously this depends upon the type of orbital involved. With l having values as defined on p. 9, m_l may have any positive or negative value equal to or less than l, including zero. Hence, for a given orbital type, there are $2l + 1$ values for m_l. For example, $l = 1$ for p orbitals, so that m_l may assume values of $+1$, 0, or -1.

The spin angular momentum of an electron, m_s is always plus or minus $\frac{1}{2}$. The quantum designations for these different types of momenta follow.

S = total spin quantum number
= sum of the m_s values for all electrons = $\frac{1}{2}$ the number of unpaired electrons.

L = resultant orbital angular momentum quantum number
= vector sum of the m_l values for all electrons (the resultant orbital angular momentum is zero for a filled subshell, hence only incompletely filled subshells need be considered in computing L).

[11] G. Herzberg, *Atomic Spectra and Atomic Structure* (New York: Dover, 1944), chap. 3.

J = total angular momentum quantum number = $L \pm S$ (the negative sign is used when a subshell is not yet half-filled).

j = $m_l \pm m_s$ for a given electron.

J may be computed from $L \pm S$ or from the resultant j's of all the individual electrons. The former scheme is used more for the lighter atoms.

The spectroscopic term symbols for atoms or monatomic ions in ground states, i.e., the states with largest L values, may be determined as follows:[12]

1. Write down the possible m_l values associated with incompletely filled subshells.
2. Place the electrons in these subshells with parallel spins until pairing becomes necessary, in such a way that the sum of m_l's has the largest absolute value.
3. Compute the S (Σm_s), L (Σm_l), and J values.
4. The symbol is used in accordance with $^{\alpha}X_{\beta}$, where
   α = the multiplicity = $2S + 1$,
   β = the J value,
   X = a letter[13] based on L, being S, P, D, F, G, H, I, ... for L equalling 0, 1, 2, 3, 4, 5, 6, ..., respectively.

For illustration, the term symbol for nitrogen with a configuration of $1s^2 2s^2 2p^3$ is obtained in the following way. Only the $2p$ orbitals are not completely filled, for which possible m_l values are $+1, 0$, and -1. The electrons are then assigned to these values in tabular form.

$$
\begin{array}{cc}
m_l & \\
+1 & \uparrow \\
0 & \uparrow \\
-1 & \uparrow \\
\end{array}
$$

This gives a total spin angular momentum S of $\frac{3}{2}$ and a resultant orbital angular momentum L of 0. The multiplicity is $2S + 1 = 4$, and J is $|L + S| = \frac{3}{2}$. Therefore, the symbol is $^4S_{3/2}$. Similarly, one gets $^3P_0$, $^3P_2$, and $^7S_3$ for carbon, sulfur, and chromium, respectively.

C, $1s^2 2s^2 2p^2$	S, $1s^2 2s^2 2p^6 3s^2 3p^4$	Cr, $1s^2 2s^2 2p^6 3s^2 3p^6 3d^5 4s^1$	
m_l	m_l	m_l (d)	m_l (s)
$+1$ $\uparrow$	$+1$ $\uparrow$ $\downarrow$	$+2$ $\uparrow$	0 $\uparrow$
0 $\uparrow$	0 $\uparrow$	$+1$ $\uparrow$	
$S = 2/2, L = 1, J = 0$	-1 $\uparrow$	0 $\uparrow$	
$^{\alpha}X_{\beta} = {}^3P_0$	$S = 2/2, L = 1, J = 2$	-1 $\uparrow$	
	$^{\alpha}X_{\beta} = {}^3P_2$	-2 $\uparrow$	
		$S = 6/2, L = 0, J = 3$	
		$^{\alpha}X_{\beta} = {}^7S_3$	

---

[12] N. W. Gregory, J. Chem. Educ., **33**, 144 (1956).

[13] Occasionally a Greek letter is used for X, e.g., Σ, Π, Δ, ... for S, P, D, ...

Corresponding subshells will not be identical in different atoms. Shielding effects of other electrons and different nuclear charges alter the orbitals in varying amounts, although the gross features will remain the same. The greater the nuclear charge, the closer will a given orbital be drawn towards the nucleus. For illustration, the outermost electron orbital for the ions Na^+, Mg^{++}, and Al^{+3} is the $2p$ orbital, and the orbital is completely filled in each case, yet the sizes decrease in the order named.

Ion	Diameter $(\overset{\circ}{A})$
Na^+	0.95
Mg^{+2}	0.65
Al^{+3}	0.50

The increasing nuclear charge exerts a greater attraction for the orbital electrons, which is reflected by the orbital size, the ionization potential, and other properties. For example, the energies of the $1s$ orbital about hydrogen and carbon are 13.6 and 284 electron-volts, respectively (1 ev = 23.06 kcal). That is, it is many times harder to remove an electron from the $1s$ orbital of carbon than from the $1s$ orbital of hydrogen. A table of corresponding atomic energy levels for the first 18 elements is given in Table 1.3.

Table 1.3. SOME ATOMIC ENERGY LEVELS (in ev)[14]

Element	$(n-1)s$	$(n-1)p$	ns	np	nd	$(n+1)s$
H			**13.6**[a]			3.40
He			**24.6**			4.77
Li	64.4		**5.39**	3.54		2.02
Be			**9.32**	6.60		2.87
B			12.9	**8.30**		3.34
C	284		16.6	**11.3**		3.77
N	400		20.4	**14.5**		4.22
O	531		28.4	**13.6**		4.47
F			37.8	**17.4**		4.73
Na		38.0	**5.14**	3.04	1.52	1.95
Mg	62.8	49.8	**7.64**	4.94	1.89	2.54
Al	86.9	72.9	10.6	**5.98**	1.96	2.84
Si		98	13.6	**8.15**	2.54	3.23
P		128	17.5	**11.0**	2.25	4.04
S		162	20.2	**10.4**	1.94	3.83
Cl		201	24.6	**13.0**		4.09

[a] Normal ionization potentials are given in boldface.

[14] H. H. Jaffe, *J. Chem. Educ.*, **33**, 25 (1956).

1.2.4 MOLECULAR ORBITALS AND COVALENT BOND FORMATION

Two hydrogen atoms may form a bond by allowing their *atomic s* orbitals to overlap. The electrons, formerly in separate atomic orbitals, may pair up to move about in the new orbital called a *molecular orbital.* Within this new orbital each electron is electrostatically attracted by two nuclei instead of one. As a result, the new system, the hydrogen molecule, is more stable than two separate hydrogen atoms by 103 kcal/mole. This is the bond energy, and it can be attributed to electrostatic forces.

When two atomic *s* orbitals combine, two *sigma* molecular orbitals are produced. In one, the time-average positions or electron density is concentrated between the nuclei and it is called a *bonding molecular orbital.* The other concentrates the electronic charge away from the zone between the nuclei and is called an *antibonding* molecular orbital. (See Fig. 1.7.) These molecular orbitals are called *sigma* orbitals because they are symmetrical about the line joining the two nuclei. Like atomic orbitals, molecular orbitals obey the Pauli exclusion principle in that only two electrons can occupy the same molecular orbital provided their spins are antiparallel.

A covalent bond arises when two atoms each donate one electron to form a shared pair in a molecular orbital; hence the covalence of an atom is determined by the number of orbitals about the atom that contain an unpaired electron. For example, from Table 1.2 one might correctly predict covalences of 3, 2, 1, and 0 for nitrogen, oxygen, fluorine, and helium, respectively.

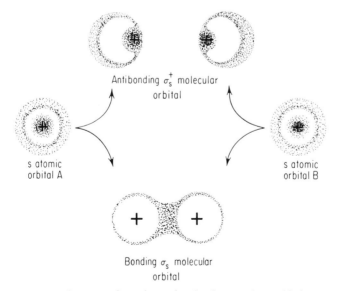

Antibonding σ_s^+ molecular
orbital

s atomic
orbital A

s atomic
orbital B

Bonding σ_s molecular
orbital

Fig. 1.7. Contours of atomic s and molecular σ_s and σ_{s^+} orbitals.

1.2.5 COVALENT BOND ANGLES

An s orbital is spherically symmetrical; hence it does not project in any direction. Thus, it can overlap another orbital equally in all directions and its bonding ability is equal in all directions. The p orbitals are mutually perpendicular to one another and, therefore, their overlap with other orbitals is greatest in directions normal to one another. Consequently, atoms using p orbitals such as those of nitrogen, oxygen, and sulfur would be expected to form bonds with interbond angles of 90° as illustrated in Fig. 1.8. By actual measurement, the H—S—H bond angle in H_2S is 92.3°.

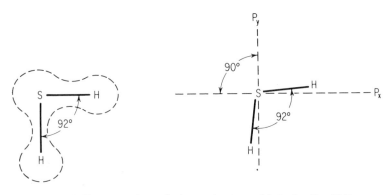

Fig. 1.8. Representation of the molecular orbitals in the H_2S molecule.

Oxygen, too, should form bonds making an angle of 90°, but the angle is larger in all noncyclic compounds of oxygen.[15] This apparent divergence from theory can be attributed to at least two factors: hybridization, and repulsion between the atoms or groups attached to oxygen. The first factor will be discussed in the next section and the latter factor here. There is considerable ionic character in the O—H bond, with hydrogen carrying a fractional positive charge and oxygen a partial negative charge. Although the hydrogen atoms in water are small enough to fit around the oxygen atom without "touching," the electrostatic repulsion between the hydrogen atoms spreads them apart to widen the H—O—H bond angle. When attached to the larger sulfur atom in H_2S the two hydrogen atoms carry smaller charges and are farther apart. Consequently, there is less repulsion between the H's, and the H—S—H bond angle is close to that expected theoretically. With larger atoms or groups, the bond angles of oxygen and sulfur are larger; however, the angles are usually smaller for sulfur than for

[15] Cf. (a) S. C. Abrahams, *Quart. Revs.*, **10**, 407 (1956); (b) M. K. Wilson and V. A. Crawford, *Ann. Rev. Phys. Chem.*, **9**, 339 (1958).

oxygen as shown below:

SOME —O— AND —S— BOND ANGLES[15]

H_2O –105°	HOD–104°	Cl_2O–110.8°	$HOCH_3$–108°
H_2S – 92.3°	HSD– 93.3°	Cl_2S–102°	$HSCH_3$– 96.5°
H_2Se– 91°			

The electron configuration of phosphorus, $1s^2 2s^2 2p^6 3s^2 3p^3$, and that of nitrogen, $1s^2 2s^2 3p^3$, show that both elements have three unpaired p electrons available for bond formation and should have bond angles of 90°. In PH_3, the H—P—H bond angles are 93.3, whereas in NH_3 the H—N—H bond angles are 106.7°. Here again, interhydrogen repulsion about the smaller nitrogen atom causes larger bond angles in NH_3 than is found for phosphorus in PH_3.

1.2.6 HYBRIDIZATION OF BOND ORBITALS

According to the electron distribution of carbon, $1s^2 2s^2 2p^2$, carbon should be bicovalent. However, in all stable compounds of carbon it is found to have a covalence of 4. To account for this fact, Linus Pauling proposed that atomic orbitals about an atom may merge or hybridize to form composite or hybrid orbitals. Thus, if carbon promotes one of its $2s$ electrons to a $2p$ orbital, the $2s$ and three $2p$ orbitals may merge to form four sp^3 hybrid orbitals containing one electron each. This process enables carbon to form four covalent bonds instead of only two, which produces more stable compounds. The energy required to promote the $2s$ electron to the $2p$ orbital is, according to the data in Table 1.3, about 120 kcal/mole. This energy is more than provided by the formation of two additional bonds permitted after the promotion and by the greater stability of sp^3 over s- or p-type bonds (see Table 1.4). The sp^3 hybrid orbital leads to stronger bonding than either an s or a p orbital because it extends out more in the direction of the attached atom, i.e., allows for greater overlapping of bonding orbitals. This is illustrated in Fig. 1.9. On the right side, towards an attached atom, the s and p orbitals are of like sign and complement each other, but on the left they are of unlike sign and diminish the portion of the resulting orbital there.

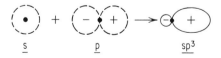

Fig. 1.9. Bounding surfaces of the cross-sectional view of s, p, and sp^3 orbitals.[16]

[16] C. A. Coulson, *Valence* (Fair Lawn, N. J.; Oxford U. P., 1952), p. 189.

Table 1.4. RELATIVE STRENGTHS OF BOND TYPES ACCORDING TO PAULING[19]

Type of orbital	Directional character	Relative strength
s	nondirectional	1.00
p	mutually orthogonal	1.73
d	slant edges of pentagonal pyramid	2.24
sp	linear	1.93
sp^3	tetrahedral	2.00
dsp^2	square planar	2.69
d^2sp^3	octahedral	2.92
dsp		3.00

The plus and minus signs assigned to orbitals have no physical significance but are used when mixing orbitals in order to determine the directional character of hybrid orbitals. Since s orbitals are spherically symmetrical, they cannot overlap as much as p orbitals and hence are weaker. For illustration, the bonds in Li_2 are largely s-type and in F_2 are chiefly p-type, and have bond strengths of 26 and 35 kcal/mole, respectively. For the same reason, various admixtures of s and p hybrid bonds should overlap more than pure s or pure p and should lead to stronger bonds. Calculations[17] and experiment[18] show that the relative bond strengths decrease in the order sp, sp^2, sp^3, p, s. Pauling and Sherman[19] proposed a different order of relative bond strengths, and although their method is a valuable one for ascertaining relative bond strengths of other types of hybrid orbitals, it does not give a satisfactory result for the s-p hybrid orbitals. Their values are given in Table 1.4.

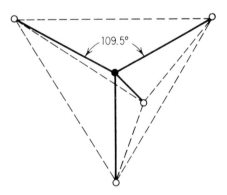

Fig. 1.10. Directions of four sp^3 hybrid orbitals (within a tetrahedron).

[17] A. Maccoll, *Trans. Faraday Soc.*, **46**, 369 (1950).
[18] A. D. Walsh, *Trans. Faraday Soc.*, **43**, 60 (1947).
[19] L. Pauling and J. Sherman, *J. Am. Chem. Soc.*, **59**, 1450 (1937).

It can be deduced that carbon does not promote its 2s electron to the 2p orbital and then form one s and three p covalent bonds, because then one bond would be different from the other three. To the contrary, it is well established that the four carbon bonds in a simple molecule such as CH_4 and CCl_4 are identical. Four identical sp^3 bonds point to the corners of a tetrahedron and therefore form angles of 109° 28' with each other (Fig. 1.10). This angle was known even before the advent of diffraction techniques. A tetrahedron fits inside a cube where apices are at opposite corners of the cube.

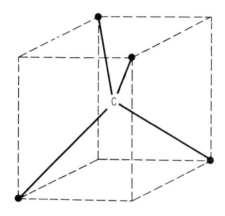

In a similar way, boron may promote one of its 2s electrons to a 2p orbital, and then the 2s and two 2p orbitals can merge to form three sp^2 hybrid orbitals. This accounts for the observation that boron is tricovalent rather than unicovalent. For instance, BCl_3 is a gas at room temperature; its melting point is − 107° and its boiling point, 13°. Hybrid sp^2 orbitals form coplanar bond angles of 120°. (See Fig. 1.11.)

If an s and a p orbital amalgamate to form two sp hybrid orbitals, each containing an electron, the hybrid orbitals have half s character and half

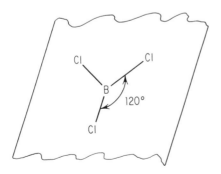

Fig. 1.11. Bond angles in BCl_3.

1.2.7 MULTIPLE COVALENT BONDS

Carbon can form sp^2 hybrid bonds as described in Sec. 1.2.6 for boron.

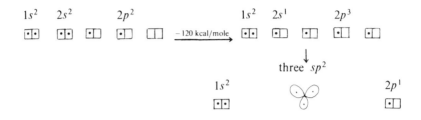

Following electron promotion and hybridization, there is a $2p$ orbital with an electron at the carbon atom. Two such atoms can form a bond through the overlap of an sp^2 hybrid orbital of each atom. Thus, in ethylene, each carbon atom uses three sp^2 hybrid orbitals: one overlaps the sp^2 orbital of the other carbon atom, and two overlap the s orbitals of two hydrogen atoms. Since three sp^2 orbitals are coplanar and form 120-degree bond angles, the three atoms attached to each carbon atom (2 H's and 1 C) are coplanar; hence all six atoms lie in the same plane. At each carbon atom there is a p atomic orbital perpendicular to the plane of the molecule and containing an unpaired electron, indicated by the propellor-shaped loop in Fig. 1.13. A more stable system results when the two p atomic

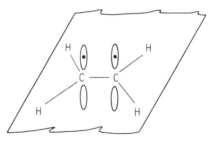

Fig. 1.13. Schematic representation of the atomic p orbitals in ethylene.

orbitals coalesce to form a molecular orbital which encompasses both nuclei. The resulting molecular orbital resembles two sausages above and below the plane of the molecule (Fig. 1.14). Such an orbital is called a *pi orbital* because of the nodal plane (i.e., a plane where the probability of finding the electron is zero) as is found in p atomic orbitals. The electrons involved are referred to as pi electrons (π) and the bond is called a π bond. Again, two atomic orbitals combine to give two molecular orbitals, a bond-

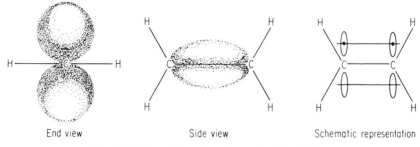

End view   Side view   Schematic representation

Fig. 1.14. Shape of the pi bonding orbitals in ethylene.

ing and an antibonding orbital (Fig. 1.15). The *p* atomic orbitals at two adjacent atoms will overlap most when they are oriented parallel to each other, but since even then the overlap is less than that of two orbitals which point towards each other, the pi-type molecular orbital is not as stable as a sigma-type molecular orbital. For instance, the energy of a carbon-carbon sigma bond is about 80 kcal while that of a carbon-carbon pi bond is only about 65 kcal. The π electrons are held less firmly and can be more easily dislocated or polarized (that is, attracted to either end of the molecular orbital by an external charge) than sigma electrons, so the pi electrons are commonly referred to as *mobile* electrons while the sigma electrons are said to be *localized.*

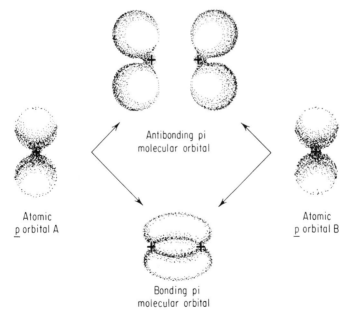

Antibonding pi
molecular orbital

Atomic
p orbital A

Atomic
p orbital B

Bonding pi
molecular orbital

Fig. 1.15. Contours of *p* atomic and pi bonding and antibonding molecular orbitals.

Pi bonds may occur between different atoms too. In an oxime $R_2C=$ N—OH, for example, sp^2 hybridization of two $2p$ and the $2s$ atomic orbitals takes place on nitrogen as well as on carbon. An sp^2-sp^2 sigma bond is formed between the two atoms, leaving a p atomic orbital on each atom to form a pi bond. The nitrogen atom thus uses two sp^2 orbitals to form sigma bonds with the carbon and oxygen atoms, and the third sp^2 orbital holds the nitrogen lone-pair. This sp^2 hybridization accounts for the C—N—O bond angle of 120° in oximes and for the existence of *syn* and *anti* isomers.

The description of a triple bond is analogous to that of a double bond. In acetylene, for example, sp hybridization occurs, with each carbon atom forming sigma bonds with a hydrogen atom and the other carbon atom. This leaves two $2p$ atomic orbitals at each carbon atom containing one electron each and perpendicular to each other. The parallel p orbitals on the carbon atoms coalesce to form two pi molecular orbitals. This gives the electron cloud a cylindrical symmetry, which can be diagrammed as in Fig. 1.16 Similarly, sp hybridization of the carbon and nitrogen atoms of an alkyl cyanide, R—C≡N, accounts for their linearity.

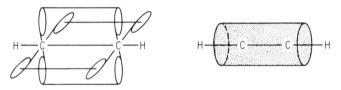

Fig. 1.16. Diagram of the molecular pi bonds in acetylene.

1.2.8 POLYCENTRIC MOLECULAR ORBITALS

In butadiene each carbon atom forms three sigma bonds. The two end carbons form two s-sp^2 bonds with hydrogen atoms and one sp^2-sp^2 bond with the inner carbon atoms, whereas the two inner carbon atoms form two sp^2-sp^2 bonds with the adjoining carbon atoms and an s-sp^2 bond with a hydrogen atom. At each carbon atom there is a $2p$ atomic orbital which is perpendicular to the plane of the molecule. As in ethylene, the $2p$ orbitals on the C_1 and C_2 atoms can form a dicentric π molecular orbital (one that encompasses two nuclei), and the $2p$ atomic orbitals on the C_3 and C_4 atoms may form a dicentric pi molecular orbital. Now, however, further stabilization results if a tetracentric π molecular orbital is formed encompassing all four nuclei (Fig. 1.17). If the double bonds were separated by more than one single bond, as in 1,4-pentadiene, the π molecular orbitals at the double bonds could not overlap and tetracentric molecular orbital formation, i.e., conjugation, would not occur.

Polycentric orbital formation in benzene is merely an extension of the

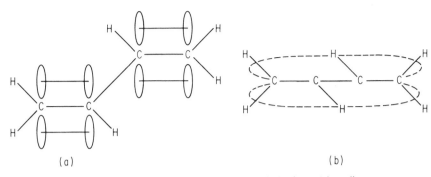

Fig. 1.17. Representation of molecular orbitals in 1,3-butadiene: (a) schematic dicentric π molecular orbitals, (b) tetracentric π molecular orbital.

process described above for butadiene. Thus, sp^2 hybridization of the atomic orbitals of the carbon atoms takes place upon bonding, and three σ molecular orbitals are formed, making angles of 120° to each other and producing a planar molecule. A p atomic orbital containing a single electron remains at each carbon atom, each perpendicular to the plane of the molecule. Since any two adjacent p orbitals may coalesce to form π orbitals, two equivalent conditions can arise, corresponding to the two Kekulé structures (Fig. 1.18). Again, additional stabilization occurs if a polycentric molecular orbital encompassing six carbon atoms is formed. This resembles two inflated inner tubes or two doughnuts, one on top of the other. Thus, reference is commonly made to the electron cloud above and below the plane of the benzene ring.

The p orbitals at the C atoms of benzene, instead of overlapping to form a set of three pi orbitals, as designated by Kekulé structures, could overlap to form two pi orbitals on opposite sides of the ring and leave a p orbital at each of the other two C atoms with an electron each. This arrangement is represented as

Any minute interaction between the two *para* atomic p orbitals to form an extremely weak pi orbital is equivalent to a *Dewar*[23] structure.

On the other hand, if an electron pair in one of the dicentric molecular orbitals of a Kekulé structure uses only the p atomic orbital at one C atom, it leaves an open p atomic orbital on the adjacent C atom. Since the elec-

[23] J. Dewar, *Proc. Roy. Soc. Edinburgh,* **6,** 82 (1867).

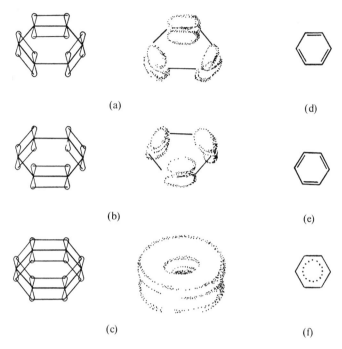

(a)   (d)

(b)   (e)

(c)   (f)

Fig. 1.18. Molecular orbitals or bonding in benzene: (a) and (b) dicentric molecular orbitals, (c) hexacentric molecular orbital, (d) and (e) Kekulé structures, (f) structural formula for the resonance hybrid of benzene.

tron pair now encompasses only one nucleus, the structure loses a certain amount of electrostatic energy and is therefore less stable than one of the Kekulé structures. This situation produces a higher electron density at the carbon atom with the filled orbital and a diminished electron density at the other carbon atom. Such a condition is diagrammed by a valence-bond structure as

Since each carbon atom has an even chance of being the one with the filled p orbital, two equivalent structures are possible.

These are referred to as ionic or polar structures of benzene. By migration of an electron pair from an adjacent double bond, there can arise two *para* ionic structures.

Consequently, two such structures are possible.

These structures are much less stable than the Kekulé structures and therefore make only a small contribution to the actual structure of benzene in its normal condition. That is to say that the actual structure of benzene more nearly resembles a Kekulé resonance hybrid structure than one of the ionic or Dewar structures. In resonance theory, then, the six π electrons of benzene can form three double bonds in one of two ways, and the structure of benzene is regarded as a hybrid of the two Kekulé structures. According to the molecular orbital theory, on the other hand, the six π electrons do not form three double bonds but move over the entire molecular frame and occupy in pairs the three π orbitals of lowest energy. Though the language of these two treatments differs, both predict two principal effects in the ground state: (1) complete delocalization of the π electrons to produce a sixfold symmetry so that all carbon-carbon bonds are equivalent and intermediate in properties between typical single and double bonds, and (2) additional thermochemical stability due to the delocalization process and measured as resonance or delocalization energy.

The formation of polycentric molecular orbitals, or conjugation, can take place to the greatest extent when the atoms are coplanar so that the p orbitals will be parallel and overlap to the maximum. Deviation from coplanarity sharply decreases the extent of overlapping of p orbitals and the degree of conjugation.

The atomic and molecular orbitals pictured in this chapter are attempts to give physical pictures to mathematical equations of quantum and wave mechanics. The quantum mechanical method is capable of answering or suggesting solutions to many puzzling molecular properties, but its application is limited by the difficulty of the mathematics involved and the complication of expressing in equation form the effects of all other electrons on each electron. The modern structural theory is less rigorous and is a qualitative scheme of describing molecules.

1.2.9 COVALENT BOND DISTANCES AND COVALENT RADII

Diffraction techniques (of X-rays, electrons, and neutrons) and spectroscopy (infrared, microwave, and polarized Raman), although highly specialized, are the most common methods for determining bond distances and angles in molecules. The experimental details and attendant difficulties cannot be described here.[24, 26] A brief account will be given of the principles involved, the results, and their significance.[25]

1.2.9(a) Diffraction Methods

This is the most direct of the physical methods of structure determination when it can be applied. When a beam of X-rays, electrons, or neutrons of wavelength 1–2 Å is allowed to impinge upon matter, the beam is scattered (diffracted) by the atoms in the molecules just as a diffraction grating diffracts a light beam. The scattered beam produces a pattern on a photographic film or other detector plate which must be interpreted in terms of the atomic arrangement within the sample. Noncrystalline samples give a pattern consisting of a series of concentric, diffuse rings, whereas crystalline powders yield sharp-ring designs. The presence of a large number of particles with all possible orientations accounts for the uniform density of X-rays in each cone. Fibrous samples give broad, elongated spots falling on curved lines perpendicular to the fiber axis. With single crystals, one obtains a series of concentric rings. X-rays may be used with solids, liquids, or gases, but organic chemists have more often used crystalline powders. Since the X-rays are scattered chiefly by the electrons of atoms, the scattering power of an atom is related to its atomic number.

Electron diffraction studies are done primarily with vapors because the charge on electrons diminishes their penetrating power. Nevertheless, any solid or liquid substance that is stable when vaporized to a pressure of a few millimeters of mercury can be studied. Also, solids can be studied in the form of films to yield transmission patterns, or in the form of powders by reflection techniques. The basic procedure is to have a well-collimated beam of monoenergetic electrons, accelerated by about 40,000 volts, intersect a fine jet of the vapor of the substance under study. The diffraction pattern is recorded on a photographic plate in preference to a film, because the plate does not shrink during processing. The scattering of the electron beam is done chiefly by the atomic nuclei, and because of their small scattering power, hydrogen atoms cannot be located precisely.[28] Electron diffraction has an advantage over X-rays in that good photographic exposures are made in a second or less while X-rays require several hours.

[24] For discussions on diffraction methods, see: J. Karle and I. L. Karle, "Electron Diffraction," and J. M. Robertson, "X-Ray Diffraction," in *Determination of Organic Structures by Physical Methods*, ed. E. A. Braude and F. C. Nachod (New York: Academic, 1955); O. Bastiansen and P. N. Skancke, *Adv. Chem. Phys.*, **3**, 323 (1961).

[25] J. C. Speakman in *Progress in Stereochemistry*, ed. W. Klyne and P. B. D. De la Mare (London: Butterworths, 1958), vol. 2, chap. 1.

[26] For discussions on spectroscopic methods, see: W. Gordy, W. V. Smith, and R. F. Trambarula, *Microwave Spectroscopy* (New York: Wiley, 1953); *Ann. Rev. Phys. Chem.*, **9**, (1958), and preceding volumes.

On the other hand, X-ray diffraction is advantageous for the study of complex and macromolecules which must be studied in the solid state. Normally, diffraction methods are not able to distinguish between optical isomers, but Bijvoet first showed how the absolute configuration of a molecule can be determined by X-ray analysis.[27]

An intricate equation has been developed which relates the intensity I of the scattered beam to the intensity I_0 of the initial beam. I is a function of all interatomic distances, bonded as well as nonbonded, and of the scattering angle ϕ. The problem then is to interpret the relative intensities and positions of the rings in the diffraction pattern in terms of molecular parameters. An attempt is made to find the best set of bond distances which will give a calculated intensity in agreement with the measured intensity. In the case of molecules whose gross structures have been determined by chemical means, methods of successive approximations to the true structure can be used. The computations are very arduous, but highly accurate results may be obtained. A formidable situation exists for compounds whose structures have not been determined by chemical or other physical methods. However, procedures have been worked out for restricting the I function that make it possible to reach satisfactory solutions. These methods involve mathematical transformations as well as the substitution of heavy atoms into the compound for "spotting." Bond distance values from diffraction methods are reliable to about ± 0.02 Å.

As already stated, the intensity of the diffracted beam is a function of the distances between all atom-pairs in the molecule, bonded and nonbonded. Thus, information is obtained not only on bond lengths but also about distances between nonbonded atoms and between neighboring molecules. For example, the conformers of 1,2-dichloroethane (cf. Sec. 3.3.1) can be distinguished, and by electron diffraction it has been estimated that at room temperature 1,2-dichloroethane consists of about 27 per cent *synclinal* (gauche) and 73 per cent antiperiplanar (*s*-trans).

In principle, then, X-ray diffraction is capable of revealing the entire structure of a molecule including not only bond lengths but the spatial arrangement of atoms making up the molecule. Although this ideal situation is not attained, it seems likely that significant approaches will be made in the near future. In the meantime, the structures of many important compounds will be solved by the present techniques.[29] Already, for ex-

---

[27] J. M. Bijvoet, *et al., Nature,* **168,** 271 (1951).

[28] Bond distances involving hydrogen atoms can be determined fairly well by neutron diffraction. Cf. G. E. Bacon and N. A. Curry, *Proc. Roy. Soc. London,* **A235,** 552 (1956); G. E. Bacon and R. Pepinsky in *Hydrogen Bonding,* ed. D. Hadzi and H. W. Thompson (New York: Pergamon, 1959), pp. 23–35.

[29] A. McL. Mathieson, *The Chemistry of Natural Products* (London: Butterworths, 1961), pp. 505 ff.

ample, with a foreknowledge of certain structural details, and in some cases by using the heavy-atom technique, X-ray analysis has provided conclusive structural evidence for many important substances such as strychnine,[30] cholesterol,[31] penicillin,[32] and vitamin B_{12}.[33] In at least one case, the formula of the alkaloid cryptopleurine was established without prior chemical knowledge about the substance.[34] For many reasons however, other physical methods will find extensive use for a long time.

1.2.9(b) Spectroscopic Methods

The theory of the absorption of light energy will be discussed in Sec. 1.2.12, but it can be said here that when a molecule absorbs energy of wavelength in the far infrared and microwave regions of the spectrum (Sec. 5.2), it undergoes certain molecular rotations. The frequencies of the absorbed energy corresponding to the transitions in rotational energy are related to the moments of inertia about some axis through the molecule; from this relationship bond distances may be derived. The accuracy of spectroscopic methods for bond distance determination, usually ± 0.005 to 0.01 Å, is greater than that for the diffraction methods.

1.2.9(c) Table of Bond Distances

Diffraction and spectroscopic measurements have yielded considerable quantitative information about the shapes and sizes of molecules during the past 30 years. A comprehensive compilation of the data has been published[35] including about 2000 substances, inorganic and organic, and giving a table of selected bond lengths accurate to ± 0.02 Å or better. Some of these values are listed in Table 1.6.

Table 1.6. SOME COMMON COVALENT BOND DISTANCES[35]

Bond	Distance (Å)	Bond	Distance (Å)
C_{sat}—C_{sat}	1.53	C—O	1.43
C=C	1.335	C=O	1.20
C≡C	1.206	N—H	1.03
C_{sat}—H	1.12	O—H	0.97
C_{arom}—C_{arom}	1.39		

[30] A. F. Peerdemann, *Acta Cryst.*, **9**, 824 (1956).

[31] C. H. Carlisle and D. Crowfoot, *Proc. Roy. Soc. London,* **A184**, 64 (1945).

[32] D. Crowfoot, C. W. Beeven, B. W. Rogers-Low, and A. Turner-Jones, in *The Chemistry of Penicillin,* edited by H. T. Clarke, J. R. Johnson, and R. Robinson, (Princeton, N. J.: Princeton University Press, 1949), p. 310.

[33] D. C. Hodgkin, *et al., Fortschr. Chem. org. Naturstoffe,* **15**, 167 (1958).

[34] J. Fridrichsons and A. McL. Mathieson, *Nature,* **173**, 732 (1954).

[35] *Interatomic Distances and Configurations in Molecules and Ions,* Chemical Society (London), Special Publication No. 11, 1958.

1.2.9(d) Covalent Radii

Pauling and Huggins[36] proposed that the length of a covalent bond, A—B, is the sum of the covalent radii, $r_A + r_B$ of the atoms A and B. For example, in ethane, chlorine, and carbon tetrachloride molecules, where carbon and chlorine exhibit their normal valences in forming essentially covalent single bonds, the bond lengths are given by the respective sums:

$$r_{C-C} = 0.77 + 0.77 = 1.54 \text{ Å}$$

$$r_{Cl-Cl} = 0.99 + 0.99 = 1.98 \text{ Å}$$

hence,

$$r_{C-Cl} = 0.77 + 0.99 = 1.76 \text{ Å}$$

which agrees with the observed C—Cl bond distance in CCl_4. Hence, with the assumption of the additivity of covalent radii, and from experimental bond distances in simple molecules where the bonds are essentially covalent, a set of covalent radii can be established. Some simple covalent radii are given in Table 1.7.

Table 1.7. SOME SIMPLE COVALENT RADII[37] (in angstroms)

Atom	Single	Double	Triple
H	0.37	..	..
Li	1.34	..	..
B	0.81	0.71	0.64
C	0.77	0.67	0.60
Si	1.17	1.07	1.00
N	0.74	0.62	0.55
P	1.10	1.00	0.93
O	0.74	0.62	0.55
S	1.04	0.94	0.87
F	0.72	0.60	..
Cl	0.99	0.89	..
Br	1.14	1.04	..
I	1.33	1.23	..

The covalent radii can be used only for first approximations because several structural factors affect bond lengths to produce significant variations from molecule to molecule. It is generally recognized that bond dis-

[36] L. Pauling and M. L. Huggins, Z. Krist., **A87**, 205 (1934).
[37] L. Pauling, *Nature of the Chemical Bond,* (3rd ed.; Ithaca, N. Y.: Cornell U. P., 1960), pp. 224, 228.

tances are affected by at least four factors:

1. Delocalization (resonance, hyperconjugation, conjugation).
2. Hybridization.
3. Electronegativity.
4. Steric conditions.

Rarely can any of these effects be demonstrated in the absence of the others although in some cases, the influence of some one factor is apparent. For example, as the electronegativities of the atoms attached to carbon in

$\diagdown$
—C—X increases, thereby increasing the electronegativity of the carbon
$\diagup$

atom too, the C—X bond contracts. Thus, the C—X bond in F_3C—X molecules is always shorter than in the corresponding H_3C—X molecules.[41] As the electronegativity of an atom increases, its valence electrons are drawn in closer to the nucleus and this decreases the effective atomic radius. Some additional examples are the following:[39, 41]

C—H[38]	
CH_3CH_2—H	1.102 Å
H_3C—H	1.094
Cl_3C—H	1.06

C—F	
H_3C—F	1.391 Å
F_3C—F	1.323

C—Cl	
H_3C—Cl	1.780 Å
H_2ClC—Cl	1.772
HCl_2C—Cl	1.763
Cl_3C—Cl	1.755
F_3C—Cl	1.72

Even the C=C bond may be shortened by the attachment of more electronegative atoms. Thus, the C=C bond length in C_2F_4 is 1.313 Å in comparison to 1.335 Å in C_2H_4.[40]

In many cases, bond shortening can be attributed to resonance delocalization (discussed in Chap. 4). However, it has occurred to a number of chemists in recent years that in evaluating bond contraction of the C—C bond relative to its length in ethane, that the effects of change in hybridiza-

---

[38] The average C—H distance in higher n-paraffins is 1.125 Å.

[39] W. F. Edgell, G. P. Muller, and J. W. Amy, *J. Am. Chem. Soc.,* **79,** 2391 (1957); J. L. Brandt and R. L. Livingston, *J. Am. Chem. Soc.,* **76,** 2096 (1954).

[40] I. Karle and J. Karle, *J. Chem. Phys.,* **18,** 963 (1950).

[41] L. S. Bartell and L. O. Brockway, *J. Chem. Phys.,* **23,** 1860 (1955). However, the chlorine atom is more easily dissociated in the CF_3 compound.

tion have been neglected.[42] That is, in calculating the bond contraction of the C—C bond in butadiene due to resonance, one should not use the ethane distance for reference but the natural length of a bond between two trigonal (sp^2-hybridized) carbon atoms.

A number of authors have shown that a carbon-carbon bond involving given states of hybridization has a fairly constant length irrespective of the types of adjacent atoms.[43-47] Some examples are given for illustration:

$$-\overset{|}{\underset{|}{C}}-C\equiv \qquad\qquad\qquad -\overset{|}{\underset{|}{C}}-C\overset{\diagup}{\underset{\diagdown}{}}$$

$CH_3-C\equiv CH$	1.459 Å		$CH_3-CH=CH_2$	1.501 Å
$CH_3-C\equiv N$	1.458		$(CH_3)_2C=CH_2$	1.505
$CCl_3-C\equiv N$	1.460		CH_3-CHO	1.501
$CH_3-C\equiv C-Cl$	1.458		CH_3-COF	1.503
$CH_3-C\equiv C-Br$	1.46		CH_3-COCN	1.490
$CF_3-C\equiv N$	1.461			
$CF_3-C\equiv CH$	1.464			
$CF_3-C\equiv C-CH_3$	1.455			
$CCl_3-C\equiv N$	1.460			
$Me_3C-C\equiv N$	1.460			
$CH_3CH_2-C\equiv CH$	1.4735			
$CH_3-C\equiv C-CN$	1.454			

Similarly, the C—H, the C—Cl, and other single bonds vary with the degree of hybridization of carbon:[46]

	C—H	C—Cl	C—Br
C_{sp3}	1.095	1.771	1.927
C_{sp2}	1.071	1.711	1.875
C_{sp}	1.058	1.631	1.795

Several empirical approaches have been used to compute the natural covalent radii of carbon in its different states of hybridization, and it can be observed in Table 1.8 that there is some variation in results.[47] The diamond value of 1.544 Å is commonly used for the $C_{sp3}-C_{sp3}$ bond length although

[42]C. A. Coulson, *Valence* (Fair Lawn N. J.: Oxford U. P., 1952); M. J. S. Dewar and H. N. Schmeising, "Conference on Hyperconjugation," Indiana University, June, 1958; H. A. Bent, J. Chem. Educ., **37**, 616 (1960).

[43]G. Herzberg and B. P. Stoicheff, Nature, **175**, 79 (1955); W. Zeil and J. F. Pfrommer, Z. Elektrochem., **61**, 938 (1957).

[44]W. Zeil, Angew. Chem., **73**, 171 (1961).

[45]R. L. Livingston and C. N. R. Rao, *J. Am. Chem. Soc.*, **81**, 3584 (1959).

[46]M. G. Brown, Trans. Faraday Soc., **55**, 694 (1959).

[47]N. S. Ham, *Revs. Pure and Applied Chem.*, **11**, 159 (1961).

Table 1.8. PROPOSED LENGTHS OF C—C BONDS IN DIFFERENT
STATES OF HYBRIDIZATION

Method	sp^3—sp^2	sp^2—sp^2	sp^3—sp	sp^2—sp	sp—sp
Experimental average[46]	1.510	1.466	1.456	1.432	1.374
Brown[46]...............................	1.505	1.466	1.459	1.420	1.374
Bernstein[48]; Costain-Stoicheff[49].......	1.502	1.460	1.466	1.418	1.376
Dewar-Schmeising[42]	1.516	1.488	1.460	1.432	1.376
Pauling, Springhall and Palmer[50a] ...	1.53	1.52	1.52	1.51	1.50
Pauling[50b]	1.52	1.50	1.50	1.48	1.46
Coulson[52]; Bak and Hansen-Nygaard[53]	1.531	1.517	1.505	1.492	1.467
Zeil[44].................................	1.506	1.470	1.461	1.425	1.380
Mulliken[54]............................	1.51	1.51	1.485	...	1.45

it has been pointed out recently that the actual value in alkanes is closer to 1.526 Å.[51]

One of the major obstacles in refining theories about chemical bonds is the indeterminacy of experimental data. This is an important point because, as has been said before, bond lengths are used as the most reliable molecular property for providing an insight into the nature of chemical bonds. The situation is worsened by the practice of comparing data obtained by different experimental techniques. For illustration, there are obtained from spectroscopic techniques what is called r_0, a value which reproduces ground state moments of inertia, and r_s, the so-called spectroscopic distance. From diffraction techniques there are reported r_m values, from the maxima in radial distribution curves, and r_g values from the centers of gravity of the peaks in the curves. By definition there is an r_e value which represents the equilibrium distance between vibrating atoms. These several definitive bond distances differ to some extent. Thus, for the C—H bond in CH_4, r_0, the spectroscopic ground state mean, r_g the ground state mean and r_e, the equilibrium distance, are respectively, 1.094 Å, 1.107 Å, and 1.085 Å. It has been pointed out that distances for a given bond when determined by different methods may differ more than the experimental accuracy of the methods themselves.[51] Hence, when looking for

[48] H. J. Bernstein, J. Phys. Chem., 63, 565 (1959).

[49] C. C. Costain and B. P. Stoicheff, J. Chem. Phys., 30, 777 (1959).

[50] (a) L. Pauling, H. D. Springall, and K. J. Palmer, J. Am. Chem. Soc., 61, 927 (1939); (b) L. Pauling, Nature of the Chemical Bond.

[51] D. R. Lide, Jr., Tetrahedron, 17, 125 (1962).

[52] C. A. Coulson, V. Henri Memorial Volume (Liege: Desoer, 1948).

[53] B. Bak and L. Hansen-Nygaard, J. Chem. Phys., 33, 418 (1960).

[54] R. S. Mulliken, Tetrahedron, 6, 68 (1959).

small variations in bond lengths, comparisons should be made with data determined by a single experimental technique.

From a critical survey of the most accurate data available, covalent radii for carbon in the tetrahedral, trigonal, and digonal states of hybridization have been recommended as follows:[51]

	Radius
C_{sp^3}	0.763 Å
C_{sp^2}	0.743
C_{sp}	0.691

1.2.10 COVALENT BOND ENERGIES[55]

Before discussing the strengths of covalent bonds, we should have a working definition of a chemical bond. Since a chemist is interested in molecular species whose structures and composition are reproducible and are sufficiently stable to permit observations of their behavior under chosen conditions, a logical definition is the following. *A chemical bond exists between two or more atoms when the forces acting between them are of sufficient strength that the group maintains its integrity under specified or assumed conditions.* On this basis, the minimum attractive force to be considered a chemical bond at room temperature is about 2 kcal/mole. Most covalent bonds have 30 to 50 times this strength, but several types of bonds will be described in Sec. 1.4 having strengths of this order of magnitude.

Although covalent bonds were described in earlier sections of this chapter in terms of molecular orbitals, the most useful physical picture or analogy for these bonds is that of a steel spring. Thus, covalent bonds have direction, tensile strength, elasticity, and resistance to stretching and bending (deformation). It follows that Hooke's law for a harmonic oscillator should be applicable to covalent bonds, and force constants assigned according to the equation $F = -kx$, where F is the force required to stretch a bond the distance x, and k is the *restoring force constant*. More will be said in Chap. 5 about the determination of bond force constants; the idea is introduced here because force constants will be mentioned occasionally before the topic of spectroscopy is taken up.

There are at least three conceivable ways of assessing the strengths of covalent bonds–in terms of

1. The energy required to stretch a bond until it snaps. This is normally called the *dissociation energy*.

[55]For a recent review and references to previous reviews, see B. E. Knox and H. B. Palmer, *Chem. Revs.*, **61**, 247 (1961); A. H. Sehon and M. Szwarc, *Ann. Rev. Phys. Chem.*, **8**, 439 (1957).

2. an energy quantity associated with each bond as it exists in a molecule, called the *bond energy*, which represents the contribution of the
bond to the total binding energy present in the molecule. Thus, the
summation of bond energies of all bonds in a molecule gives the
heat of formation of the molecule from its atoms.
3. the force it takes to stretch a given bond an infinitesimal amount.
This evaluation is in terms of bond force constants.

Since chemical changes involve the making and breaking of bonds, a
knowledge of the resistance of a bond to small alterations in length is not
adequate for most purposes. Consequently, bond force constants do not
offer a satisfactory scale, and bond dissociation energies and bond energy
terms constitute the most commonly used bases for evaluating bond
strengths. There are several experimental methods for measuring these two
quantities. However, before considering the principles on which the experimental techniques are based, let us examine further the limitations of
these two interpretations of bond strength.

First, let us point out that other methods have been proposed for assessing bond strengths. One suggestion[56] was to use ionization potentials of
bonding electrons. It was argued that the more tightly the electrons are
bound, the stronger is the bond and the higher is the ionization potential.
Another scale was based on a relationship with bond distances, the bond
strength varying inversely with bond distance.[57] Such methods can be
highly precise in certain cases, but they do not lend themselves to wide
applicability.

The dissociation energy, $D(\text{R}-\text{X})$, of a bond R—X is the energy
change for the reaction

$$\text{R}-\text{X} \longrightarrow \overset{.}{\text{R}}{}^{0} + \overset{.}{\text{X}}{}^{0} \tag{1.1}$$

carried out in the ideal gas state (zero pressure and $0°$ K) with the products
in their ground states. The difference in the heat of reaction at $0°$ K and
$25°$ C is only about 1 kcal/mole. This is usually less than the experimental error in measurements of bond strengths, and a temperature correction is rarely worthwhile. This concept of bond strength–the dissociation energy–is simple, but there are certain limitations to its use. For example, the CH_3 radical is planar and uses sp^2 orbitals, but the bonds in
CH_4 are tetrahedral (sp^3 orbitals). The C–H bond dissociation energy in
methane, according to Eq. (1.1), will therefore include not only the energy
to break the $H_3\text{C}-\text{H}$ bond, but also the energy changes accompanying the
readjustment in orbital bonding.

The bond energy term or thermochemical bond energy carries even less
preciseness. It is an energy quantity assigned to each bond in a molecule

[56] A. D. Walsh, *Trans. Faraday Soc.*, **42**, 779 (1946).

[57] G. Glockler, *J. Chem. Phys.*, **21**, 1242 (1953).

so that the sum over all bonds is equal to the heat of formation, i.e., heat of atomization of the molecule. The heat of atomization of a compound, ΔH_f, is defined by Eq. (1.2) for a reaction in the ideal gas state and for molecules without zero point energy.

$$C_l H_m O_n \longrightarrow lC + mH + nO \qquad (1.2)$$

This concept looks straightforward too, but there are two drawbacks:

1. The bond energy of a given bond is more than the energy liberated from the overlap of electron clouds of the two bonded atoms. There is a small additional effect for nonbonded atoms. Furthermore, the bond strength should increase with an increase in electronegativity of one or both bonded atoms, because the bonding of electrons in a molecular orbital is related to the bonding in the atomic orbitals involved. The electronegativities, of course, are affected by other atoms attached to the bonded atoms.

The general procedure of determining bond energy terms uses thermochemical data. For example, the R—X bond energy term, E_{R-X}, is one nth the heat of atomization of the compound RX_n, and E_{R-Y} is one nth the heat of atomization of RY_n. Then, the heat of formation of the compound $RX_a Y_b$ is the sum $a \cdot E_{R-X} + b \cdot E_{R-Y}$. This method assumes that the energy term for a given bond is constant from molecule to molecule. Obviously this is not true, for then two isomers such as neopentane and n-pentane would have the same heats of formation. Here, then, is one limit of accuracy to bond energy terms. For a specific example, one can compute the E_{C-H} bond energy term as 1/4 the heat of atomization of methane. Then, the E_{C-C} bond energy term may be derived from the heat of atomization of ethane ($\Delta H_f(C_2H_6)$) and E_{C-H}

$$E_{C-C} = \Delta H_f(C_2H_6) - 6E_{C-H} \qquad (1.3)$$

Similarly, the E_{C-C} term could be derived from the heat of atomization of propane:

$$E'_{C-C} = \tfrac{1}{2}(H_f(C_3H_8) - 8E_{C-H}) \qquad (1.4)$$

However, E_{C-C} will not equal E'_{C-C} exactly. If this is done for higher n-alkanes, the value of E_{C-C} changes regularly to approach a limit. A reasonable thing to do then is to take an average E_{C-C} bond energy value. If this value were then used with the $\Delta H_f(C_2H_6)$ to compute E_{C-H}, and the E_{C-H} so obtained used to calculate the heat of formation of methane, the value thus computed would differ from that measured for methane. Thus, it is apparent that a certain amount of juggling of values must be done to choose the best set of bond energy terms. Fortunately the corrections to bond energy terms from nonbonded atoms is relatively small, and bond energy terms are still very useful. They have the advantage over dissociation energies in that (1) only a few dissociation energies are known, and (2) most reactions involve not free radicals but stable reactant and product molecules. Consequently, the use of bond energy terms has been fruitful and of sufficient accuracy for most purposes.

2. The second major difficulty in the establishment of bond energy terms is the definition of the states of the atoms from the atomization of a molecule. For example, the ground state of carbon is the $3P$ state, which has the electronic configuration $1s^2 2s^2 2p^2$. In most saturated compounds, however, carbon is quadrivalent, and it might be argued that not a $3P$ but a $5S$ carbon ($1s^2 2s^1 sp^3$) should represent the ground state. The energy of this state differs from that of the $3P$ state by the promotional energy of an electron from the $2s$ to the $2p$ orbital or 120 kcal. Furthermore, a tetrahedral carbon atom uses hybridized orbitals; that is, carbon is in a "valence state" which is calculated by Van Vleck[58] to be 164 kcal above the ground state. The important point here is not so much the question of which atomic state, $3P$ or $5S$, to choose for the reference state, but the fact that the valence state of carbon will vary from compound to compound and be reflected in the bond energy term. This is another reason why an average bond energy term is chosen.

For maximum usefulness, the most general definition is to regard the heat of atomization as the heat liberated in the conversion of a substance in the ideal gas state at $25°$ C to the atomic elements in their ground states at this temperature.[59]

1.2.10(a) Measurement of Bond Strengths

There are three common sources of energy for rupturing the bond R—X in order to measure its dissociation energy according to Eq. (1.1): (1) electromagnetic radiation in the ultraviolet and visible regions of the spectrum, (2) kinetic energy from a beam of electrons, and (3) thermal energy. Our brief discussion will follow this sequence, and will simply introduce the techniques; detailed descriptions may be found in writings concerned solely with this topic.[60,61]

I. Spectroscopic method.[60] This method consists of measuring the molecular band spectrum of a diatomic molecule and picking out bands whose frequencies correspond most closely to a classical harmonic vibrational

[58] J. H. Van Vleck, J. Chem. Phys., 2, 20 (1934) and earlier papers.

[59] T. L. Cottrell, The Strengths of Chemical Bonds (2nd ed.; New York; Academic, 1958) p. 107; L. Pauling, The Nature of the Chemical Bond (3rd ed.; Ithaca, N. Y.: Cornell U. P., 1960), chap. 3.

[60] T. L. Cottrell, The Strengths of Chemical Bonds.

[61] M. Szwarc, Chem. Revs., 47, 75 (1950).

series.[62] The bands converge, and sometimes can be observed until they form a continuous spectrum. The spectrum is due to absorption of energy for atomic vibrations (in addition to other forms as are discussed in Chap. 5) which is quantized, but after the vibrational energy is sufficient to disrupt the molecule into atoms, any further absorption of energy is in the form of atomic kinetic energy. The kinetic energy is not quantized, so the corresponding part of the spectrum appears as a continuum. The energy required to dissociate the molecules into atoms may be computed from the frequency where the continuous spectrum begins. The absorption bands are weaker near the point of convergence, and often extrapolation is required to determine the limit. One other difficulty is the fact that covalent molecules are dissociated into two atoms, one in the normal state and the other in an electronically excited state. This does not prohibit the use of the method, for the excess atomic excitation energy can be determined from atomic spectra or approximation techniques, and subtracted from the spectroscopic dissociation energy of the diatomic molecule. Extensive compilations of dissociation energies are available[63] from which calculations of bond energies have been made. This spectroscopic method of determining bond dissociation energies cannot be used for polyatomic molecules because their spectra are too complicated for analysis.

II. Electron Impact Method.[64,65] Electrons of known energy are allowed to impinge on gaseous molecules to produce ionization and dissociation. Under certain conditions, the lowest energy required to produce a given ion by dissociation and ionization, called the *appearance potential,* is equal to the sum of the bond dissociation energy and the ionization potential of the fragment. Normally, the ionized particles are identified by mass spectrometry. Results from this method are usually consistent with results from other methods.

III. Thermal methods.[61] Two different approaches are used to determine bond strengths by thermal (pyrolytic) methods. One is to measure the rate of some process and relate it to thermodynamic properties through assumptions about the mechanism of the process; the other approach is to measure the energy change for the reaction shown in Eq. (1.1) either directly or by a set of equilibria.

[62]G. Herzberg, *Molecular Spectra and Molecular Structure* (2nd ed.; Princeton, N. J.; Van Nostrand, 1950), Chap. VII.

[63]A. G. Gaydon, *Dissociation Energies and Spectra of Diatomic Molecules* (London; Chapman and Hall, 1947).

[64]T. L. Cottrell, *The Strengths of Chemical Bonds*, chap. 5.

[65]F. H. Field and J. L. Franklin, *Electron Impact Phenomena and the Properties of Gaseous Ions*, (New York: Academic, 1957).

III(a). Kinetic methods.[66] The principle in this approach is to derive the activation energy for the dissociation of a particular bond. Either a unimolecular decomposition of a molecule into fragments is brought about,

$$R_1 - R_2 \rightleftharpoons R_1 \cdot + R_2 \cdot \qquad (1.5)$$

or a molecule is reacted with a radical to give a different radical and molecule.

$$CH_4 + Br \cdot \rightleftharpoons CH_3 \cdot + HBr \qquad (1.6)$$

In a reaction expressed by Eq. (1.5), the reasonable assumption is made that the recombination of the radical fragments formed in the dissociation process does not require any activation energy and, therefore, the activation energy of the dissociation is equal to the bond dissociation energy. The activation energy is derived from the temperature coefficient of the rate constant for the dissociation process. Values of bond dissociation energies so obtained are generally self-consistent and in substantial agreement with results obtained from other methods. This fact provides justification for the assumption of zero activation energy for combination of free radicals.

Studies are made sometimes in a flowing system and the concentration of radicals determined by mass spectrometry, mirror removal techniques, or absorption spectrophotometry.

III(b). Thermal Equilibrium Methods. The heat of dissociation of the bond R—X from Eq. (1.1) can be derived if the equilibrium concentrations of RX, R·, and X· are known over a temperature range. By using the Van't Hoff equation,

$$\frac{d(\ln K)}{d(1/T)} = \frac{-\Delta H}{R} \qquad (1.7)$$

where K, T, ΔH, and R are the equilibrium constant, absolute temperature, heat of dissociation, and gas constant (1.99 calories/mole), respectively, one may determine dissociation energies from reaction constants, and the only limitations are the measurements themselves.

(i) The *effusion method* allows a small constant flow of gas at a constant low pressure to escape through a small orifice. The rate of escape of the various species in the equilibrium mixture is related to their partial pressures, and hence relative concentrations may be deduced.

(ii) In the *equilibrium flow method,* the dissociation equilibrium is

[66]A. H. Sehon and M. Szwarc, *Ann. Rev. Phys. Chem.,* **8,** 445 (1957).

established in a flowing system and the concentration of dissociation products determined, usually spectroscopically.

(iii) *Explosion, flame, and detonation methods* involve essentially the measurement of maximum temperatures (flame method), maximum pressures (explosion method), or maximum detonation velocities reached. Dissociation energies may then be derived from these data and the necessary specific heats and thermal data.

(iv) Miscellaneous methods based on thermal conductivity measurements, molecular beam analysis, and chemiluminescence intensity measurements are useful but rather specialized techniques, and are not widely used.

(v) The most widely applicable method of deriving "average" bond energy terms is from measurement of *heats of combustion* of substances and subsequent calculation of heats of formation. This method is particularly good because heats of formation of compounds cannot be computed theoretically, and an empirical method is needed. Bond energy terms are established such that the summation over all bonds in a molecule gives its heat of formation. The heat of combustion is defined as the change in heat content per mole, ΔH_c°, when the compound reacts with oxygen in its standard state to form gaseous CO_2 at one atmosphere and liquid water at 25° C, and forming other products in their standard states, if elements other than carbon, hydrogen, and oxygen are present in the compound. The heats of formation of CO_2 and H_2O from the elements in their standard states have been determined very accurately by the National Bureau of Standards.

The heat of combustion of a compound leads to the sum of all its bond energies and not to the energy of an individual bond. For instance, the value of the C—H bond energy is taken as one-fourth the energy absorbed in the reaction $CH_4 \longrightarrow C\cdot + 4\ H\cdot$, although it is known from spectroscopic and electron impact methods that the energies required to break the first and last C—H bonds are 101 and 80 kcal,[27] respectively. Heats of atomization are not determined directly but through the application of Hess's law, i.e., use of a cycle to reach a given point,

$$CH_4 \xrightarrow[4E_{C-H}]{\text{quantity sought}} C\cdot + 4\ H\cdot$$

$$\downarrow {-C_{CH_4}} \qquad \uparrow {S_C + 2D_{H_2}}$$

$$CO_2 + 2\ H_2O \xrightarrow[C_{C+2C_{H_2}}]{} C_s + 2\ H_2$$

where E_{C-H} is the C—H bond energy, C_{CH_4}, C_C, and C_{H_2} are the heats of combustion of methane, carbon, and hydrogen, S_C is the heat of sublimation of carbon (graphite), and D_{H_2} is the dissociation energy of hydrogen, all at constant pressure and 25° C.

$$
\begin{array}{rcll}
 & & Energy\ change \\
 & & kcal/mole \\
CH_{4(g)} + 2\,O_{2(g)} = CO_{2(g)} + 2\,H_2O_{(l)} & 212.8 & (1.8) \\
CO_{2(g)} = C_{graphite} + O_{2(g)} & -94.0 & (1.9) \\
C_{graphite} = C_{(g)} & -170.9 & (1.10) \\
2\,H_2O_{(l)} = 2\,H_{2(g)} + O_{2(g)} & -136.6 & (1.11) \\
2\,H_{2(g)} = 4\,H_{(g)} & -208.4 & (1.12) \\
\hline
CH_{4(g)} = 4\,H_{(g)} + C_{(g)} & -397.1 & (1.13)
\end{array}
$$

$$
C{-}H_{bond\ energy} = \frac{397.1}{4} = 99.3\ kcal/mole
$$

Then, from the heat of combustion of ethane and a knowledge of the C—H bond energy, one gets the C—C bond energy. Similarly, bond energy values may be obtained for C=C and C≡C bonds from the heats of combustion of ethylene and acetylene. Extension of this procedure to simple alcohols, ketones, etc., will give C—O, C=O, and other bond energies. As was pointed out on p. 42, bond energy terms are usually "average" or "best value" quantities. A set of bond energies is given in Table 1.10. Bond energies are used primarily for computing heats of formation of compounds and are not to be confused with bond dissociation energies. The latter apply to specific bonds within a given molecule and usually differ by a small amount from bond energies. For example, the H_3C—H bond energy and bond dissociation energy are 101 and 98.8 kcal, respectively. Naturally, the dissociation energy and the bond energy for a diatomic molecule are identical. Some useful bond dissociation energies are listed in Table 1.9.

Notice in the illustration above that the heat of sublimation of carbon [Eq. (1.10)] is needed for determining carbon bond energies from heats of

Table 1.9 SOME BOND DISSOCIATION ENERGIES[55,60]

Bond	D (kcal)	Bond	D (kcal)
H—H	103.2	H_3C—CH_3	83
CH_3—H	101	ϕCH_2—CH_3	63
CH_3CH_2—H	96	ϕCH_2—$CH_2\phi$	47
$(CH_3)_2CH$—H	94	CH_3—CN	103
$(CH_3)_3C$—H	89	CH_3—CF_3	117
—C—H	80	ϕ—ϕ	103
$CH_2{:}CHCH_2$—H	76.5	$CH_2{:}CHCH_2$—$CH_2CH{:}CH_2$	38
ϕ—H	102	ϕ_3C—$C\phi_3$	11
$C_6H_5CH_2$—H	77.5		
F_3C—H	103		
HO—H	117.5		

combustion. This quantity was a point of considerable controversy for two decades. A wide variety of experiments have been performed to determine the heat of sublimation of carbon, including spectroscopic, electron impact appearance potentials, photochemical, and high-temperature equilibrium measurements. The most favored value in the 1930's was 124 kcal; then the consensus swung to a value of 170 kcal in the late 1940's. Then followed a period of heated conflict between the values of 140 and 170. Now 170 kcal is almost universally accepted for the heat of sublimation of carbon. A review by Kern[67] discusses the principal experimental methods used for this determination, points out the uncertainties attendant upon each method, and summarizes the arguments.

A set of bond energies can be established from each value of the heat of sublimation of carbon. The first and most widely used set was that of Pauling, based on a value of 124 kcal. Adoption of the 170-kcal value necessitates a revision of many of Pauling's values. Pitzer[68] has done this; Table 1.10 includes some of his results.

From the data in Table 1.10 one may compute the heat of formation of a simple covalent compound. For illustration, the heat of formation of trimethylamine from bond energies is

$$9(C\!-\!H) + 3(C\!-\!N) = 9(98.8) + 3(69.7) = 889.2 + 209.1 =$$
$$1098 \text{ kcal/mole.}$$

This may be compared with the experimental value. From the measured heat of combustion of trimethylamine, 588 kcal/mole, and from the heats of formation of the other substances in the reaction,

$$2(CH_3)_3N + 10.5\,O_2 \longrightarrow 6\,CO_2 + 9\,H_2O + N_2 + 1176 \text{ kcal}$$

one may derive the heat of formation of trimethylamine:

$$\Delta H = E_{\text{products}} - E_{\text{reactants}}$$
$$\Delta H = 6E_{CO_2} + 9E_{H_2O} + E_{N_2} - 2E_{(CH_3)_3N} - 10.5E_{O_2} = 1176 \text{ kcal}$$

where E is the heat of formation of a given compound. Hence,

$$2E_{(CH_3)_3N} = 6E_{CO_2} + 9E_{H_2O} + E_{N_2} - 10.5E_{O_2} - 1176$$
$$= 6(410.7) + 9(244.9) + 278.2 - 10.5(146.2) - 1176$$
$$E_{(CH_3)_3N} = 1118 \text{ kcal/mole}$$

Thus, there is only a 20-kcal or 2% difference between the calculated and measured heats of formation of trimethylamine. Similar agreement will be found for many simple compounds, but only for molecules in which atoms

[67] D. M. Kern, *J. Chem. Educ.,* **33**, 272 (1956).
[68] K. S. Pitzer, *J. Am. Chem. Soc.,* **70**, 2140 (1948).

Table 1.10. Some Covalent Bond Energies[59, 68]

Elements		Hydrides		Chlorides		Misc.	
			Single bond energies (kcal/mole)				
H—H	104.2	H—H	104.2	H—Cl	103.2	C—F	105.4
C—C	83.1	C—H	98.8	C—Cl	78.5	C—Br	65.9
N—N	38.4	N—H	93.4	N—Cl	47.7	C—I	57.4
O—O	33.2	O—H	110.6	O—Cl	48.5	C—N	69.7
F—F	36.6	F—H	134.6	F—Cl	60.6	C—Si	69.3
Si—Si	42.2	Si—H	76	Si—Cl	85.7	Si—O	88.2
P—P	51.3	P—H	76.4	P—Cl	79.1	Si—F	129.3
S—S	50.9	S—H	81.1	S—Cl	59.7	Si—Br	69.1
Cl—Cl	58.0	Cl—H	103.2	Cl—Cl	58.0	N—F	64.5
Br—Br	46.1	Br—H	87.5	Br—Cl	52.3	O—F	44.2
I—I	36.1	I—H	71.4	I—Cl	50.3	O—Cl	48.5
						I—Br	42.5

Bond	Single	Double	Triple
	Multiple bond energies (kcal/mole)		
C—C	83	145	198
N—N	38	97.6	225
O—O	33	96	
P—P	51		116
S—S	51	101	
C—N	70	135	
C—O	84	179 (Ketones)	250
S—O		120	

Compound	ΔH_f	Compound	ΔH_f
	Relevant heats of formation* (kcal/mole)		
O_2	146.2	$(H_2O)_{liquid}$	244.9
N_2	278.2	CO_2	410.7
$(Br_2)_{gas}$	46.2	SO_2	297.4
$(I_2)_{solid}$	51.2	HF	147.5

* These values were adjusted so that use of bond energies from this table gives reasonable results.

exhibit normal covalences. Deviations are attributable to resonance, intra-molecular strain, or highly polar bonds (Cf. Chaps. 2 and 4).

1.2.11 BOND LENGTH-BOND ENERGY RELATIONSHIPS

Many empirical relationships have been drawn between the various bond characteristics of bond energy, bond length, bond force constant, bond dipole, electronegativity, ionization potentials of the bonded atoms, and other atomic or molecular properties.[69] For example, it has been shown that for a given bond type, e.g. C—C, C—H, etc., the bond energy in various compounds will vary inversely with the first,[70(a)] second,[70(b)] or third power[71] or even with a power series[72] of the interatomic distance. Also, equations based on quantum theory have been developed for predicting or correlating bond energies, bond force constants, and interatomic distances.[73] All of these relationships are usually quite limited in their application. They do, however, help illuminate the nature of chemical bonds and may be useful for computing bond energies from other parameters with little loss in accuracy.

1.2.12 MOLECULAR ABSORPTION OF ENERGY

The energy of a molecule in the gaseous state may be expressed as the summation of its translational plus its internal energy. The translational energy is not quantized and therefore a molecule may gain or lose any finite quantity of this form of energy. On the other hand, the internal energy–electronic, vibrational, and rotational–is quantized. Consequently, molecules may gain or lose only integral amounts of these three forms of energy, say through collisions or through the absorption or emission of light energy. Chemists are able to learn a great deal about electronic structure and bonding in molecules by measuring changes in their internal energies. The internal energy of a molecule is conveniently represented by diagrams such as Fig. 1.19. The position of a molecule on such a scale is called its *potential energy* or *energy state*.

The potential energy of a substance is defined as the negative value of the energy that would be required to dissociate a compound into its atoms to infinite distances. Therefore a compound is considered more stable, the lower is its potential energy on the negative scale. This is best explained by the diagram in Fig. 1.20. Two isomers of potential energy X and Y on an arbitrary scale would require amounts of energy represented by the distances XX' and YY' for dissociation into atoms. Also, if they were burned, they would liberate amounts of energy represented by the distances XZ and YW. Since A and B are isomers, the combustion products are identical. Thus, B is more stable than A, has the greater energy of forma-

[69] E. M. Layton, Jr., R. D. Kross, and V. A. Fassel, *J. Chem. Phys.*, **25**, 135 (1956).

[70] (a) L. Pauling, *J. Phys. Chem.*, **58**, 662 (1954); (b) H. O. Jenkins, *Trans. Faraday Soc.*, **51**, 1042 (1955).

[71] H. Feilchenfeld, *J. Phys. Chem.*, **61**, 1133 (1957).

[72] G. Glockler, *Tetrahedron*, **15**, 87 (1961); M. L. Huggins, *J. Am. Chem. Soc.*, **75**, 4126 (1953).

[73] Cf. E. R. Lippincott and R. Schroeder, *J. Am. Chem. Soc.*, **78**, 5171 (1956), and references cited therein.

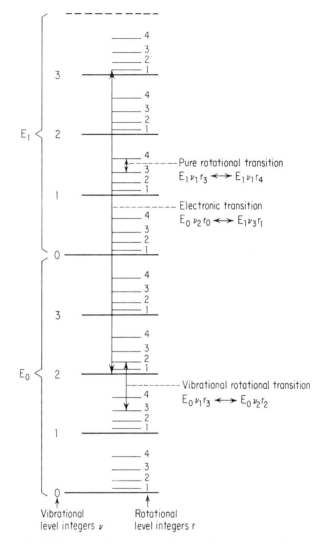

Fig. 1.19. Schematic energy level diagram for a simple molecule.

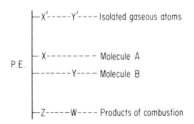

Fig. 1.20. Schematic diagram of the relative stabilities of two isomeric
molecules, their products of combustion, and their constituent atoms.

tion from its atoms, and has the smaller heat of combustion. The lower line could represent the products of a different reaction, such as hydrogenation. Hence, of two isomers, the one with the smaller heat of hydrogenation (liberated) per mole of H_2 absorbed would be the more stable. Strictly, this view does not apply to other than isomers, but in general, it holds in a semiquantitative way for closely similar compounds.

If a molecule gains a small amount of energy, say of the order of magnitude of that from a light source in the far infrared region of the spectrum (about 1 kcal/mole), this will be only enough energy to bring about a transition between rotational levels, no matter in which vibrational state or electronic state it may be. The result will be a change in the modes of rotation of atoms or groups about a given axis in the molecule. If the light source is of greater energy, such as that of the near infrared [see Table 1.11 and Table 1.12], the quanta of energy are sufficiently large (ca. 10

Table 1.11. ENERGY CONVERSION CHART FOR SPECTROSCOPY

Electron-volts	Ergs per molecule	Calories per mole	Wave numbers (cm^{-1})
1	1.602×10^{-12}	23,053	8067
6.242×10^{11}	1	1.439×10^{16}	5.036×10^{-5}
4.34×10^{-5}	6.95×10^{-17}	1	0.35
1.2395×10^{-4}	1.986×10^{-16}	2.86	1

Spectral region	Approximate wavelength (Å)	Approximate energy (cal/mole)
Microwave	10^7–10^8	10
Far infrared	(2×10^5)–10^7	10^3
Near infrared	10^4–(2×10^5)	10^4
Visible	4000–8000	5×10^4
Near ultraviolet	2000–4000	10^5
Far ultraviolet	1–2000	10^6

kcal/mole) to produce vibrational and rotational transitions. The molecules will then undergo changes in modes of atomic vibrations and rotations. Finally, if the energy change is greater (10–250 kcal/mole), such as that from ultraviolet light, changes in all three forms of internal energy may occur. Changes in electronic energy correspond to alterations in electron configurations of molecules which usually differ by one or more valence bonds. The electronic energy level of a molecule under normal conditions is called its ground state, and the succeeding higher electronic levels represent the first, second, ..., excited states, with energies E_0, E_1, E_2, ..., respectively. Similarly, at each electronic plateau, there are the ground and the first, second, ..., excited vibrational states, and for each

Table 1.12. INTERCONVERSION CHART FOR INFRARED-VISIBLE-ULTRAVIOLET SPECTROPHOTOMETRY.

Wave number
$\nu'(\text{cm}^{-1})$

	100 200	1000 10,000			100,000
Spectral region	Far infrared	Near infrared	Visible	Quartz	Vacuum Ultraviolet
Molecular processes	Rotation of molecules and intermolecular vibrations in crystals	Atomic vibrations in molecules	Electronic motions in molecules		
Type spectra	Pure rotation	Rotation-vibration	Electronic band spectra		
Recording devices	Thermopile or bolometer		Photographic plate Photoelectric cell		

Wavelength   1000   100   50 20 10 5 2   1000   400   200   100

⎵_____⎵   ⎵_____⎵
        microns, μ millimicrons, mμ

Units:

Wavelength (λ): Å = angstrom unit = 10^{-8} cm = $10^{-4}\mu$
1 nm = nonameter = 10^{-9}m = 1 m u
Wave number (ν'): Waves per centimer = cm^{-1}
Frequency (ν): Vibrations per second
Interrelations: $\nu' = 1/\lambda = \nu/c$, where c = speed of light $\simeq 3 \times 10^{10}$ cm/sec
Energy (kcal/mole) = $[12,395/\lambda(\text{Å})] \times 23.06$ [e.g., E of 4000 Å = $(12,395/4000) \times 23.06 = 71.5$ kcal/mole]

vibrational level there are the ground and excited rotational states. [See Fig. 1.19.]

One of the best methods of studying internal energy changes of molecules is through spectroscopy. The sample is placed between a light source and a recorder. A prism, grating, or similar device is used to resolve the light beam into its component wavelengths. A photographic plate or photoelectric cell serves as a recorder for the ultraviolet and visible regions, and thermopiles or bolometers are used for the infrared region. A spectrum of the compound is obtained by hand-plotting or automatically recording the relative absorptions of light at the various wavelengths of light against the values of the wavelengths themselves. In actual practice with infrared spectra, wavelengths are commonly replaced by their reciprocals, *wave numbers*. Also, the amounts of absorption may be expressed as *absorbancy* (optical density), *per cent transmission*, or *molar absorptivity* (molar extinction coefficient).

Spectra are designated *ultraviolet, visible,* and *infrared* depending upon the region in which they are measured. Absorption and emission spectra, together with Raman, nuclear magnetic resonance, microwave, and other forms of spectroscopy are powerful tools for all types of chemical research. No one type is universally the best; each is used as a complement rather than a substitute for the others. Their applications will be discussed at length in Chap. 5.

1.2.13 MAGNETIC SUSCEPTIBILITY [74,75]

From classicial physics we have learned that a negative charge moving in a closed orbit is equivalent to a current in a coil of wire and will produce a magnetic field. When an atom, with its attendant electrons moving in closed orbits, is placed in a magnetic field, the external field superposes an angular velocity of precession on the electronic motions. This produces on a system, with random orientation in the external field, a small magnetic moment in opposition to the external field. Thus, the magnetism, called *diamagnetism*, will be found in all atoms regardless of whether or not they also possess permanent moments. Diamagnetism depends only on the effective radius of the electronic orbits and is essentially temperature independent. For illustration, F^-, Ne, Na^+, and Mg^{++} are isoelectronic, but their diamagnetisms decrease in this order because the increasing nuclear charge decreases the orbital radii.

	F^-	Ne	Na^+	Mg^{++}
Mag. susc./g-ion	-11	-7.6	-5	-3×10^{-6} esu

On this basis, we can expect the magnetic susceptibility of a covalently bonded atom to increase as the negative formal charge on the atom increases. Similarly the diamagnetic susceptibility will be smaller the higher is the oxidation state of an ion:

Cr^{+2}	-15	Mn^{+2}	-14	Pb^{+2}	-28
Cr^{+3}	-11	Mn^{+3}	-10	Pb^{+4}	-26
Cr^{+4}	-8				

P. Pascal measured the diamagnetic susceptibilities of many compounds and showed that their susceptibilities X_m can be closely approximated by the expression

$$X_m = \Sigma \, n_i x_i + \lambda$$

where n_i is the number of atoms of susceptibility x_i in the molecule and λ is a structural parameter (sometimes called a constitutive constant or exaltation) which depends upon the nature of the bonding between the atoms. Pascal empirically established a set of atomic susceptibilities x_i and struc-

---

[74] P. W. Selwood, *Magnetochemistry* (2nd ed.; New York: Interscience, 1956).

[75] C. C. Hutchison, Jr., in *Determination of Organic Structures by Physical Methods,* ed. E. A. Braude and F. C. Nachod (New York: Academic, 1955), chap. 7.

tural parameter constants λ, some of which are given in Tables 1.13 and 1.14.

Table 1.13   PASCAL'S CONSTANTS (x_i) FOR SOME ELEMENTS

(10^{-6} cgs units)

H..	-2.93	F	-11.5	Li	-4.2
C..	-6.00	Cl	-20.1	Na	-9.2
N (open chain)	-5.57	Br	-30.6	K	-18.5
N (ring)...................................	-4.61	I	-44.6	Si	-13.0
N (monoamide)	-1.54	S	-15.0	B	-7.0
N (diamide, imide)	-2.11	Se	-23.0		
O (alcohol, ether)......................	-4.61	Te	-37.3		
O (aldehyde, ketone)..................	$+1.72$	P	-10.0		
O (carboxyl, ester, etc.)	-3.36	As	-21.0		

Table 1.14. PASCAL'S STRUCTURAL PARAMETER CONSTANTS,

λ (10^{-6} cgs units)[74, 75]

C=C............................	$+5.5$	C—Cl.............................	$+3.1$
C≡C............................	$+0.8$	C—Br	$+4.1$
C=C—C=C	$+10.6$	C—I	$+4.1$
H_2C=CH—CH_2...............	$+4.5$	$C_3^\alpha, C_3^\gamma, C_3^\delta, C_3^\epsilon$...............	-1.3
N=N	$+1.85$	$C_4^\alpha, C_4^\gamma, C_4^\delta, C_4^\epsilon$....................	-1.55
C=N	$+8.15$	C_3^β, C_4^β............................	-0.5
C≡N	$+0.8$	C_Δ	$+4.1$
$C_{\text{arom (in one ring)}}$ ·················	-0.24	$C_\square$....................................	$+3.05$
$C_{\text{arom (in two rings)}}$ ·················	-3.1	$C_{\square}$....................................	-0.98
$C_{\text{arom (in three rings)}}$ ·················	-4.0	$C_\bigcirc$	$+0.86$

C_Δ, etc., in Table 1.14 refer to cycloaliphatic rings. C_3^α, etc., refer to carbon atoms in α, β, γ, δ, or ϵ positions with respect to oxygen atoms attached to 3 or 4 other atoms excepting hydrogen. Pascal's constants may be used to provide supporting evidence for the proposed structure of a compound just as Parachor values are used. For illustration, if we assume that cycloöctatetraene has an aromatic ring, we would calculate its magnetic susceptibility to be

$$X_m \times 10^6 = 8x_C + 8x_H + 8\,\lambda_{\text{Carom}}$$
$$= 8(-6.00) + 8(-2.93) + 8(-0.24)$$
$$= -73.36 \text{ cm}^3/\text{mole}$$

whereas, if we assume a nonaromatic structure, we have

$$x_m \times 10^6 = 8x_C + 8x_H + 2\,\lambda_{C=C-C=C}$$
$$= 8(-6.00) + 8(-2.93) + 2(10.6)$$
$$= -50.24 \text{ cm}^3/\text{mole}$$

This latter value is in good agreement with the observed value of -51.9×10^{-6} cm^3/mole, and substantiates the nonaromatic physical and chemical properties of cyclooctatetraene. Similar calculations for benzene give -37.1 and -55.02×10^{-6} cm^3/mole for a nonaromatic and an aromatic ring, respectively. The measured value is -54.79×10^{-6} cm^3/mole, which in this case is in agreement with the aromatic character of benzene.

The constants in Tables 1.13 and 1.14 should not be used to distinguish structures whose calculated magnetic susceptibilities are closer than several units, because the specific atomic increments are affected by several additional factors not indicated in the table, such as ionic character and forces between nonbonded atoms.

It is noteworthy that aromatic carbon atoms and, therefore, aromatic rings have large negative structural parameter constants. This provides evidence that the π electrons circulate around the ring and thereby execute large orbital motions to produce relatively large diamagnetic moments.

In addition to diamagnetism, some substances exhibit a magnetic character of much larger magnitude. Reference was made in Sec. 1.2.2 to the spin of electrons. Since a rotating charge creates a magnetic field, a spinning electron will produce a magnetic dipole and cause the atom to have a permanent magnetic moment called *paramagnetism*. If an atom has more than one electron, the magnetic dipoles associated with each spinning electron may or not cancel each other. It can be expected, however, that any molecule with an odd number of electrons is certain to be paramagnetic. A very large paramagnetism is called *ferromagnetism*, and is confined to the solid state. Neither diamagnetism nor paramagnetism is observed in the absence of an external magnetic field, because diamagnetism is an *induced* magnetism and, owing to random orientation of molecules, paramagnetic substances do not have an excess magnetism in any one direction.

1.2.13(a) Experimental Methods

The magnetic susceptibilities of substances can be measured by many techniques.[76, 77] Probably the most common method, devised by Quincke for liquids and modified by Gouy for solids, is applied to substances *en masse*. It is based on the difference in weight of a sample when in and when not in a magnetic field. The experimental set-up is diagrammed in Fig. 1.21. A cylinder of the substance A is suspended from a balance with one end in a homogeneous field between the magnetic poles M and M'. Obviously, the greater the magnetic susceptibility of the substance, the greater will be the force with which it is drawn into the field; this force can

[76] L. J. Brubacher and F. E. Stafford, *J. Chem. Educ.*, **39**, 574 (1962).
[77] S. Kirschner, M. J. Albinak, and J. G. Bergman, *J. Chem. Educ.*, **39**, 576 (1962); L. J. Brubacher and F. E. Stafford, *ibid.*, **39**, 574 (1962).

To balance

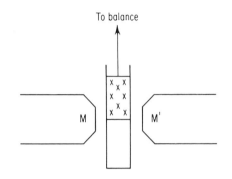

Fig. 1.21. Diagrammatic sketch of the Gouy method of measuring magnetic susceptibilities.

be measured by a sensitive balance. The balance is standardized by measuring the susceptibility of a primary standard, such as copper sulfate, sodium chloride, water, or air, whose susceptibilities are known very accurately. Special modifications of this method have been devised to measure the susceptibilities of liquids or strongly paramagnetic substances.

A second general method of determining magnetic susceptibilities makes use of the effect of a magnetic field upon a stream or beam of atoms or molecules in a vacuum tube, as was done in the classic Stern-Gerlack experiment. There are a number of experimental difficulties to this method, and although its application is limited, it has revealed atomic magnetic phenomena which are masked by atomic interaction in the *en masse* measurements.

In the Gouy method, the force acting on the sample is given by the expression

$$f = \tfrac{1}{2}(k_1 - k_2)(H_1^2 - H_2^2)A = g\Delta w,$$

where k_1 and k_2 are the magnetic susceptibilities per unit volume of the sample and surrounding atoms, respectively; H_1 and H_2 are the field strengths between the pole pieces and at the upper end of the sample; A is the cross-sectional area of the sample, g is the gravitational constant, and Δw is the apparent change in weight on application of the field.

The molar magnetic susceptibility of a substance, X is found equal to

$$N\alpha + \frac{N\mu^2}{3kT}$$

where N is Avogadro's number, k is Boltzmann's constant, α is the molecular diamagnetic susceptibility, T is the absolute temperature, and μ is the permanent magnetic dipole moment. The permanent magnetic moment yields the most information concerning the structure of a substance. To determine μ, one measures X, computes α from Pascal's constants, and then calculates μ. The second procedure, which is probably more accurate, is to measure X at various temperatures and determine the slope of the line when X is plotted against $1/T$. The slope is equal to $N\mu^2/3k$, from which one may calculate μ. For a substance with n unpaired electrons, $\mu = \sqrt{n(n+2)}$ Bohr magnetons. The Bohr magneton (B.M.) is the common unit of magnetic susceptibility and is equal to 5589 ergs/gauss/gram-atom. For a substance with one unpaired electron, then, μ will be close to $\sqrt{1(1+2)} = 1.73$ B.M.

The two most common usages of magnetic susceptibility data by organic chemists are for ascertaining the free radical character of compounds and for providing information about bond-types in organometallic compounds. This latter use will be demonstrated in Sec. 1.4 and the former in Sec. 4.8.2. A more recent development based on the magnetic properties of atoms will be taken up in the section on nuclear magnetic resonance spectroscopy.

1.3 Polar Bonds.   *1.3.1 IONIC BONDS*

Before discussing other types of bonds commonly found in organic substances, we can briefly consider certain polar bonds. The strongest of these is the ionic bond, which would be found, for example, in a gaseous sodium chloride molecule or an ion-pair in a concentrated aqueous salt solution. A close approximation of its strength is given by the expression

$$f = \frac{e_1 e_2}{r}$$

where f is the interionic force of attraction, e_1 and e_2 are the ionic charges in esu, and r is the interionic distance. For illustration, the strength of an ionic bond between two oppositely charged monovalent ions of gaseous molecules is of the order of 125 kcal/mole. Few organic substances possess ionic bonds, so little will be said about them.

1.3.2 ION-DIPOLE BONDS

A second type of polar bond is that between an ion and a polar molecule. For instance, the dipolar molecules H_2O, NH_3, and CH_3OH are strongly attracted by cations as in $Fe(H_2O)_6^{+3}$. The force of attraction is strong enough for the complex ion to behave as a single atomic aggregate, but sometimes the exact composition is difficult to determine precisely.[78] These bonds are commonly found in solvates of crystallization (ammoniates, hydrates, alcoholates). Since the charge on a polar molecule is usually less than a unit charge, the ion-dipole bond is not as strong as an ionic bond.

[78] J. P. Hunt and H. Taube, *J. Chem. Phys.*, **18**, 757 (1950).

Its weakness is shown by the fact that the solvate is usually lost over sulfuric acid at room temperature or driven off by mild heating.

STUDY QUESTIONS

1. List all four quantum numbers for each of the electrons in the outermost shell of the argon atom.

2. Write the electron structures of elements having atomic numbers 21, 24, 34, 46, and 72. How many unpaired electrons does each element have?

3. Calculate the wavelength in Å of the two principal spectral lines of lithium.

4. Work out the ground-state spectroscopic term symbols for oxygen, potassium, cobalt, Zn^{++}, and Er^{+3}. What is the term symbol for. carbon having the excited electron distribution $1s^2 2s^1 2p^3$?

5. What energy would it take to promote a $2s$ and a $2p$ electron of sulfur to $3d$ orbitals? Since it requires so much energy, why is it that sulfur forms stable compounds in which 12 electrons are in its valence shell?

6. What is one major shortcoming of Lewis' theory of covalent bonding?

7. Why is the following statement incorrect? "The valence electron of a carbon atom underwent a transition to the $2d$ orbital." Would $3d$ in place of $2d$ be permissible?

8. Explain the fact that the first and second ionization potentials of calcium (6.11 and 11.87 ev respectively) are each lower than the first and second ionization potentials of scandium (6.56 and 12.80 ev) but the third ionization potential of calcium (51.21 ev) is much higher than that of scandium (24.75 ev).

9. What is an argument against carbon's using four sp^3 hybrid bonds in ethylene instead of three sp^2 and one pi bond?

10. Why is it an inadequate argument to say that the carbon-carbon double bond is weaker than two single bonds chiefly because of strain?

11. Explain the occurence of SiF_6^{-2}, SF_6, and PF_6^{-1} molecular species but not the corresponding CF_6^{-2}, OF_6, or NF_6^{-1} species.

12. Offer an explanation in terms of molecular orbitals for the observation that cyclobutadiene is so unstable that it has never been isolated.

13. Draw a picture of the orbitals of allene, $CH_2{=}C{=}CH_2$.

14. Would you predict the C—Cl bond in CF_3Cl to be longer or shorter than that in CCl_4, and on what basis do you make your prediction?[79]

15. Offer an explanation for the $4d^{10} 5s^0$ electron configuration of Pd instead of $4d^8 5s^2$.

[79] Compare with observed results, L. S. Bartell and L. O. Brockway, *J. Chem. Phys.*, **23**, 1860 (1955).

16. If a value of 126 kcal rather than 170 is chosen for the heat of sublimation of graphite, what difference in bond energy is found for the C—C bond? Does this affect the difference between the C—C and C=C bond energies?

17. The equilibrium constant for dissociation of molecular bromine into atoms is 6.18×10^{-12} at $600°$ K and 2.55×10^{-1} at $1600°$ K. Estimate the Br—Br bond energy and compare your value with that in Table 1.10.

18. Offer an explanation for the ≡C—CN bond distance of only 1.38 Å observed in H—C≡C—CN and CH_3—C≡C—CN. Note that this is shorter than the carbon-carbon bond distance in benzene.[80]

19. Predict the relative ionization potentials of arsenic (at. no. 33) and selenium (at. no. 34).

20. Predict the relative atomic volumes of copper and potassium and give the basis of your prediction.

21. What justification is there for postulating the hybridization of atomic orbitals for bonding purposes?

22. Which should be the better solvent for nitromethane, benzene or cyclohexane?

23. Which atom of naphthalene should have the larger diamagnetic susceptibility, an α carbon atom, a β carbon atom, or one of the carbon atoms common to both rings?

24. Explain the fact that chlorine, bromine, and iodine readily form the X_3^- ion, where X is one of the halogens, but fluorine does not form such an ion.

25. Which should have the larger diamagnetic susceptibility of each pair: Na^+ or K^+; argon or krypton; $S^=$ or $O^=$?

26. The magnetic susceptibility of ethyl benzoylacetate is -115.2×10^{-6} cm^3/mole. Is this value closer to the magnetic susceptibility calculated for its keto or its enol tautomer?

27. What bond angles would you predict for the hydronium ion? If the experimental H—O—H angle were about 110°, what shape would you give the ion?

28. On what basis would you expect the C—D and N—D bonds to be cleaved in reactions more slowly than C—H and N—H bonds, respectively?

29. Offer an explanation for the trends in C—H bond distances and force constants in the following two series:

Compound	Force constant	Bond distance
CH_3F	4.7×10^5 dynes/cm	1.109 Å
CH_3Cl	4.9	1.101
CH_3Br	4.95	1.100
CH_3I	5.0	1.100
CH_4	5.0	1.094
C_2H_4	5.1	1.087
C_2H_2	5.9	1.059

[80]Cf. A. A. Westenberg and E. B. Wilson, Jr., *J. Am. Chem. Soc.*, **72**, 199 (1950).

30. Predict the relative first ionization potentials for zinc[30] and galium[31]; phosphorus[15] and sulfur[16]. The superscripts are atomic numbers.

31. The C—H bond distance in benzene is 1.08 Å. On this basis how does the electronegativity of the C_6H_5 group compare with those of the CH_2=CH— and HC≡C— groups?

32. Predict the relative C—H bond distances in CH_3—CH_3, CH_4, CF_3CH_3.[81]

33. Offer an explanation for the relative C—C bond distances in ethane (1.545 Å) and ethyl chloride (1.52 Å), and for the fact that the α C—H bond of ethyl chloride (1.089 Å) is slightly shorter than that of the β C—H bond (1.092 Å).

34. Predict the relative C—Cl bond distances in CCl_2F_2 and CF_3Cl.

35. The C=C bond energy is less than twice the C—C bond energy but the C=O bond energy is somewhat greater than twice that of the C—O bond. Explain.

36. Based on the covalent radii of hybridized carbon atoms proposed in this chapter, what length would you predict for the C_1—C_1' bond in biphenyl? The experimental value is 1.507 Å in the solid state. How can you explain the difference between your prediction and the measured value?

37. What type of hybridization would you propose for the nitrogen atom of pyridine?

1.4 Coordinate covalent bonds

In the previous sections we have seen that when the atomic orbitals about two atoms coalesce to form a molecular orbital, the two single electrons formerly in each atomic orbital may pair up and be associated with both nuclei, i.e., form a *covalent* bond. However, it is possible for the atomic orbitals of two atoms to overlap and for two electrons from only one of the atoms to use the arising molecular orbital for bond formation. For example, the unshared electron pair on the nitrogen atom of ammonia can serve to form a covalent bond with a proton according to the equation

$$
\left. \begin{array}{ccc}
& \text{H} & \quad\quad \text{H} \\
& \overset{..}{\cdot\cdot} & \quad\quad \overset{..}{\cdot\cdot} \\
\text{H} : \overset{..}{\text{N}} : \; + \; \text{H}^+ & \longrightarrow & \text{H} : \overset{..}{\text{N}} : \text{H} \\
& \text{H} & \quad\quad \text{H}
\end{array} \right]^{+}
$$

In the resulting ammonium ion NH_4^+ all four N—H bonds are identical, as shown by the spectroscopic and other properties of the ion. In order to distinguish the two modes of formation of the covalent bond, the bond formed when one atom donates both electrons is called a *coordinate covalent* bond.

Most often fractional charges arise on two atoms when they form a co-

[81]Cf. L. F. Thomas, J. S. Heeks, and J. Sheridan, Z. Elektrochem., **61**, 935 (1957).

ordinate covalent bond. For instance, when trimethylamine and tri-
methylboron react to form a coordinate covalent bond,

$$
\begin{array}{ccc}
\underset{|}{\overset{Me}{|}} \quad \underset{|}{\overset{Me}{|}} & & \overset{Me}{|} \overset{Me}{|} \\
Me-N : + B-Me & \longrightarrow & Me-N : B-Me \\
\underset{Me}{|} \quad \underset{Me}{|} & & \underset{Me}{|} \underset{Me}{|}
\end{array}
$$

the nitrogen atom suffers a loss in negative charge about its nucleus and
the boron atom gains an equivalent negative charge. Accordingly, a better representation of the complex molecule is

$$
\begin{array}{c}
\overset{Me}{|} \quad \overset{Me}{|} \\
Me-N^{\delta+}-B^{\delta-}-Me \\
\underset{Me}{|} \quad \underset{Me}{|}
\end{array}
$$

where the δ signs represent fractional charges. Supporting this view is the
fact that the N—B bond has a force constant[82] (3.7×10^5 dynes/cm.)
typical of an ordinary covalent bond, and a dipole moment (3.92 Debye
units) commensurate with a large ionic character. The charges shown are
only fractional unit charges and are called *formal charges*. A formal
charge is the resultant of the positive kernel charge and the negative
charge of valence electrons after equal distribution of bonding electrons.
Of course, formal charges are only crude approximations of the charge distribution because bonding electrons are not shared equally between atoms
of different electronegativities. For simplicity, the delta signs are usually
omitted.

As another example, trimethylamine oxide has the structure

$$
\begin{array}{c}
CH_3 \\
| \\
H_3C-{}^+N-O^- \\
| \\
CH_3
\end{array}
$$

Its polar or saltlike character is revealed by its dipole moment (5.02 D)
which is in the range for ion-pairs (6.2 D for KCl), by its very low solubility in ether and high solubility in water, and by its relatively high melting
point (208° C). Owing to the ionic or polar character of many coordinate
covalent bonds, they have been given several names such as, semi-ionic
bond (Noyes), dative bond (Branch, Menzies), coordinate link (Sidgwick),
and semipolar double bond (Lowry, Sugden). It was shown many years
ago that although the ionic attraction of the coordinate covalent bond in
these nitrogen compounds may be regarded as a fifth valence of nitrogen,

[82]H. J. Becher and J. Gubeau, *Z. anorg. Chem.*, **268**, 131, 273 (1952).

one of the bonds of a so-called pentavalent nitrogen is different from the other four. Meisenheimer[84] prepared the isomeric salts $(CH_3)_3NOCH_3^+OH^-$ and $(CH_3)_3NOH^+OCH_3^-$. Their properties were consistent with the structures I and II.

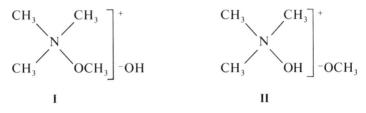

            I   II

This valency of nitrogen is understood now, since the nitrogen atom can accommodate only 8 electrons in its valence shell. Therefore, it can form only four covalent bonds. Phosphorus, on the other hand, can have a covalence greater than four by using its $3d$ orbitals. For instance, pentaphenyl phosphorus, $\phi_5 P$, is soluble in nonpolar solvents, can be recrystallized from cyclohexane, melts at 124°, and has no dipole moment.[83] Thus, it is a typical covalent compound with phosphorus forming five covalent bonds. In contrast to this, phosphorus forms only four covalent bonds in the salt $\phi_4 PI$, m.p. 334–344°.

1.4.1. CHELATES

(a) General features. Chelate compounds are now fairly common in chemistry and are finding use in almost every type of chemical activity from analytical and industrial chemistry to biochemistry. For example, reagents that form metal chelates are used extensively in qualitative as well as quantitative analyses. Dimethylglyoxime, 8-hydroxyquinoline (oxine), cupferron, Fehling's and Benedict's solutions, o-phenanthroline, and ethylenediamine tetraacetic acid (EDTA)[84] are examples of substances used frequently in analytical procedures. The use of chelons, compounds which form soluble complexes and may be used for titrating metal ions, has markedly altered the analytical approach to metal ion analysis. Many water-soluble chelates are used to soften water, to enable agricultural products to absorb vital metal ions from the soil through their roots, or to separate various mixtures of ions through solvent extraction. So far, the most successful way to separate the rare earth elements in large quantities is through the use of ion exchangers with chelate-forming solutions.

[83] G. Wittig, *Angew. Chem.*, **63**, 15 (1949).

[84] J. Meisenheimer, *Ann.*, **397**, 273 (1913); (a) M. B. Johnston, A. J. Barnard, Jr., and H. A. Flascha, *J. Chem. Educ.*, **35**, 601 (1958); (b) C. N. Reillay, R. W. Schmid, and F. S. Sadek, *J. Chem. Educ.*, **36**, 555 (1959); (c) G. Schwarzenbach, *et al.*, *Helv. Chim. Acta*, **31**, 678 (1948) and earlier papers.

Chlorophyll, the heme portion of hemoglobin, and cytochromes are special chelates which are indispensable for life processes.

The term *chelate*, suggested by Morgan and Drew and pronounced *key'-late*, is derived from the Greek work *chela* for claw and appropriately describes this class of compounds. They consist of a partial circle of atoms which close up the ring by holding a given atom in a molecular claw. Owing to the range of normal covalent bond angles, 5- and 6-membered rings are the most stable. For a ring of single bonds only, the 5-membered ring is usually the most stable,[85] whereas 6-membered rings have maximum stability when there are two double bonds in the ring. The copper chelates of glycine and salicylaldehyde are typical examples of these two groups of chelates, respectively.

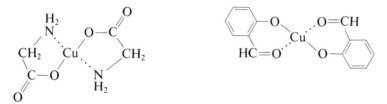

The dotted line is used to indicate the coordinate covalent bond, which may vary from an essentially covalent bond to one of primarily ionic character. Amino nitrogen and carbonyl oxygen are the most common neutral atoms to form chelate rings through coordination. Chelates are found with varying polar properties, and range from the high melting, water-soluble, salt-like chelates to the nonpolar, volatile, liquid chelates soluble in organic solvents. An example of the latter type is aluminum isovalerylacetonate, which is a liquid at room temperature.

As mentioned in Sec. 1.3.2, ions in solution are surrounded by a sheath of solvent molecules or by other molecules in solution.

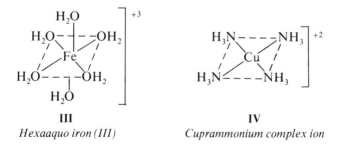

III   IV

Hexaaquo iron (III)   *Cuprammonium complex ion*

The solvating substances are dipolar molecules held by ion-dipole forces, and they reduce the charges on the metal ion. The coordination number

[85]H. Irving, R. J. P. Williams, D. J. Ferrett, and A. E. Williams, *J. Chem. Soc.*, 3494 (1954).

is six for most ions, but it is eight for some such as W^{+4} and Mo^{+4}, four for ions such as Cu^{+2}, Zn^{+2}, and Mg^{+2}, and two for some such as Hg^{+2} and Ag^{+1}. When the bonding is largely covalent, there will be definite bond angles. In other instances, as with the alkali metal ions, only ion-dipole bonds are formed and no definite structure or formula can be assigned. In such cases there is a dynamic equilibrium between hydrating and bulk solvent molecules, and only an average hydration number can be assigned. When a chelating substance is added to a metal ion solution, two or more of the solvating molecules may be replaced and the reversible reaction between chelate and solvate is shifted in favor of chelation.

Extensive reviews on chelates and coordination compounds are available[86,88] but the properties of most interest from the standpoint of this book are the bonding and charge distribution in chelates. Accordingly, we will discuss primarily the bonding and structural parameters that greatly affect the stabilities of chelates. First, let us briefly describe the methods used for studying chelates.

1.4.2 METHODS OF STUDYING CHELATES[86,89]

The process of chelation can be expressed by the simple reversible equation

$$M^{+n}(H_2O)_x + n\,HKe \rightleftharpoons MKe_n + n\,H^+ + x\,H_2O \qquad (1.14)$$

where $M^{+n}(H_2O)_x$ is a hydrated metal ion in solution, HKe is the chelating agent, and MKe_n is the resulting chelate compound. For example, one can write

$$Cu^{+2}(H_2O)_4 + 2\,CH_3C(OH){=}CH{-}COCH_3 \rightleftharpoons$$

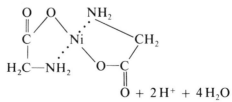

$$+ 2\,H^+ + 4\,H_2O \qquad (1.15)$$

$$Ni^{+2}(H_2O)_4 + 2\,\overset{+}{H_3N}{-}CH_2CO_2^- \rightleftharpoons$$

$$+ 2\,H^+ + 4\,H_2O \qquad (1.16)$$

[86] A. E. Martell and M. Calvin, *Chemistry of the Metal Chelate Compounds* (Englewood Cliffs, N.J.: Prentice-Hall, 1952).

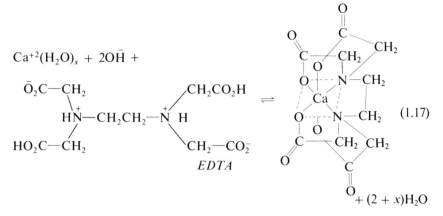

$$\text{(1.17)}$$

Normally, chelate formation obeys the laws of mass action, and the equilibrium between a metal ion M and a chelating agent Ke can be expressed by the simple equation

$$M + x\,Ke \rightleftharpoons MKe_x \qquad (1.18)$$

where MKe_x represents the chelate. The equilibrium constant K, called the *formation constant* or the *stability constant*, is then

$$K = \frac{[MKe_x]}{[M][Ke]^x} \qquad (1.19)$$

where the brackets designate activities. Like other thermodynamic equilibrium constants, thermodynamic formation constants can be determined by (1) making measurements at various concentrations and extrapolating to infinite dilution, (2) calculating activity coefficients from theoretical relationships, or (3) working at very high dilutions where K approaches the thermodynamic value.

Several experimental methods have been developed for determining stability constants.[86,87] The most common procedures involve a titration technique. For example, Eqs. (1.15) to (1.17) show that as chelation takes place with certain chelating agents, the pH of the solution drops, and this can be followed potentiometrically. Figure 1.22 illustrates the characteristic titration curves for EDTA in the presence of various metal ions. Curve I is the titration curve obtained in the presence of potassium ions upon the addition of potassium hydroxide. This ion does not form a chelate, and the

[87] F. J. C. Rossotti and H. Rossotti, *The Determination of Stability Constants* (New York: McGraw-Hill, 1961).

[88] *Chemistry of the Coordination Compounds,* ed. J. C. Bailar (New York: Reinhold, 1956), chap. I; "Conference on Coordination Compounds," *Revs. Pure and Applied Chem.*, **4**, 1–110 (1954) ; "Ions of the Transition Elements," *Disc. Faraday Soc.*, no. 26 (1958).

[89] A. E. Martell, *J. Chem. Educ.*, **29**, 270 (1952).

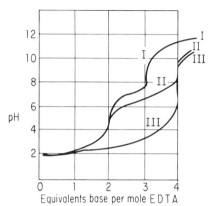

Fig. 1.22. Characteristic titration curve for EDTA in the presence of
K^+ (I), Cd^{+2} (II), and Ca^{+2} (III) ions.

curve is almost identical to the normal titration curve of the amino acid
alone. Curve III shows the effect of the presence of an ion that forms a
very stable chelate. The equivalent amount of hydrogen ion liberated during the titration suppresses the pH until the end point is approached.
Curve II is typical of the titration of EDTA in the presence of an ion that
forms a chelate of intermediate stability. Hence, the pH drop in the
central buffer region of the titration curve gives a measure of the relative
stability of the chelates of various ions with a given chelating agent.[90]
Equations for deriving the stability constants from titration curves have
been developed in several forms.[86,87,91]

Since chelation is a reversible reaction and associated with pH, it follows that the more stable the chelate the lower the pH required for dissociation. Also, since the most stable chelate would have the lowest equilibrium
concentration of metal ion in solution, then the more stable the chelate, the
higher the concentration of hydroxide ion needed for precipitation of the
metal ion. These two relationships are employed frequently in the separation of ions by ion exchangers, fractional precipitation, or solvents.[92]   For
illustration, at a pH of 5, oxine (8-hydroxyquinoline) precipitates tungsten,
iron, and aluminum ions. However, only tungsten will precipitate in the
presence of EDTA because the latter forms stable, soluble chelates with
the iron and aluminum ions at this pH. Then, after the tungsten-oxine
chelate has been filtered off, the pH may be raised to 8–9 wherein the

[90]Cf. L. A. Maley and D. P. Mellor, *Austral. J. Sci. Res.*, Ser. A, **2**, 579 (1949), on
stability constants of amino acids.

[91]Cf. J. Bjerrum, Metal Ammine Formation in Aqueous Solution (Copenhagen: P. Haase
and Sons, 1941); M. Calvin and K. W. Wilson, *J. Am. Chem. Soc.*, **67**, 2003 (1945); J. C.
Sullivan and J. O. Hindman, *J. Am. Chem. Soc.*, **79**, 1028 (1957); L. G. Sillen, F. J. Rossotti, and H. S. Rossotti, *Acta Chem. Scand.*, **9**, 1166 (1955) and **10**, 186–214 (1956).

[92]A. E. Martell and M. Calvin, *Chemistry of the Metal Chelate Compounds*, chap. 9.

oxine will precipitate the iron. This may be filtered off and leave the aluminum in solution. In this fashion, a mixture of the three ions may be resolved.

The other principal methods[93(a)] of determining stability constants involve the measurement of the equilibrium concentration of metal ion in solution by conductivity, emf, polarography,[93(b)] or solubility. Also, a measure of the relative stability of a chelate, that is, how firmly the metal ion is held by the chelating agent, can be obtained from the rates of ion exchange,[93(c)] polarographic reduction potentials,[93(d)] or spectroscopy.[93(e)] A word of caution should be given in the use of spectroscopy for determining relative stabilities of chelates. Although some relationships between stability constants and wavelengths of maximum absorption (λ_{max}) of chelates have been observed,[94] they hold only for restricted series. The difficulty is that absorption maxima of chelates are a function of several parameters, such as charge density and available orbitals on the metal ion, and the combined effects may preclude a simple relationship between λ_{max} and stability constants for a mixed group of chelates.[94(b),(c)] As with visible and ultraviolet spectra, there are certain limited correlations between infrared spectra and stabilities of chelates, but there is no general relationship.[95] On the other hand, the techniques of spectrophotometry offer a good method of determining stability constants.[96]

1.4.3 BONDING IN CHELATES

The essential difference between chelates and the so-called Werner coordination compounds, such as III, is that two or more of the ligands in a chelate are joined by a chain of atoms. Although there may be quantitative differences in stability, the bonding and stereochemical properties of both types of complexes are quite similar. Consequently, the bonding in the two may be considered in a single discussion.

The most prominent theories proposed[97] to describe the bonding in coordination compounds have been the electrostatic, the electron-pair repul-

[93] (a) *Ibid.*, chap. 3; (b) C. F. Hiskey, Symposium on "The Chemistry of Chelate Compounds," held at Polytechnic Institute of Brooklyn, 1952, p. 12; (c) A. W. Adamson, Symposium on "The Chemistry of Chelate Compounds," p. 18; (d) H. F. Holtzclaw, A. H. Carlson, and J. P. Collman, *J. Am. Chem. Soc.*, **78**, 1838 (1956); (e) H. Irving and D. H. Mellor, *J. Chem. Soc.*, 3457 (1955).

[94] K. Yamasaki and K. Sone, *Nature*, **166**, 998 (1950); (b) R. H. Holm and F. A. Cotton, *J. Am. Chem. Soc.*, **80**, 5658 (1958); (c) G. Charette, G. Neirynck, and Ph. Teyssie, *J. Phys. Chem.*, **65**, 735 (1961).

[95] L. J. Bellamy and R. F. Branch, *J. Chem. Soc.*, 4491 (1954).

[96] Cf. Sec. 5.5.4.

[97] "Ions of the Transition Elements," *Disc. Faraday Soc.*, no. 26 (1958). Another proposal was the quanticule theory of K. Fajans, *Chem. Eng. News*, **27**, 900 (1949).

sion theory,[98] the valence bond, the molecular orbital, and the ligand field theories.   Before we consider the structure-stability relationships of chelates, it is appropriate to compare briefly the essential features of the two theories most popular at this time.

Valence Bond Theory. The valence bond theory, developed for complexes by Pauling,[101] proposes that a number of orbitals on the central metal atom equal to the number of ligands are available for coordinate covalent bond formation with the ligands.   The directional characteristics of the atomic pure or hybrid orbitals about the center atom determine the stereochemical properties of the complexes.   The spatial arrangements of the most common bond-types were given in Table 1.5.

In order to account for the different magnetic properties of a given metal ion in various complexes, Pauling proposed that the central atom would use one type of hybrid orbital with certain ligands and a different orbital type for other ligands.   He postulated that in most cases the magnetic moment of a complex could be used to classify the orbital bond-type, which he designated "essentially covalent" and "essentially ionic." For illustration, the bivalent nickel ion has 26 electrons which will fill the $1s$, $2s$, $2p$, $3s$, and $3p$ orbitals, and eight electrons will go into the $3d$ subshell. According to Hund's rule, two electrons in the $3d$ subshell are unpaired, and simple ionic nickelous salts should have a magnetic character corresponding to two unpaired electrons, as they actually do.   A complex of Ni(II) can be formed in which the ligands form coordinate covalent bonds through the use of sp^3 or dsp^2 orbitals.   The latter arrangement is made possible by a pairing up of the two unpaired electrons in the $3d$ orbitals to make available an open $3d$ orbital.   These electron arrangements may be diagrammed as follows, where the orbitals hybridized for bonding are enclosed by the dashed lines.

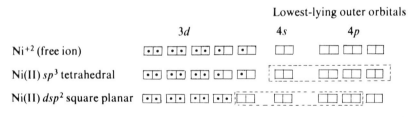

---

[98]The shapes of simple covalently bonded molecules and ions have been qualitatively explained in terms of electron-pair repulsions which tend to keep the electrons as far apart as possible [cf. R. J. Gillespie, *J. Am. Chem. Soc.*, **82**, 5978 (1960), and references cited therein].   The method assumes electron pairs repel one another, and the repulsions decrease in the following order: lone-pair vs. lone-pair > lone-pair vs. bond pair > bond pair vs. bond pair, and multiple bond vs. multiple bond > multiple bond vs. single bond > single bond vs. single bond.

Accordingly, a tetrahedral complex of nickel should have a magnetic character corresponding to two unpaired electrons. Nickel acetylacetone is an example of such a paramagnetic compound whose structure has been verified by X-ray diffraction measurements. In a complex with dsp^2-type bonds, the nickel has no unpaired electrons and should be diamagnetic, i.e., have very little magnetic character. Examples are $Ni(CN)_4^{-2}$, whose structure has been found by X-ray diffraction to be planar, and the ion bis-$(\alpha,\alpha'$-dipyridyl)Ni^{+2}.

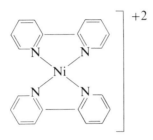

Nickel bis-(α,α'-dipyridyl) ion

It must be pointed out that although Pauling used the terms "essentially ionic" and "essentially covalent" to distinguish the bond-types in coordination complexes, he did not mean that there were ionic bonds in the classical sense between the central ion and surrounding ligands. The terms merely designated whether or not the complex had the same number of unpaired electrons as the free ion. For example, the magnetic criterion would classify the acetylacetone chelate of Fe(III) as being ionic. However, it is volatile, and soluble in organic liquids–properties typical of covalent compounds. Since the terms essentially ionic and essentially covalent were misleading, Pauling has substituted the terms *hypoligated* and *hyperligated*, respectively.[99] In one case, orbitals of the valence shell are hybridized for bond formation; in the other case, orbitals from an inner shell (penultimate shell) are incorporated. Accordingly, the two types have been referred to as "outer orbital" and "inner orbital" complexes.[102] Other terms proposed are "normal" and "penetration" complexes,[103] "higher level" and "lower level" complexes,[104] "high-spin" and "low-spin" com-

[99] L. Pauling, *The Nature of the Chemical Bond,* pp. 162–163.

[100] Cf. F. Basolo and R. G. Pearson, *Mechanisms of Inorganic Reactions* (New York: Wiley, 1958), pp. 46 ff.

[101] L. Pauling, *op. cit.,* chap. 5; cf. D. H. Busch, *J. Chem. Educ.,* **33,** 376, 498 (1956).

[102] H. Taube, *Chem Revs.,* **50,** 69 (1952).

[103] W. Biltz, *Z. anorg, allgem, Chem,* **164,** 245 (1927)

[104] F. H. Burstall and R. S. Nyholm, *J. Chem. Soc.,* 3570 (1952).

plexes,[105] and "spin-paired" and "spin-free" complexes. In general, the high electronegative atoms fluorine and oxygen favor *outer orbital bonding* since they tend to hold the bonding electrons about themselves. Low electronegativity of the ligand atoms and large positive charge on the central ion favor *inner orbital* bonding since these factors will allow the central ion to pull in the electrons from the ligand atoms. Thus, the hexafluorocobalt(III) ion CoF_6^{-3} is an outer orbital complex while the hexamminecobalt(III) ion $Co(NH_3)_6^{+3}$ is an inner orbital complex. Usually, the outer orbital complexes undergo rapid reversible exchange of complexed components with uncomplexed components.[102,106]

The coordinate covalent bonds in these complexes are most often sigma bonds, but when the central atom has d electrons and the ligand has vacant orbitals perpendicular to the line joining the two atoms (or can have by resonance), then a reverse-donation may occur. For illustration, carbon monoxide ($\bar{C}{\equiv}O^+$) may react with a metal to produce a $\bar{M}{-}C{\equiv}O^+$ bond, but the back-donation makes the $M{=}C{=}O$ structure a major contributor to the resonance hybrid. This π bond between the metal and carbon not only gives the bond a double-bond character, and therefore greater strength, but it prevents the accumulation of negative charge on the metal which would destabilize the system.[107] For example, nickel tetracarbonyl, $Ni(CO)_4$, is diamagnetic and the nickel is in the zero oxidation state. X-ray diffraction reveals it to be tetrahedral, therefore, inner orbital bonding (square planar for nickel) does not occur. If nickel were to promote its two $4s$ electrons into the $3d$ subshell, it could then use its $4s$ and $4p$ orbitals to form four sp^3-type bonds. This would account for the tetrahedral configuration and the diamagnetism. However, it has been found that the $C{-}O$ bond distance is greater than that of a triple bond and that the $Ni{-}C$ distance is considerably less than that expected for a single bond.[108] Here, double bonding between the nickel and carbon atoms would explain the observed bond distances as well as the great stability, small magnetic character, and steric structure of $Ni(CO)_4$.

The effect of double bonding is revealed by the difference in structures and stereochemistry of the complex ions $Ni(en)_2^{+2}$ and $Ni(dipy)_2^{+2}$, where en stands for ethylenediamine and dipy for α,α-dipyridyl. The magnetic character of $Ni(en)_2^{+2}$ corresponds to two unpaired electrons, which indicates it has the outer orbital tetrahedral configuration for which π bonding

[105]J. S. Griffith and L. E. Orgel, *Quart. Revs.*, **11**, 381 (1957).

[106]H. C. Clark and A. L. Odell, *J. Chem. Soc.*, 3431, 3435 (1955).

[107]Occasionally a δ bond may be formed in which parallel d orbitals are used on the central and ligand atoms and two nodal planes cut the bond axis. Cf. H. H. Jaffe, *J. Phys. Chem.*, **58**, 185 (1954); D. P. Craig, A. Maccoll, R. S. Nyholm, L. E. Orgel, and L. E. Sutton, *J. Chem. Soc.*, 332 (1954).

[108]L. Pauling, *Nature of the Chemical Bond*, p. 332.

between Ni and N should be neglible. However, the dipyridyl complex has the planar structure previously shown, and the π electron clouds of the aromatic rings are in a favorable position for π bonding with the d orbitals on the nickel atom. The infrared spectra of a number of coordination complexes support this notion.[109] Similarly, Hearon[113] attributed the much greater stability of histidine chelates over those of other α-amino acids to the formation of partial Co–N double bonds.

One final example of the effect of double bonding on the stability of coordination compounds is the behavior of NF_3 and PF_3 towards BF_3 and transition ions. BF_3 coordinates readily with NF_3, but in spite of BF_3 being one of the strongest electron acceptors known, it does not coordinate with PF_3.[110] Thus, the lone-pair electrons on phosphorus in PF_3 are not available for ordinary σ bond formation. However, with atoms which can donate electron pairs to form double bonds, PF_3 rather than NF_3 has the greater tendency for coordination. Thus, PF_3 coordinates with the iron in hemoglobin whereas NF_3 does not.[111] NF_3, of course, does not have available orbitals for double bond formation while phosphorus makes use of its $3d$ orbitals. PF_3 also complexes readily with Pt(II).[112]

In spite of the great success of the valence bond theory for describing the bonding in these complexes, there are some failures. For example, the complex $Ni(dipy)_3^{+2}$ is paramagnetic to the extent of two unpaired electrons. According to valence bond theory, this fact and its resolution into optical isomers[114] would suggest the sp^3 tetrahedral structure for the complex. However, it is very unlikely that only four bonds are used for bonding. Instead, the view may be taken that the complex has the outer orbital sp^3d^2-type σ bonds as well as some π bonding. Also, the valence bond theory is usually applied to the ground states of coordination compounds and is particularly poor for interpreting their ultraviolet and X-ray absorption spectra. Nevertheless, the use of the valence bond theory is often justified in its simplicity.

The molecular orbital (M.O.) theory differs from the valence bond theory chiefly in the fact that the valence electrons are not paired up for sigma bond formation, but are assumed to move independently in molecular orbitals which extend over all the nuclei of the system.[115, 116] M.O.'s are constructed from overlapping atomic orbitals (A.O.), and the number of M.O.'s formed is equal to the number of A.O's used. Half of the M.O.'s

[109] D. H. Busch and J. C. Bailar, *J. Am. Chem. Soc.*, **78**, 1137 (1956).

[110] J. W. Irvine and G. Wilkinson, *J. Am. Chem. Soc.*, **73**, 5501 (1951).

[111] G. Wilkinson, *Nature*, **168**, 514 (1954).

[112] J. Chatt and A. Williams, *J. Chem. Soc.*, 3061 (1951).

[113] J. Hearon, *J. Natl. Cancer Inst.*, **9**, 1 (1948).

[114] F. Basolo, *Chem. Revs.*, **52**, 459 (1953).

[115] J. W. Linnett, *Disc. Faraday Soc.*, no. 26, 8–12 (1958).

[116] L. E. Sutton, *J. Chem. Educ.*, **37**, 498 (1960).

will be bonding, i.e., more stable than the original atomic orbitals, and half will be antibonding, that is, less stable than the original A.O.'s.

Ligand Field Theory.[117]   The crystal field theory, first proposed by Bethe,[118] was developed as an extension of electrostatic theory for treating an orderly arrangement of interacting particles as occurs in a crystal lattice. First Kossel in 1920, and later Fajans, Van Arkel, Garrick, and others, showed that by picturing complexes as point charges and dipoles, a good account could be given for the properties of many coordination compounds. The basic idea was that the ligands (anions or dipolar molecules) are attracted to the center cation by simple electrostatic forces. The anions or negative poles of the dipolar molecules produce a field of negative charge about the cation. From a knowledge of the charges and sizes of the central ion and the charges, dipole moments, and polarizabilities of the ligands, one may calculate energies of formation of many coordination complexes. Also, certain predictions can be made regarding the relative tendencies for complexes to undergo substitution reactions via S_N1 and S_N2 pathways.[119] Crystal field theory is also able to explain the magnetic properties[120] and visible spectra of certain paramagnetic salts.[121] However, little use was made of the crystal field theory by chemists until Orgel[122] showed that by incorporating some of the concepts of molecular orbital theory, much better interpretations could be given to the spectra, stability, and other properties of coordination compounds. This combined approach of M.O. and crystal field theories is now called *ligand field theory.*[105]

The theory is based on the supposition that the five d orbitals of a central metal ion, which are equal in energy in the gaseous metal ion, have different energies in the presence of the electrostatic field of the ligands in a coordination compound. The orbitals pointing towards ligands are of higher energy than those pointing away from the ligands because the electrons on the central ion tend to avoid those regions where the negative field of the surrounding ligands is greatest. Preferential filling of the orbitals farthest away from the ligands, rather than random filling of the d orbitals as dictated by simple electrostatic theory, brings about a gain in bonding energy called crystal field stabilization energy (Δ).

[117] L. E. Orgel, *An Introduction to Transition Metal Chemistry, Ligand Field Theory* (London: Methuen and Co., 1960); C. J. Ballhausen, *Introduction to Ligand Field Theory* (New York: McGraw-Hill, 1962).

[118] H. Bethe, *Ann. Physik.* (5) 3, 133 (1929).

[119] R. G. Pearson, *J. Chem. Educ.,* **38,** 164 (1961).

[120] R. Schlapp and W. G. Penney, *Phys. Rev.,* **42,** 666 (1932); J. H. Van Vleck, *Theory of Electric and Magnetic Susceptibilities* (London, Oxford U.P., 1932).

[121] R. Finkelstein and J. H. Van Vleck, *J. Chem. Phys.,* **8,** 790 (1940); H. Hartman, *Theorie der Chemischen Bindung,* (Berlin: Springer-Verlag, 1954), p. 221.

[122] L. E. Orgel, *J. Chem. Soc.,* 4756 (1952).

In a coordination compound, the z axis is taken as the major axis and the central metal ion is on this axis. For a coordination number of four, there are two principal geometric arrangements, the tetrahedral and the square planar configurations. In the square planar arrangement, the $d_{x^2-y^2}$ orbital has the highest energy because it is nearest the negative charges. This has been vividly illustrated by Pearson[123] as shown in Fig. 1.23. An orbital which points to a ligand is raised in energy (lower sta-

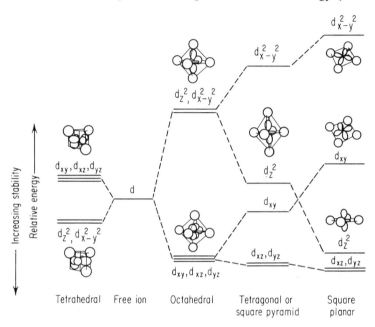

Fig. 1.23. Chart and models of the crystal field splittings of d orbitals of central ion in regular coordination complexes of various arrangements. Redrawn from Pearson.[123]

bility) because then an electron in this orbital is repulsed more by the negatively charged ligand. The d_{xy} orbital is next in energy since it is still in the plane of the negative charges, but has nodes along the two axes described by the ligand atoms (x and y axes). The d_{z^2} orbital is next to the lowest in energy because it has only a small probability in the plane of the ligands. The lowest-energy d orbitals are the degenerate d_{xz} and d_{yz} orbitals which point away from the ligands and have nodes in the plane of the ligands. The relative energies of the tetrahedral arrangement are just the reverse of the square planar.

For a square pyramid, the relative energies of the d orbitals are the same as for the square planar structure except for the effect of two addi-

[123] R. G. Pearson, *Chem. Eng. News*, June 29, 1959, p. 72. Copyright 1959 by the American Chemical Society. Reprinted with permission.

tional charges along the symmetry axis. This charge decreases the energy of the d_{xy} orbital below that of the d_{z^2} orbital.

The geometric arrangement for a coordination number of six is with the six negative charges at the corners of an octahedron. If the six ligands are identical, then the triply degenerate d_{xz}, d_{yz}, and d_{xy} orbitals are more stable than the doubly degenerate d_{z^2} and $d_{x^2-y^2}$ orbitals by an amount denoted $10D_q$. The two groups are commonly designated t_{2g} and e_g, respectively. An energy diagram for this model is given in Fig. 1.24.[124,125] The quantity $10D_q$, representing Δ, may be divided into two

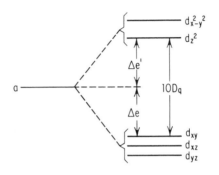

Fig. 1.24. Energy diagram for an octahedral ligand field. Redrawn from Maneh and Fernelius.[124]

portions, Δe and $\Delta e'$. The stabilization portion is Δe, and $\Delta e'$ is a destabilization energy from any electrons occupying the e_g orbitals. When the d orbitals are completely filled, the energy lost must equal the energy gained. Since the low-energy orbitals can accommodate six electrons and the upper ones can hold four electrons, we have

$$6 \Delta e = 4 \Delta e' \quad \text{and} \quad 6 \Delta e + 4 \Delta e' = 10D_q$$

Therefore,

$$\Delta e = 4D_q, \quad \Delta e' = 6D_q$$

Hence, the relative energies of the d orbitals for the octahedral complex, in terms of D_q, are

d_{xy}	d_{xz}	d_{yz}	d_{z^2}	$d_{x^2-y^2}$
-4	-4	-4	6	6

When an electron enters a t_{2g} orbital there is a stabilization of $-4D_q$, and of $+6D_q$ when it enters an e_g orbital. For a distribution of, say, six

[124]W. Maneh and W. C. Fernelius, *J. Chem. Educ.*, **38**, 192 (1961).

[125]P. George and D. S. McClure, *Progress in Inorganic Chemistry*, vol. 1 (New York: Interscience, 1959), pp. 381 ff.

electrons in the lower levels and two in the upper, the crystal field stabilization energy would be $(6 \times -4D_q) + (2 \times 6D_q) = -12D_q$. The system
is more stable by $12D_q$ than it would be if the d orbitals had not split in
relative energies. CFSE values for one to ten d electrons for an octahedral
complex are given in Table 1.15.

If there are fewer than ten electrons in the d subshell, there will be
alternative distributions of the electrons among the t_{2g} and e_g orbitals. Two
types of interactions between the electrons tend to spread out the electrons over as many orbitals as possible. One is the electrostatic repulsion, which is greater when two electrons occupy the same orbital than
when in separate orbitals. The second is the exchange energy, which is
zero for electrons of opposed spins and is negative (stabilizing) for electrons with parallel spins.

The dependence of this exchange energy upon distribution among orbitals may be illustrated as follows.[116] For a d^5 spin-free configuration
$(t_{2g}\alpha)^3(e_g\alpha)^2$, there are $4 + 3 + 2 + 1 = 10$ exchange interactions,
i.e., ten combinations of interchanging the electrons. For a d^5 spin-paired
configuration $(t_{2g}\alpha)^3(t_{2g}\beta)^2$, e.g.,

there are $2 + 1 + 1 = 4$ exchange interactions. Thus, the spin-free state is
six interaction units (π_e) more stable than the spin-paired state. For a d^4
configuration with a spin-free distribution $(t_{2g}\alpha)^3(e_g\alpha)^1$ there are
$3 + 2 + 1 = 6$ exchange interactions, and for the spin-paired distribution $(t_{2g}\alpha)^3(e_g\beta)^1$ there are three interactions, giving a stabilization of $3\pi_e$ to the spin-free state.

Similar analyses can be made for d^1 to d^{10} configurations, and the results are given in Table 1.15.[116] The reference point of zero energy for the
ligand field effect is taken to be that for random filling of the five d orbitals,
that is, the energy of the d orbitals of the complexed metal ion before
splitting occurs. Only for the d^4–d^7 configurations is there a choice of electron distribution, because with three or fewer electrons the t_{2g} orbitals fill
one by one with parallel spins, and with eight to ten electrons the three
t_{2g} orbitals are already filled and the electrons must go into the e_g orbitals.

Different ligands, such as ions, H_2O, amines, etc., produce different degrees of energy separation (Δ) of the orbitals, usually in the range 20 to 50
kcal/mole. The value of Δ depends primarily on the charge on the central
ion and on the nature of the ligands. For a given central ion, Δ for the
common ligands increases approximately in the order: I^-, Br^-, Cl^-, OH^-,
RCO_2^-, F^-, urea, H_2O, EDTA, pyridine, NH_3, ethylenediamine, NO_2^-,
and CN^-. This is known as the *spectrochemical* series, and is based on the

Table 1.15 Ligand Field Stabilization Energies in D_q Units for an Octahedral Complex[116]

	Number of Electrons													
Number of electrons:	1	2	3	4		5		6		7		8	9	10
				Spin-free	Spin-paired	Spin-free	Spin-paired	Spin-free	Spin-paired	Spin-free	Spin-paired			
Electron distribution:														
e_g				1		2		2		2	1	2	3	4
t_{2g}	1	2	3	3	4	3	5	4	6	5	6	6	6	6
Resultant spins	1	2	3	4	2	5	1	4	0	3	1	2	1	0
Spin exchange interaction (π_e)	0	−1	−3	−6	−3	−10	−4	−10	−6	−11	−9	−13	−16	−20
Electrostatic electron repulsion (π_c)	0	0	0	0	+1	0	+2	+1	+3	+2	+3	+3	+4	+5
Energy in ligand field (D_q)	−4	−8	−12	−6	−16	0	−20	−4	−24	−8	−18	−12	−6	0

shift to shorter wavelengths of the absorption maximum of the central ion produced by the presence of the ligand.[126] It is apparent that Δ is not based on electrostatic forces alone. When Δ is large (strong crystal field), the ligand can "compress" the electrons into the t_{2g} orbitals to give a spin-paired complex. If Δ is small (weak crystal field), then the repulsion between paired-up electrons will be the dominant factor and the electrons will occupy different orbitals as far as possible. The complex will then have a maximum magnetism (spin-free complex). For example, $Fe(H_2O)_6^{+3}$ is a spin-free complex, but the large crystal field of the CN^- ions in $Fe(CN)_6^{-3}$ makes it a spin-paired complex. Pauling's valence bond theory would describe these as "essentially ionic" and "essentially covalent," respectively.

When the d subshell is filled, there can be no crystal field stabilization. Thus, zinc in Zn(II) complexes has ten d electrons and the complexes are less stable than those of Ni(II) or Cu(II) for which the $3d$ subshell is not completely filled.

The magnitude of Δ ($10D_q$) can be approximated by quantum mechanical calculations or it can be determined experimentally from visible absorption spectra.[124] The visible spectrum of a complex is believed to involve the transition of d electrons (or f electrons when appropriate) from lower to higher energy levels within the same subshell. For example, the strong-field complex $Co(NH_3)_6^{+3}$ has six d electrons in the three t_{2g} orbitals. Light absorption at the longest wavelengths will correspond to removing one of these electrons and putting it into an e_g orbital. The final state will be one of two triply degenerate states depending upon the choice of e_g orbitals, and absorption bands associated with the two transitions will be observed for such d^6 complexes. The hydrated manganese and ferric ions are examples of weak-field complexes in which Δ is too small to prevent the electrons from spreading into separate orbitals. The same is true of the hydrated ferrous ion which has six d electrons, but where the sixth goes into one of the t_{2g} orbitals.

The ligand field theory also offers a satisfactory account of certain unusual bond distances. For example, the crystal lattice of manganese trifluoride is built up of irregular octahedra and has three different Mn—F distances in the lattice: 1.79, 1.91, and 2.09 Å.[127] It is supposed that the electrostatic field of the fluoride ions splits the d orbitals of the Mn^{+3} ion into a lower triplet t_{2g} and upper doublet e_g, and that Δ is not

[126] R. Tsuchida, *Bull. Chem. Soc. Japan,* **13**, 388, 436, 471 (1938); K. Fajans, *Naturwissenschaften,* **11**, 165 (1923). For a review of the relative affinities of ligand atoms see S. Ahrland, J. Chatt, and N. R. Davies, *Quart. Revs.,* **12**, 265 (1958); T. M. Dunn in *Modern Coordination Chemistry,* ed. J. Lewis and R. G. Wilkins (New York: Interscience, 1960), p. 266.

[127] M. A. Hepworth and K. H. Jack, *Acta Cryst.,* **10**, 345 (1957); M. A. Hepworth, K. H. Jack, and R. S. Nyholm, *Nature,* **179**, 211 (1957).

large. The four d electrons in Mn^{+3} will therefore be unpaired and will be distributed one in each of the three t_{2g} orbitals which point in between the fluoride ions, and one in the d_{z^2} orbital. The charge on the last electron will repel the F^- ion on the z axis; this accounts for the large interionic distance of 2.09 Å. Similarly in CrF_2, in which Cr^{+2} is isoelectronic with Mn^{+3}, the Cr—F distance is 2.43 Å along the z axis but only 2.01 and 1.98 Å along the x and y directions.

Crystal field theory alone does not account for the relative stabilities of several ligand-types; the explanation is assumed to be that the theory does not recognize π bonding. Accordingly, the combined use of crystal field and M.O. theories, referred to as ligand field theory, offers the best approach to date for interpreting various properties of coordination compounds, such as their stabilities, spectra, magnetic character, rates of reactions, redox potentials, and stereochemical properties.

This section has dealt primarily with the theories of bonding in chelates. It should be pointed out that empirical approaches have been used too. For illustration, some correlations between types of bonding and infrared spectra of chelates have been drawn. It has been found,[128(a)] for example, that when the carboxylate peak (C=O stretch) of amino acid chelates is in the region 1550–1610 cm^{-1}, the metal-oxygen bonding is primarily ionic; when this peak is in the 1630–1660 cm^{-1} region, the bonding is essentially covalent; and when the peak occurs between these two regions, the bonding is probably of intermediate ionic and covalent character. On this basis, for example, it was concluded that the bonding in the EDTA chelates of Al(III), Ce(III), and Bi(III) is primarily ionic, whereas in the EDTA chelates of V(III), Cr(III), Fe(III), Co(III), Ti(IV), Th(IV), Mo(VI), the bonding is chiefly covalent.[128(b)]

1.4.4 STRUCTURAL PARAMETERS AND CHELATE STABILITY

Section 1.4.3 discussed the nature of the metal-ligand bond in coordination compounds and it was found that the stereochemistry and stability of chelates depend upon the cation and the type of ligands involved. The important properties of these compounds that affect the stability of the chelate can be grouped as shown in Table 1.16. The first two groups affect the stability of coordination compounds in general and will be discussed only briefly.

1. **Charge Density.** Other things being equal, the stability of the chelate ring should increase with the ionic charge and decrease with the ionic radius

---

[128](a) Cf. D. T. Sawyer and P. T. Paulsen, *J. Am. Chem. Soc.,* **80,** 1597 (1958), and references cited therein; (b) D. T. Sawyer and J. M. McKinnie, *J. Am. Chem. Soc.,* **82,** 4191 (1960).

Table 1.16 STRUCTURAL PARAMETERS AFFECTING THE
STABILITY OF COORDINATION COMPOUNDS

Metal ion	Complexing compound	Chelating agent
1. Charge density	3. Basicity	5. Resonance effects
2. Available orbitals	4. Spatial requirements	6. Entropy effects
		7. Steric effects

of the metal ion. In general,[129] such a relationship is observed for chelates of high ionic character (such as those of the alkali metals and alkaline earth metals), and adherence to the relationship is sometimes used as a criterion for distinguishing ionic from covalent bonding.[130]

2. Available Orbitals. Considerable discussion has already been given to the dependence of stereochemical, magnetic, stability, and other properties of chelates on the type of orbitals used in the coordinate covalent bonding. In comparing the stabilities of chelates of a given chelating agent with various ions, usually there is a good linear relationship between stability constants and the ionization potentials of the central ions.[131,132] Since electron pairs from ligand atoms occupy vacant orbitals on the central metal ion, the energy required to remove an electron from these orbitals should be a good measure of the coordinate covalent bond strength.[131(a)] Thus, a plot of the last ionization potentials of the metals to produce the specific ions, i.e., the second ionization potential for divalent ions and the third ionization potential for trivalent ions, is found to be linearly related to the stability constants of metal chelates with a given chelating agent. Other empirical relationships have been drawn between stability constants and such properties as the electronegativity of the metal,[131(c)] or with the product of electronegativity and hybrid bond strength.[131(a)] The stability of complexes formed from bivalent ions of the first transition series usually follows the order, Mn < Fe < Co < Ni < Cu > Zn, irrespective of the ligand.[133] Except for zinc, this sequence follows the order of the second ionization potentials of the elements [cf. Table 1.17].

3. Basicity of Ligand Atoms. Coordinate covalent bonding is equivalent to neutralization in the Lewis sense, and we might expect to find a strong

[129] H. J. Emeleus and J. S. Anderson, *Modern Aspects of Inorganic Chemistry* (2nd ed.; London: Routledge and Kegan-Paul, 1952), p. 166.

[130] M. M. Jones, *Science,* **121,** 371 (1955).

[131] (a) M. Calvin in *The Mechanism of Enzyme Action,* ed. W. D. McElroy and B. Glass, (Baltimore, Md.: Johns Hopkins Press, 1954), p. 255; (b) H. Freiser, *Rec. Chem. Progress,* **14,** 202 (1953); C. L. Van Panthaleon Van Eck, *Rec. trav. chim.,* **72,** 50, 529 (1953); (c) W. C. Fernelius, *et al., J. Am. Chem. Soc.,* **76,** 379 (1954).

[132] M. Calvin and N. Melchoir, *J. Am. Chem. Soc.,* **70,** 3270 (1948); H. Irving and R. J. P. Williams, *Nature,* **162,** 746 (1948).

[133] H. Irving and R. J. P. Williams, *J. Chem. Soc.,* 3192 (1953).

Table 1.17 The Ionization Potentials of the
First Transition Metal Series

Metal	Ionization Potential (in ev)		
	First	Second	Third
Sc	6.56	12.80	24.75
Ti	6.83	13.57	24.47
V	6.74	14.65	29.31
Cr	6.76	16.49	30.95
Mn	7.43	15.64	33.69
Fe	7.90	16.18	30.64
Co	7.86	17.05	33.49
Ni	7.63	18.15	35.16
Cu	7.72	20.29	36.83
Zn	9.39	17.96	39.70

parallel in stability of chelates with the basicity of ligand atoms.   This
was first shown to be the case by Calvin[134] and his coworkers for a large
number of copper chelates. They found a linear relationship between stability constants and pK_a of the chelating agents. The weaker is the acid
strength of a chelating agent HKe, i.e., the greater is the base strength of
the ion of the complexing agent, the more stable is the chelate. That is,
there is the same relative order of attraction of the chelate ion for protons
as for metal ions. This is only a restricted generality, of course, for other
structural factors may upset the relationship.

In a series of chelates of type V

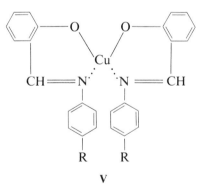

V

where R may be varied to change the basicity of the nitrogen atom, the
order of increasing stability of V is found to be in the order $R = NO_2 <$
$SO_3Na < C_6H_5 < H < CH_3 < OH < OCH_3$. With the exception of the

[134]M. Calvin and K. W. Wilson, *J. Am. Chem. Soc.*, **67**, 2003 (1945); M. Calvin and
R. H. Bailes, *J. Am. Chem. Soc.*, **68**, 949 (1946).

inverted order of the last two, this is also the order of increasing base strength of the correspondingly p-substituted anilines.

It is to be expected, then, that factors which affect the basicity of the donor atoms of chelating agents will affect the stability of the chelates. One such factor is the inductive effect. For example, α-amino acids readily form chelates, but when electron-withdrawing groups are on the amino nitrogen atom, e.g., the N-nitroamino acids,

$$CH_2{-}COOH$$
$$|$$
$$O_2N{-}NH$$

they may have little tendency to form chelates.

4. Spatial Requirements. It has been shown that not only chelates but co-ordination complexes in general are more stable the greater is the base strength of the ligands.[135] For example, the log of the stability constants of silver ion towards primary amines varies linearly with the pK_a of the amines.[135)a)] Thus, the affinities of the proton and the silver ion towards the amines are quite similar. Similarly, the crowding of groups about the nitrogen atom in the amine not only lowers its affinity for protons,[136] but also lowers its tendency to complex with metal ions.[135]

The steric effect on chelate stability will be discussed below (item 7).

5. Resonance Effects. Calvin[134,137] and his group were also the first to show that a major factor contributing to the stability of chelate rings is resonance —for example, among forms such as **VI** (a) and (b).

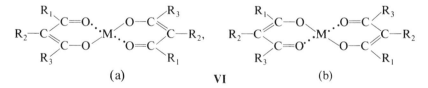

(a)   **VI**   (b)

They even suggested that there might be some degree of benzenoid resonance of type **VII** in each ring,[142]

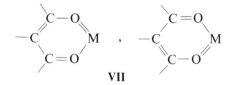

VII

---

[135](a) R. J. Bruehlman and F. H. Verhoek, *J. Am. Chem. Soc.,* **70,** 1401 (1948); (b) J. Bjerrum, *Chem. Revs.,* **46,** 381 (1950).

[136] For a discussion of this effect, see Sec. 3.4.

[137] M. Calvin, *et al., J. Am. Chem. Soc.,* **70,** 3270, 3273 (1948); **68,** 557 (1946).

in which the metal back-donates d electrons. Evidence has accumulated in recent years to support this proposal.[139-141] For example, in *tris*-(acetylacetonato)-iron(III), the chelate ring is planar, the two M—O distances are of equal length, the two C—C bonds are of equal length (1.39 Å, the same as in benzene), and the two C—O bonds are of equal length (1.28 Å, between the single- and double-bond distances).[138] Furthermore, in addition to the extraordinary hydrolytic and thermal stability, many chelates of 1,3 diketones readily undergo electrophilic *substitution* such as halogenation, acetylation, formylation, and nitration.[140] It is noteworthy that the introduction of *m*-directing groups into one ring deactivates the other ring. The rings are extremely inert towards nucleophilic reagents.

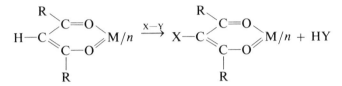

For resonance of type VI the six-membered ring must have two double bonds, and any effect which diminishes the double-bond character of these bonds will decrease the stability of the chelate.[134,143] Thus, cross-conjugation with the chelate ring has such a destabilizing effect. For illustration, VIII is a typical stable chelate whereas IX is difficult to prepare and is unstable in solution.

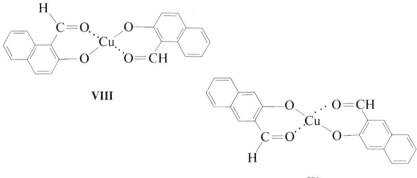

[138] R. B. Roof, Jr., *Acta Cryst.,* **9,** 781 (1956).

[139] A. H. Maki and B. R. McGarvey, *J. Chem. Phys.,* **29,** 31 (1958).

[140] J. P. Collman, R. A. Moss, H. Maltz, C. C. Heindel, and E. T. Kittleman, *J. Am. Chem. Soc.,* **83,** 531 (1961); *Chem. and Ind.* (London), 1213 (1960).

[141] K. Nakamoto, P. J. McCarthy, and A. E. Martell, *J. Am. Chem. Soc.,* **83,** 1272 (1961).

[142] For comments not in agreement, see R. H. Holm and F. A. Cotton, *J. Am. Chem. Soc.,* **80,** 5658 (1959); R. W. Kluiber, *J. Am. Chem. Soc.,* **82,** 4839 (1960).

[143] T. J. Lane, C.S.C., A. Sam, and A. J. Kandathil, *J. Am. Chem. Soc.,* **82,** 4462 (1960).

This can be attributed to the fact that the carbon-carbon bond of the chelate ring in VIII is the C_1—C_2 bond of a naphthalene ring whereas in IX it is the C_2—C_3 bond of a naphthalene ring. Since the bond order[144] of the C_1—C_2 bond of naphthalene is greater than that of the C_2—C_3 bond, the carbon-carbon bond of VIII has a greater double-bond character than in IX. Consistent with this observation, it is found that the C=C bond in the chelate rings of X, XI, XII, and XIII have progressively lower bond orders, and this is the order of the decreasing stability of their copper[134,137] and hydrogen chelates[145] (intramolecular hydrogen bonding).

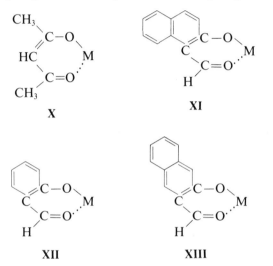

Another illustration of this cross-conjugation effect on the chelate resonance is found in the chelates of acetoacetic esters.

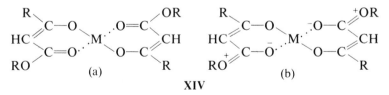

XIV

Hydrogen and metal chelates of acetoacetic esters are much less stable than those of acetylacetone (X), which can be attributed to the cross-conjugation of the ester group resonance as in XIV(b). It is noteworthy that this decrease in stability occurs in spite of the fact that the ester group resonance increases the electron density at the carbonyl oxygen atoms.

---

[144]The bond order is a number to express the degree to which a given bond resembles a single (= 1), double (= 2), or a triple (= 3) bond. Bond orders are discussed in Sec. 4.6.

[145]I. M. Hunsberger, *J. Am. Chem. Soc.*, **72**, 5626 (1950).

The chelate ring resonance may also involve the metal ion. For illustration, the structures of chelates of α,α'-dipyridyl or o-phenanthroline are resonance hybrids of forms XV(a), (b), and (c).

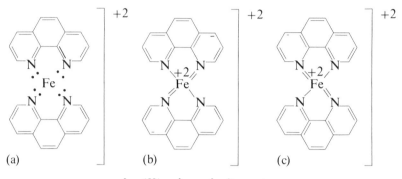

Iron(II) o-phenanthroline cation   **XV**

Not only do infrared spectra[146] indicate some double-bond character for the metal-nitrogen bonds, but it is significant that chelation renders the o-phenanthroline nucleus more susceptible to coupling with diazonium salts[147] (i.e., increases their electron density) and the chelates have an unusually high stability.[148]

Other outstanding examples of this resonance stabilization of chelates are the naturally occurring pigments such as chlorophyll, heme, and the phthalocyanines. Resonance among forms such as XVI, in which only the porphyrin ring is shown, accounts for the fact that these compounds are not destroyed by concentrated mineral acids[149] and sometimes may be sublimed at elevated temperatures without decomposition.[150]

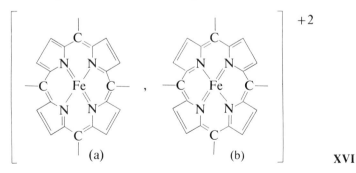

XVI

[146] D. H. Busch and J. C. Bailar, *J. Am. Chem. Soc.*, **78**, 1137 (1956).

[147] V. I. Kuznetsov, *Chem. Abs.*, **45**, 1452 f. (1952).

[148] G. K. Schweitzer and J. M. Lee, *J. Phys. Chem.*, **56**, 195 (1952); G. T. Morgan and F. H. Burstall, *J. Chem. Soc.*, 2213 (1931).

[149] S. Granick and H. Gilder, *Advances in Enzymology*, **7**, 305 (1947).

[150] R. P. Linstead, *et al.*, *J. Chem. Soc.*, 1744 (1936).

6. Entropy Effects. The free energy of formation of a chelate may be determined from the relationship

$$\Delta F = \Delta H - T\Delta S = -RT \ln K$$

where K is the stability constant and the other symbols have their usual thermodynamic meaning. Also, by measuring K at two or more temperatures, one may determine ΔH. This permits a calculation of ΔS, the entropy change for chelation. This has been done for many chelates,[150] and it has been found in some cases that the entropy factor is quite significant. For example, the heats of formation of the complexes $Cd(NH_3)_4^{+2}$ and $Cd(NH_2CH_3)_4^{+2}$ are practically the same, so that the greater stability of the latter complex can attributed to the observed increase in entropy.

Several factors may be responsible for the entropy effect in chelation. The simplest interpretation might be to attribute it to an increase in translational degrees of freedom by the larger number of molecules released in chelate formation.[151(a)] However, it has been pointed out that the change in translational entropy is severalfold larger than the "chelation effect" and that entropy contribution from other changes, such as for cyclization and solvation, must be considered.[152] The entropy of cyclization may be approximated from entropy changes accompanying ring-closure reactions, e.g.,

$$n\text{-hexane} \longrightarrow \text{cyclohexane} + H_2.$$

It is observed that a change in freedom of rotation has a marked effect on the stability of chelates. The pairs of chelates XVII and XVIII, and XIX and XX, have almost identical structures except for the presence of an additional chelate ring in each pair. By joining the groups attached to the donor nitrogen atoms there results a much more stable chelate as shown by their half-wave reduction potentials.[151(a)] The more negative the $E_{1/2}$ value, the more stable is the chelate. On the other hand, the increase in stability will be lessened if there is some strain in forming the third ring. Thus the stability of XXI is between that of XIX and XX.

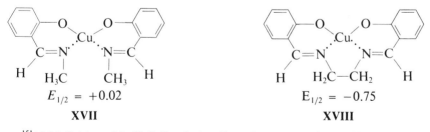

$$E_{1/2} = +0.02 \qquad\qquad E_{1/2} = -0.75$$

XVII **XVIII**

[151](a) M. Calvin and R. H. Bailes, *J. Am. Chem. Soc.*, **68**, 949 (1946); (b) C. G. Spike and R. W. Parry, *ibid.*, **75**, 2726 (1953); (c) R. M. Izatt, W. C. Fernelius, C. G. Haas, and B. P. Block, *J. Phys. Chem.*, **59**, 170, 235 (1955); L. Sacconi, G. Lombardo, and P. Paoletti, *J. Chem. Soc.*, 848 (1958).

[152]F. H. Westheimer and L. L. Ingraham, *J. Am. Chem. Soc.*, **60**, 1668 (1956).

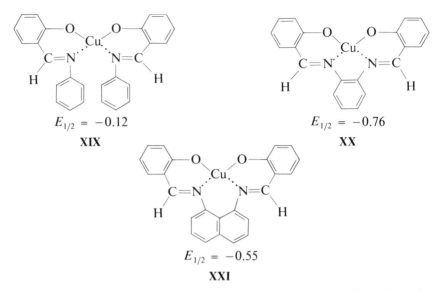

$$E_{1/2} = -0.12$$
XIX

$$E_{1/2} = -0.76$$
XX

$$E_{1/2} = -0.55$$
XXI

Another example of the increase in stability of complexes brought about by ring formation is the unusual stability of chelated boronites. For example, ethyl acetoacetyl boronites, unlike dialkyl- and diphenylboronites, are completely stable in the atmosphere and are inert to cold water and dilute acids.[153]

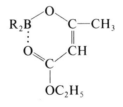

An ethyl acetoacetyl boronite

7. Steric Effects. Spatial requirements may affect the stability of chelates in two ways. Ring strain may weaken the chelate ring, or spatial interference may "mechanically" block ring formation around the metal ion. For example, the formation constant of the silver-ammonia complex is larger than that of the silver-ethylenediamine chelate. This reversal in the usual order of stability of ammonia and ethylenediamine complexes can be attributed to the weakened Ag—N bonds in the Ag(en)$^+$ chelate. Silver normally uses linear *sp* orbitals, which would be under severe strain in the cyclic structure.

$$H_2N\cdots Ag\cdots NH_2 \Big]^+$$
$$CH_2-CH_2$$

[153]W. Gerrard, M. F. Lappert, and R. Shafferman, *Chem. and Ind.*, 722 (1958).

The steric effect shows up most commonly through its hinderance to chelate formation. For example, 1,10-phenanthroline is used in analytical chemistry as an indicator owing to its formation of the red $[Fe(phen)_3]^{+2}$ ion, where phen stands for phenanthroline. However, even though the nitrogen atoms in 2,9-dimethyl-1,10-phenanthroline are more basic than the parent compound, the dimethyl derivative does not even produce a color with ferrous ions.[154]

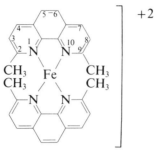

This can be attributed to the spatial interference of the methyl groups which prevent the close approach of the phenanthroline ligands for chelate formation.

For similar reasons, substitution of alkyl groups on the nitrogen atoms of ethylenediamine decreases the stability of the complexes with metal ions relative to the ethylenediamine complexes.[155] Isopropyl groups, e.g., i—$PrNH$—CH_2CH_2—$NHPr$—i and N-isopropylglycine, actually block the formation of the ordinary type of complex with nickel and copper ions.[156]

Sometimes the size of the metal ion is critical for chelate formation. For example, oxine forms a chelate with the Mg^{+2} iron but not with the Be^{+2} ion.

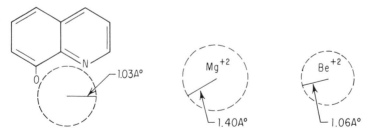

Apparently, the ionic size of the beryllium ion is just a little too small to form the chelate. On the other hand, owing to crowded spatial conditions

[154]M. Yasuda, K. Sone, and K. Yamasaki, *J. Phys. Chem.,* **60,** 1667 (1956).

[155]H. M. Irving and J. M. M. Griffiths, *J. Chem. Soc.,* 213 (1954).

[156]F. Basolo and R. K. Murmann, *J. Am. Chem. Soc.,* **76,** 211 (1954); F. Basolo and Y. T. Chen, *J. Am. Chem. Soc.,* **76,** 953 (1954).

in hexamethylacetylacetone, $(CH_3)_3C-C(OH)=CH-CO-C(CH_3)_3$, it preferably binds small ions and can be used to separate the small Li^+ ion from the other alkali metal ions.[157]

As stated at the beginning of Sec. 1.4.1, this discussion of chelates has been concerned primarily with the coordinate covalent bonding in chelates and with structural parameters which profoundly affect their stabilities. Some aspects of particular interest, for example, would have been their reversible oxygen-carrying abilities,[158] the role of chelates in biological systems,[159] and the use of chelates in analytical separations. The uses and applications of chelates are of tremendous value but are beyond the scope of this book.

1.5 Molecular Bonds

There are several classes of compounds which owe their existence to what is probably best described as an *intermolecular coordinate covalent bond*. This is a bond very similar to the coordinate covalent bond just discussed, but instead of the electron pair being provided by a single atom it is supplied by a group of atoms. It will be described in detail presently, at which time it will become clear why it is called here a *molecular bond*. Types of substances containing such a bond are the "sandwich" compounds, the molecular addition compounds, and CT complexes.

1.5.1 METALLOCENES [160, 161]

One of the exciting rewards of laboratory work is that occasionally there will be entirely unexpected results which, if recognized, will open up a new area of science or will yield a product of high commercial value. Many chemical discoveries were made by accident. One of the most financially successful was the discovery of the production of dynamite by Alfred Nobel. Other familiar examples are the vulcanization of rubber by Charles Good-

---

[157] G. A. Guter and G. S. Hammond, *J. Am. Chem. Soc.,* **78,** 5166 (1956).

[158] M. Calvin, *et al., J. Am. Chem. Soc.,* **68,** 2254, 2263, 2267, 2273 (1946); R. H. Bailes and M. Calvin, *J. Am. Chem. Soc.,* **69,** 1886 (1947); L. F. Larksworthy and R. S. Nyholm, *Nature,* **183,** 1377 (1959).

[159] R. J. P. Williams, *Biol. Revs. Cambridge Phil. Soc.,* **28,** 381 (1953); *The Mechanism of Enzyme Action,* ed. W. D. McElroy and B. Glass (Baltimore Johns Hopkins Press, 1954), p. 221 (M. Calvin), p. 257 (I. M. Klotz), and p. 291 (E. L. Smith, N. C. Davis, E. Adams, and D. H. Spackman).

[160] For an extensive recent review of metallocenes, see E. O. Fischer and H. P. Fritz in *Advances in Inorganic Chemistry and Radiochemistry,* ed. H. J. Emeleus and A. G. Sharpe, vol. 1 (New York: Academic Press, 1959), pp. 55–115.

[161] G. Wilkinson and F. A. Cotton, *Progress in Inorganic Chemistry,* vol. 1 (New York: Interscience, 1959), p. 1; M. D. Rausch, *J. Chem. Educ.,* **37,** 568 (1960).

year, lead tetraethyl by Thomas Midgley, synthetic dyes by William Perkin, radioactivity by Henri Becquerel, the urea inclusion complexes by Friederich Bengen, and triphenylmethyl free radicals by Moses Gomberg. Such was also the case in 1951 when Kealy and Pauson[162] discovered ferrocene by accident. They were attempting to prepare fulvalene by oxidizing cyclopentadienemagnesium bromide with anhydrous ferric chloride in ether solution. Instead of getting the expected fulvalene, they isolated an unusually stable iron-containing orange product whose analysis agreed with the formula $C_{10}H_{10}Fe$. This was later given the name *ferrocene* to indicate its aromatic character.[164]

Fulvalene

The methylene hydrogen atoms of cyclopentadiene may be replaced to produce three different types of bonds to the carbon atom.

1. The hydrogens are acidic enough to be replaced by an active metal or a Grignard reagent to yield an essentially ionic bond.

$$\begin{array}{c} CH{=}CH\\ |\qquad\quad\\ CH{=}CH \end{array}\!\!\!\!CH_2 + Na \longrightarrow \begin{array}{c} CH{=}CH\\ |\qquad\quad\\ CH{=}CH \end{array}\!\!\!\!CH^- Na^+ + \tfrac{1}{2}H_2$$

$$\begin{array}{c} CH{=}CH\\ |\qquad\quad\\ CH{=}CH \end{array}\!\!\!\!CH_2 + RMgX \longrightarrow \begin{array}{c} CH{=}CH\\ |\qquad\quad\\ CH{=}CH \end{array}\!\!\!\!CH^- MgX^+ + RH$$

Normally, the alkali, the alkaline earth, and the rare earth metals form this type of salt. The salts have the color of the cation, hydrolyze in water, react with the air, and are insoluble in hydrocarbons but may be moderately soluble in ether.

2. A second type of bond with the cyclopentadienyl ring is a covalent bond to another carbon atom or to a silicon atom. For example, 5,5-dimethylcyclopentadiene and 5-cyclopentadienylsilane are typical organic compounds.

$$\begin{array}{c} CH{=}CH\\ |\qquad\quad\\ CH{=}CH \end{array}\!\!\!\!C(CH_3)_2 \qquad\qquad \begin{array}{c} CH{=}CH\\ |\qquad\quad\\ CH{=}CH \end{array}\!\!\!\!CH{-}Si(CH_3)_3$$

5,5-dimethylcyclopentadiene   *5-cyclopentadienyltrimethylsilane*

[162] T. J. Kealy and P. L. Pauson, *Nature,* **168,** 1039 (1951). A convenient preparation of ferrocene from sodium cyclopentadienide and ferrous chloride is given by G. Wilkinson in *Organic Synthesis,* vol. 36, ed. N. J. Leonard (New York; Wiley, 1956).

[163] J. D. Dunitz, L. E. Orgel, and A. Rich, *Acta Cryst.,* **9,** 373 (1956); E. A. Seibold and L. E. Sutton, *J. Chem. Phys.,* **23,** 1967 (1955).

[164] R. B. Woodward, M. Rosenblum, and M. C. Whiting, *J. Am. Chem. Soc.,* **74,** 3458 (1952).

It is significant that the cyclopentadienyl ring in these compounds still undergoes the Diels-Alder reaction, as does also cyclopentadiene.

3. A third type of metal-cyclopentadienyl bond is a molecular bond. This third type of bond is formed primarily with the transition elements which have available d orbitals. The most extensively studied compound of this type is *bis*-(cyclopentadienyl)-iron, $(C_5H_5)_2Fe$, commonly called *ferrocene*.[170] Ferrocene is an orange, crystalline solid, which melts at 173–174° and boils near 249°. It is soluble in common organic solvents, such as benzene, ether, and alcohol; it is insoluble in water; and it is unaffected by alkali and boiling concentrated hydrochloric acid. Crystalline samples of these fairly covalent metal-organics have been studied by X-ray and electron diffraction[163] and found to consist of the metal packed between two parallel cyclopentadienyl rings, which explains their common name of *sandwich compounds*. A more dignified name is *metallocene*.

The covalent character of the metallocenes is apparent from their solubility, volatility, and other properties. This indicates that each $C_5H_5^-$ ion donates an electron pair to the metal ion. Ferrocene is diamagnetic, hence its six $3d$ electrons are paired up to make available two open $3d$ orbitals.

However, the electron pair does not come from the former methylenic carbon alone. If it did, each ring would still have two typical double bonds and would have properties resembling those of cyclopentadiene. To the contrary, ferrocene does not undergo a Diels-Alder reaction with maleic anhydride, it is not hydrogenated over a platinum catalyst, it undergoes *substitution* reactions rather than addition reactions, it does not polymerize, and side chains may be oxidized without affecting the rings. All of these properties are typical for benzene but not for cyclopentadiene. Furthermore, infrared spectra and diffraction studies show that all C—C bond lengths are the same, about 1.4 Å, and that there is only one type of C—H bond in the cyclopentadienyl rings.[165] Thus, each ring may be regarded as a complete resonance hybrid of the five equivalent forms

in which there are six π electrons in the ring. This is the situation for benzene and other aromatic rings.[166]

[165] E. R. Lippincott and R. D. Nelson, *Spectrochim. Acta*, **10**, 307 (1958).

[166] The similarity in physical and chemical properties of benzene, cyclopentadienyl, and other *aromatic* rings is discussed in Sec. 4.9.

To account for the covalent and aromatic character of ferrocene-type compounds, they have been given the pentagonal antiprismatic structure XXII, where M is the metal.

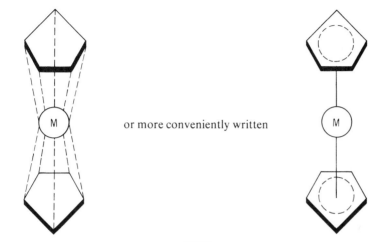

or more conveniently written

XXII

It is implied that the metal interacts equally with each carbon atom of the ring and that the bonding is covalent. The bond is well described by the term *intermolecular coordinate covalent bond,* but for brevity will be called a *molecular bond.* Thus, we will define a molecular bond as one in which two or more atoms of a molecular species donate π electrons to another species to form a delocalized covalent bond. As with coordinate covalent bonds, the covalent or ionic character of molecular bonds will vary but will generally be more covalent than ionic.

The molecular bond, in ferrocene for example, represents exactly what is meant by the term covalent bond: one in which both components share electron pairs and act as if the electron pairs belonged solely to each component. For illustration, the iron in ferrocene is diamagnetic only because its $3d$ electrons are paired up to make available two d orbitals for an electron pair from each cyclopentadienide ion. At the same time, each cyclopentadienyl group can have an aromatic character only if it has the three pairs of π electrons. Thus, the metal and the rings act as if each still has the bonding electron pairs. Nevertheless, there is no net charge on the cyclopentadienyl rings. This is shown by the values of the dissociation constants of ferrocenedicarboxylic acid in aqueous alcohol.[164]

$$\begin{array}{lll}
\text{Ferrocenedicarboxylic acid} & K_1 & 3.1 \times 10^{-7} \\
& K_2 & 2.7 \times 10^{-8} \\
\text{Benzoic acid} & K & 2.4 \times 10^{-7}
\end{array}$$

That is, the value for K_1 is very nearly the same as that of benzoic acid, in which the COOH group is attached to an uncharged ring. One may conclude, therefore, that the ferrocenyl group is also neutral.[167] If it is true that the cyclopentadienyl rings in ferrocene are substantially uncharged, then the iron also must be neutral because ferrocene is a neutral substance.

A large number of metallocenes have been prepared and studied since their discovery in 1951. Several different aromatic rings, such as indene, azulene, benzene, and others, will also form these metallocenes.[169] In many metallocenes, carbon monoxide or nitric oxide molecules are found in place of one of the aromatic rings.

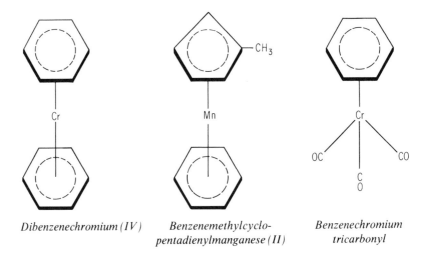

Dibenzenechromium (IV)   Benzenemethylcyclo-   Benzenechromium
                        pentadienylmanganese (II)   tricarbonyl

Metallocenes undergo most of the typical aromatic reactions such as acylation, arylation, metalation, various condensations, sulfonation, etc., and even formation of relatively stable carbonium ions.[170, 171] Thus, all of the general types of benzene derivatives are known for the ferrocene series. Most oxidizing agents oxidize the iron to the ferric state to produce ferricinium ions, $(C_5H_5)_2Fe^+$. Owing to this ease of oxidation of the iron,

[167] Dipole moments[168] show that inductive effects of the phenyl and ferrocenyl groups are approximately the same. However, the 20-fold greater basicity of ferrocenylamine over that of aniline suggests that the n, π electron-donor resonance of the amino group in ferrocenylamine is less than in aniline.

[168] P. L. Pauson, *Quart. Revs.*, **9**, 400 (1955).

[169] E. O. Fischer and H.-P. Fritz, *Angew. Chemie*, **73**, 353 (1961).

[170] For a summary of derivatives of ferrocene, see K. Plesske, *Angew. Chem.*, **74**, 301, 347 (1962).

[171] J. H. Richards and E. A. Hill, *J. Am. Chem. Soc.*, **81**, 3484 (1959).

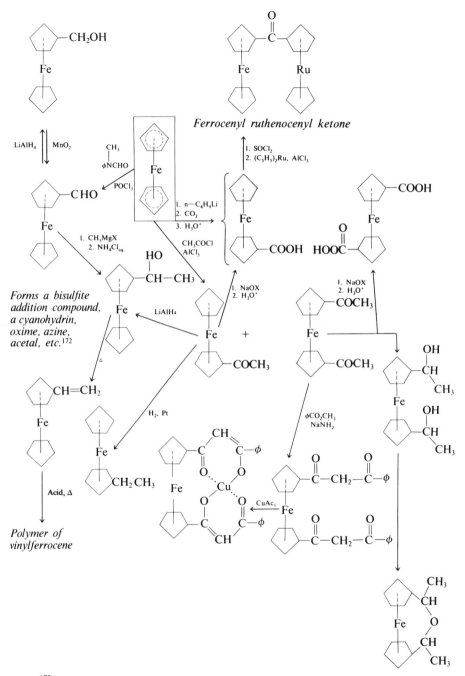

Ferrocenyl ruthenocenyl ketone

Forms a bisulfite addition compound, a cyanohydrin, oxime, azine, acetal, etc.[172]

Polymer of vinylferrocene

[172] P. J. Graham, R. V. Lindsey, G. W. Parshall, M. L. Peterson, and G. M. Whitman, *J. Am. Chem. Soc.*, **79**, 3416 (1957).

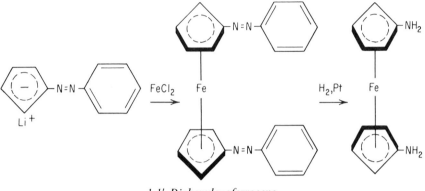

1,1'-Diphenylazoferrocene
black needles, m.p. 183-5°[173]

ferrocene has not been halogenated or nitrated directly, although the sulfo-[174] and the halo-derivatives[175] have been prepared by indirect methods.

The existence of a sandwich configuration does not necessarily imply molecular bonding. For illustration, Mn^{+2} appears to form an ionic sandwich-type compound with cyclopentadienide ion.[176] A chemical test for detecting the occurrence of an ionically bound cyclopentadienide group has been proposed which is based on the tendency for an ionic compound to ionize in moderately polar media.[176(a)]

$$(C_5H_5)_2M \rightleftharpoons C_5H_5M^+ + C_5H_5^-$$

The addition of Fe^{+2} ions should bring about the formation of ferrocene just as do the ionic sodium and Grignard cyclopentadienides.[178] Cobaltocene and nickelocene, which have molecular bonding, yield no trace of ferrocene even on refluxing with ferrous chloride in tetrahydrofuran solution for several hours. By contrast, $(C_5H_5)_2$ Mn reacts instantaneously and quantitatively with ferrous chloride at room temperature to give ferrocene and manganous chloride. Furthermore, the $C_5H_5^-$ ion in the ionic compounds no longer has an aromatic character. For illustration, maleic anhydride reacts with C_5H_5Na, $(C_5H_5)_2Mn$, and $(C_5H_5)_2Mg$ to give similar orange-red adducts. Ferrocene, as stated previously, does not react with maleic anhydride.

Other chemical properties, such as rapid hydrolysis in water, and several physical properties, such as the mass spectra and magnetic data, also suggest Mg^{+2} and Mn^{+2} sandwich compounds to be ionic. For instance, ferrocene, cobaltocene, and nickelocene are nonconducting in liquid ammonia,

[173] G. R. Knox, *Proc. Chem. Soc., (London)*, 56, (1959).

[174] V. Weinmayr, *J. Am. Chem. Soc.*, **77**, 3009 (1955).

[175] A. N. Nesmeyanov, *et al.*, *Doklady Akad. Nauk S.S.S.R.*, **100**, 1009 (1955).

[176] (a) G. Wilkinson, F. A. Cotton, and J. M. Birmingham, *J. Inorg. Nucl. Chem.* **2**, 95 (1956); (b) F. A. Cotton and L, T. Reynolds, *J. Am. Chem. Soc.*, **80**, 269 (1958).

whereas the cyclopentadienides of sodium, magnesium, and manganese(II) are conducting.[176(a)] On the other hand, a recent infrared spectroscopic study of $Mg(C_5H_5)_2$ indicates that $Mg(C_5H_5)_2$ is covalent but has weak metal-ligand bonds. The weakness of these bonds may account for the apparent ionic nature of $Mg(C_5H_5)_2$. The tendency of Mg^{+2} and Mn^{+2} to form ionic rather than molecular bonds can be explained in terms of the electron distributions of these ions. The Mn^{+2} ion has a half-filled $3d$ subshell and the Mg^{+2} has the rare-gas structure of neon. Thus, the filled or half-filled subshells are unusually stable in the $+2$ ionic states. This explanation receives support in the fact that manganese forms $C_5H_5Mn(CO)_3$ and $[C_5H_5Mn(CO)_2NO]^+$ in which the metal is isoelectronic with Fe(II) and forms molecular bonds. 5-Methylcyclopentadiene gives the same types of sandwich compounds as cyclopentadiene.[177] Thus, dimethylferrocene is covalent while manganese(II) methylcyclopentadienide is ionic. The cobalt(III) complex, $(C_5H_5)_2CoCCl_3$, is ionic too.[178] Unlike cobaltocene, which has $Co{-}C_5H_5$ molecular bonds, the trichloromethyl derivative shows the presence of two types of $C{-}H$ bonds, it undergoes a Diels-Alder reaction with maleic anhydride, and it reacts with ferrous chloride to produce small amounts of ferrocene. Thus, at least one ring has lost is aromatic character.

The aromatic character of organic groups in metallocenes varies like that of benzene and other aromatic hydrocarbons. For example, benzene does not undergo the Diels-Alder reaction under the normal conditions, naphthalene does to something less than 1 per cent, and other aromatic hydrocarbons do in slightly higher but still small amounts. Similarly, ferrocene and cyclopentadienylmanganese tricarbonyl[179] are completely inert towards maleic anhydride but the $(C_5H_5)_2M$ compounds of vanadium, chromium, cobalt, and nickel react in an undetermined way. This does not mean that the latter metallocenes are not aromatic but that the energy states of the metals affect the aromatic character of the ring and the ease of oxidation or reduction of the metal. For example, the reaction of $(C_5H_5)_2Co$ with maleic anhydride appears to be not a Diels-Alder addition to the rings but some interaction with the metal.[176(a)]

It is interesting to compare the relative rates of electrophilic substitution of ferrocenyl and phenyl groups. From competitive acylation reactions, the order of decreasing reactivity is[180]

alkylferrocene > ferrocene > anisole >

$$CH_3C_5H_4Mn(CO)_3 > C_5H_5Mn(CO)_3 > benzene$$

[177] L. T. Reynolds and G. Wilkinson, *J. Inorg. Nucl. Chem.,* **9,** 86 (1959).

[178] S. Katz, J. F. Weiher, and A. F. Voigt, *J. Am. Chem. Soc.,* **80,** 6459 (1958).

[179] T. S. Piper, F. A. Cotton, and G. Wilkinson, *J. Inorg. Nucl. Chem.,* **1,** 165 (1955).

[180] J. Kozikowski, R. E. Maginn, and M. S. Klove, *J. Am. Chem. Soc.,* **81,** 2996 (1959); M. Rosenblum, *J. Am. Chem. Soc.,* **81,** 4530 (1959). Compare E. McArnett and R. D. Bushick, *J. Org. Chem.,* **27,** 111 (1962).

The greater reactivity of ferrocene is easily understood in view of the fact that the neutral cyclopentadienyl group would have a negative charge were it to have its full complement of π electrons and this would attract the electrophilic reagent. The donor character of the organic component in metallocenes is also revealed by the increase in acidity of an organic acid or decrease in basicity of an organic base through metallocene formation. The following data illustrate this point, where the pK_a's of free and complexed organic moieties are compared.[169]

Ar in Ar: Cr(CO)$_3$	pK_a	pK_a of free Ar
ϕOH	6.51	9.89
ϕCOOH	4.52	5.16
ϕCH$_2$COOH	5.02	5.64
	pK_b	pK_b
ϕNH$_2$	13.31	11.70

A description of the molecular bonds in these metallocenes has been quite a challenge to theoreticians, and several different views have been expressed.[181] One prominent school proposes that the attainment of a rare-gas electron structure about the metal has much to do with the stability of metallocenes.[182] This would be analogous to the bonding found in stable coordination complexes such as the $Fe(CN)_6^{-4}$ ion in which the metal atom accepts electron pairs from the ligands to fill its $3d$, $4s$, and $4p$ orbitals. For illustration, the isoelectronic complexes $(C_5H_5)_2Fe$, $(C_5H_5)_2Ru$, $(C_5H_5)_2Os$, and $(C_5H_5)_2Co^+$ have the maximum stability among metallocenes and have 18 electrons in the penultimate shell of the metal.

Isoelectronic complex	Outer occupied orbitals about the metal
$(C_5H_5)_2Fe$	$3s^2\ 3p^6\ 3d^{10}$
$(C_5H_5)_2Co^+$	$3s^2\ 3p^6\ 3d^{10}$
$(C_5H_5)_2Ru$	$4s^2\ 4p^6\ 4d^{10}$
$(C_5H_5)_2Os$	$5s^2\ 5p^6\ 5d^{10}$

It is noteworthy that metallocenes of these metals in other oxidation states, in which this rare-gas configuration does not occur, such as $(C_5H_5)_2Co$ and $(C_5H_5)_2Fe^+$, are much less stable in air and more sensitive to hydrolysis. On the other hand, others maintain that the properties of the metallocenes are best explained in terms of molecular bonding between the metal and the organic moieties.

The dependence on available d orbitals for molecular bonding, rather than on s, p, or f orbitals, suggests that the d orbitals of the metal overlap

[181] See E. O. Fischer and H. P. Fritz, p. 93 fn. 160, and references cited there.
[182] Cf. J. W. Linnett, *Trans. Faraday Soc.*, **52**, 904 (1956).

with the π orbitals of the rings. The magnetic and other properties of these compounds can be explained if, according to valence bond theory, one supposes that the metal uses $d^2\,sp^3$ (sp^3 or dsp^2 for coordination number of four) hybrid orbitals for the metal-ring molecular bond (see Table 1.18).

Table 1.18. ELECTRONIC CONFIGURATION OF METALS IN METALLOCENES ACCORDING TO VALENCE BOND THEORY

Metal	Example metallocene	Magnetism in number of unpaired electrons	Occupied orbitals nd	$(n+1)s$	$(n+1)p$
Ti(IV)	$(TiCp_2OH)^+$	0	☐ ☐ ☐ [xx] [xx]	[xx]	☐ ☐ ☐
Ti(III)	$TiCp_2^+$	1	[•] ☐ ☐ [xx] [xx]	[xx]	☐ ☐ ☐
Cr(I)	$Cr\phi_2^+$	1	[••] [••] [•] [xx] [xx]	[xx]	☐ ☐ ☐
Cr(III)	$CrCp_2^+$	3	[•] [•] [•] [xx] [xx]	[xx]	☐ ☐ ☐
V(III)	VCp_2^+	2	[•] [•] ☐ [xx] [xx]	[xx]	☐ ☐ ☐
Mn(II)	$MnCp_2$ (ionic)	5	[•] [•] [•] [•] [•]	[•]	☐ ☐ ☐
Fe(II)	$FeCp_2$	0	[••] [••] [••] [xx] [xx]	[xx]	☐ ☐ ☐
Fe(III)	$FeCp_2^+$	1	[••] [••] [•] [xx] [xx]	[xx]	☐ ☐ ☐
Co(II)	$CoCp_2$	1	[••] [••] [•] [xx] [xx]	[xx]	☐ ☐ ☐
Co(III)	$CoCp_2^+$	0	[••] [••] [••] [xx] [xx]	[xx]	☐ ☐ ☐
Ni(II)	$NiCp_2\,(sp^3\,?)$	2	[••] [••] [••] [•] [•]	[xx]	[xx] ☐ ☐
Ni(III)	$NiCp_2^+(dsp^2\,?)$	1	[••] [••] [••] [•] ☐	☐	☐ ☐ ☐

Cp = cyclopentadienide ion; $\phi = C_6H_6$; · = metal electrons; x = Cp electrons. Dotted line around hybridized bonding orbitals.

Hybrid $d^2\,sp^3$ or sp^3 orbitals are proposed rather than pure d, s, or p orbitals, because X-ray absorption edge measurements on ferrocene indicate that $4p$-level orbitals are involved in the molecular bond.[183] The weakness of this valence-bond description is that it proposes a single bond between the metal and each ring. There are reasons to believe that, in the regions between the metal and each ring, there are as many as three pairs of electrons. A strong advocate of this view is E. O. Fischer,[184] who proposes that the three pairs of π electrons of each ring form a total of six coordinate covalent bonds with the metal. The metal thereby completes its electron shell and assumes its usual coordination number and octahedral shape.

[183] E. O. Fischer, *Rec. trav. chim.*, **75**, 629 (1956).
[184] E. O. Fischer and W. Pfab, *Z. Naturforsch.*, **7b**, 377 (1952).

It is significant that substitution of electron-donating groups on the ferrocene rings greatly facilitates the ease of oxidation of the Fe(II), while electron-withdrawing groups have the opposite effect. For example, amino- and hydroxy-ferrocenes are rapidly and irreversibly oxidized in air. In contrast to this, 1,1'-diacetylferrocene is not oxidized by ferric chloride, although ferrocene itself is. On a quantitative basis, it has been found that the oxidation potentials of p-substituted phenylferrocenes vary linearly with the Hammett sigma constants of the *para* substituents.[185] These observations are in accord with expectation, namely, that the molecular orbitals of the iron and organic rings overlap and any push or pull effect on the electrons of the rings will have a similar effect on the electrons about the metal. Furthermore, any withdrawal of electrons from one ring can diactivate the second ring towards electrophilic substitution. For illustration, the ferrocenyl ring is sufficiently nucleophilic to be formylated with N-methyl-formanilide and phosphorus oxychloride, but only one formyl group can be introduced. After the first group enters, it withdraws electrons not only from the substituted ring but also from the second ring through the metal.

The importance of three pairs of π electrons in the donor ring for molecular bond formation is revealed by the fact that *bis*-indenyl compounds may be hydrogenated in the benzene ring, but only two moles of hydrogen per ring are taken up.[160] The π electrons of the third double bond of the benzene ring must be tied up in the five-membered ring to form the metal-ring molecular bond.

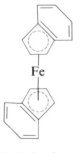

Bis-(indenyl)-iron

Molecular orbital treatments of the bonding in these metallocenes have proposed that the six π electrons of each cyclopentadienide ion and the d electrons of the metal ion are incorporated into the valency shell of the metal nd, $(n + 1)s$, $(n + 1)p$ orbitals to approach that of the inert element.[186] Thus, the complex would have a maximum stability when the total of these

[185] J. G. Mason and M. Rosenblum, *J. Am. Chem. Soc.*, **82**, 4206 (1960).

π and d orbitals is 18. There is general but not complete agreement on which bonding and antibonding orbitals are occupied.

Chemical and physical properties of the *bis*-cyclopentadienyls show that rotation of the rings with respect to each other may occur at normal temperatures in all but the solid state.[187] In the solid state, three conformations are possible for *bis*-substituted metallocenes. *Bis-p*-chlorophenylferrocene is reported to have a *cis* configuration,[188] *bis*-indenyliron has a *gauche* configuration,[189] and ferrocenedicarboxylic acid has the *trans* conformation.[162] Meso (XXIII) and racemic (XXIV) isomers of tetrasubstituted ferrocenes have been isolated as a result of the absence of rotation of the rings in the solid state.[190]

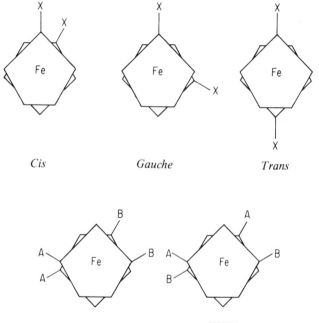

| Cis | Gauche | Trans |

| XXIII | XXIV |

[186] A. D. Liehr and C. J. Ballhausen, *Acta Chem. Scand.,* **11**, 207 (1957); J. W. Linnett, *Trans. Faraday Soc.,* **52**, 904 (1956); W. E. Moffitt, *J. Am. Chem. Soc.,* **76**, 3386 (1954); J. D. Dunitz and L. E. Orgel, *J. Chem. Phys.,* **23**, 954 (1955); H. H. Jaffe, *J. Chem. Phys.,* **21**, 156 (1953).

[187] M. Rosenblum and R. B. Woodward, *J. Am. Chem. Soc.,* **80**, 5443 (1958); P. L. Pauson, *Quart. Revs.,* **9**, 400 (1955).

[188] D. A. Semenow and J. D. Roberts, *J. Am. Chem. Soc.,* **79**, 2741 (1957).

[189] J. Trotter, *Acta Cryst.,* **11**, 355 (1958).

[190] K. L. Rinehart and K. L. Motz, *Chem. and Ind. (London),* 1150 (1957); R. E. Benson and R. V. Lindsey, *J. Am. Chem. Soc.,* **79**, 5471 (1957).

It is rather difficult to prepare metallocenes with heterocyclic rings because of the donor character of the lone-pair electrons on the hetero atom, which tends to form a typical *interatomic* coordinate covalent bond.[191] The thiophene ring is one of the weaker groups with respect to this donor function, and recently carbonylthiophene metallocenes of chromium[192] and iron[193] were prepared. The donor function of the nitrogen atom of the pyridine ring can be blocked by quarternarization. This was done by formation of the N-methiodide salt and it was found that the salt easily forms a metallocene with molybdenum hexacarbonyl.[194] The tricarbonyl-1-methylpyridinemolybdenum iodide is a yellow, crystalline salt, soluble in ethanol and water, but not very soluble in nonpolar solvents.

The aromatizing effect of the metal ion in metallocenes is further revealed by the properties of cyclooctatetraeneiron tricarbonyl, $C_8H_8Fe(CO)_3$. It is produced in a 60–70 per cent yield from iron pentacarbonyl and cyclo-öctatetraene.[195] It is a deep red, crystalline compound which melts at 92° and is very soluble in organic solvents. Its nuclear magnetic resonance spectrum indicates that all eight carbon atoms are equivalently bonded to iron. Also, the cyclooctatetraene ring in the compound no longer adds bromine in a carbon tetrachloride solution. This indicates that the molecular bond involves an overlap of the iron d orbitals with a π orbital extending over all eight carbon atoms of the ring.

Another interesting type of metallocene is one involving a cyclohepta-trienyl ring. Metallocenes of this aromatic ring are difficult to prepare.[196] When metal carbonyls are reacted with cycloheptatriene, the reaction produces not tropylium compounds ($C_7H_7^-$ rings), but a cycloheptatriene compound in which there is no loss of hydrogen.[196]

$$C_7H_8 + M(CO)_6 \longrightarrow C_7H_8M(CO)_3 + 3\,CO$$

in contrast to the reaction with cyclopentadiene:

$$C_5H_6 + M(CO)_6 \longrightarrow C_5H_5M(CO)_3 + 3\,CO + \tfrac{1}{2}H_2$$

where M = Cr or Mo. The cycloheptatriene-metal carbonyls are orange-red, crystalline compounds, may be sublimed without decomposition, and are soluble in most organic solvents. Absorption spectra of the compounds suggest that the six olefinic carbon atoms of the cycloheptatriene rings are almost planar and the methylenic carbon atom is out of the plane.

[191] Cf. S. S. Nigam and R. S. Nyholm, *Proc. Chem. Soc., (London)*, 321 (1957).

[192] E. O. Fischer and K. Öfele, *Chem. Ber.*, **90**, 2532 (1957); **91**, 2395 (1958).

[193] R. Burton, M. L. H. Green, E. W. Abel, and G. Wilkinson, *Chem. and Ind. (London)*, 1592 (1958).

[194] B. Moore and G. Wilkinson, *Proc. Chem. Soc., (London)*, 61 (1959).

[195] T. A. Manuel and F. G. A. Stone, *Proc. Chem. Soc., (London)*, 90 (1959).

[196] R. B. King and F. G. A. Stone, *J. Am. Chem. Soc.*, **81**, 5263 (1959); E. W. Abel, M. A. Bennett, R. Burton, and G. Wilkinson, *J. Chem. Soc.*, 4559 (1958).

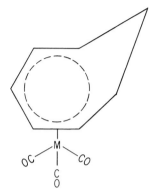

Apparently, the six π electrons form a delocalized system approximating that of benzene which to some extent "by-passes" the methylene group. When the cycloheptatriene compound is treated with trityl fluoroborate in methylene chloride, the latter reagent readily snatches a hydride ion from the cycloheptatriene ring to produce the tropenium compound.[197]

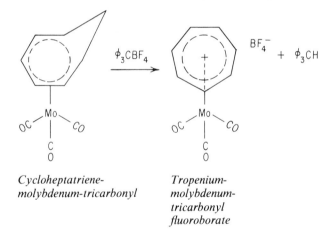

Cycloheptatriene-
molybdenum-tricarbonyl

Tropenium-
molybdenum-
tricarbonyl
fluoroborate

The tropenium compound is insoluble in water or pentane and very soluble in acetone, acetonitrile, or 96 per cent sulfuric acid. Its nuclear magnetic resonance spectrum verified the presence of the symmetrical seven-membered ring.

The high potential commercial value of the metallocenes lies in the fact that they are stable metal-containing organic substances. Thus, the presence of the metal portion may make them useful catalysts for industrial processes and as antiknock agents. The organic portion may lead to many valuable products for which benzene or naphthalene derivatives are now

[197] H. J. Dauben, Jr., *et al., J. Am. Chem. Soc.,* **83,** 497 (1961); **80,** 5570 (1958).

used, such as dyes, fertilizers, explosives, textiles, plastics, lubricants, and many other commodities.

STUDY QUESTIONS

1. What is the difference between d^2sp^3 and sp^3d^2 bonding?

2. What is the order of relative energies of the d orbitals in crystal field splitting for a linear triatomic structure?

3. Why would standardized solutions of ammonia or sodium cyanide be poor titrants for the determination of Cu^{+2} or Cd^{+2} with which they form stable complexes?

4. Oxine and 4-methyl-oxine form chelates with Zn^{+2} and Al^{+3} ions; however, 2-methyl-oxine forms a chelate with Zn^{+2} but not with Al^{+3}. Offer an explanation.

5. Explain the observations that, when glycine is added to dilute cupric acetate, it reduces the molar conductance by 50 per cent but when an equivalent amount of β-alanine or of γ-aminobutyric acid is added, the conductance of cupric acetate is changed only 10 per cent or less.

6. Which solution would have the lowest and which the highest concentration of cupric ions after the following are added to separate 100-ml portions of 0.1M cupric acetate: (a) 0.005 mole of α,α-dipyridyl, (b) 0.005 mole of ethylenediamine, (c) 0.01 mole of ammonia. Give the basis for your answer.

7. Why would Cu^+ be expected to be the most stable monovalent ion among the first transition series?

8. What line of reasoning may be used to deduce from its dissociation constants that ferrocenedicarboxylic acid has the *trans* configuration?

9. Describe the iron-nitrogen bonds in structure XV(a). Should a plus charge be written on the nitrogen atoms?

10. Offer an explanation for the fact that Co(III) coordination compounds are quite stable whereas Co(II) complexes are easily oxidized.

11. $Co(Cl)_4^=$ has a magnetic moment corresponding to 3 unpaired electrons. Give an electron distribution about the cobalt which is consistent with its observed tetrahedral structure.

12. Write an electron distribution for copper in $Cu(H_2O)_4^{+2}$. It has one unpaired electron and is square coplanar. Does your distribution predict that the ion should be more easily oxidized or reduced?

13. Work out the energies of the d orbitals in terms of D_q for a tetrahedral arrangement and calculate the CFSE for an ion of 8 d electrons.

1.5.2 CHARGE-TRANSFER AND SIGMA COMPLEXES

It has been known for many years that certain substances combine in a $1:1$ molar ratio to form crystalline addition products referred to as *molecular addition compounds*. These solid compounds, such as the picrates and trinitrobenzenoates, are commonly used in the isolation, purification, molecular weight determination, or identification of organic substances. More recently, a similar association has been observed to occur in solution between certain types of compounds, and these products are sometimes called *pi complexes*. In these two groups of substances, referred to here as *charge-transfer* complexes (CT), always one component (A) is an electrophilic substance and the other component (B) is an electron-donor compound (see Table 1.19). The intercomponent bonding has been referred to most often as a charge-transfer interaction which involves several types of forces. Complex formation can be described by the equation[198]

$$A + B \rightleftharpoons \quad (A \cdots B), (\overset{-}{A}\overset{+}{-}B), (\overset{+}{A}\overset{-}{-}B) \qquad (1.20)$$

$$\text{(a)} \qquad \text{(b)} \qquad \text{(c)}$$

$$\textbf{XXV}$$

Structure XXV is a resonance hybrid of forms (a), (b), and (c). Form (a) makes the major contribution to the ground or normal state of the complex, in which the dotted line represents weak Coulombic forces (primarily van der Waals, dipole-dipole, ion-dipole, dipole-induced dipole forces and even hydrogen bonds). Forms (b) and (c) contribute primarily to the excited states of the complexes, with (c) of much less significance than (b) for most types of complexes. Forms (b) and (c) contain a molecular bond. That is, there is a *delocalized intermolecular coordinate covalent bond* in which the electron pair is provided not by a specific atom but by two or more atoms in B and is shared with two or more atoms in A. Form XXV(b) for a toluene-bromine complex, for example, can be regarded as a resonance hybrid of forms XXVI(a), (b), (c), (d), etc.,

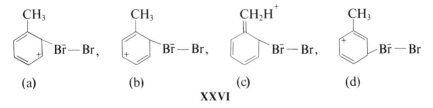

$$\text{(a)} \qquad \text{(b)} \qquad \text{(c)} \qquad \text{(d)}$$

$$\textbf{XXVI}$$

[198] R. S. Mulliken, *J. Am. Chem. Soc.,* **74,** 811 (1952). Cf. W. Brackman, *Rec. trav. chim.,* **68,** 147 (1949). For a simple, lucid molecular-orbital description of these CT complexes, see M. J. S. Dewar and A. R. Lepley, *J. Am. Chem. Soc.,* **83,** 4560 (1961).

Table 1.19. EXAMPLES OF CHARGE-TRANSFER COMPLEXES[211]

Electrophilic + reagent A +	Electron donor B	$\rightleftharpoons$ Charge-transfer complex $\rightleftharpoons$ (A ... B), (A$\overset{+}{-}$B), (A$\overset{+}{-}$B)
Polynitro compounds	Arenes	Picrates
Picric acid	Alkenes	Quinhydrones
2,4,7-Trinitrofluorenone	Alkynes[208]	Benzene-silver perchlorate
1,3,5-Trinitrobenzene	Cycloalkenes[209]	
Tetranitromethane[199]	Alkyl halides[210]	Etc.
Carbonyl compounds	Amines	
Quinone		
Chloranil		
Flavones[200]		
Maleic anhydride[201]		
Oxalyl chloride[202]		
Halogen compounds		
Halogens		
Hydrogen halides[203]		
Chloroform[204]		
Acidic gases[207]		
O_2, SO_2, CO_2, O_3		
Transition ions		
Ag^+, Cu^{++}		
Tetracyanoethylene[205]		
Pyridinium ions[206]		

[199] D. L. Hammick, *et al., J. Chem. Soc.,* 763, 1350 (1938); 1463 (1936).

[200] F. Cramer and G. H. Elschneg, *Chem. Ber.,* **89**, 1 (1956).

[201] W. G. Barb, *Trans. Faraday Soc.,* **49**, 143 (1953); E. R. Garrett and R. L. Guile, *J. Am. Chem. Soc.,* **75**, 3958 (1953).

[202] B. D. Saksena and R. E. Kagarise, *J. Chem. Phys.,* **19**, 994 (1951).

[203] D. Cook, Y. Lupien, and W. G. Schneider, *Can. J. Chem.,* **34**, 957, 964 (1956).

[204] L. W. Reeves and W. G. Schneider, *Can. J. Chem.,* **35**, 251 (1957).

[205] R. E. Merrifield and W. D. Phillips, *J. Am. Chem. Soc.,* **80**, 2778 (1958).

[206] E. M. Kosower and J. C. Burbach, *J. Am. Chem. Soc.,* **78**, 5838 (1956).

[207] D. F. Evans, *J. Chem. Soc.,* 345 (1953); W. G. Barb, *Proc. Roy. Soc. (London),* **A212**, 66 (1952); L. J. Andrews and R. M. Keefer, *J. Am. Chem. Soc.,* **73**, 4169 (1951); T. W. Nakagawa, L. J. Andrews, and R. M. Keefer, *J. Am. Chem. Soc.,* **82**, 269 (1960).

[208] H. J. Lucas and W. S. Dorsey, *J. Am. Chem. Soc.,* **78**, 1665 (1956); D. Cook, Y. Lupien, and W. G. Schneider, *Can. J. Chem.,* **34**, 957 (1956).

[209] F. S. Mathews and W. J. Lipscomb, *J. Am. Chem. Soc.,* **80**, 4745 (1958).

[210] L. J. Andrews and R. M. Keefer, *J. Am. Chem. Soc.,* **73**, 5733 (1951); **74**, 1891 (1952).

[211] (a) L. J. Andrews, *Chem. Revs.,* **54**, 713 (1954); (b) G. Briegleb, *Elektronen-Donator-Acceptor Komplexe* (Heidelberg: Springer-Verlag, 1961).

or for a trinitrobenzene-toluene complex, in which the planes of the components are parallel but not necessarily face-to-face,

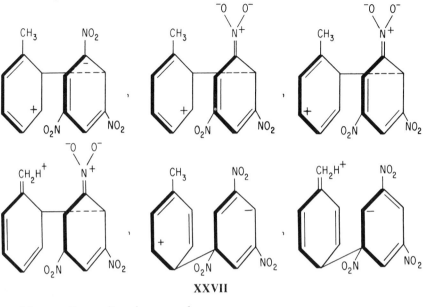

XXVII

and for an alkene-silver ion complex,

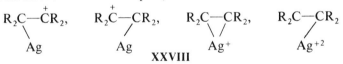

XXVIII

For simplicity, these can be diagrammed:

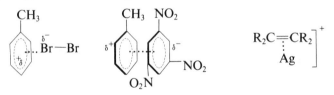

Complex formation in solution is detected by studying the physical properties of the solution and noting a deviation from ideal behavior. Such properties have included vapor pressure,[212] viscosity,[213] refractive index,[214] dielectric constant,[215] conductivity,[247, 259] surface tension;[216] absorption of infrared, visible, or ultraviolet radiation; optical dichrosim,[227] nuclear

[212] C. C. Addison and J. C. Sheldon, *J. Chem. Soc.,* 1937 (1957).

[213] G. H. Locket, *J. Chem. Soc.,* 1501 (1932).

[214] E. C. McLure, A. Ogilvie, and T. J. Rose, *J. Chem. Soc.,* 67 (1955).

[215] C. H. Giles, T. J. Rose, and D. G. M. Vallance, *J. Chem. Soc.,* 3799 (1952).

[216] E. Ferroni and G. Gabrielli, *J. Phys. Chem.,* **60,** 1258 (1956).

magnetic resonance,[204] and melting points.[204] In addition, dipole moments, magnetic susceptibility, and distribution coefficients[217] have been measured to study CT complex formation. The deviations may appear as maxima or minima, or there may be some abrupt change in the physical property. Of course, it is also necessary to show that the deviations are actually due to the formation of CT complexes.

Diffraction studies of solid charge-transfer complexes show that the crystals consist of alternate layers of the two components about 3–3.5 Å apart.[218] Diffraction measurements on benzene-silver perchlorate crystals[219] reveal that the silver ion lies above a carbon-carbon bond of the aromatic ring. Diffraction studies on crystals of the benzene-bromine complex indicate that the axis through the two bromine atoms is perpendicular to the plane of the benzene ring and passes through its center.[220] This structure for the latter complex is supported by infrared spectroscopic studies too.[221] Several different properties of the charge-transfer complexes support the use of XXV as a good working model for the structures of CT complexes:

1. The infrared or Raman spectra of charge-transfer complexes closely resemble the summation of spectra of the components A and B.[212] This indicates that XXV(a) makes a large contribution to the ground state of the complex. Actually, certain bond vibrational frequencies of A and B are shifted, sometimes as much as 150 cm^{-1}.[222, 223] Thus, the initial bonding within A and B has been disturbed by complex formation, as is to be expected, but only enough to change the bond orders a certain fraction.[224] For example, an X-ray diffraction study[219] of the $AgClO_4$—C_6H_6 complex indicates that the silver ion lies above a carbon-carbon bond of the benzene ring and that this bond is shortened from the usual 1.39 Å to 1.35 Å while the two adjacent bonds are lengthened to 1.43 Å. These values correspond to bond orders of 1.55 and 1.80 in comparison to the normal value of 1.67. Also, the ring carbon-carbon bond angles are altered. Instead of all being 120°, two are 115.6° and four are 122.2°. The strength of the charge-transfer bond in this complex is estimated to be 25–50 kcal.[225]

Furthermore, in complexes with A components of the type X—Y, e.g., an arene-halogen complex, which can be represented by formula XXIX,

---

[217] M. Davies and H. E. Hallam, *J. Chem. Educ.,* **33**, 322 (1956).

[218] For a survey of diffraction studies on CT complexes, see O. Hassel and Chr. Romming, *Quart. Revs.,* **16,** 1 (1962).

[219] H. G. Smith and R. E. Rundle, *J. Am. Chem. Soc.,* **80,** 5075 (1958).

[220] O. Hassel, *J. Mol. Phys.,* **1,** 241 (1958).

[221] E. E. Ferguson, *J. Chem. Phys.,* **26,** 1357 (1957); **25,** 577 (1956).

[222] R. N. Haszeldine, *J. Chem. Soc.,* 4145 (1954); R. D. Kross and V. A. Fassel, *J. Am. Chem. Soc.,* **79**, 38 (1957); E. E. Ferguson, *Spectrochim. Acta,* **10,** 123 (1957); D. L. Glusker and H. W. Thompson, *J. Chem. Soc.,* 471 (1955).

[223] H. J. Taufen, M. J. Murray, and F. F. Cleveland, *J. Am. Chem. Soc.,* **63,** 3500 (1941).

[224] J. Chatt and L. A. Duncanson, *J. Chem. Soc.,* 2939 (1953).

[225] B. D. Tildesley and A. G. Sharpe, *Research,* **6,** 515 (1953).

$$A\cdots X{-}Y, \qquad \overset{-}{A}{-}X\cdots\overset{+}{Y}$$

(a)   (b)

XXIX

it has been observed that as the formation constant of the complex becomes larger, the infrared absorption frequency of the X—Y bond decreases.[226] This indicates an increasing contribution of XXIX(b) to the ground state. The fact that these bonds become infrared-active reveals the development of charge asymmetry in the complex. In fact, there is a fairly good linear relationship between E_a and $\Delta k/k$ for several charge-transfer complexes of the halogens (and also hydrogen-bond complexes $A\cdots H{-}X$).[226] E_a is the increase in charge on atom Y (in XXIX) brought about by complex formation and $\Delta k/k$ is the relative change in force constant of the bond X—Y. Thus, as the contribution of XXIX(b) increases, the bond between X and Y becomes weaker.

2. The intercomponent distances in the charge-transfer complexes (3–3.5 Å) are too large for a typical covalent bond between components, and show that although the molecular π orbitals of each component overlap in a direction perpendicular to the planes of the component molecules, the penetration is not deep. Nevertheless, the complexes have a large polarizability perpendicular to the planes of the components, as revealed by the fact that their absorption of polarized light is greatest when the electric vibrations are normal to the parallel planes of the two components.[227] Also, the delocalization of positive charge on B is facilitated by the presence of a second adjacent benzene ring parallel to that attached to A:[228]

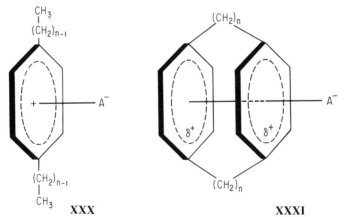

XXX   **XXXI**

[226] W. B. Person, R. E. Erickson, and R. E. Buckles, *J. Am. Chem. Soc.,* **82**, 29 (1960) and earlier papers; J. Collin, L. D'Or, and R. Alewaeters, *J. Chem. Phys.,* **23**, 397 (1955); *Rec. trav. chim.,* **75**, 862 (1956).

[227] K. Nakamoto, *J. Am. Chem. Soc.,* **74**, 1739 (1952).

[228] D. J. Cram and R. H. Bauer, *J. Am. Chem. Soc.,* **81**, 5971 (1959).

Accordingly, with a given A, the λ_{max} of XXXI is found at longer wavelengths than that of XXX, which implies on the basis of empirical observations that XXXI is the more stable. This transannular effect was estimated[228] to range from 2 to 14.4 kcal/mole.

3. Dipole moments reveal a shift in charge density with complex formation. For example, iodine and benzene alone have no electric dipole moments but the iodine-benzene complex has a moderate dipole moment (~ 1 D).[229] Similarly, 1,3,5-trinitrobenzene, p-nitrobenzene, and stannic chloride[230] do not have dipole moments when measured in inert solvents such as carbon tetrachloride but do have moments when measured in complex-forming solvents such as benzene, naphthalene, or dioxane.

Magnetic susceptibility data on charge-transfer complexes also confirm the contribution of the polar form XXV(b) to the ground state of the complexes.[231] The diamagnetism of the complexes exceeds the sums of the values of their components by amounts up to 16×10^{-6} cm^3/mole. This is four times the difference in magnetic susceptibilities between the keto and enol tautomers of ethyl benzoylacetate, for example, and is almost the difference (18×10^{-6}) one would get between an aromatic and nonaromatic structure for benzene. The enhanced diamagnetism of charge-transfer complexes implies that there is a greater delocalization of charge in the complex.[232]

The ground-state structure of a complex from two nonpolar components can be represented by the formula XXXII and the excited state by XXXIII. A quantum mechanical treatment of dipole moment data on charge-transfer complexes has led to an evaluation of the coefficients in XXXII and XXXIII.[198] The dipole moments and calculated coefficients[233] of several complexes are listed in Table 1.20. As expected, the coefficients show that the nonpolar form makes the major contribution to the ground state whereas the ionic form is the principal contributor to the excited state. It is important to realize, however, that in spite of the relative smallness of b in XXXII, the molecular bond accounts for a large fraction of the bonding energy and may even be the major force. This is due to the relative

[229] R. S. Mulliken, J. chim. phys., 51, 341 (1954); G. Kortum and H. Walz, Z. Elektrochem., 57, 73 (1953); G. Briegleb, and J. Czekalla, Z. Elektrochem., 59, 184 (1955); F. Fairbrother, J. Chem. Soc., 1051 (1948).

[230] H. Tsubomura, Bull. Chem. Soc. Japan, 27, 1 (1954).

[231] S. S. Bhatnager and C. L. Lakra, Ind. J. Phys., 8, 43 (1933); N. S. Rao and S. R. Govindarajan, Proc. Ind. Acad. Sci., 15A, 35 (1942); R. C. Sahney, S. L. Aggarwal, and M. Singh, J. Ind. Chem. Soc., 23, 335 (1946); C. Courty, Bull. soc. chim. France, Mem., 5, 84 (1938).

[232] Charge-transfer complexes of a few large polynuclear aromatic hydrocarbons such as perylene or violanthrene have marked conductivities and decreased diamagnetisms [H. Akamatsu, H. Inokuchi, and Y. Matsunaga, Bull. Chem. Soc. Japan, 29, 213 (1956)]. These unusual properties appear to be related to an increase in diradical character of the hydrocarbons owing to complexation.

magnitudes of covalent bond energies ($>$ 50 kcal/mole) compared to polarization forces ($<$ 7 kcal/mole). For illustration, the fraction R of the total ground state binding energy in these complexes provided by the molecular bond is also given in Table 1.20.

$$[a(A, B) + b(A \overset{-}{\text{—}} \overset{+}{B})] \qquad [a'(A, B) + b'(A \overset{-}{\text{—}} \overset{+}{B})]$$

XXXII   **XXXIII**

Table 1.20. Ground- and Excited-State Resonance
Contributions in Charge Transfer Complexes **XXXII** and **XXXIII**[233]

Complex	Dipole moment	a	b	a'	b'	I	R
Hexamethylbenzene-trinitrobenzene........	0.87	0.962	0.193	0.290	0.986	3.8	58
Stilbene-trinitrobenzene........	0.82	0.964	0.186	0.284	0.988	3.5	70
Naphthalene-trinitrobenzene ..	0.69	0.969	0.168	0.266	0.99	2.8	51
Durene-trinitrobenzene........	0.55	0.975	0.045	0.244	0.994	2.1	47
Hexamethylbenzene-chloranil .	1.00	0.957	0.209	0.306	0.983	4.4	45
Benzene-iodine ..	0.72	0.97	0.17	0.27	0.99	2.8	100
Pyridine-iodine..........	4.5	0.86	0.50			25	
Triethylamine-iodine..........	11.3					59	

I = Percentage ionic character of XXXII.
R = Percentage contribution of the resonance energy to the total binding energy of XXXII.

Contradictory to earlier views, it appears that form (c) of **XXV** can make a contribution to the stability of metal ion-olefin complexes.[233] This would explain the fact that only transition metal ions and metals form these complexes. The metal ions react in valency states for which the energy to remove an electron from a dp hybrid bond is not prohibitive. Thus, Cu^{++} ion, for example, does not form an isolable complex, presumably because the structure $\overline{B}$—Cu^{+++} would be energetically improbable, where B represents a donor molecule.

Related to the charge-transfer complexes are what have been called *sigma complexes*.[234] Aromatic compounds react with HCl—$AlCl_3$ or

---

[233]S. P. McGlynn, *Chem. Revs.*, **58**, 1113 (1958); B. E. Douglas, *J. Am. Chem. Soc.*, **75**, 4839 (1953).
[234]H. C. Brown and J. D. Brady, *J. Am. Chem. Soc.*, **74**, 3570 (1952).

HF—BF$_3$ mixtures, for example, to produce salts that ionize in non-aqueous, ion-supporting solvents such as liquid hydrogen fluoride or sulfuric acid. The reaction can be represented by the equation

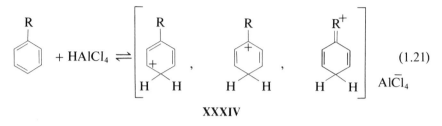

$$(1.21)$$

XXXIV

where the carbonium ion **XXXIV** is a resonance hybrid of several forms and in which there is a covalent bond between the reagent and a specific carbon atom of the aromatic ring. Such an ion has been established as an intermediate in nitration where there is a nitro group in place of the additional hydrogen atom. These carbonium ions are not molecular association products having molecular bonds, but their relationship makes it interesting to compare the two types.[235,236]

1. The first noticeable difference between charge-transfer (CT) and σ complexes is their color. The CT complexes are usually colorless or light yellow, while the sigma complexes are orange or deeper and in some cases almost black.[237] As in the triphenylmethane-type dyes, the excited states of the sigma complexes are greatly stabilized by resonance which decreases the energy difference between ground and excited states and brings about light absorption in the visible region of the spectrum.

2. The second distinction between CT and sigma complexes is the marked electrical conductivity of the sigma complexes, whereas the CT complexes are nonconducting.[238,239] This conductivity of the sigma complexes confirms their ionized state in solution.

3. The third difference is the isotope exchange which takes place with sigma complexes. When arenes are mixed with DCl—AlCl$_3$ or DF—BF$_3$, there is an exchange of deuterium for hydrogen. This satisfies expectation,

[235] R. S. Mulliken ("Symposium on Molecular Physics at Nikko," Japan, 1953) has referred to these as "outer complex" and "inner complex," respectively.

[236] The CT complexes have been further classified into two categories, "general," where the component A is located symmetrically over B and exemplified by the arene-halogen complexes, and "localized," in which A is not symmetrically located over B, such as with the arene-Ag$^+$ complexes. The distinction between these two subclasses lies mostly in the steric effect of substituents upon complex stability, the "localized" group being more sensitive to steric requirements. However, we will not make a distinction between these two subdivisions of CT complexes.

[237] H. Akamatsu, H. Inokuchi, and Y. Matsunaga, *Nature*, **173**, 168 (1954).

[238] F. Fairbrother, *J. Chem. Soc.*, 180 (1950).

[239] H. C. Brown and J. D. Brady, *J. Am. Chem. Soc.*, **74**, 3570 (1952).

for when the sigma complex reverts back to the arene, either the C—H bond or the C—D bond will break. When the C—H bond breaks, the recovered aromatic will contain deuterium. No such exchange occurs in the CT complexes with DCl or TCl.[239]

An equilibrium apparently exists between an aromatic compound, its CT complex, and its sigma complex according to the equation[240]

$$\text{Ar} + \text{HX} \rightleftharpoons \underset{\substack{CT \\ complex}}{\text{Ar}:\text{HX}} \rightleftharpoons \underset{\substack{Sigma \\ complex}}{(\text{ArH})\overset{+}{X}} \rightleftharpoons \text{ArH}^+ + \text{X}^- \qquad (1.22)$$

In media unfavorable to the existence of the ionic sigma complex, such as media of low dielectric constant, and in the absence of catalysts, only the easily formed CT complex is detectable. For instance, solutions of HCl in aromatic compounds are colorless or pale yellow and nonconducting.[239] If a reagent is added that will combine with the halide ion, the equilibrium is shifted towards the right. Thus, when salts such as aluminum chloride or boron trifluoride are added to the Ar : HX mixture, the mixture becomes colored and conducting. Mixtures of $\text{HX} + \text{AlX}_3 + \text{Ar}$ form red oils that are highly conducting, but these oils are not formed in the absence of any one of the three substances.[242] Liquid hydrogen fluoride is a solvent of high dielectric constant; aromatic substances dissolve in it to form limited amounts of the sigma complex. This is evident because hydrogen fluoride solutions of aromatic compounds have a conductivity and visible color. When boron trifluoride is added to these solutions in increasing amounts, their conductivities and colors progressively increase until one mole-equivalent of BF_3 has been added, and then the conductivities level off. This indicates that the equilibrium has been shifted almost completely to the right. In the absence of steric effects, the order of magnitude of equilibrium constants for sigma complexes is 100-fold larger than that for CT complexes.[241]

Sulfuric acid, too, is a polar medium in which the ionic sigma complex is stable. Thus, aromatics undergo isotope exchange in D_2SO_4 as a result of sigma complex formation. For illustration, C_6D_6 and other deutero-aromatics have been prepared by mixing the aromatic compound with D_2SO_4 or DCl—AlCl$_3$.[243]

Similarly, iodine forms only the CT complex with mesitylene since

[240] R. A. Zingaro and W. E. Tolberg, *J. Am. Chem. Soc.,* **81,** 1353 (1959).

[241] H. Tsubomura, *J. Am. Chem. Soc.,* **82,** 40 (1960).

[242] H. C. Brown and W. J. Wallace, *J. Am. Chem. Soc.,* **75,** 6268 (1953) and references cited therein; H. Luther and G. Pockels, *Z. Elektrochem.,* **59,** 159 (1955).

[243] V. Gold and F. A. Long, *J. Am. Chem. Soc.,* **75,** 4543 (1953); A. Klit and A. Langseth, *Nature,* **135,** 956 (1956); C. K. Ingold, C. G. Raisin, and C. L. Wilson, *J. Chem. Soc.,* 915 (1936).

mesitylene is not an ionizing solvent. However, pyridine is an ionizing solvent, and iodine forms a CT complex with it.[244] The infrared spectrum of iodine in pyridine is markedly different from that of pyridine alone[245] and the solution is conducting.[246]

The CT-σ complex equilibrium is also shifted towards σ-complex formation by resonance stabilization of the latter. For example, tetraphenyl-ethylenes, particularly those having groups in the *para* position which will readily accept a positive charge, react with halogens to form deeply colored, conducting solutions.[247] The solutions range in color from red to almost black depending upon the substituents and the temperature.

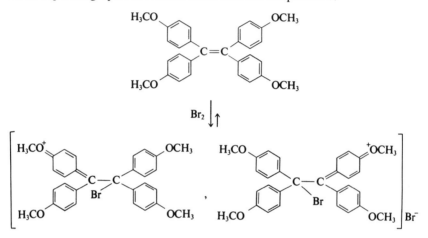

An interesting gradation in color is found in the complexes of tetracyanoethylene. The colors with benzene, xylene, durene, hexamethylbenzene, and N,N-dimethyl-*p*-toluidine are yellow, orange, red, violet, and green.[249]

As a CT complex changes over to a sigma complex, say for example in arene-halogen complexes, as the arene-halogen bond gets stronger, the interhalogen bond should get weaker and longer. In agreement with this expectation, it is found that the normal I—I bond distance (2.67 Å) is increased to 2.85 Å in the unusually stable violanthrene-iodine CT complex[248] and to 2.90 Å in the pyridine-iodine sigma complex.[250(a)]   Similarly, in the

[244]S. Nagakura, *J. Am. Chem. Soc.*, **80**, 520 (1958).

[245]F. Millich and G. Oster, *J. Am. Chem. Soc.*, **81**, 1357 (1959); E. K. Plyler and R. S. Mulliken, *J. Am. Chem. Soc.*, **81**, 823 (1959).

[246]L. F. Audrieth and E. J. Birr, *J. Am. Chem. Soc.*, **55**, 668 (1933).

[247]R. E. Buckles, *et al.*, *J. Am. Chem. Soc.*, **80**, 5055 (1958); **74**, 1171 (1952).

[248]H. Akamatsu, Y. Matsunaga, and H. Kuroda, *Bull. Chem. Soc. Japan*, **30**, 618 (1957).

[249]*Chem. Eng. News*, **38**, 114 (1960).

[250](a) G. Dallinga, *Acta Cryst.*, **7**, 665 (1954); (b) O. Hassel, *Mol. Phys.*, **1**, 241 (1958).

dioxane-Br_2 complex there are chains of alternate dioxane and bromine molecules in which the arrangement of atoms is $>$O$\cdots$Br$\cdots$Br$\cdots$O$<$. The Br—Br distance, 2.31 Å, is slightly greater than that in the Br_2 molecule (2.28 Å).[250(b)]

The effects of substituents on the stabilities of charge-transfer and sigma complexes are in the expected directions. For illustration, the relative stabilities of a number of substituted benzene complexes with various electrophilic reagents are given in Table 1.21. It can be observed there that, in general, increased stability is associated with an increase in electron-donor ability of B and electron pulling power of A. Hence, electron-donating groups in B or electron-withdrawing groups in A lead to greater complex stability.[251] Polynitro rather than mononitro compounds, for instance, are used for the formation of solid CT complexes, and hexanitroso-benzene is one of the more powerful complex-forming compounds.[252] The most powerful complexing agent reported so far is tetracyanoquinodime-thane.[253]

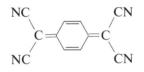

Tetracyanoquinodimethane

The sequences in the several columns of Table 1.21 are not identical because the effects of induction, resonance, solvation, and steric requirements operate independently. Because of steric factors, for example, the introduction of an electron-donating group into B or of an electron-withdrawing group into A does not always produce the expected increase in stability.[261] The relative stabilities of the benzene- and mesitylene-silver ion complexes is a case in point. Towards all other electrophilic reagents, mesitylene produces the more stable complex owing to the electron-donating effect of the methyl groups. In the silver ion complex, the ion is above a carbon-carbon bond of the aromatic ring, and the methyl groups prevent a close approach to the ring. Another notable example of the steric effect is found in hexaethylbenzene. CT complexes normally become more stable as the number of methyl or ethyl groups is increased. However, hexaethylbenzene is an abnormally weak π-electron donor owing to partial screening of the π-electron cloud by six large ethyl groups.[262] For il-

[251]C, A. Buehler, *et al., J. Am. Chem. Soc.,* **53**, 4094 (1931); R. Foster, D. Ll. Hammick, and P. J. Placito, *J. Chem. Soc.,* 3881 (1956).

[252]A. S. Bailey and J. R. Case, *Proc. Chem. Soc., (London),* 176 (1957).

[253]D. S. Acker, *et al., J. Am. Chem. Soc.,* **82**, 6508 (1960); *Chem. Eng. News,* **40**:9, 86 (1962).

Table 1.21. Relative Stabilities of Some Molecular Complexes

Compound	Solubility of HCl[239]	Charge-Transfer Complexes					Sigma Complexes		
		ICl[254]	Ag$^+$[255]	TCNE[205]	TNB[256]	CA[257]	HBF$_4$[258]	Liquid HF[259]	Rate of Halogenation[260]
C_6H_5F	0.97		0.19	0.39	0.57				
C_6H_5Cl	0.87		0.29	0.31	0.84				
C_6H_5Br	0.85	0.59	0.40	0.62	1.15				
C_6H_5I	0.84		2.07						
C_6H_6	1.00	1.00	1.00	1.00	1.00	1.00		0.09	0.0005
C_6H_5Me	1.51	1.61	1.22	1.85	1.96	1.67	0.01	0.63	0.157
$C_6H_5CH_2Me$	1.74	1.63	1.12		1.87				0.13
$C_6H_5CHMe_2$	2.03	1.63	1.16		1.78				0.08
$C_6H_5CMe_3$	2.23	1.63	0.96		2.25				0.05
$1,2\text{-}C_6H_4Me_2$	1.85	2.3	1.2	3.49	2.69	3.5	2.0	1.1	2.1
$1,4\text{-}C_6H_4Me_2$	1.64	2.8	1.09	3.82	2.55	2.97	1.0	1.0	1.0
$1,3\text{-}C_6H_4Me_2$	2.07	2.57	1.26	3.00	2.37	2.8	20	26	200
$1,2,4\text{-}C_6H_3Me_3$	2.23				2.59	3.4	40	63	340
$1,2,3\text{-}C_6H_3Me_3$	2.39						40	69	400
$1,3,5\text{-}C_6H_3Me_3$	2.61	8.5	0.75	8.7	3.45	3.9	2800	140	80,000
$1,2,4,5\text{-}C_6H_2Me_4$		7.88				10	120	400	1,400
$1,2,3,4\text{-}C_6H_2Me_4$	2.67					8.84	170	13,000	2,000
$1,2,3,5\text{-}C_6H_2Me_4$	2.74					8.24	5,600	16,000	240,000
C_6HMe_5		11.9		61.5		17.8	8,700	29,000	360,000
C_6Me_6		42		132		30.2	89,000	97,000	

Me = CH_3. TNB = trinitrobenzene. TCNE = tetracyanoethylene. CA = chloranil.

lustration, the relative rates of reaction of ozone with some methyl- and ethylbenzenes are as follows:[262]

Benzene = 1

C_6H_5Me	1	12	C_6H_5Et
$1,3\text{-}C_6H_4Me_2$	28	40	$1,3\text{-}C_6H_4Et_2$
$1,3,5\text{-}C_6H_3Me_3$	150	143	$1,3,5\text{-}C_6H_3Et_3$
C_6Me_6	8750	120	C_6Et_6

Again owing to the steric effect, cis-2-butene gives a more stable CT complex with silver ion than does the trans isomer.[263,265]

The relative basicities of the halobenzenes appear to be in the order $\phi I > \phi Br > \phi Cl > \phi F$, in spite of the results based on the solubilities of HCl in aromatics by vapor-pressure measurements. Thus, towards Ag^+, TCNE, and TNB, as well as from shifts in the H—X stretching frequency of various proton donors (e.g., HCl, CH_3OH, pyrrole, and phenylacetylene) when mixed with the halobenzene,[266] there is the decreasing order of relative basicities $\phi H > \phi I > \phi Br > \phi Cl > \phi F$.

In the absence of steric effects, it is not unusual to find correlations of CT complex stability with such parameters as

1. the polarizability of B.[267]
2. the ionization potential of B.[256,257]
3. the dipole moment of B.[264]
4. the electronegativity of substituents in B.[264]
5. the polarizing power of A.[239]
6. λ_{max} of the complex.[205]

Each of these six properties is directly or indirectly affected by the degree of operation of polarization forces in the ground states of the complexes. The greater is the polarizability of B, the more stable is the complex. It is

[254]L. J. Andrews and R. M. Keefer, J. Am. Chem. Soc., 73, 4169 (1951).

[255]L. J. Andrews and R. M. Keefer, J. Am. Chem. Soc., 74, 4500 (1952).

[256]G. Briegleb, Z. Elektrochem., 59, 184 (1955).

[257]N. H. Smith, Ph.D. Thesis, University of Chicago, 1955. Compare R. Foster, D. Ll. Hammick, and B. N. Parsons, J. Chem. Soc., 555 (1956).

[258]D. A. McCaulay and A. P. Lien, J. Am. Chem. Soc., 73, 2013 (1951).

[259]M. Kilpatrick and F. E. Luborsky, J. Am. Chem. Soc., 75, 577 (1953).

[260]H. C. Brown and J. D. Brady, J. Am. Chem. Soc., 74, 3570 (1952).

[261]S. D. Ross, M. Bassin, and I. Kuntz, J. Am. Chem. Soc., 76, 4176 (1954).

[262]T. W. Nakagawa, L. J. Andrews, and R. M. Keefer, J. Am. Chem. Soc., 82, 269 (1960); 77, 2545 (1955),

[263]K. N. Trueblood and H. J. Lucas, J. Am. Chem. Soc., 74, 1338 (1952).

[264]L. N. Ferguson and A. Y. Garner, J. Am. Chem. Soc., 76, 1167 (1954).

[265]P. D. Gardner, R. L. Brandon, and N. J. Nix, Chem. and Ind., (London), 1363 (1958).

[266]G. A. Olah, S. J. Kuhn, and S. H. Flood, J. Am. Chem. Soc., 83, 4581 (1961).

[267](a) H. D. Anderson and D. Ll. Hammick, J. Chem. Soc., 1089 (1950); (b) L. J. Andrews and R. M. Keefer, J. Am. Chem. Soc., 72, 3113 (1950).

observed, for example, that Hammett's meta sigma constants parallel equilibrium constants for CT complex formation between silver ion and monosubstituted benzenes. This correlation suggests that polarization forces are more important than the molecular bond in the ground state of CT complexes. Furthermore, the easier it is to take an electron from B, the more stable is the complex. For example, the relative stabilities of CT complexes of trinitrobenzene and of choranil have been found to be inversely proportional to the ionization potentials of the B components,[256] and the relative stabilities of a series of quinhydrones have been found to parallel the oxidation potentials (and spectra[268]) of the respective quinones. Thus, the lower is the ionization potential of B (I_p) and the greater is the electron affinity of A (E_a), the stronger is the CT bond.[269] This generalization has been related to ultraviolet spectra in the form $\Delta E = I_p - E_a + C$, where ΔE is the transition energy corresponding to the CT bond and C is a constant.[270] Such an equation has also been the basis for computing ionization potentials of polynuclear aromatic hydrocarbons.[271] Ionization potentials of arenes are obtained directly from photoionization measurements, electron impact studies, and vacuum ultraviolet Rydberg spectra of the vapors. However, these methods are not applicable to hydrocarbons with low volatilities, so that the indirect determination of ionization potentials from the absorption spectra of their CT complexes fills an important gap.

Another noticeable difference between the CT complexes and the sigma complexes is the importance of ground-state resonance for the latter. In both types, stability increases with the number of electron-donating methyl groups in B, but the sigma complexes of *m*-xylene, among the dimethylbenzenes, and of mesitylene, among the trimethylbenzenes, are outstandingly stable (see Table 1.21). This can be explained in terms of the resonance of the complexes. In *m*-xylene, for example, no matter which *ortho* or *para* position is attacked by the proton, the intermediate ion is stabilized by resonance involving both methyl groups,

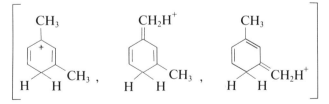

268 W. H. Hunter and E. H. Noethey, *J. Phys. Chem.,* **37,** 875 (1933).

269 E. M. Kosower and J. A. Skorcz, *J. Am. Chem. Soc.,* **82,** 2195 (1960).

270 G. Briegleb and J. Czekalla, *Angew. Chem.,* **72,** 401 (1960); R. Foster, *Tetrahedron,* **10,** 96 (1960).

271 A. Streitwieser, Jr., *J. Am. Chem. Soc.,* **82,** 4123 (1960); J. B. Birks and M. A. Slifkin, *Nature,* **191,** 761 (1960).

whereas the intermediate ion from *o*- or *p*-xylene is stabilized by resonance involving only one *or* the other methyl group.

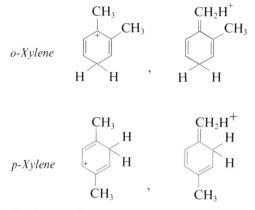

A similar completely complementary resonance occurs only for mesitylene among the trimethylbenzenes.

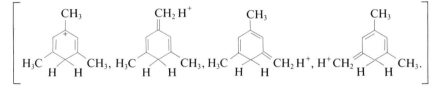

It has already been shown that steric requirements may reduce the stability of a charge-transfer complex. If either component is nonplanar, the distance between planes is increased, which decreases both the overlap of molecular orbitals and the polarization of B by A, and thereby a much weaker charge-transfer bond is produced.[272] For examples, *trans*-stilbene forms a picrate but the nonplanar *cis* isomer does not. β-Phenylnaphthalene forms a picrate but the α isomer does not. In the latter compound, the *peri* hydrogen atom prevents the phenyl group from being coplanar with the naphthalene ring. Similarly, the relative stabilities of the picric acid complexes of alkyl-substituted naphthalenes,[273] of trinitrobenzene complexes of biphenyls,[274] and of trinitrobenzene,[275] chloranil,[276] and iodine[277]

[272]M. S. Newman in *Steric Effects in Organic Chemistry* (New York: Wiley, 1956), chap. 10; M. Orchin, *J. Org. Chem.*, **16**, 1165 (1951); L. H. Klemm, J. W. Sprague, and H. Ziffer, *J. Org. Chem.*, **20**, 200 (1955); J. G. Traynham and M. F. Sehnnert, *J. Am. Chem. Soc.*, **78**, 4024 (1956).

[273]P. D. Gardner, R. L. Brandon, N. J. Nix, and I. Y. Chang, *J. Am. Chem. Soc.*, **81**, 3413 (1959).

[274]C, E. Castro, L. J. Andrews, and R. M. Keefer, *J. Am. Chem. Soc.*, **80**, 2322 (1958).

[275]S. D. Ross and M. M. Labes, *J. Am. Chem. Soc.*, **79**, 76 (1957).

[276]N. H. Smith, Ph.D. Thesis, University of Chicago, 1955.

[277]H. Tsubomura, *J. Am. Chem. Soc.*, **82**, 40 (1960).

complexes of substituted anilines are found to decrease with increasing non-planarity of the B component.

The ultraviolet and visible spectra of charge-transfer complexes have been studied extensively.[233] The intense absorption exhibited by these complexes, usually in the 240 to 320 mμ region, has been associated with the E $\rightarrow$ N transition in which an electron jumps from B to A.[198] Hence, it is called a charge-transfer transition (c-t). Generally, there is a linear relationship between the ionization potential (I_p) of B and λ_{max} for complexes of different donors with the same acceptor.[278] It has been pointed out,[279] however, that there is little theoretical basis to expect a linearity; indeed, several persons have reported deviations from linearity.[280] Recently there has been developed a nonlinear theoretical relationship between I_p and λ_{max}.[281] Nevertheless, within a group of closely related donors, linearity is not uncommon.

Orgel and Mulliken[282] proposed that pairs of certain molecules, e.g., iodine and n-heptane, may exhibit "contact" c-t spectra through the absorption of light when the two molecules come together during a chance encounter. Thus, solid CT complexes possess "compound" c-t spectra, whereas iodine plus n-heptane gives rise to a "contact" c-t spectrum.[283] Charge-transfer complexes in solution exhibit a mixture of the two types of spectra. Mulliken's original theory of charge-transfer complexes[198] predicted a parallel correlation between the binding energy of the complex and the intensity of the c-t band. Because an inverse relationship is observed in most cases, at variance with theory, numerous studies have been made of the variation of the intensity of the c-t band with stability of a series of complexes of similar donor molecules.[233,284,285] A recent proposal has been offered to explain this anomaly.[285]

The c-t bands of CT complexes exhibit small bathochromic shifts and increased intensities when measured at high pressures[286] or low tempera-

[278]S. H. Hastings, J. L. Franklin, J. C. Schiller, and F. A. Matsen, *J. Am. Chem. Soc.,* **75,** 2900 (1953); S. P. McGlynn and J. D. Boggus, *J. Am. Chem. Soc.,* **80,** 5096 (1958); H. McConnell, J. S. Ham, and J. R. Platt, *J. Chem. Phys.,* **21,** 66 (1953); R. Foster, *Nature,* **183,** 1253 (1959); D. Booth, F. S. Dainton, and K. J. Ivin, *Trans. Faraday Soc.,* **55,** 1293 (1959).

[279]R. S. Mulliken, *Rec. trav. chim.,* **75,** 845 (1956).

[280]R. Foster, *Nature,* **181,** 337 (1958); C. Reid and R. S. Mulliken, *J. Am. Chem. Soc.,* **76,** 3869 (1954); S. Nagakura, *J. Am. Chem. Soc.,* **80,** 524 (1958).

[281]G. Briegleb and J. Czekalla, *Z. Elektrochem.,* **63,** 6 (1959).

[282]L. E. Orgel and R. S. Mulliken, *J. Am. Chem. Soc.,* **79,** 4839 (1957).

[283]D. F. Evans, *J. Chem. Phys.,* **23,** 1436 (1954).

[284]W. N. White, *J. Am. Chem. Soc.,* **81,** 2912 (1959); J. N. Murrell, *J. Am. Chem. Soc.,* **81,** 5037 (1959).

[285]G. Briegleb and J. Czekalla, *Z. physik. Chem.,* **24,** 37 (1960).

[286]R. E. Gibson and O. H. Loeffler, *J. Am. Chem. Soc.,* **62,** 1324 (1940).

tures.[287] This has been attributed to changes in solvent structure and to shifts of the equilibrium constants towards greater concentration of the complexes with increasing pressure and decreasing temperature.

The effect of solvent upon c-t absorption bands is to shift the band to shorter wavelengths with increasing dielectric constant of the solvent.[288] This "blue shift" can be attributed partly to the effect of the solvent upon the degree of dissociation of the CT complex and partly to the orientation of solvent molecules around the solute molecules. In the ground state, the orientation of solvent molecules is favorable to the charge distribution of the CT complex molecules. Upon excitation, the charge distribution of the complex molecules is markedly altered and the solvent molecules are no longer orientated for strong binding to the solute molecules. The more polar the solvent, the greater is the loss in solvent stabilization upon excitation and the shorter is the wavelength of absorption.[289]

A valuable use of the ultraviolet spectra of CT complexes is for the determination of their formation constants in solution. A large majority of the charge-transfer complexes dissociate so readily that they resist isolation. Consequently, use must be made of physical methods for determining their relative stabilities. Cryoscopic, immiscible solvent distribution, vapor pressure, solubility, spectroscopic, and electromotive force measurements are the most common physical methods used.[211] The general equation for the equilibrium in 1:1 complex formation is

$$B + A \rightleftharpoons BA \qquad (1.23)$$

The concentration equilibrium constant is expressed in the usual way.

$$K_c = \frac{(C_{BA})}{(C_B - C_{BA})(C_A - C_{BA})} \qquad (1.24)$$

where C_{BA} = concentration of complex BA at equilibrium,
C_B = initial concentration of B,
C_A = initial concentration of A.

The absorbance A of the mixture at any wavelength for a 1-cm cell is given as

$$A = C_{BA}\epsilon_{BA} + (C_A - C_{BA})\epsilon_A + (C_B - C_{BA})\epsilon_B \qquad (1.25)$$

where the ϵ's are absorptivities. In most cases, the complex is found to absorb in a region where absorption by A or B, or both, is negligible.[290]

---

[287]J. Ham, *J. Am. Chem. Soc.*, **76**, 3875 (1954); D. E. Schuler and R. H. Schuler, *J. Am. Chem. Soc.*, **76**, 3092 (1954).

[288]E. M. Kosower, *J. Am. Chem. Soc.*, **80**, 3253–3270 (1958).

[289]G. J. Brealey and M. Kasha, *J. Am. Chem. Soc.*, **77**, 4462 (1955).

[290]S. Ainsworth and E. Rabinowitch (*Science, 131*, 303 (1960)) have pointed out that the spectra of certain complexes do not differ from the summations of spectra of their components, which is attributed to delayed electron transfer after electronic excitation of one of the components.

Several procedures have been developed for determining K_c, most of which consist of making a plot of some function of the concentration of components vs. the observed absorbance and then calculating ϵ_{BA} and K_c from the intercept and slope of the graph.[205,273,291] From K_c and its temperature coefficient, heats of formation and entropy values have also been determined.[205,292] It should be pointed out that the partition method, in which the distribution coefficient of A between water and a nonpolar solvent is measured with and without B in the nonpolar phase, usually gives a higher value for the equilibrium constant than does the spectrophotometric method. This has been explained[293] by saying that the partition method measures complexation through polarization forces as well as through charge-transfer bonding.

Recently, several workers have used infrared intensities for determining formation constants of charge-transfer complexes.[294] The same principles are used in computing the thermodynamic constants from the spectral data as were used in the visible-ultraviolet region of the spectrum. However, the absorption intensities of the CT complexes are much smaller in the infrared region than they are in the ultraviolet, which decreases the accuracy of the results. Nevertheless, the formation constants obtained for the two spectral regions usually compare favorably. For illustration, the formation constants for the dioxane-iodine complex determined from infrared and ultraviolet measurements are 0.7 and 0.86, respectively,[294(c)] and for the benzene-ICl complex, the constants are 0.7 and 0.54, respectively.[294(a)] The infrared region can be used when the CT-spectrum is barely detectable in the ultraviolet region.[294(a,b)]

Also, the solvent affects the magnitude of the equilibrium constant and the heat of formation of a CT complex.[295] For illustration, the spectrophotometrically determined equilibrium constants between tetracyanoethylene (TCNE) and o-xylene in three different solvents,[205] and the heats of formation of quinhydrone in three different solvents are as follows:[296]

[291]Cf. N. J. Rose and R. S. Drago, *J. Am. Chem. Soc.*, **81,** 6138 (1959) and references cited therein; M. Brandon, M. Tamres, and S. Searles, *J. Am. Chem. Soc.*, **82,** 2131 (1960); *J. Phys. Chem.*, **65,** 654 (1961); R. L. Scott, *Rec. trav. chim.*, **75,** 787 (1956).

[292]R. S. Drago and N. J. Rose, *J. Am. Chem. Soc.*, **81,** 6141 (1959); T. M. Cromwell and R. L. Scott, *J. Am. Chem. Soc.*, **72,** 3825 (1950); C. Walling, E. R. Briggs, K. B. Wolfstirn, and F. R. Mayo, *J. Am. Chem. Soc.*, **70,** 1537 (1948); M. Brandon, M. Tamres, and S. Searles, *J. Am. Chem. Soc.*, **82,** 2131 (1960).

[293]S. D. Ross and I. Kuntz, *J. Am. Chem. Soc.*, **76,** 74 (1954).

[294](a) A. I. Popov, R. E. Humphrey, and W. B. Person, *J. Am. Chem. Soc.*, **82,** 1850 (1960); (b) H. Yamada and K. Kozima, *J. Am. Chem. Soc.*, **82,** 1543 (1960); (c) D. L. Glusku and H. W. Thompson, *J. Chem. Soc.*, 471 (1955).

[295]G. Briegleb, *et al., Z. physik. Chem.*, **B31,** 58 (1936); **B32,** 305 (1936).

[296]A. Kuboyama and S. Nagakura, *J. Am. Chem. Soc.*, **77,** 2644 (1955).

Solvent	K (TCNE:o-Xylene)	Solvent	$-\Delta H$ (Phenol:Hydro- quinone)
$CHCl_3$	9.46	n-Heptane	6.6 kcal/mole
CH_2Cl_2	6.97	CCl_4	4.3
$(C_2H_5)_2O$	2.95	H_2O	1.2

The variation with solvent can be attributed to the competitive complexation of component A with the solvent.

The limiting extent of polarization in a CT complex would be for complete electron transfer to occur. TCNE, and more so, tetracyanoquinomethane TCNQ, are such strong complexing agents that they do just that. With copper, iodine ion, or other easily oxidized substances, TCNQ will form a CT complex with complete electron transfer.

$$Cu + TCNQ \rightleftharpoons (\overset{+}{Cu}—TCNQ \cdot^-)$$

The ion pair contains the $\overset{-}{TCNQ} \cdot$ ion-radical which is paramagnetic. These CT complexes are usually close to black in color. With lithium iodide, a stable, paramagnetic complex is formed ($\overset{+}{Li}—\overset{-}{TCNQ}$) which reacts with various cations to form other similar complexes.

$$\overset{+}{Li}—\overset{-}{TCNQ} \cdot \xrightarrow{M^+} M\overset{+}{—}TCNQ^- \cdot$$

The cation M^+ can also be one from various trialkylammonium ions. These latter complexes, $R_3\overset{+}{NH}—TCNQ \cdot$, react with excess TCNQ to form an unusual crystalline, highly magnetic complex $Q \cdot$ of the general formula $R_3\overset{+}{NH}—\overset{-}{TCNQ} \cdot —TCNQ$. The unusual property of these $Q \cdot$ complexes is their appreciable electrical conductivity in the solid state.[253] For instance, whereas the electrical resistance R_e for metals is in the range 10^{-3}–10^{-5} ohm-cm, R_e for most organic compounds is 10^{12}–10^{14} and is 10^{-2}–10^3 for the $Q \cdot$ complexes. The crystals are composed of TCNQ species stacked above one another with the cation at one edge. As might be

expected, the lowest resistivity for these compounds is perpendicular to the planes of the rings. Although the formula for Q · indicates that two different types of TCNQ species are present, they apparently are equivalent, with each sharing the odd electron, because only one infrared cyanide frequency is observed.

Uses of CT complexes. One interesting practical application of CT complexes is the preparation of aromatic compounds from aliphatics. It has been found that disubstituted acetylenes may be polymerized in the presence of metal carbonyls to give a mixture of molecular complexes which generally are well crystallized, stable, and soluble in organic solvents.[297] For example, dimethylacetylene condenses with iron pentacarbonyl to give hydroquinone-iron tricarbonyl.[298] The latter compound may then be reduced to yield hydroquinone.

$$Fe(CO)_5 + CH_3-C\equiv C-CH_3 \xrightarrow{h\nu}$$

Similarly, triarylchromium compounds bring about the condensation of disubstituted acetylenes to benzene derivatives, a reaction in which CT complexes apparently serve as intermediates.[299] For illustration, triphenylchromium(III) tetrahydrofuranate reacts with diaryl- or dialkylacetylenes (DMA) to give a mixture of products (see page 123). In the same fashion, diphenylacetylene is condensed to hexaphenylbenzene plus 1,2,3,4-tetraphenylnaphthalene. The triphenylchromium-THF need not be isolated for promoting the condensation. For example, the cyclization of 2-butyne will take place when it is added to a mixture of magnesium, bromobenzene, and chromium trichloride tetrahydrofuranate.

Hence, it is seen that charge-transfer complexes have more than açademic interest.[300] Mention has already been made of the use of solid CT complexes (molecular addition compounds) for the isolation, resolution, purification, or identification of amines and hydrocarbons.[302] Picrates, for example, have been used for the determination of molecular weights by

[297]W. Hübel, et al., J. Inorg. Nucl. Chem., **9**, 204 (1958).

[298]H. W. Sternberg, R. Markby, and I. Wender, J. Am. Chem. Soc., **80**, 1009 (1958).

[299]W. Herwig, W. Metlesics, and H. Zeiss, J. Am. Chem. Soc., **81**, 6203 (1959); W. Hübel, et al., Angew. Chem., **73**, 680 (1961).

[300]D. Booth, Sci. Progress, **48**, 435 (1960).

[301]M. Green and R. F. Hudson, Proc. Chem. Soc., (London), 323 (1957); A. E. Comyns and H. J. Lucas, J. Am. Chem. Soc., **79**, 4339 (1957); G. Karagounis, E. Charbonnier, and E. Floss, J. Chromatog., **2**, 84 (1959).

[302]M. Orchin and E. O. Woolfolk, J. Am. Chem. Soc., **68**, 1727 (1946).

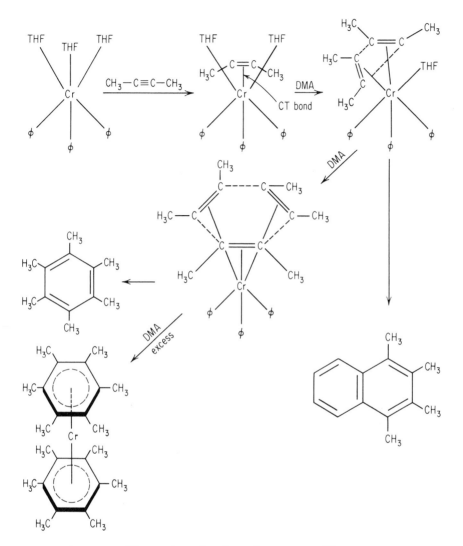

spectrophotometry[305] or by titration in aqueous[306] or nonaqueous media.[307] Racemic mixtures have been resolved through fractional crystallization or precipitation of CT complexes[301] and by molecular complexation chromatography, in which an optically active complexing agent is impregnated on an absorbent in a column.[303(a)] As to be expected, adsorption is favored by planarity of a molecule and by an increased tendency to form a CT-type complex.[304] Hydrocarbons have been separated by gas

[303]L. H. Klemm, *et al., J. Chromatog.,* **3,** 364 (1960) and earlier papers; B. Smith and R. Ohlson, *Acta Chem. Scand.,* **16,** 351 (1962).

[304]L. H. Klemm, D. Reed, L. A. Miller, and B. T. Ho, *J. Org. Chem.,* **24,** 1468 (1959).

phase chromatography using silver nitrate in ethylene glycol as the stationary phase. Evidently differential CT-complexation permits separation of saturated from unsaturated hydrocarbons and of various types of unsaturated hydrocarbons.[303(b)]

Charge-transfer complexes are also formed in biological systems. For example, proteins combine with carotenes to form deeply colored lipoproteins. The most common one is visual purple, the substance required for night vision. It consists of the yellow carotenoid, retinene, bound to a protein to give the intensely colored photosensitive visual purple.

Charge-transfer complexes may also be found of value to serve as drugs or fertilizers or even explosives. For example, CT complexes between biurets and alkylisocyanurates are found[308] to provide good protection against electroshock and psychomotor seizures. The unpleasant effects of chloral hydrate, such as its smell, taste, and irritation of the gastrointestinal tract, are removed through molecular complex formation with antipyrine to produce an effective nonhabitforming sedative. CT complexes between 4,4'-dinitrocarbanilide (DNC) and several pyrimidines, par-

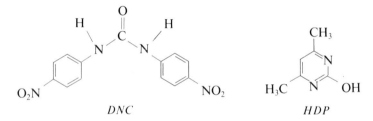

ticularly 2-hydroxy-4,6-dimethylpyrimidine (HDP), have significant antiparasitic activity not shown by either component.[309] The DNC:HDP addition compound has only about one-tenth the antimalarial potency of quinine but it does not exhibit some of the side effects of quinine. Most recently, the Dow Chemical Company announced two complex-forming polymers of N-vinyl-5-methyl-2-oxazolidinone which form complexes with a large number of organic compounds. The complexes frequently retain the biological properties of the original substances. For examples, the complex with sodium saccharin has the sweetness of saccharin without the bitter aftertaste, the iodine complex has the biocidal activity of iodine but does not "burn" when applied to the skin, and the phenol complex has the

[305]K. G. Cunningham, G. W. Dawson, and F. S. Spring, *J. Chem. Soc.*, 2304 (1951); V. Boekelheide and J. C. Godfrey, *J. Am. Chem. Soc.*, **75**, 3679 (1953).

[306]E. K. Anderson, *Acta Chem. Scand.*, **8**, 157 (1954).

[307]J. S. Fritz, *Anal. Chem.*, **24**, 306 (1952); J. R. Clark and S. M. Wang, *Anal. Chem.*, **26**, 1230 (1954).

[308]W. J. Close, *J. Am. Chem. Soc.*, **75**, 3619 (1953).

[309]A. C. Cuckler, C. M. Malanga, A. J. Basso, and R. C. O'Neill, *Science*, **122**, 244 (1955).

same bactericidal activity as free phenol but does not have the phenol odor and is less hygroscopic than phenol. However, it is possible that these complexes are not charge-transfer complexes but inclusion compounds as discussed in Sec. 1.7.3.

STUDY QUESTIONS

1. In which solvent should hydrogen chloride have the greater solubility, benzene or cyclohexane?
2. What are the relative acid strengths of benzene and ethane? their relative base strengths? Give the basis for your answer.
3. How would you attempt to show that osmocene is, or is not, ionic?
4. In which solvent would the infrared absorption stretching frequency for the I—Cl bond be the smaller, in toluene or p-xylene? Give the basis for your reply.
5. Explain the fact that the Br_2-ethylene complex has no significant conductivity but that the Br_2-tetra-(p-methoxyphenyl)-ethylene complex has a marked conductivity.
6. Considerable evidence[311] indicates that the C=C bond has a greater nucleophilic character than the C≡C bond. Which class of compound should give the more stable CT compound?[208,310]

1.6 Hydrogen bonds[312] (see also Sec. 5.4.3).

It is early observed in the study of organic chemistry that most compounds containing O—H groups tend to have unexpectedly high boiling points and large water solubilities. This property of OH-containing compounds leads to the recognition that when a hydrogen atom is attached to a highly electronegative atom, it has an affinity for a second electronegative atom, and this attraction has a marked effect upon the properties of the molecules involved. In the case of hydroxy compounds, the hydrogen atom is attached to the highly electronegative oxygen atom and has an affinity for the oxygen atom of a second OH group. This attraction weakly binds different molecules so that more energy is required to separate the liquid molecules for vaporization, or it causes water to attach itself to foreign molecules so

[310] J. Chatt and L. A. Duncanson, *J. Chem. Soc.*, 2939 (1953).

[311] D. I. Miller, *J. Org. Chem.*, **21**, 247 (1956); R. Daniels and L. Bauer, *J. Chem. Educ.*, **35**, 444 (1958) and references cited therein.

[312] (a) G. C. Pimentel and A. L. McClellan, *The Hydrogen Bond* (San Francisco: Freeman and Co., 1960); (b) *Hydrogen Bonding*, ed. D. Hadzi and H. W. Thompson, (New York: Pergamon, 1959).

that their solubility in water is increased. The hydrogen bond (H bond) plays a very prominent role in our daily lives. For example, it is primarily responsible for the structures of proteins, it is important in determining the shapes of the nucleic acids and hence controls cell development to some degree, and it is a big factor in the action of many adhesives, the liquid state of water at room temperature, the binding of many dyes, and several biological phenomena. The use of the concept of H bonding to explain various phenomena was slow to gain prominence, but over the past two decades a tremendous number of studies have been made of the H bond, and its importance has become recognized.

Hydroxylic and amino compounds associate primarily in the liquid and solid states to form polymeric aggregates with a pattern, for example, like that of alcohols,

where R represents an alkyl group and n is an indefinite integer. A few classes of compounds, notably the carboxylic acids and oximes,[314] tend to form dimers predominantly.[315] Thus, in the solid state, the carboxylic acids crystallize in head-to-head orientation.[316]

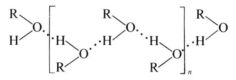

Carboxylic acid dimer   *Oxime dimer*

H bonding may also occur between two atoms of the same molecule as in o-fluorophenol or in a β-diketone.

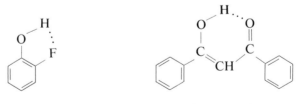

o-Fluorophenol   *Dibenzoylmethane*

[313]T. S. Moore and T. F. Winmill, *J. Chem. Soc.,* 1635 (1912); G. Oddo and E. Puxeddu [*Gass. chim. ital.,* **36,** 1 (1906)] had previously proposed a divided valency for hydrogen in order to account for some unusual properties of azo compounds.

[314]B. Jerslev, *Nature,* **180,** 1410 (1957).

[315]Cf. D. L. Marrin and F. J. C. Rossotti, *Proc. Chem. Soc., (London),* 60 (1959).

[316]R. Brill and K. H. Meyer, *Z. Krist.,* **67,** 570 (1928).

This *intra*molecular H bonding is a form of chelation while the *inter*-molecular hydrogen bonding is referred to as *association*.

Moore and Winmill[313] first proposed the existence of H bonds to explain the weakness of ammonia and amines in contrast to the strong quaternary ammonium hydroxides. Pfeiffer[317] introduced the H bond into organic chemistry, and it was later generalized by Latimer and Rodebush in 1920.[318] First let us examine the nature of the H bond, and then consider some of the properties of molecules which are greatly affected by H bonding.

1.6.1 THE NATURE OF THE H BOND FORCE[319,320]

The use of the term "bond" for the attractive forces associated with the H bond has drawn criticism from some persons because it has much less strength than covalent bonds and is of much greater variability in length. Average energies of various types of H bonds are listed in Table 1.22. The question is often raised, "How weak can an interatomic force be and still be regarded as a chemical bond?" For instance, strengths of H bonds have been measured down to 1 kcal/mole. It is convenient to refer to these attractive forces as "bonds," and most often they should be regarded as chemical bonds in accordance with the working definition of a chemical bond adopted on p. 39. In the case of the weak H bonds, it is admittedly a debatable matter at what point the H bond interaction may still be regarded as a "bond" rather than a nonbonding attractive force. It has been pointed out[321] that the change in entropy accompanying intermolecular H bonding is quite large (loss of three degrees of translational and three degrees of rotational freedom with a gain of one degree of vibrational). This is much larger than the entropy change occuring with intramolecular H bonding. Consequently, very weak H bonds are more likely to be observed among the intramolecular type.

It has been convenient to divide the H bond energy into four components:[320] (i) electrostatic interactions, (ii) delocalization effects, (iii) dispersion forces, and (iv) repulsive forces. Of course, all interatomic forces are *electrostatic;* however, the above classification is made for the sake of "bookkeeping" and to gain a clearer understanding of the hydrogen bond. The term "electrostatic" in (i) refers to the forces that would arise if the charges on the atoms could be regarded as point charges without any de-

[317]P. Pfeiffer, *Ann.*, **398**, 137 (1913).
[318]W. M. Latimer and W. H. Rodebush, *J. Am. Chem. Soc.*, **42**, 1419 (1920).
[319]C. G. Cannon, *Spectrochim. Acta*, **10**, 341 (1958).
[320]C. A. Coulson, cf. reference 312(b), pp. 339 ff.
[321]H. H. Jaffe, *J. Am. Chem. Soc.*, **79**, 2373 (1957).

Table 1.22. H Bond Energies

Energies of Some H Bond Types			
Type of bond	Mean energy (kcal/mole)	Type of bond	Mean energy (kcal/mole)
O—H···N	7	N—H···O	2.3
O—H···O	6	N—H···N	2–4
C—H···O	2.6	N—H···F	5
		F—H···F	7

Some Specific H Bond Energies[322]		
Bond	Substance	Energy (kcal/mole)
F···H···F⁻	KHF₂, solid	27
F—H···F	(HF)₆, vapor	6.8
F—D···F	(DF)₆, vapor	6.85
O—H···O	H₂O, ice	6.4
	(CH₃COOH)₂, vapor	7.64
	(CH₃COOH)₂, in C₆H₆	4.85
	(C₆H₅COOH)₂, in C₆H₆	4.4
	(o-HO—C₆H₄COOH)₂, in C₆H₆	2.8
	o-HO—C₆H₄COOH , intramolecular	4.7
	(CH₃OH)₄, vapor	6.05
	(C₆H₅OH)₂, in C₆H₆	2.4
O—D···O	(CH₃COOD)₂, vapor	7.95
	(CF₃COOD)₂, vapor	6.96
O—H···Cl	o-Cl—C₆H₄OH, gas, intramolecular	2.8
	o-Cl—C₆H₄OH, in CCl₄, intramolecular	1.7
N—H···F	NH₄F, crystal	5.0
N—H···O	C₆H₅NH₂:OC(C₆H₅)₂, in CCl₄	2.0
N—H···N	NH₃, crystal	1.3
C—H···N	(HCN)₂, vapor	3.3
	(HCN)₃, vapor	4.4
C—H···O	(CH₃CHO)₂, vapor	2.61
	(CH₃)₂CO:HCCl₃	2.7
C—H ··· π electrons	Alcohol: arene	2–4

formation from polarization. Forces in (ii) arise from the fact that mutual polarization of the electron clouds about the atoms does occur, and an account is taken of this distortion in terms of delocalization effects. The small electrostatic interactions resulting from instantaneous charge dis-

[322]M. M. Davies, *Ann. Repts. Chem. Soc.*, **43**, 5 (1946); A. W. Searcy, *J. Chem. Phys.*, **17**, 210 (1949); M. D. Taylor, *et al.*, *J. Am. Chem. Soc.*, **73**, 315 (1951); W. Weltner, Jr., and K. S. Pitzer, *J. Am. Chem. Soc.*, **73**, 2606 (1951); A. N. Campbell and E. M. Kartzmark, *Can. J. Chem.*, **38**, 652 (1960).

tributions of electrons in motion produce the dispersion forces, and the forces under (iv) are the result of the repulsions between inner-shell electrons during the close approach of the atoms brought together by the H bond. Let us discuss these four effects separately to see what contributions they make to the H bond energy.[323] Since most studies have been made on the O—H···O type of H bond, the discussion will be directed to such bonds, but it is assumed that what is said applies in general to the other types of H bonds.

(i) *Electrostatic interactions.* The fact that H bonds are found only between highly electronegative atoms suggests that dipole-dipole forces play a dominant role in the H bond. With this in mind, several persons have made calculations based on classical electrostatic theory to show that the H bond energy can be accounted for by computing the electrostatic force between the bond dipole along O_A—H and the dipole of the H—O_B—H molecule

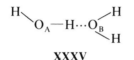

XXXV

pointing towards O_A in **XXXV**.[324] Unfortunately, the close agreement between such calculations and observed bond energies led some persons to attribute the entire H bond energy to such electrostatic forces. However, logic would dictate that there must at least be certain repulsive forces operating to prevent the bond from collapsing. Furthermore, if the electrostatic interactions were the only contributing factor, one might expect a correlation with dipole moments. This is not so, for CH_3NO_2 and CH_3CN have large dipole moments but do not form H bonds with hydroxy compounds to any significant extent.[325] As a generality, it is to be expected that the H bond strength will increase (a) with increasing polarity of the A—H bond in A—H···B, (b) with an increase in electron-donor character of B, (c) with the stability of the polar structure $\overset{\delta-}{A}$—H···$\overset{\delta+}{B}$, depending on the relative electronegativities of A and B, (d) and with greater linearity of the H bridge. Thus, C—H bonds normally do not form H bonds, but when the electronegativity of the carbon atom is increased by the attachment of other atoms or by orbital hybridization (see Sec. 1.2.9), the C—H bond becomes sufficiently polar to participate in H bonding. For examples,

[323] A. M. Benson, Jr. and H. G. Drickamer, *J. Chem. Phys.*, **27**, 1164 (1957).

[324] E. Bauer and M. Magat, *J. phys. radium*, **9**, 319 (1938); E. J. W. Verwey, *Rec. trav. chim.*, **60**, 887 (1940); **62**, 127 (1942); F. E. Harris and B. J. Alder, *J. Chem. Phys.*, **21**, 1031 (1953); J. A. Pople, *Proc. Roy. Soc.*, **A205**, 163 (1951); H. Harms, *Z. physik. Chem.*, **B43**, 257 (1939).

[325] Y. Sato and S. Nagakura, *Sci. Light*, **4**, 120 (1955); S. Nagakura and M. Gouterman, *J. Chem. Phys.*, **26**, 881 (1957).

C—H···Cl, C—H···F, C—H···O, and C—H···N bonds exist in CHCl$_3$, CHF$_3$, (CH$_3$CHO)$_2$, and (HCN)$_2$,[326] respectively, as well as in a number of other substances. Even an acetylenic C—H bond is fairly polar and forms H bonds.[329] In accordance with (c) above, spectroscopic data indicate that the O—H···N bond is stronger than the O—H···O bond,[327] while the N—H···O bond is much weaker.[328] This might be expected since oxygen is more electronegative than nitrogen, which makes the polarized structure $\overset{\delta-}{O}$—$\overset{\delta+}{H}$···N more stable than $\overset{\delta-}{O}$—$\overset{\delta+}{H}$···O. The electronegativity of sulfur is rather low, so that S—H···S bonds between S—H groups are too weak to affect transition temperatures or lead to association, and are often not detected.[330] For instance, the boiling points of R—SH compounds are much lower than those of the corresponding R—OH compounds. However, precise spectroscopic measurements reveal that S—H···S bonds do exist, although they are weak.[331] In more polar compounds, such as sulfoxides and phosphinodithioic acids (R$_2$PS · SH), S—H···S, S—H···O, and S—H···N bonds are more easily detectable.[332]

Most estimates put the electrostatic contribution to the H bond energy of an O—H···O bond at approximately 6 kcal/mole.

(ii) Delocalization effects.   Although electrostatic interactions are important for the formation of H bonds, it was pointed out above that such forces cannot represent the whole phenomenon. An alternative model (XXXVI) would be to regard the O—H···O bond as a resonance hybrid of forms XXXVI (a) to (e).

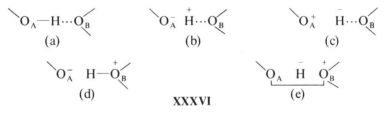

The electrostatic interactions (i) involve primarily forms XXXVI (a), (b), and (c), with (b) making the major contribution. The delocalization effects (ii) are concerned with form (d) and, to a smaller degree, form (e). One experimental observation that provides support for this model comes from

[326]R. H. Cole, *J. Am. Chem. Soc.,* **77**, 2012 (1955).

[327]H. H. Freedman, *J. Am. Chem. Soc.,* **83**, 2900 (1961).

[328]I. M. Klotz and J. S. Franzen, *J. Am. Chem. Soc.,* **82**, 5241 (1960).

[329]A. W. Baker and G. H. Harris, *J. Am. Chem. Soc.,* **82**, 1923 (1960).

[330]D. Plant, D. S. Tarbell, and C. Whiteman, *J. Am. Chem. Soc.,* **77**, 1572 (1955).

[331]S. Forsén, *Acta Chem. Scand.,* **13**, 1472 (1959); R. A. Spurr and H. F. Byers, *J. Phys. Chem.,* **62**, 425 (1958); A. Menefee, D. Alford, and C. B. Scott, *J. Chem. Phys.,* **25**, 370 (1956).

the measurement of the intensity of infrared absorption by the O—H bond near 3 microns.[334] The intensity of an infrared absorption is proportional to the square of the change in dipole moment during excitation. On this basis, the O—H bond dipole can account for only about 30 per cent of the observed intensities. This suggests that there is a much larger fluctuation in charge in the H bond than in a free O—H bond. A second experimental observation in support of this model (XXXVI) comes from nuclear magnetic resonance measurements. It is found that the absorption by the hydroxyl hydrogen of methanol is temperature dependent whereas that of the methyl hydrogen atoms is not. This has been interpreted[335] to imply that the hydroxyl hydrogen is less shielded by electrons than the CH_3 hydrogens. That is, as the proton of the H bond vibrates, there is more movement of charge about it than about methyl hydrogen atoms, and thus, the electrons of the O_A—H bond and of the O_B oxygen atom are partially delocalized as implied by forms (d) and (e). Interpretation of other n.m.r. and spectroscopic data on H bonding[336] add further evidence for delocalization forces in H bonds. For example, an analysis of infrared spectroscopic data shows that as the negative charge on O_A increases, the covalent character of the O_A—H bond decreases.[337]

The delocalization effect is greater the more available is an electron pair on the donor atom. Thus, the N—H···N bond of associated ammonia molecules is much weaker than the O—H···O bond of water for two reasons: the smaller ionic character of the N—H bond decreases the electrostatic energy, and there is only one unshared electron pair on the NH_3 molecule whereas there are two pairs on the oxygen atom of H_2O. The N—H···N bond has an estimated strength of 1.3 kcal/mole. However, evidence of the contribution of delocalization effects comes from the fact that O—H···N bonds are generally stronger than O—H···O bonds. If electrostatic forces were the only type, the latter bond would be the stronger, but the greater stability of the polar structures —O $\overset{+}{\text{H—N}}$ over —O $\overset{+}{\text{H—O}}$, thereby increasing the delocalization of bonding electrons, results in the O—H···N bond being the stronger.[338]

[332] G. Allen and R. O. Colclough, *J. Chem. Soc.,* 3912 (1957); W. Gordy and S. C. Stamford, *J. Am. Chem. Soc.,* **62,** 497 (1940); D. Barnard, J. M. Fabian, and H. P. Koch, *J. Chem. Soc.,* 2442 (1949).

[333] Successful calculations of observed properties have been obtained by using only forms (a) and (d) [E. R. Lippincott and R. Schroeder, *J. Chem. Phys.,* **23,** 1099, 1131 (1955); *J. Phys. Chem.,* **61,** 921 (1957)].

[334] N. D. Coggeshall, *J. Chem. Phys.,* **18,** 978 (1950).

[335] C. A. Coulson, *Research,* **10,** 149 (1957).

[336] C. Reid and T. M. Connor, *Nature,* **180,** 1192 (1957); L. Paoloni, *J. Chem. Phys.,* **30,** 1045 (1959).

[337] W. B. Pearson, R. E. Erickson, and R. E. Buckles, *J. Am. Chem. Soc.,* **82,** 29 (1960).

[338] H. H. Freedman, *J. Am. Chem. Soc.,* **83,** 2900 (1961).

Coulson[320] has made an additional observation which substantiates the operation of delocalization effects in H bonds. The sum of the van der Waals radii of hydrogen and oxygen is 2.6 Å, whereas the $H \cdots O_B$ distance in water is only 1.6 Å. Hence, some covalent bonding must occur between the H and O_B, atoms because normally interatomic repulsion rises rapidly for interatomic distances much less than the sum of the van der Waals radii in the absence of covalent bonding. As a result of the unusually short interatomic distances of the H bond, associated liquids generally have larger densities and smaller molar volumes than similar nonassociated compounds.[339] Thus, again we can conclude that forms (d) and (e) contribute to the hybrid structure XXXVI, or in other words, there is a delocalization of the charge clouds about H and O_B.

There is another important feature of H bonds which is related to the delocalization forces. As the strength of an H bond increases, the $O_A \cdots O_B$ distance decreases and the H atom moves towards the center.[340] Thus, as the delocalization forces increase, the $H \cdots O_B$ distance decreases and the O_A—H distance increases slightly. This relationship is illustrated in Fig. 1.25. The curve suggests that if the $O_A \cdots O_B$ distance is sufficiently

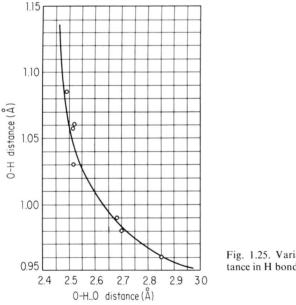

Fig. 1.25. Variation of O_A—H $\cdots$ O_B distance in H bonds.[340(a)]

---

[339] Page 53 of reference 312(a).

[340](a) K. Nakamoto, M. Margoshes, and R. E. Rundle, *J. Am. Chem. Soc.*, **77**, 6480 (1955); (b) G. C. Pimentel and C. H. Sedarholm, *J. Chem. Phys.*, **24**, 639 (1956).

short, the O_A—H distance will equal the H$\cdots O_B$ distance.[341] This supposition appears to be the case in the maleate anion[342] and in chelates of dimethylglyoxime.[343,345]

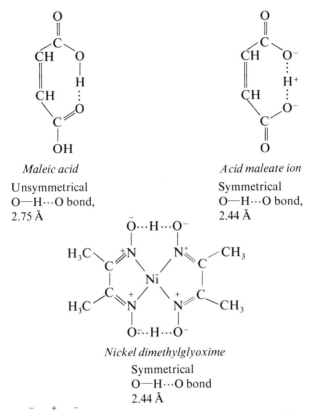

Maleic acid	A cid maleate ion
Unsymmetrical	Symmetrical
O—H$\cdots$O bond,	O—H$\cdots$O bond,
2.75 Å	2.44 Å

Nickel dimethylglyoxime
Symmetrical
O—H$\cdots$O bond
2.44 Å

Similarly, the F$\cdots$H$\cdots$F bond appears to be symmetrical[346] and of unusually great strength (ca. 27 kcal/mole), in contrast to the strength of a typical unsymmetrical F—H$\cdots$F$^-$ bond (6.8 kcal/mole). This means that

[341]One of the shortest, reasonably accurate $O_A\cdots O_B$ distances found in the literature is 2.417 $\pm$ 0.018 Å in crystalline sodium hydrogen diacetate.[344]

[342]H. M. E. Cardwell, J. D. Dunitz, and L. E. Orgel, *J. Chem. Soc.,* 3740 (1953).

[343]L. E. Godycki, R. E. Rundle, R. C. Voter, and C. J. Banks, *J. Chem. Phys.,* **19,** 205 (1951); J. Fujita, A. Nakahara, and R. Tsuchida, *J. Chem. Phys.,* **23,** 1205 (1955). For contradiction, see R. Blinc and D. Hadzi, *J. Chem. Soc.,* 4536 (1958).

[344]W. Fuller, *J. Phys. Chem.,* **63,** 1705 (1959); J. C. Speakman, *Proc. Chem. Soc. (London),* 316 (1959).

[345]Infrared spectral data suggest that the H bond in crystalline di-*p*-chlorophenyl hydrogen phosphate ((ϕO)$_2$PO$\cdot$OH) is symmetrical. Cf. D. Hadzi and A. Novak, *Proc. Chem. Soc., (London),* 241 (1960).

[346]E. F. Westrum and K. S. Pitzer, *J. Am. Chem. Soc.,* **71,** 1940 (1949); S. W. Peterson and H. A. Levy, *J. Chem. Phys.,* **20,** 704 (1952).

the potential energy of the system changes from a double minimum to a single minimum function. One of the most successful internuclear potential functions can be used to predict relationships between properties of the H bond and the $O_A \cdots O_B$ distance.[347]

Finally, the relatively recent demonstration of H bonds involving π electrons provides additional evidence for the operation of delocalization effects in H bonds. For example, intramolecular H bonds occur between an OH group and the π electrons of a benzene ring or of an ethylenic bond, and intermolecular H bonds arise between $CDCl_3$ and the benzene ring when $CDCl_3$ is dissolved in benzene.

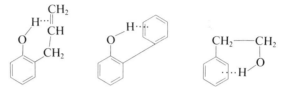

Several types of experimental data substantiate the formation of such bonds with energies of 2 to 4 kcal/mole.[348] The bonds apparently have a strong contribution from XXXVI(d) owing to the ease of polarization of π-electron clouds. As is to be expected, substituents which increase the basicity of the π electrons in the ethylenic group strengthen the H bond and electron-withdrawing groups weaken the H bond.[349]

The importance of the π or lone-pair electrons on the donor atom of an H bond is shown by the fact that β- and γ-hydroxy aliphatic amines exhibit intramolecular H bonds:

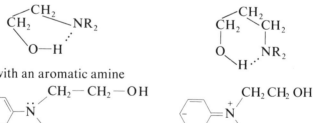

However, with an aromatic amine

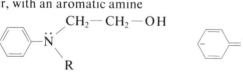

the nitrogen lone-pair electrons are shared with the ring, which virtually precludes intramolecular H bonding.[351]

[347] E. R. Lippincott and R. Schroeder, *J. Chem. Phys.*, **23**, 1099, 1131 (1955); *J. Phys. Chem.*, **61**, 921 (1957).

[348] See the following articles and references cited therein: P. R. Schleyer, D. S. Trifan, and R. Bacskai, *J. Am. Chem. Soc.*, **80**, 6691 (1958); A. W. Baker, *et al.*, *J. Am. Chem. Soc.*, **81**, 4524 (1959); R. W. West, *J. Am. Chem. Soc.*, **81**, 1614 (1959); footnote 31 in L. P. Kuhn *et al.*, *J. Am. Chem. Soc.*, **81**, 6472 (1959); C. M. Huggins and G. C. Pimentel, *J. Phys. Chem.*, **60**, 1615 (1956); W. Beckering, *J. Phys. Chem.*, **65**, 206 (1961); L. W. Reeves and W. G. Schneider, *Can. J. Chem.*, **35**, 251 (1957).

[349] A. W. Baker and A. T. Shulgin, *J. Am. Chem. Soc.*, **80**, 5358 (1958); **81**, 4524 (1959).

Various estimates have been made of the percentage contribution of forms (d) and (e) to the resonance hybrid XXXVI.[350] For intermolecular bonds, the values center around 10 per cent, but in systems where the donor atom (O_B) is part of a pi-electron system, the contribution of form (d) may increase to 25 to 30 per cent. As an estimate, it has been proposed that the delocalization effects contribute about 8 kcal to the total O—H···O bond energy.[320]

(iii) Dispersion forces. Pitzer and coworkers[352] have presented convincing arguments to show that dispersion forces between inner shells of non-bonded atoms are of significant magnitudes and have a definite effect on dissociation energies and the conformations of molecules. Thus, the anomalously low dissociation energy of fluorine as compared to chlorine, bromine, and iodine may be partially attributed to the absence of dispersion forces between inner-shell electrons on the fluorine atoms.[353] It is likely that such forces occur between the inner shells of the bridged atoms of an H bond, particularly for the stronger, shorter H bonds.[340,354,355] Estimates[354] of the magnitude of these dispersion forces in H bonds are about 3 kcal/mole.

(iv) Repulsive forces. As stated above, there must be some counteracting repulsive force in an H bond because the other types of forces are all attractive and would shorten the H bond until it collapsed. This point explains the fact that such bonds are essentially unique to hydrogen and deuterium.[356] For illustration, the electronegativities of lithium and so-

[350]R. Grahn, Arkiv för Fysik (in English), 15: 23, 257 (1959); C. A. Coulson and U. Danielsson, 8, 245 (1954); H. Tsubomura, Bull. Chem. Soc. Japan, 27: 7, 445 (1954); L. Pauling, J. chim. phys., 46, 435 (1949); J. R. Hulett, J. A. Pegg, and L. E. Sutton, J. Chem. Soc., 3901 (1955).

[351]M. St. C. Flett, Spectrochim. Acta, 10, 21 (1957).

[352]K. S. Pitzer and E. Catalano, J. Am. Chem. Soc., 78, 4844 (1956); J. Chem. Phys., 23, 1735 (1955).

[353]On the other hand, R. S. Mulliken [J. Am. Chem. Soc., 77, 884 (1955)] pointed out that the greater strength of the Cl—Cl bond in Cl_2 compared to the F—F bond in F_2 can be attributed to the $3d$-π bonding in Cl_2. He concluded that only a small amount of d-π character is needed for a pronounced increase in double-bond character, and he estimated that only 5 per cent d-π character leads to 20 per cent double-bond character in the Cl—Cl bond. Presumably a similar situation exists in Br_2 and I_2. The fluorine valence shells would require unreasonable amounts of energy to accommodate more than eight electrons and therefore does not exhibit this d-π bonding.

[354]E. J. W. Vervey, Rec. trav. chim., 60, 887 (1941).

[355]A. D. Cohen and C. Reid, J. Chem. Phys., 25, 790 (1956).

[356]In a few instances, bifurcated H bonds

$$A—H\overset{\cdot\cdot B}{\underset{\cdot\cdot B}{}}$$

have been proposed. The evidence is usually open to question; in some cases, refinement of the data has repudiated the earlier evidence. [Cf. K. Nakamoto, M. Margoshes, and R. E. Rundle, J. Am. Chem. Soc., 77, 6480 (1955).]

dium are each less than that of hydrogen, and would give the O—Li or O—Na bonds greater dipole character, but still no lithium or sodium bonds have been shown to exist.[357] The reason for this absence of such bonds is, primarily, that the K and L shell electrons of lithium or sodium repel the O_B charge-cloud to prevent its close approach. Hydrogen and deuterium atoms have no inner-shell electrons to produce such repulsive forces. Estimates[354,358] of this repulsive force have ranged from 8 to 60 kcal, but a value of 8 kcal/mole is more consistent with the overall observed H bond energy.

The contributions from these four types of forces (i) to (iv) are summed up in Table 1.23. The total is of the same order of magnitude as observed

Table 1.23. ESTIMATED CONTRIBUTIONS TO THE
O—H···O BOND ENERGY[320]

Type of force	Energy (kcal)
(i) Electrostatic	+6
(ii) Delocalization	+8
(iii) Dispersion	+3
(iv) Repulsive	−9
Total	+8
Experimental	+6

experimentally. However, we cannot overlook the fact that any one item in the summation may be considerably greater or less, while the other items differ in the opposite direction to give a correct total. In fact, it appears that the repulsive energy should be larger and the delocalization energy smaller, to make the electrostatic energy the most important contributor. It is obvious that much more quantitative work needs to be done before a good theoretical model for the H bond can be constructed.

1.6.2 EFFECTS OF H BONDING ON PHYSICAL PROPERTIES[359]

Essentially all physical properties are affected by H bonding, but we will limit this discussion to those which are most prominently altered, such as transition temperatures, water solubility, thermal stability, and a few others. Spectral properties will be deferred to Chap. 5.

(i) Transition temperatures. The boiling point is the temperature at which the thermal agitation of molecules (kinetic energy) is sufficient to overcome the

[357]Some evidence for the existence of lithium bonds has been offered but, even so, the "bonds" are too weak to be regarded as chemical bonds. [Cf. A. Rodionov et al., Chem. Abstracts, **52**, 6869b (1958).]

[358]N. D. Sokolov, Doklady Akad. Nauk S.S.S.R., **58**, 611 (1947).

[359]L. N. Ferguson, J. Chem. Educ., **33**, 267 (1956).

intermolecular attractive forces in the liquid state. It is logical to expect the boiling point of a compound to be larger the heavier are its molecules and the stronger are the intermolecular forces. The forces between alkane molecules are among the weakest intermolecular forces, so that the boiling points of alkanes are taken as reference points for given molecular weights, and they are spoken of as having *normal* boiling points. For illustration, in Table 1.24 it can be seen that the boiling points of ethers and alkanes of comparable molecular weights are not far apart, but the boiling points of alcohols with equivalent molecular weights are considerably higher. The reason is that the alcohol molecules are held together by hydrogen bonds and require more energy to separate the molecules for vaporization.

Table 1.24. BOILING POINTS OF n-ALKANES, ETHERS, AND
ALCOHOLS OF COMPARABLE MOLECULAR WEIGHTS

n-Alkanes	Ethers	Alcohols
$CH_3CH_2CH_3$	$CH_3\!-\!O\!-\!CH_3$	CH_3CH_2OH
$-45°$	$-25°$	$78°$
$CH_3CH_2CH_2CH_3$	$CH_3\!-\!O\!-\!CH_2CH_3$	$CH_3CH_2CH_2OH$
$-0.5°$	$8°$	$98°$
$CH_3(CH_2)_3CH_3$	$CH_3CH_2\!-\!O\!-\!CH_2CH_3$	$CH_3CH_2CH_2CH_2OH$
$36°$	$35°$	$118°$
$CH_3(CH_2)_4CH_3$	$CH_3CH_2\!-\!O\!-\!CH_2CH_2CH_3$	$CH_3(CH_2)_2CH_2OH$
$69°$	$61°$	$138°$
$CH_3(CH_2)_5CH_3$	$(CH_3CH_2CH_2)_2O$	$CH_3(CH_2)_4CH_2OH$
$98°$	$89°$	$156°$
$CH_3(CH_2)_7CH_3$	$(CH_3CH_2CH_2CH_2)_2O$	$CH_3(CH_2)_6CH_2OH$
$151°$	$141°$	$194°$

Another illustration of the effect of intermolecular hydrogen bonding on boiling points is found in a comparison of the boiling points of poly-hydric alcohols and their ethers.

$$
\begin{array}{llll}
\text{CH}_2\text{OH} & \text{CH}_2\text{OC}_2\text{H}_5 & \text{CH}_2\text{OC}_2\text{H}_5 & \text{CH}_2\text{OC}_2\text{H}_5 \\
| & | & | & | \\
\text{CHOH} & \text{CHOH} & \text{CHOH} & \text{CHOC}_2\text{H}_5 \\
| & | & | & | \\
\text{CH}_2\text{OH} & \text{CH}_2\text{OH} & \text{CH}_2\text{OC}_2\text{H}_5 & \text{CH}_2\text{OC}_2\text{H}_5
\end{array}
$$

b.p. =   290°   230°   191°   185°

$$
\begin{array}{lll}
\text{CH}_2\text{OH} & \text{CH}_2\text{OCH}_3 & \text{CH}_2\text{OCH}_3 \\
| & | & | \\
\text{CH}_2\text{OH} & \text{CH}_2\text{OH} & \text{CH}_2\text{OCH}_3
\end{array}
$$

b.p. =   197°   125°   84°

As the OH groups are successively covered by alkyl groups to block hy-drogen bonding, the boiling points progressively decrease in spite of the increase in molecular weights.

Sulfur is much less electronegative than oxygen, giving S—H bonds a much smaller ionic character than O—H bonds. Accordingly, thiols form only very weak hydrogen bonds. For illustration, the boiling points of the alcohols listed below are higher than those of the corresponding thiols.

Alcohol	b.p.	b.p.	Thiol
HOH	100°	−62°	HSH
CH₃OH	66°	6°	CH₃SH
CH₃COOH	119°	93°	CH₃COSH

This is due to stronger bonding occuring in OH compounds as shown by the fact that sulfur compounds, owing to larger molecular weights, ordinarily have higher boiling points than the oxygen compounds. Two illustrations are:

$$(CH_3)_2O \qquad -24° \qquad 38° \qquad (CH_3)_2S$$
$$(C_2H_5)_2O \qquad 35° \qquad 92° \qquad (C_2H_5)_2S$$

Similarly, tertiary amines have lower boiling points than isomeric primary or secondary amines, because the latter associate through N—H···N bonds. For example, 2-methylpyrrolidine boils at a higher temperature than its isomer, N-methylpyrrolidine. Comparisons of this type should be made only for molecules having similar shapes so that the van der Waals attractions will be approximately the same.

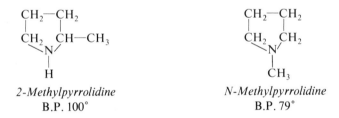

2-Methylpyrrolidine   N-Methylpyrrolidine
B.P. 100°   B.P. 79°

The effect of intramolecular H bonding on transition temperatures is opposite to that of intermolecular H bonding. For illustration, the *ortho* isomers of hydroxy nitro and carbonyl compounds have lower melting points than the respective *meta* or *para* isomers. In this case, chelation ties up the *ortho* OH groups and prevents association from occurring, which would otherwise raise the melting points.

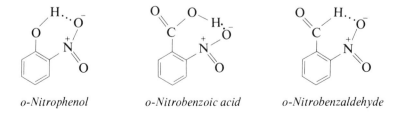

o-Nitrophenol   *o-Nitrobenzoic acid*   *o-Nitrobenzaldehyde*

Compound	Ortho isomer m.p.	Para isomer m.p.
Nitrophenol	44°	114°
Nitrobenzoic acid	144°	241°
Nitrobenzaldehyde	44°	106°
Dihydroxybenzene	104°	169°

Nitration of a substance usually brings about an elevation in its boiling point, but the nitration of resorcinol in the 2 position and of catechol in the 3 position actually lowers their boiling points.[360] These decreases can be attributed to intramolecular H bonding.

    2-Nitroresorcinol   *3-Nitrocatechol*

1,2-Diols can form five-membered cyclic rings through H bonding, and this has an obvious boiling point-lowering effect.[361]

1,2-Diols	B.P.	B.P. of other isomers	
Butanediol-1,2	191°	Butanediol-1,3	203°
Butanediol-2,3	183°		
		⎰ Pentanediol-1,4	219°
Pentanediol-2,3	188°	⎱ Pentanediol-1,5	238°
		Pentanediol-2,4	197°

Chelated compounds also have lower sublimation temperatures than their associated isomers, and sometimes the difference offers a means of separating the isomers. For example, 4(7)-nitrobenzimidazole sublimes at atmospheric pressure whereas the 5(6)-isomer does not.[362] Cryoscopic measurements reveal that the 4(7)-isomer is also less associated in solution.

  4(7)-Nitrobenzimidazole   *5(6)-Nitrobenzimidazole*

[360]L. Hunter, *Report of a Symposium on the Hydrogen Bond* (London: The Royal Institute of Chemistry, 1949), p. 1.
[361]C. H. Giles, *et al., J. Chem. Soc.,* 559 (1956).
[362]J. L. Rabinowitz and E. C. Wagner, *J. Am. Chem. Soc.,* **73,** 3030 (1951).

(ii) Vapor states. The comparisons made so far have all been qualitative in nature. Quantitative measurements are always more meaningful. In the reaction for association,

$$n\ A \rightleftharpoons A_n \qquad (1.26)$$

n is the number of monomeric molecules of A that combine through H bonds to give a polymer of degree of association n, and the ratio of the molecular weight of the polymer to that of the monomer is simply A_n/A. Then from ebullioscopic or cryoscopic measurements, the ratio of the observed molecular weight M_0 to that of the monomer M will be the association factor β.

$$\beta = M_0/M$$

The greater the concentration of solute, the closer is the approach of the solute molecules, and consequently, the greater is the degree of association. Thus for molecules that associate to form primarily dimers, such as the carboxylic acids, β will approach 2 as a limit with increasing concentration of solute. However, most classes of compounds tend to form linear polymers, as water does, and the degree of association then exceeds 2. Two excellent examples are alcohols and phenols, which have been studied quite extensively by spectroscopic methods (cf. Sec. 5.4.3).

Quantitative measurements of association in the vapor state are made by determining deviations from perfect-gas behavior. At low pressures, a vapor will obey fairly closely the ideal gas law $PV = nRT$, where n is the number of moles of gas present. This can be rearranged to give $P/T = nR/V$, and it becomes evident that at constant volume, the ratio of P to T at various temperatures will be constant for a given sample of gas. Now, if association occurs, n moles of gas will reduce to n' moles of gas, where $n' = n/\beta$, and β is the association factor. The new gaseous state can be represented by the equation, $P_1 V_1 = n' R T_1$. If the volume is held fixed, i.e., $V = V_1$, then from the combination of these four equations we get the association factor β:

$$\frac{P/T}{P_1/T_1} = \frac{n}{n'} = \beta$$

Hence, if the P/T ratio is measured at an elevated temperature T, where the substance is essentially monomeric, the ratio of the P/T value at temperature T to that at a lower temperature T_1 will give the association factor at temperature T_1. If complete dissociation does not occur at a reasonable temperature, an alternative, and probably more reliable, procedure is to make a calculation from the equation $PV = nRT$ for the pressure P that would prevail if a given quantity of material were completely monomeric at a chosen temperature. Then, the actual pressure P_1 is measured for the same conditions, and the ratio P/P_1 will give the association factor.

A second technique for determining the degree of association in the vapor state is to make vapor density measurements. From the gas law, the molecular weight of a gaseous sample is given by the equation $M = dRT/P$, where d is the vapor density. If association occurs, the mean molecular weight of a sample can be expressed as $M_0 = d_0 RT/P$, and the ratio of $M_0/M = d_0/d = \beta$ will give the association factor β. Therefore, the density d_0, temperature, and pressure of a sample are measured at a chosen set of conditions and compared with the density calculated from the formula weight under the same conditions.

A third method of studying association in the vapor state, not to mention the powerful spectroscopic methods discussed in Chap. 5, is through the measurement of heat capacities.[363] The heat capacity of a gas can be expressed in terms of the heat capacity of an ideal gas, the pressure, and the degree of association. Such measurements on methyl alcohol[363(a)] gave data that could best be explained by assuming the formation of a tetramer.[364]

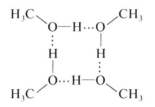

The authors point out, however, that this method does not actually distinguish between the formation of tetramers and the formation of an appropriate mixture of trimer, tetramer, pentamer, etc. This was the first strong evidence for the occurrence of association of alcohols in the vapor state. It was later supported by infrared spectroscopic studies.[365] Presumably it requires one H bond per monomer unit to give a stable polymer in the vapor state. The geometry is not favorable for the formation of a dimeric alcohol molecule with two H bonds, and although a trimer with three H bonds is sterically possible, it appears that the tetramer has the more favorable steric requirements to give a stable polymer.[366] The heat of association for the tetramer was found to be 24.2 kcal, or 6.05 kcal per

[363](a) W. Weltner, Jr., and K. S. Pitzer, *J. Am. Chem. Soc.*, **73**, 2606 (1951); (b) J. D. Lambert, *et al.*, *Trans. Faraday Soc.*, **37**, 421 (1941); *Proc. Roy. Soc.*, **A204**, 424 (1950); (c) W. Weltner, Jr., *J. Am. Chem. Soc.*, **77**, 3941 (1955).

[364]It is interesting in this connection that F. J. Llewellyn, E. G. Cox, and T. H. Goodwin [*J. Chem. Soc.*, 883 (1937)] found from an X-ray diffraction study of crystalline pentaerythritol that the molecules occur in clusters of four with the same arrangement as proposed by Weltner and Pitzer for methanol.

[365]A. Ens and F. E. Murray, *Can. J. Chem.*, **35**, 170 (1957).

[366]However, nuclear magnetic resonance data on *t*-butyl alcohol in carbon tetrachloride solution are interpreted best in terms of a monomer-trimer equilibrium [M. Saunders and J. B. Hyne, *J. Chem. Phys.*, **29**, 253 (1958)].

bond. This value is slightly higher than that (5.8 kcal) determined from heats of mixing[367] and also from infrared spectroscopy (5.64 kcal) in carbon tetrachloride solution.[368] The value for the vapor state is higher than those in solution because there is a small contribution from van der Waals attraction. Interactions with the solvent counteract this contribution when in solution.

The association of carboxylic acids has been the object of considerable interest,[369] perhaps because at low pressures and in dilute solutions essentially only monomeric and dimeric species are present and because a large variety of acids are available for studying the effects of structure on the H bond energy. Several different methods have been used to study the association of acids: in solution, for example, by isopiestic measurements,[370] dielectric constant measurements,[371] infrared spectroscopic measurements,[368,372] and solvent distribution measurements.[373] In the vapor phase, vapor density,[374] vapor pressure,[375] spectroscopic,[372,376] sound velocity,[377] and heat capacity measurements[377] have been made. There are some conflicting results in the literature, but precise measurements by a single investigator indicate that the smaller is the ionization constant of the acid

$$(RCOOH)_2 \rightleftharpoons 2\ RCOOH^{378}$$

Acid	K'_{100mm}	ΔF_{100mm} (kcal/mole)	ΔH $\pm\ 0.05$ kcal/mole	$10^5\ K_a$
CF_3COOH	435	0.415	14.05	50,000
HCOOH	301	0.686	14.11	1.75
CH_3COOH	92	1.570	15.27	1.34
C_2H_5COOH	89	1.594	15.18	1.51

[367] G. von Elbe, J. Chem. Phys., **2**, 73 (1934).

[368] W. C. Coburn, Jr., and E. Grunwald, J. Am. Chem. Soc., **80**, 1318 (1958).

[369] For an extensive review see G. Allen and E. F. Calden, Quart. Revs., **7**, 255 (1953).

[370] F. T. Wall and F. W. Banes, J. Am. Chem. Soc., **67**, 898 (1945); F. T. Wall and P. E. Rouse, J. Am. Chem. Soc., **63**, 3002 (1941).

[371] A. A. Maryott, M. E. Hobbs, and P. M. Gross, J. Am. Chem. Soc., **71**, 1671 (1949); H. A. Pohl, M. E. Hobbs, and P. M. Gross, J. Chem. Phys., **9**, 408, 415 (1941).

[372] R. H. Gillette, J. Am. Chem. Soc., **58**, 1143 (1936).

[373] E. N. Lassettre, Chem. Rev., **20**, 259 (1937).

[374] E. W. Johnson and L. K. Nash, J. Am. Chem. Soc., **72**, 547 (1950); H. C. Ramsperger and W. C. Porter, J. Am. Chem. Soc., **48**, 1267 (1926); A. S. Coolidge J. Am. Chem. Soc., **50**, 2166 (1928); T. M. Fenton and W. E. Garner, J. Chem. Soc., 694 (1930); F. H. MacDougall, J. Am. Chem. Soc., **58**, 2585 (1930).

[375] M. D. Taylor, et al., J. Am. Chem. Soc., **78**, 2950 (1956); O. R. Foz and J. Marcillo, Chem. Abstracts, **44**, 8716 (1950).

[376] R. C. Herman, J. Chem. Phys., **8**, 252 (1940); G. B. B. Sutherland, Trans. Faraday Soc., **36**, 889 (1940); R. E. Kagarise, J. Chem. Phys., **27**, 519 (1957).

[377] C. O. Strother and W. T. Richards, J. Chem. Phys., **4**, 566 (1936).

[378] M. D. Taylor, et al., J. Am. Chem. Soc., **78**, 2950 (1956).

the stronger is the H bond.[371,378,380] This trend is understandable, for as the electronegativity of R increases, thereby diminishing the contribution of the polar form to the carbonyl resonance

$$C{=}O, \quad \overset{+}{C}{-}O^-$$

and decreasing the electron density on the carbonyl oxygen atom, the H bond is weakened while proton dissociation from the OH group is facilitated. The intermolecular H bond energy in phenols also increases with decreasing acid strength of the phenols.[379]

(iii) **Water solubility.** The reciprocal H bonding between the OH group of hydroxylic compounds and water markedly increases the water solubility of the hydroxylic compound. When a compound has a large ratio of OH groups to hydrocarbon groups, the compound will have a significant solubility in water. For example, sugars and certain starches are very soluble in water, and even polyvinyl alcohol, a polymer of large molecular weight,

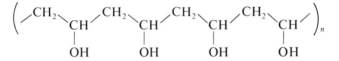

is quite soluble in water. Also, the success of nonionic detergents is due to the powerful solubilizing effect of hydroxyl groups. These detergents are usually derivatives of di- and triethanolamines or of the condensation products of ethylene oxide with alcohols or phenols. Unlike the cationic or anionic "soaps," where the water-soluble portions of the molecules are ionic, the water-soluble portions of the nonionics are neutral hydroxyl, ether, or amino groups which dissolve in water primarily as a result of hydrogen bonding.

On the other hand, liquid ethers and esters are nonassociated, which makes them have much lower boiling points than their isomeric alcohols and acids. Water may form hydrogen bonds with ethers and esters, but ethers and esters do not have groups for also forming hydrogen bonds with water. This lack of co-association of esters with water causes the esters to have much lower water solubilities than their isomeric acids, but the effect is insignificant in the case of the ethers (Table 1.25).

Owing to association with water molecules, primary and secondary amines are quite soluble in water. The primary amines up to C_5 and the secondary amines up to C_4 are completely miscible with water at room temperature, whereas even the first tertiary amine, trimethylamine, is only 41 per cent soluble and the higher tertiary amines are practically insoluble.

[379]M. M. Maguire and R. West, *Spectrochim. Acta,* **17,** 369 (1961).
[380]M. L. Huggins, *J. Org. Chem.,* **1,** 407 (1936).

Table 1.25 Boiling Points and Water Solubilities of Some Isomeric Ethers and Alcohols, and of Some Isomeric Esters and Carboxylic Acids*

Molecular formula	Alcohol	Boiling point (°C)		Ether	Water solubility (%) near room temp.		Alcohol
$C_4H_{10}O$	n-Butyl	118	35	Diethyl	7.5	9	n-Butyl
$C_5H_{12}O$	n-Pentyl	138	62	Ethyl n-propyl	sl.s.	2.7	n-Pentyl
$C_6H_{14}O$	n-Hexyl	157	91	Di-n-propyl	sl.s.	0.6	n-Hexyl
$C_6H_{14}O$	Isohexyl	158	69	Di-isopropyl	0.2	v.sl.s.	Isohexyl
$C_6H_{14}O$	Isohexyl	158	83	n-Propyl isopropyl	0.5	v.sl.s.	Isohexyl
$C_8H_{18}O$	n-Octyl	195	142	Di-n-butyl	0.05	sl.s.	n-Octyl
	Acid			*Ester*			*Acid*
$C_2H_4O_2$	Acetic	118	32	Methyl formate	30	∞	Acetic
$C_3H_6O_2$	Propionic	141	57	Methyl acetate	33	∞	Propionic
$C_3H_6O_2$	Propionic	141	54	Ethyl formate	11	∞	Propionic
$C_4H_8O_2$	n-Butyric	168	81	n-Propyl formate	2.2	∞	n-Butyric
$C_4H_8O_2$	n-Butyric	168	77	Ethyl acetate	9	∞	n-Butyric
$C_4H_8O_2$	n-Butyric	168	80	Methyl propionate	0.5	∞	n-Butyric

*Values taken from *Lange's Handbook of Chemistry.*

This effect is probably due to a steric effect rather than lack of N—H···O bonding because tertiary amines with the R groups tied back by ring formation, such as in pyridine, are soluble in water.

When the OH group of an hydroxylic compound is tied up by chelation, association with water is hindered and the water solubility then approaches that of a similar compound which lacks the OH group. One practical application of this contrasting effect of chelation and association upon physical properties is made in the separation by steam distillation of a mixture of *ortho* and *para* hydroxy-carbonyl or nitro compounds. In the case of the *ortho* isomers, association of the OH group with water molecules is diminished owing to its chelation with the adjacent carbonyl or nitro group.

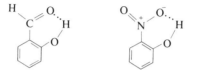

Consequently, the *ortho* isomers are only sparingly water soluble and are much more volatile than the *para* isomers. As a combined result of decreased water solubilities and increased vapor pressures, the *ortho* isomers can be steam distilled so much more rapidly than the *para* isomers that a practical separation of two isomers may be made. This decrease in association of chelated compounds will also permit the resolution of *ortho-para* mixtures by sublimation.[384]

There is a simple method of differentiating between chelated and associated compounds, which consists of determining the differences in melting points of a substance when dry and when in contact with water.[381] The depression in melting point when wet is much smaller for chelated than for associated compounds. For instance, *o*-nitrophenol gives a wet melting-point depression of 1° while the depression is 56° for the *meta* isomer, and 74° for the *para* isomer. Additional examples are given in Table 1.26. Presumably this marked difference in wet melting-point depressions of chelated and associated compounds is due to the ability of an associated compound to associate also with water, which increases their mutual solubilities. There results a considerable water content in the eutectic mixture, whose melting point is therefore much lower than that of the pure compound. Since water is much less soluble in the chelated compound, as well as in a substance which is incapable of forming H bonds, the water content of the eutectic mixture will be small, and so will the wet melting-point depression. Similarly, *m*- and *p*-fluorobenzoic acids are much more associated in solution than is *o*-fluorobenzoic acid. In this case, the *o*-fluoro

[381]A. M. Stock, W. E. Donahue, and E. D. Amstutz, *J. Org. Chem.,* **23,** 1840 (1958); N. V. Sidgwick, *et al., J. Chem. Soc.,* 1202 (1915); W. Baker, *et al., J. Chem. Soc.,* 49 (1937); H. O. Chaplin and L. Hunter, *J. Chem. Soc.,* 484 (1939).

Table 1.26. WET MELTING-POINT DEPRESSIONS FOR SOME
ISOMERIC HYDROXY COMPOUNDS[382,383]

Chelated compounds		Associated compounds	
1-Hydroxy-2-acetylnaphthalene	2°	1-Hydroxy-4-acetylnaphthalene	44°
1-Acetyl-2-hydroxynaphthalene	2°		
2-Hydroxy-3-acetylnaphthalene	6°		

2-Hydroxy-	5°	4-Hydroxy-	35°
3-Chloro-2-hydroxy-	7°	3-Chloro-4-hydroxy-	36°
3-Bromo-2-hydroxy	5°	3-Bromo-4-hydroxy-	50°

$SO_2C_6H_5$ ... R ... R

R = OH, R′ = H	12.5°	R = H, R′ = OH	51°
R = OH, R′ = OCH₃	10.5°	R = OCH₃, R′ = OH	51°
R = NH₂, R′ = H	11°	R = H, R′ = NH₂	32.5°
R = NH₂, R′ = OCH₃	13°	R = OCH₃, R′ = NH₂	28°

atom ties up the hydroxyl group through chelation, which is not possible in the *meta* and *para* isomers.

(iv) Ionization of carboxylic acids. When the anion of an acid is stabilized by intramolecular hydrogen bonding, there is a marked increase in the dissociation of the acid.[360] For illustration, the ionization constants ($\times$ 10^5) for the isomeric hydroxy- and methoxybenzoic acids in water are:

	Ortho	Meta	Para
HO—	105	8.3	2.9
CH₃O—	8.1	8.2	3.4

It is apparent that the *o*-hydroxy isomer has an abnormally large dissociation, and it is the only acid in this group whose anion is stabilized by

[382] E, D. Amstutz, J. J. Chessick, and I. M. Hunsberger, *Science,* **111,** 305 (1950).
[383] L. N. Ferguson and I. Kelly, *J. Am. Chem. Soc.,* **73,** 3707 (1951).
[384] L. N. Pino and W. S. Zehrung, *J. Chem. Educ.,* **31,** 476 (1954).

chelation. Its dissociation is 17 times that of benzoic acid, and that of 2,6-dihydroxybenzoic acid is 800 times as large, which can be attributed to an even greater stabilization by hydrogen bonding.

Salicylate ion

2,6-Dihydroxybenzoate ion

When the dissociating H atom is involved in a H bond, more energy is required for its removal, and the observed dissociation constant will be abnormally low. For illustration, *o*-halophenols are weaker acids than the *m*- or *p*-isomers.[385]

o-Halophenol

Spectroscopic evidence for the chelated structure of *o*-halophenols is given in Chap. 5. The acid weakening effect of *ortho* H bonding groups makes it possible to analyze mixtures of *o*- and *p*-hydroxybenzoic acids, because the phenolic hydroxyl group of the *para* isomer is acidic enough to give a break in the titration curve near pH 10, while the *ortho* isomer does not give this inflection. Hence, titration to the first inflection point near pH 6 corresponds to neutralization of the carboxyl of both acids and indicates the total amount of acid present. Titration to the second break represents neutralization of the *para* hydroxyl, and the distance between breaks indicates the amount of the *para* isomer in the mixture.[386]

It has been pointed out[387,390] that H bonding is partly responsible for the large K_1 to K_2 ratio for some dicarboxylic acids. Thus, the K_1/K_2 ratio is 32 for fumaric acid and 26,000 for maleic acid.[391] Statistically, K_1/K_2 for a dibasic acid should be greater than four, based on the fact that there is a ratio of 2:1 for the number of protons that may dissociate in the undissociated and monodissociated forms and a factor of 2:1 for the number of sites the proton may recombine with the dianion or the monoanion. As the two carboxyl groups approach each other, they exert electrostatic effects on each other. The CO_2^- group of the fumarate ion has a mild retarding electrostatic effect on the dissociation of the second COOH group

[385]D. H. McDaniel and H. C, Brown, *J. Am. Chem. Soc.*, **77**, 3759 (1955).
[386]L. N. Ferguson, J. C. Reid, and M. Calvin, *J. Am. Chem. Soc.*, **68**, 2502 (1946).
[387]D. H. McDaniel and H. C. Brown, *Science*, **118**, 370 (1953).

and decreases K_2 with respect to K_1. By contrast, in the maleate ion, the CO_2^- group has a much larger attractive electrostatic effect on the proton of the second $COOH$[388] and also the ion is stabilized by the strong H bond. Both effects retard the dissociation of the second proton to give the larger K_1/K_2 ratio.[389]

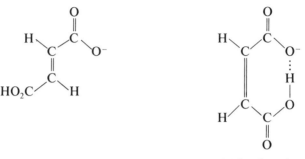

Acid fumarate ion   *Acid maleate ion*

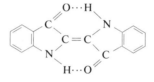

Trans-Indigo

(v) Stereoisomerism. H bonding may have a strong influence on the spatial configuration of a molecule or in hindering its isomerization.[392] For example, the *trans* isomer of indigo is so stabilized by H bonding that it resists photochemical isomerization to the *cis* isomer.[393] On the other hand, the N,N'-diacetyl derivative and the sulfur analogue, in which the N—H···S bonds are too weak to be effective, readily undergo isomerization. Similarly, intramolecular H bonding apparently makes the *cis* isomer of the platinium chelate of pyridine-2-aldoxime more stable than the *trans* isomer.[394]

[388] F. H. Westheimer and O. T. Benfey, *J. Am. Chem. Soc.*, **78**, 5309 (1956).

[389] It has been suggested that the H bonding has only a negligible effect in the maleate ion (R. E. Dodd, R. E. Miller, and W. F. K. Wynne-Jones, *J. Chem. Soc.*, 2790 (1961).

[390] H. H. Jaffe, L. D. Freedman, and G. O. Doak, *J. Am. Chem. Soc.*, **76**, 1548 (1954).

[391] G. Dahlgren, Jr., and F. A. Long, *J. Am. Chem. Soc.*, **82**, 1305 (1960).

[392] L. Hunter, in *Progress in Stereochemistry*, vol. 1, ed. W. Klyne (New York: Academic, 1954), chap. 6.

[393] W. R. Brode, E. G. Pearson, and G. M. Wyman, *J. Am. Chem. Soc.*, **76**, 1034 (1954); **73**, 1487 (1951).

[394] C. F. Liu and C. H. Liu, *J. Am. Chem. Soc.*, **83**, 2615 (1961).

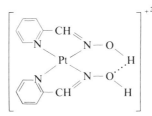

In the alicyclic and bicyclic diols, H bonding may be a factor in the relative stability of certain conformations. The detection of such intramolecular H bonding has facilitated the determination of the structures of certain diols.[396]

In another example, Pauling, Corey, and Branson investigated the configuration of the peptide chains of fibrous proteins and postulated that their configuration should be one that permits good H bonding.[397] Based on this and other factors, their proposed structure, known as the α-helix, is generally accepted now as being correct.[398] In this structure each N—H bond of the peptide group forms an N—H···O bond with the near-by carbonyl oxygen atom on the next turn of the helix.

Thus, H bonds have a definite stabilizing effect, and in some cases, certain substances owe their existence to the presence of H bonds.[399] For example, enediols are ordinarily too unstable to be isolable, but pyridine- and quinoline-2-aldehydes can be reduced to give stable enediols.[395] This unusual stability is attributable to the presence of two H bonds in the structures.

Similarly, H bonds are a major factor responsible for the enol content of β-diketones (Sec. 4.8.4) and other tautomeric equilibria,[400] and for the formation of gas hydrates (Sec. 1.7.3). Simple carboxylic acids exist as *cis*

[395]C. A. Buehler, J. W. Addlebury, and D. M. Glenn, *J. Org. Chem.*, **20**, 1350 (1955).

[396]H. Kwart and W. G. Vosburgh, *J. Am. Chem. Soc.*, **76**, 5400 (1954).

[397]L. Pauling, R. B. Corey, and H. R. Branson, *Proc. Nat. Acad. Sci. U.S.*, **37**, 205 (1951).

[398]F. H. C, Crick, *Sci. Progress*, **42**, 205 (1954).

[399]E.g., some of the inclusion compounds [M. L. Huggins, *J. Chem. Educ.*, **34**, 480 (1957)].

[400]G. Cilento, E. C. Miller, and J. A. Miller, *J. Am. Chem. Soc.*, **78**, 1718 (1956); C. H. Giles, *et al.*, *J. Am. Chem. Soc.*, **78**, 72 (1956).

monomeric or as dimeric species depending on the environmental conditions.

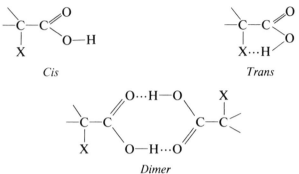

Cis   *Trans*

Dimer

However, when proton acceptors are α to the carboxyl group, as in methoxyacetic acid, the intramolecularly H bonded *trans* isomer will also be present. The presence of all three species can be detected by infrared spectroscopy.[401]

(vi) **Adsorption,** Hydrogen bonding is a very important factor in the process of dyeing textiles. A striking illustration can be given as follows:[402] If a piece of pure cotton and another of cellulose acetate are dipped into a warm dyebath containing a water-soluble blue dye and a water-insoluble red dye, when the fabrics are withdrawn and rinsed in hot water, the cotton will be colored pure blue and the cellulose acetate will be pure red. On the other hand, the fabrics may be dipped in another pair of dyes and this time have the opposite colors.

Pontamine Sky Blue 6BX	⟶	Cotton, blue
Celanthrene Red 3BN		Acetate, red
Pontamine Fast Scarlet 4BA	⟶	Cotton, red
Celanthrene Pure Blue BRS		Acetate, blue

What happens is that each fabric selectively adsorbs a particular type of dye. The first two dyes of the above pairs are water soluble, and the same hydrogen bonding groups that make them water soluble bind them to cellulose through hydrogen bonds with the cellulose OH groups. Most of these OH groups of cellulose are covered by acetyl radicals in cellulose acetate, giving it the general characteristics of an ester. It then adsorbs dyes that tend to be insoluble in water through binding forces such as dipole-dipole and van der Waals forces.

[401] M. Oki and M. Hirota, *Spectrochim. Acta,* **17,** 583 (1961).
[402] I wish to acknowledge here my indebtedness to the E. I. du Pont Chemical Company for providing samples of the dyes used in these experiments.

(vii) Miscellaneous effects.[403]   In addition to the several physical properties discussed above, many others are affected by H bonding.   Some such properties are color, heat of mixing, heat of vaporization,[404] dipole moments,[405] refractive index,[406] viscosity,[407] polarographic reduction potentials,[408] titration curves in nonaqueous solvents,[409] relative stabilities of chair and boat conformations of cyclic compounds,[410] heats of combustion,[411] and several types of absorption spectra. In fact, H bonding is likely to affect all physical properties. Sometimes, however, it will be difficult to single out the role of H bonding or make quantitative interpretations.   The most powerful method for studying H bonding is spectroscopy, but we will postpone this discussion until spectroscopy in general is taken up in Chap. 5.   Actually, it is difficult to say much about H bonds without including the results of spectroscopic measurements.

It can be mentioned here that steric requirements sometimes prohibit H bonding.   For example, di-o-t-alkylphenols and tri-t-alkylcarbinols are monomeric. Similarly, indigo is highly associated in the solid phase but with large groups in the 4,4′ or 7,7′ positions, association is essentially absent.[412] The large groups about the OH groups in these compounds prevent close approach of the molecules and thereby weaken or entirely block the formation of H bonds.

Steric requirements may interfere with H bonding in another way. o-Nitroacetanilide exhibits intramolecular H bonding.

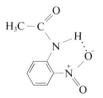

However, when substituents such as the Br, NO_2, or CH_3 group are placed $ortho$ to the NO_2 or the $NHCOCH_3$ group, they prevent the H bond form-

[403]Chap. 2 of reference 312(a).

[404]A. Bondi and D. J. Simkin, $A.$ $I.$ $Ch.$ $E.$ Journal, 3, 473 (1957); R. W. Taft and H. H. Sisler, J. Chem. Educ., 24, 175 (1947).

[405]B. Eda and K. Ito, Bull. Chem. Soc. Japan, 29, 524 (1956); 30, 164 (1957); J. R. Hulett, J. A. Pegg, and L. E. Sutton, J. Chem. Soc., 3901 (1955).   An extensive discussion of dielectric polarization of associated molecules (through H bonds and dipole-dipole forces) is given by W. Hückel in Theoretical Principles of Organic Chemistry, vol. II [Princeton, N. J.: (Elsevier) Van Nostrand, 1958], pp. 318 ff.

[406]C. H. Giles, et al., J. Chem. Soc., 72 (1956) and earlier papers.

[407]L. A. K. Staveley and P. F. Taylor, J. Chem. Soc., 200 (1956).

[408]M. J. Astle and W. V. McConnell, J. Am. Chem. Soc., 65, 35 (1943).

[409]A. T. Shulgin and H. O. Kerlinger, J. Org. Chem., 25, 2037 (1960).

[410]See Sec. 3.3.2.

[411]O. Bastiansen, Acta Chem. Scand., 3, 415 (1949).

[412]J. Weinstein and G. M. Wyman, J. Am. Chem. Soc., 78, 2387 (1956).

ing groups from lying coplanar with the ring. This makes the distance between the bridged electronegative atoms too large for an H bond, and the compounds become associated through intramolecular H bonds. For illustration, *o*-nitroacetanilide is chelated, as evidenced by its wet melting-point depression, but when groups are introduced adjacent to the NO_2 or NHAc group, chelation is blocked and the compounds easily associate with water.[413]

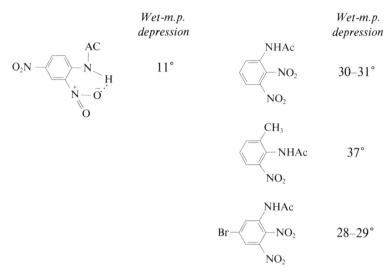

Wet-m.p. depression

11°

Wet-m.p. depression

30–31°

37°

28–29°

An example of steric facilitation rather than steric hindrance to H bonding was noted in the case of *o*-nitrophenols with alkyl groups *ortho* to the OH group.[414]

Apparently, the alkyl group forces the OH group to form an H bond with the nitro group in all molecules and also increases the H bond strength over that found in *o*-nitrophenol.

It is noteworthy that most intramolecular H bonds involve either a five-membered ring with only single bonds or one double bond, or a six-membered ring with two double bonds.

Most of the effects of H bonding on physical properties are summarized in Table 1.27. Qualitative comparisons are made with the prop-

[413] H. O. Chaplin and L. Hunter, *J. Chem. Soc.*, 375, 1034 (1938).
[414] J. C. Dearden and W. F. Forbes, *Can. J. Chem.*, **38**, 1852 (1950).

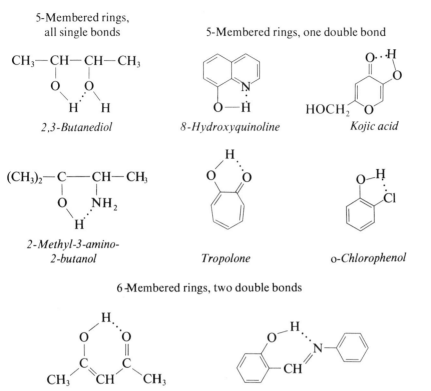

5-Membered rings,
all single bonds

2,3-Butanediol

2-Methyl-3-amino-
2-butanol

5-Membered rings, one double bond

8-Hydroxyquinoline

Kojic acid

Tropolone

o-Chlorophenol

6-Membered rings, two double bonds

Acetylacetone

Salicylaldehyde-anil

erties of a non-H bonding compound such as a hydrocarbon. The effects on spectra will be discussed in Chap. 5 but are included in the table for organization.

1.6.3 EFFECTS OF H BONDS ON CHEMICAL PROPERTIES

One noticeable example of H bonding modifying the usual properties of a functional group is where O—H···O=C or N—H···O=C bonds obliterate the typical carbonyl properties. For example, in diaroylmethanes

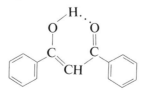

the strong H bonds tie up the carbonyl group, and the compounds do not form Schiff bases or add HCN. The OH group is tied up too, for the com-

Table 1.27. QUALITATIVE EFFECTS OF H BONDS ON
SOME PHYSICAL PROPERTIES

Property	Intramolecular H bonds	Intermolecular H bonds
Transition temp.	Close to normal	Increased
Vapor pressure	Close to normal	Decreased
Mixed melting points	Slightly depressed	Greatly depressed
Molecular weight	Close to normal	Increased
Water solubility	Decreased	Increased
Solvent power	Close to normal	Increased
Ionization	Decreased	Increased
Isomer stability	Increased	Close to normal
Adsorption on		
polar surfaces	Close to normal	Increased
Infrared spectra:		
Stretching freq.	Decreased	Increased
Bending freq.	Increased	Decreased
Effect of environment	Small	Large
Electronic absorption	Large increase	Small increase or decrease
NMR chemical shift	Shifts to lower field	Shifts to lower field
Other misc. properties:		
Molar volume	Small decrease	Large decrease
Viscosity	Close to normal	Higher
Dielectric constant	Relatively low	Relatively high
Surface tension	Close to normal	Higher
Phototropy[415]	Observed	Not observed

pounds do not undergo acetylation with acetic anhydride, nor give methane when treated with methyl magnesium iodide, nor give nitrogen with diazomethane. Similarly, the H bond in nickel dimethylglyoxime is so strong that the OH group is not acetylated by acetic anhydride nor does it give methane with methyl magnesium iodide.[416] For the same reason, *o*-hydroxyazo compounds, unlike the *para* isomers, are insoluble in alkali, cannot be methylated with diazomethane, and are difficult to acylate.[417]

Another example of the effect of H bonding on chemical properties grew out of a study of the enzymatic deamination of certain keto acid amides.[418]

$$HO_2C-CO-CH_2-CONH_2 \xrightarrow[\text{enzyme}]{H_2O} HO_2C-CO-CH_3 + NH_3 + CO_2$$

[415]M. D. Cohen, Y. Hirshberg, and G. M. J. Schmidt in *Hydrogen Bonding,* ed. D. Hadzi and H. W. Thompson, (New York: Pergamon, 1959), p. 293.

[416]R. C. Voter, C. V. Banks, V. A. Fassel, and P. W. Kehres, *Anal. Chem.,* **23,** 1730 (1951).

[417]C. Smith and A. D. Mitchell, *J. Chem. Soc.,* **93,** 843 (1908).

[418]A. Meister, *Federation Proceedings,* **14,** 683 (1955).

It was found that those keto amides having no more than two methylene groups between the keto group and the amide group and having at least one amide hydrogen atom exist in chelated structures.

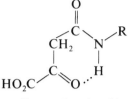

α-Ketosuccinamic acid

In contrast to keto acid amides in general, the chelated ones are unusual in that they do not undergo enzymatic deamination nor do they give 2,4-dinitrophenylhydrazones. Thus, H bonding has prevented one of the strongest reactions of carbonyl groups, the formation of 2,4-dinitrophenylhydrazones.

A number of cases have been reported in the literature in which the mechanism or kinetics of a reaction are markedly influenced by the stabilization of a reaction intermediate through H bonding.[419] For instance, chelated *o*-hydroxy-aldehydes and ketones often react with amines to form Schiff bases much more rapidly than their associated isomers.[420] The order is reversed for reactions such as oxidations or reductions because the chelated isomers are stabilized by H bonding. The usual rule that equatorial esters are hydrolyzed faster than axial esters is reversed when there is a β—OH to produce an intramolecular H bond.[421]

1.6.4 H BONDING IN BIOLOGICAL SYSTEMS

Hydrogen bonding plays an important role in biological systems too. For example, a large quantity of water, over 50 per cent of their weight, is retained by living cells in plants and animals, and most of this water is attached to proteins by H bonds. Mention was made earlier of the role that H bonds play in constraining fibrous protein molecules to the α-helical configuration. For instance, when a polypeptide is placed in D_2O instead of H_2O, more of the polypeptide exists in a random form.[422] This can be attributed to less hydrogen bonding occurring between D_2O and the polypeptide to hold the molecule in the helical structure. It appears that the

[419]H. A. Shah and R. C. Shah, *Nature, 142,* 163 (1938); S. Seshadri and P. L. Trivedi, *J. Org. Chem., 22,* 1633 (1957); A. R. Surrey, *et al., J. Am. Chem. Soc., 81,* 2887 (1959); M. Szwarc and J. Smid, *J. Chem. Phys., 27,* 421 (1957).

[420]G. Vavon and P. Montheard, *Bull. soc. chim., France, 7,* 551 (1940).

[421]H. B. Henbest and B. J. Lovell, *J. Chem. Soc.,* 1965 (1957).

[422]M. Calvin, J. Hermans, Jr., and H. A. Scheraga, *J. Am. Chem. Soc., 81,* 5048 (1959).

O—D···O bonds are slightly stronger than O—H···O bonds and that D_2O is self-associated more than H_2O. Consequently, solutes in D_2O do not form intermolecular hydrogen bonds to the same extent that they do in H_2O.[423]

Others have noted the large number of compounds having physiological activity that can form H bonds, and it is highly probable that H bonding contributes to the success of many drugs either by aiding their solubility and diffusion through cell fluids or by binding them to nucleic acids and other body constituents for physiological actions.

Summary

From the foregoing discussion, it is observed that H bonding has a profound effect upon a wide variety of properties of substances. In recent years, H bonding has been the subject of considerable interest. A large number of quantitative data are being accumulated which will enable chemists to construct a more accurate model of the H bond. Although H bonds are relatively weak compared to typical covalent and ionic bonds, they do have very pronounced effects upon the properties of compounds. In some cases–for example, the action of nonionic detergents or the dyeing of textiles–H bonds are the key factors for the success of commercial processes.

Much more will be said about H bonds in Chap. 5 on spectroscopy.

STUDY QUESTIONS

1. Offer an explanation for the following observations:
   (a) Ethyl propionate boils at a lower temperature than propionic acid even though the ester has the larger molecular weight.
   (b) Propyleneimine boils at a higher temperature (67°) than does its isomer, N-methyl-ethyleneimine (27.5°).
   (c) Triethylamine is slightly soluble in water whereas pyridine is miscible with water in all proportions.
   (d) Tropolone does not form a 2,4-dinitrophenylhydrazone.
   (e) Quinoline-8-carboxylic acid is a much weaker acid than any of the isomeric quinoline carboxylic acids.
   (f) 4-Methoxy-10-methylacridine is demethylated much more readily than the 1-, 2-, or 3-methoxy isomers under the same conditions.[424]
   (g) Only 8.2 g of phenol dissolves in 100 g of water at 15° but the two become completely miscible above 65°.

[423]G. Dahlgren, Jr., and F. A. Long, *J. Am. Chem. Soc.*, **82**, 1303 (1960).
[424] G. M. Badger, *Revs. Pure and Applied Chem.*, **7**, 66 (1957).

2. Predict the following, and in each case give the basis for your prediction:
   (a) The relative solubilities of *ortho* and *para* fluorobenzoic acids in water.
   (b) The relative solubilities of *ortho* and *para* nitrophenols in benzene.
   (c) The relative melting points of 8-hydroxyquinoline and of the 2-hydroxy isomer.
   (d) The possibility of separating 8-hydroxyquinoline from the 4-hydroxy isomer by steam distillation.
   (e) The relative solubilities in water of $CHCl_3$, $CHBr_3$, and C_6H_5Br.
   (f) The relative solubilities in water of trimethylamine and isobutane.
   (g) The better solvent for benzoic acid, petroleum ether or ethyl ether.
   (h) The order of relative H bond strengths in the *o*-halophenols.[425]
   (i) The relative boiling points of acetamide, N-methylacetamide, and N,N-dimethylacetamide.
   (j) Which would have the larger wet melting-point depression, *p*-nitroacetanilide or *o*-nitroacetanilide.

3. Fatty peracids, $R—CO_3H$, are monomeric in benzene solution, which can be attributed to intramolecular H bonding.

Should this H bond have an acid strengthening or acid weakening effect?[426]

4. The isomers tropine and pseudotropine are each believed to have one of the bicyclo structures

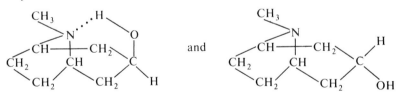

What measurements would you make to assign the proper structures to each compound?[427]

5. Spectroscopic and X-ray diffraction measurements indicate that pure formic acid at room temperature is polymeric; however, cryoscopic measurements in benzene indicate that formic acid is dimeric in the solvent. How do you interpret these results?

6. The molecular weight of *p*-bromophenol in benzene by cryoscopic measurements is 185.[428] On the assumption that essentially only dimers are produced, what is the degree of association at the experimental concentration?

[425] A. W. Baker, *J. Am. Chem. Soc.*, **80**, 3598 (1958).
[426] D. Swern, *et al., J. Am. Chem. Soc.*, **77**, 5537 (1955); **80**, 4850 (1958).
[427] B. L. Zenitz, *et al., J. Am. Chem. Soc.*, **74**, 5564 (1952).
[428] W. F. Anzilotti and B. C. Curran, *J. Am. Chem. Soc.*, **65**, 610 (1943).

7. In the solid state, both OH groups of 2,3-dihydroxyacetophenone are tied up by some type of H bonding, but in solution one of the OH groups is free. Propose structures for the compound in the solid state and in solution.

8. The benzoin condensation of quinaldehyde N-oxide yields a very stable enediol; however, the infrared spectrum exhibits no bands for the presence of free OH groups. Assign a possible structure to the enediol.[429]

9. Predict which compound will form the stronger H-bond, 2-hydroxy-4-nitro-biphenyl or 2-hydroxy-4'-nitrobiphenyl.[430]

    Which conformation should be the most stable, and which the least stable, A, B, or C?[431]

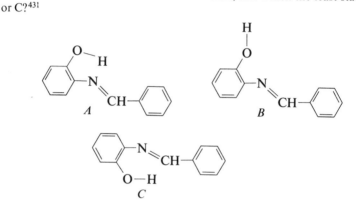

1.7 Nonbonding intermolecular forces

There are two types of ubiquitous intermolecular forces, which differ primarily in magnitude and effective range: van der Waals and dipole forces.

1.7.1 VAN DER WAALS ATTRACTION

Although the negative charges of the electrons in a neutral molecule are balanced by the positive charges on the nuclei, the electrons are in constant motion, and the center of density of the negative charges (i.e., a point which may be regarded as the time-average position for all of the negative charges) does not coincide continuously with the center of density of the positive charges. This situation produces small instantaneous local dipoles; that is, areas with a positive and negative end which behave as small electric magnets. When molecules are close enough, these dipoles attract each other like magnetic bars, causing the molecules to cling to one another. Such attraction is called *van der Waals attraction*. The greater the area over which molecules may come in close contact, the greater is the overall van

[429] C. A. Buehler, L. A. Walker, and P. Garcia, *J. Org. Chem.,* **26,** 1410 (1961).

[430] M. Oki and H. Iwamura, *Bull. Chem. Soc. Japan,* **31,** 769 (1958).

[431] A. W. Baker and A. T. Shulgen, *J. Am. Chem. Soc.,* **81,** 1523 (1959).

der Waals attraction. For straight-chain hydrocarbons, the forces are about 1.0 kcal per CH_2 unit, which explains the regular increase in boiling point with increasing chain length within a homologous series. Branching of a chain decreases the area over which a molecule may "touch" other molecules; accordingly, the boiling points of isomers decrease with the degree of branching. For example, the boiling points of normal, iso, secondary, and tertiary-butyl alcohols are 117°, 107°, 100°, and 83°, respectively. Van der Waals forces become weaker in proportion to the seventh power of the distance between molecules: $F \propto (1/d^7)$. A short separation of molecules markedly decreases the van der Waals force of attraction; hence, they are effective only for short intermolecular distances; in other words, they are very short-range forces.

1.7.2 DIPOLE ASSOCIATION

The dipoles that arise from the unequal sharing of electrons by covalently bonded atoms are referred to as *bond dipoles,* and their magnitudes are indicated by the size of their *bond moments* (Table 2.11). Bond dipoles in different molecules attract one another; this is called *dipole-dipole attraction.* Dipole-dipole forces vary inversely as the fourth power of the distance between molecules: $F \propto (1/d^4)$. Thus, they too are effective only for short distances but are of longer range than van der Waals forces. The effects from dipole association are the same as from hydrogen bonding, only to a smaller extent. Thus, compounds made up of bonds having large bond dipoles are somewhat polar. This is reflected in those properties which involve the separation of molecules, such as boiling points and heats of

Table 1.28. SOME PROPERTIES REFLECTING POLAR CHARACTER OF VARIOUS CLASSES OF COMPOUNDS OF COMPARABLE MOLECULAR WEIGHTS

Compound	Class	Mol. wt.	B.P. (°C)	Heat of vaporization (kcal/mole)	Trouton's constant
$CH_3CH_2CH_2CH_3$	Alkane	58	0.6	5.3	19.4
CH_3CH_2Cl	Alkyl chloride	64.5	13	6.0	20.5
$(CH_3CH_2)_2O$	Ether	74	34.6	6.2	20.2
CH_3-COCl	Acid chloride	78.5	52	6.2	21.5
$CH_3-CO-CH_3$	Ketone	58	56	7.2	21.9
$CH_3-CO_2CH_3$	Ester	74	57.5	7.3	22.1
CH_3CH_2CN	Nitrile	55	97	7.4	20
CH_3NO_2	Nitroalkane	61	99.9	8.2	22.1
$CH_3CH_2CH_2OH$	Alcohol	60	98	9.9	26.6
CH_3COOH	Carboxylic acid	60	118	11.6	29.6
CH_3-CONH_2	Amide	59	222		

vaporization. The greater the association, the greater is the energy required to separate molecules for vaporization (Table 1.28). Now, related to heats of vaporization is Trouton's constant–the ratio of the molar heat of vaporization to the absolute boiling point of a substance. This constant is found to be a useful index for the relative polarity of organic compounds (see Table 1.28). Knowledge of the relative polarity of organic compounds is of particular value when seeking a solvent for a substance. One looks among the polar liquids, i.e., alcohols and acids, for a solvent for a polar compound and among the nonpolar liquids for a solvent for a nonpolar substance.

1.7.3 INCLUSION COMPOUNDS[432]

For decades, the choleic acids, the blue color of starch-iodine mixtures, and the hydrate of chlorine gas were chemical oddities. Suddenly, following the accidental discovery of the crystalline urea complex of octyl alcohol by Bengen in 1940, there was a tremendous burst of activity and interest in these compounds by the oil companies. It was soon discovered that these complexes, referred to as *inclusion compounds,* have several valuable commercial and laboratory uses.

The inclusion compounds are of two general types, the cage or *clathrates* (Gr. = lock) and the *channel* compounds.

Channel	*Clathrates*
Urea complexes	Quinols
Cyclodextrins	Gas hydrates
Choleic acids	Etc.
Biphenyls	
Etc.	

These compounds have one underlying principle in common: their formation depends on the spatial "fitting-in" of the guest molecules into the crystal lattice cavities or the "holes" of liquid aggregates of *host* molecules. There is no chemical affinity between the host and guest molecules in the usual sense, e.g., inclusion compounds of even the inert gases have been formed. Inclusion compound formation depends upon the size and shape of the guest molecules and the reciprocal size of the cavities created by the host molecules. This brings about a very close contact of the molecules, and the short-range van der Waals forces become significant factors for compound formation.

---

[432] L. Mandelcorn, *Chem. Rev.,* **59,** 827 (1959); F. D. Cramer, *Revs. Pure and Applied Chem.,* **5,** 143 (1955); J. W. Smith, *Sci. Progress.,* **38,** 698 (1950); H. M. Powell, *Endeavour,* **9,** 154 (1950); K. A. Kobe and L. R. Reinhard, *J. Chem. Educ.,* **36,** 300 (1959).

1.7.3(a) Dimensional Requirements

Urea complexes. *Guests: n-alkanes and their straight-chain derivatives.* In the presence of straight-chain hydrocarbons, urea crystallizes in the form of parallel tubes or helixes with the urea molecules arranged stepwise in head-to-tail hydrogen bonding and forming hexagonal unit cells.[433] The diameter of the central channel is ca. 5 Å (Fig. 1.26), which is just the right size to

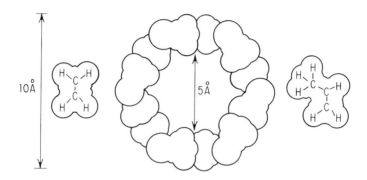

Fig. 1.26. Dimensions of the urea channel compared to the van der Waals diameters of long-chain and branched-chain hydrocarbon molecules.

hold straight-chain hydrocarbon molecules or their straight-chain derivatives in a planar, zig-zag configuration.[433, 434] Nuclear magnetic resonance data indicate that the guest molecules may execute only torsional oscillations about an axis parallel to the channel.[435] On the other hand, branched chains are too large to fit into the channel and rarely form inclusion compounds with urea. Compound formation occurs most readily with straight chains of six carbon atoms or more. With sufficiently long carbon chains, certain lightly branched chains will also form urea inclusion compounds. Thus, 2-methylalkanes above 2-methyldecane will form stable compounds at 25°.[436] About 0.7 molecules of urea are required per CH_2 group of the guest molecule. X-ray diffraction investigations[433] show that urea normally crystallizes in a tetragonal structure, but in a helical inclusion compound, the N—H···O bond distances are 0.05 Å shorter than in tetragonal urea. Apparently in the presence of the guest molecules urea can crystallize in the helical structure, and the complex owes its stability largely to the formation of strong H bonds and van der Waals forces between the closely packed molecules. The heats of formation of the urea complexes is about 1 kcal/

[433] A. E. Smith, *Acta Cryst.*, **5**, 224 (1952).

[434] W. Schlenk, Jr., *Ann.*, **565**, 204 (1949).

[435] D. F. R. Gilson and C. A. McDowell, *Nature*, **183**, 1183 (1959).

[436] R. W. Schiessler and D. D. Neiswender, Jr., *J. Org. Chem.*, **22**, 697 (1957).

mole of urea or 1–2 kcal per CH_2 unit of the guest molecule. This is the order of magnitude of energies for certain physical processes such as the heat of vaporization of *n*-alkanes or their heats of adsorption on silica gel.

Thiourea complexes. *Guests: branched-chain aliphatics, cycloalkanes, $CHCl_3$, durene, 2-bromoethane.* Thiourea forms inclusion compounds very similar in structure to the urea complexes.[437] Although the unit cell is rhombo-hedral, the helical structure resembles that of urea with a central channel of larger diameter (ca. 7 Å).[438] The straight-chain hydrocarbons are too slender to support the thiourea helixes and accordingly do not form com-plexes.

Choleic acids. *Guests: almost all classes of organics.* The steroid desoxy-cholic acid (XXXVII) forms inclusion compounds, called *choleic acids,* with a wide variety of organic molecules.[439] In the presence of the guest mole-cules, desoxycholic acid crystallizes in an open structure leaving hollow

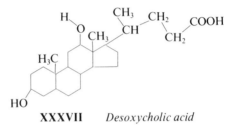

XXXVII   *Desoxycholic acid*

channels in the center (Fig. 1.27).[440] Certain other steroids form inclusion compounds too, and it is probable that they have a channel structure as well. For instance, cortisone and cholic acid form blue iodine compounds, and aqueous solutions of sodium desoxyribonucleate and other purines dissolve many aromatic amines and polynuclear hydrocarbons presumably by inclusion compound formation.[441] 4,4'-Dinitrobiphenyl forms channel-type inclusion compounds with certain 4,4'-substituted biphenyls (see Fig. 1.28).[443]

Cyclodextrins. *Guests: halogens, fatty acids, aromatics.* Amylose and some of its degraded dextrins form channel-type inclusion compounds with

[437] B. Angla, *Compt. rend.,* **224,** 402, 1166 (1947).

[438] H. U. Lenne, *Acta Cryst.,* **7,** 1 (1954).

[439] L. F. Fieser, *The Chemistry of Natural Products Related to Phenanthrene* (2nd ed.; New York: Reinhold, 1937), pp. 129, 368.

[440] Y. Go and O. Kratky, *Z. physik. Chem.,* **B26,** 439 (1934).

[441] J. Booth, E. Boyland, and S. F. D. Orr, *J. Chem. Soc.,* 598 (1954).

[442] R. F. Marschner, *Chem. Eng. News,* **33:** 6, 495 (1955).

[443] B. W. Rapson, D. Saunder, and N. Thael-Stewart, *J. Chem. Soc.,* 1110 (1946); *Proc. Roy. Soc.,* **A190,** 508 (1947).

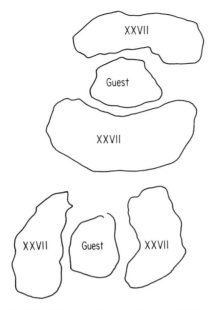

Fig. 1.27. Choleic acid from view parallel to the channels.

iodine and a number of other substances.[444] These cyclodextrins have a crystalline pattern of a hexagonal helix (see Fig. 1.29)[445] and are of three classes with respect to channel diameter[446] (see Table 1.29). It can be seen there that compound formation has a definite dependency on the size of the guest molecule and the bore of the tube of the cyclodextrin. For instance, bromobenzene is too large to fit into the α-cyclodextrin channel and does not form an inclusion compound, but it does form a compound with the β- or γ-cyclodextrin. There is a similar trend with the halogens. The cyclo-

Table 1.29. CHARACTERISTICS OF THE CYCLODEXTRINS[446, 447]

Cyclodextrin	Glucose units per ring	Channel diam. (Å)	Guest molecules
α	6	6	Cl_2, Br_2, I_2, aliphatics, benzene derivatives with small substituents.
β	7	8	Br_2, I_2, many organics.
γ	8	10–11	I_2, only large organic molecules.

[444] K. Freudenberg, et al., Ann., **518**, 102 (1935); Chem. Ber., **71**, 1596 (1938); **83**, 296 (1950); D. French, et al., J. Am. Chem. Soc., **64**, 1651 (1942); **71**, 354 (1949).
[445] R. E. Rundle, J. Am. Chem. Soc., **69**, 1769 (1947).
[446] F. D. Cramer, Revs. Pure and Applied Chem., **5**, 143 (1955).
[447] H. Schlenk and D. M. Sand, J. Am. Chem. Soc., **83**, 2312 (1961).

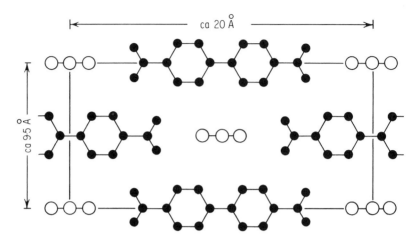

Fig. 1.28. 4,4′-Dinitrobiphenyl inclusion compound structure from view parallel to the channels.[443]

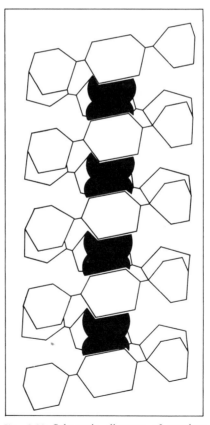

Fig. 1.29. Schematic diagram of amylose inclusion compounds.[442]

dextrins also form inclusion compounds in solution; this accounts for the blue color formed by iodine and starch solutions.[448] Apparently, even in solution the starch components have a helical structure.[449]

Quinols. *Guests: SO_2, CH_3OH, CH_3CN, C_2H_4, HCO_2H, CO_2, O_2, HCl, H_2S, argon, krypton, xenon.* The first clathrate compound, hydroquinone-H_2S, was reported by Wöhler in 1849. The *quinols*, which are hydroquinone[451] and phenol[450] inclusion compounds, have been studied extensively by H. M. Powell. Compound formation arises by three hydroquinone molecules forming a cup through H bonds and two such units forming a cage for the guest molecules (Fig. 1.30). Still, compound forma-

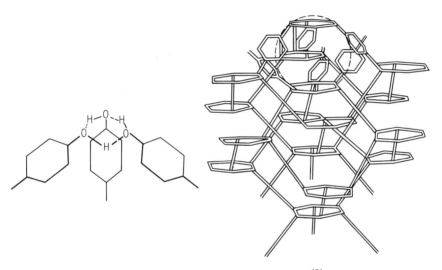

Fig. 1.30. Structure of quinol clathrates.[454]

tion is dependent upon the size of the guest molecules. Hydroquinone, for example, will form quinols with methyl alcohol and argon but not with ethyl alcohol (too large) or helium (too small).

Hydrates. *Guests: gases (CH_4, CO_2, SO_2, Cl_2, Kr, etc.), salts (ammonium salts, etc.).* The gas[458] and salt[455] hydrates consist of crystalline compounds in which water molecules form cavities within which foreign molecules are trapped. In one prominent type, the cubic unit cell is 12 Å on an edge, formed by two dodecahedra and six tetrakaidecahedra in which the polyhedra are made up of 20 or so water molecules held together by H bonds

[448] F. D. Cramer, *Chem. Ber.*, **84**, 855 (1951).
[449] J. Hollo and J. Szejtli, *Periodica Polytechnica*, **1**, 25 (1957).
[450] M. von Stackelberg, *Rec. trav. chim.*, **75**, 902 (1956).
[451] H. M. Powell and B. D. P. Wetters, *Chem. and Ind.*, *(London)*, 256 (1955) and earlier papers; L. Mandelcorn, *Chem. Revs.*, **59**, 827 (1959).

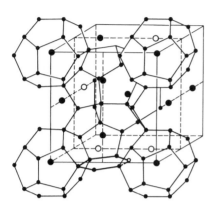

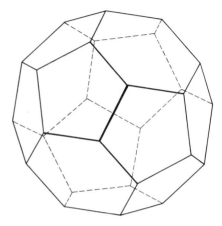

Fig. 1.31. A unit cell of a 12-Å gas hydrate.[458] Only the chambers of the front half of the unit cell are shown. The smaller dots represent the water molecules and the larger dots indicate positions of guest molecules.

Fig. 1.32. A hexakaidecahedron formed by 28 H-bonded water molecules in the 17-Å hydrate crystals.[452]

[Fig. 1.31]. Another common hydrate crystal, such as found for chloroform hydrate ($CHCl_3 \cdot 17H_2O$), is composed of 17 Å cubic cells with hexakaidecahedra formed from 28 water molecules (Fig. 1.32).

The first gas hydrate, chlorine hydrate ($6Cl_2 \cdot 46H_2O$) was discovered by Davey in 1810. Among other things, the gas hydrates are now used for desalting seawater.[456] Formation of gas hydrates in natural gas lines sometimes causes the lines to become "plugged." It has recently been proposed that liquid water has a gas hydrate-type structure.[453]

Miscellaneous inclusion compounds. In most instances it is impossible to predict which combinations of compounds will form inclusion compounds. Many strange combinations have been discovered, but only in a relatively few cases have the structures been studied by diffraction techniques. Some examples[457] can be given here; others will be mentioned in the discussion on uses of inclusion compounds.

[452] L. Pauling, *Science,* **134**, 15 (1961).

[453] L. Pauling in *Hydrogen Bonding* ed. D. Hadzi and H. W. Thompson (New York: Pergamon Press, 1959), p. 1.

[454] H. M. Powell, *J. Chem. Soc.,* 61 (1948).

[455] Cf. *Chem. Eng. News,* **39**, 40 (1961).

[456] Cf. *Chem. Eng. News,* **38**, 60 (1960).

[457] G. B. Barlow and A. C. Clamp, *J. Chem. Soc.,* 393 (1961).

[458] M. von Stackelberg, *et al., Proc. International Conf. Coord. Compounds,* (1955), p. 408, and earlier papers; L. Pauling and R. E. Marsh, *Proc. Natl. Acad. Sci. U.S.,* **38**, 112 (1952).

Ammonia solutions of nickel cyanide form inclusion compounds in which the nickel cyanide molecules are in planar arrays and the ammonia molecules, bonded to nickel atoms, project above and below each plane. Each guest molecule is trapped in a cavity bound by two planes of nickel cyanide and by vertically aligned pairs of ammonia molecules.[459] Again, compound formation is governed by specific reciprocal spatial relationships. For example, benzene, pyridine, pyrrole, aniline, and phenol will form nickel ammonia cyanide compounds whereas toluene and chlorobenzene will not.

The so-called "molecular sieves," natural semipermeable membranes such as the zeolites, also have channel-type architectural structures. They are being used more and more for resolving mixtures by selectively screening substances which will pass through their tubular channels.[460] However, here the channel structure is rigid and capable of sustaining itself in the absence of the guest molecules; accordingly, these are not classed as inclusion compounds and will not be discussed further.

1.7.3(b) General Properties of Inclusion Compounds.

The most common way of preparing the inclusion compounds is to crystallize the host substance in the presence of the guest molecules. If the host is soluble in the guest component, one merely crystallizes the host from a solution in which the guest is the solvent. Otherwise, a common solvent is used which is itself not clathrated. The urea complexes, for example, are easily made by mixing hot methanolic solutions of urea and of the guest compound and allowing the inclusion compound to crystallize upon cooling. The quinol-inert gas clathrates are obtained by crystallizing hydroquinone under pressure of the noble gas. Inclusion compounds of n-butyl 3,5-dinitrobenzoate are formed when the ester is recrystallized from certain hydrocarbons or their long-chain derivatives (e.g., hexadecane, methyl stearate).[461]

As a rule, inclusion compounds melt at a temperature near the normal melting point of the host, although a few, such as the choleic acids, melt as much as 10° C above the melting point of desoxycholic acid. The inclusion compounds may be decomposed thermally or by dissolving away the host molecules. Thermal decomposition may involve sublimation of the host, change of the crystalline clathrate structure to a nonclathrate structure of the host, diffusion and escape of the guest molecules, desorption of the

[459] J. H. Rayner and H. M. Powell, *J. Chem. Soc.,* 319 (1952).
[460] W. Bradley, *J. Am. Chem. Soc.,* **67,** 975 (1945).
[461] E. H. White, *J. Am. Chem. Soc.,* **77,** 6081 (1955).

guest molecules from the surface of the clathrate, or any combination of these processes.[462]

Some of the inclusion compounds are soluble in water without decomposition; others, such as the cyclodextrins, may be formed and kept in solution. For example, the choleic acids dissolve in alkali and offer a means of retaining hydrocarbons in aqueous solution, although the guest molecules are still shielded from the solvent molecules.

Certain physical properties of guest molecules are unaffected by inclusion compound formation while other properties are altered considerably. It appears that magnetic character is not significantly modified, and therefore inclusion compounds provide a convenient means of studying the magnetic susceptibility of certain compounds. For instance, nitric oxide or nitrogen dioxide can be studied at very low temperatures without their liquefaction or dimerization which otherwise would occur.[463] An inclusion compound also serves as a good medium for studying compounds by X-ray diffraction.[474]

On the other hand, some properties of guest molecules are markedly altered by inclusion compound formation. Most familiar is the dark color of cyclodextrin-iodine compounds. The λ_{max} of iodine is shifted 50–100 $m\mu$ to longer wavelengths with a 100-fold increase in intensity in the inclusion compound.[446] X-ray diffraction measurements indicate that all distances between adjacent iodine atoms are the same, 3.06 Å. This is longer than the I—I bond in molecular iodine, and suggests a delocalization of the iodine bonding electrons–probably facilitated by the polar molecular environment of the cyclodextrin molecules and perhaps even involving some change-transfer interaction.

Another property that is changed upon inclusion-compound formation is redox potential. For example, the redox potential of methylene blue is -0.027 v; it goes up to $+0.021$ v upon the addition of cyclodextrin.[464]

1.7.3(c). Uses of Inclusion Compounds

The most common application of an inclusion compound, of course, is the starch-iodine reaction used in analytical chemistry. It is interesting to note, in this connection, that if the starch has included some other compound such as a fatty acid, then it will not absorb iodine to give the blue color. Otherwise, the general uses of the inclusion compounds fall into three catagories: (i) resolution of mixtures, (ii) storing substances, (iii) transport of compounds.

[462] E. E. Aynsley, W. A. Campbell, and R. E. Dodd, *Proc. Chem. Soc., (London),* 210 (1957); L. Mandelcorn, *Chem. Rev.,* **59**, 836 (1959).

[463] A. H. Cooke, *et al., Proc. Roy. Soc.,* **A225**, 112 (1954); D. F. Evans and R. E. Richards, *J. Chem. Soc.,* 3295 (1952).

[464] F. D. Cramer, *Chem. Ber.,* **86**, 1582 (1953).

(i) The wave of interest in inclusion compounds stemmed from the use of the urea complexes for the separation of straight-and branched-chain hydrocarbons.[465] It is well-known that branched-chain hydrocarbons give better motor fuels than do straight-chain hydrocarbons, and removal of the latter through their urea complexes will upgrade a petroleum product. One only has to mix the fuel with a saturated aqueous solution and, after allowing it to stand for a given period, run off the upgraded fuel. Many fats and waxes have little or no commercial value because of high fatty acid content. Removal of the free acid is seldom undertaken because of the formation of emulsions which are hard to handle. Treatment with moist urea, however, will easily remove the fatty acids in the form of their complexes, and leave behind usable oil or wax. In other instances, fatty acids are isolated from crude oils in relatively pure condition by means of their urea complexes. Saturated molecules form urea inclusion complexes more readily than unsaturated derivatives because the deviation from the regular zig-zag chain structure, which has the optimum cross section for urea complex formation, is greater, the more double bonds there are in the chain. On this basis, for example, oleic, linoleic, and linolenic acids can be separated readily in 90–95 per cent purity.[465] *Cis-trans* isomers, e.g., maleates and fumarates, can readily be separated by urea complexation.[467] The separation of benzene and cyclohexane, whose boiling points are less than one degree apart, is no elementary laboratory task. Now, it can be done by simply treating a mixture with wet thiourea and filtering out the cyclohexane complex. The cyclohexane can be recovered from its complex by shaking the latter in water, whereupon the thiuorea is dissolved away.

Resolution by *clathration*[466] is a rapidly expanding field of investigation. One general method consists of forming a clathrate from a suitable mixture of transition metal cation, a basic nitrogen compound, and an anion.[468] Inclusion compounds similar to the ammoniacal nickel cyanide compounds mentioned previously are formed, and by varying any one of the three constituents–the cation, the anion, or the base–a variety of mixtures may be resolved, sometimes in quantitative yields. The process is of particular interest to industry because it offers a means of separating mixtures. Resolution of products has been a deterrent in commercializing the coal hydrogenation process. Mixtures of the xylenes, ethylbenzene, and other hydrocarbons are normally difficult or expensive to fractionate by conventional means.

---

[465] W. J. Zimmerschied, R. A. Dinerstein, A. W. Weitkamp, and R. F. Marschner, *Ind. Eng. Chem.,* **42,** 1300 (1950); E. V. Truter, *Chem. and Proc. Eng.,* **35,** 3 (1954); D. Swern, *Ind. Eng. Chem.,* **47,** 216 (1955).

[466] The term suggested by H. M. Powell [*Nature,* **163,** 566 (1949)].

[467] J. Radell, J. W. Connolly, and W. R. Cosgrove, Jr., *J. Org. Chem.,* **26,** 2960 (1961).

[468] W. D. Schaeffer, W. S. Dorsey, D. A. Skinner, and C. G. Christian, *J. Am. Chem. Soc.,* **79,** 5870 (1957); F. V. Williams, *J. Am. Chem. Soc.,* **79,** 5876 (1957).

The dehydration of *o*-thymotic acid (2-hydroxy-3-isopropyl-6-methyl-benzoic acid) with concentrated phosphoric acid gives a cyclic trimer XXXVIII that will form clathrate inclusion compounds with methyl and

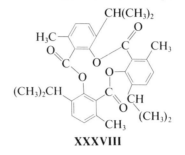

XXXVIII

ethyl alcohols, *n*-hexane, chloroform, benzene, and other compounds. The trimer is unusual in that steric requirements prevent the large ring from being planar. It exists in two stereoisomeric forms which differ by having a left-handed or right-handed spiral configuration. This has led to the resolution of racemic mixtures by clathration.[469] Other racemic mixtures, such as *dl*-2-chloroöctane or *dl*-*sec*-butyl bromide, have been resolved by means of fractional crystallization of suitable inclusion compounds.[470]

(ii) It has been found that substances may be stored in the form of their inclusion compounds for protection. For instance, the autooxidation of oleic acid does not occur when the acid is in the form of the urea complex.[471] Vitamin A palmitate and other polyunsaturated compounds have been stabilized in the form of their cholic acid or cyclodextrin inclusion compounds.[472] One objective here is to find a host substance which is easily metabolized and will form a stable inclusion compound with unstable nutrient substances such as vitamin A. The inclusion compounds would then be a convenient way of dispensing the drugs.

The clathrates of the inert gases provide a convenient method of dispensing the gases without resorting to high-pressure cylinders. The volume of gas present within the crystals is more than 70 times that of the crystals themselves.

An ingenious use of inclusion compounds resulting from their capacity to hold molecules in a fixed position is the stereospecific polymerization of dienes. For example, the diene guest molecules in a thiourea complex are aligned in a regular order as schematically shown in Fig. 1.33. This holds the molecules in a rigid vise during polymeriyation, and produces a polymer

---

[469] A. C. D. Newman and H. M. Powell, *J. Chem. Soc.*, 3747 (1952).

[470] H. M. Powell, *Nature*, **170**, 155 (1952); W. Schlenk, Jr., *Experimentia*, **8**, 337 (1952); W. Schlenk, Jr., *Angew. Chem.*, sample English issue, May, 1961, p. 26.

[471] H. Schlenk and R. T. Holman, *Science*, **112**, 19 (1950).

[472] H. Schlenk, D. M. Sand, and J. A. Tillotson, *J. Am. Chem. Soc.*, **77**, 3587 (1955).

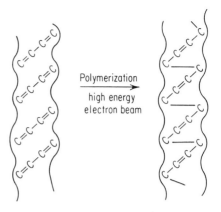

Fig. 1.33. Schematic representation of diene polymerization in a thiourea canal.[473]

with a completely ordered *trans*-1,4-structure. As a consequence the polymer has some highly desired properties.[473]

(iii) Inclusion compounds may have a very important biological function: the transportation of substances through cell membranes. Mention was made earlier of the fact that aqueous solutions of several different purines will dissolve many aromatic amines and polynuclear hydrocarbons. One theory on the mechanism of assimilation of fats in the intestines is that certain bile acid salts form some type of complex (probably an inclusion compound) with the fats of fatty acids in the intestines and "carry" the latter through the intestinal walls. It is well established that bile acid salts are good solubilizers of lipophilic substances.[474]

[473]J. F. Brown and D. M. White, presented before the Polymer Chemistry Section at the 133rd American Chemical Society meeting, April, 1958.
[474]P. Ekwall, A. Sten, and A. Morman, *Acta Chem. Scand.*, **10**, 681 (1956).

CHAPTER *II*

It was stated in the introduction that this text is presenting a modern structural theory of organic chemistry, in which properties of organic molecules are interpreted and predicted on the basis of valence-bond structures plus the judicious application of resonance, H bonding, and inductive and steric effects. The inductive effects are a manifestation of differences in electronegativities, and we shall now consider electronegativity and related topics.

2.1 Relative atomic electronegativities

Chemists are always seeking correlations between molecular properties and chemical constitution in order (1) to be able to interpret observed properties, and (2) to be able to plan the structure of a molecule that would have a given desired property. These correlations are usually developed

ELECTRONEGATIVITY AND

ELECTRIC DIPOLE MOMENTS

by logical semi-theoretical or by empirical methods. Many reliable relationships have been found between the structures of molecules and such properties as their color, index of refraction, acidity or basicity, shock and thermal stability, chemical reactivities, and, to a limited extent, certain biological activities (chemotherapy). Probably the most fundamental correlation developed was the periodic table. Another widely used basic relationship has been a scale of relative atomic electronegativities.

The electronegativity of an atom is defined as the intrinsic power of an atom in a molecule to attract electrons within the molecule. As we shall see, this concept is incorporated into the modern structural theory of organic chemistry to interpret many properties which otherwise would be anomalous, such as acid and base strengths, bond distances, ionic character as manifested through dipole moments, volatilies and solubilities, redox potentials, spectra, H bond strengths, and many chemical and biological properties.

Several methods[1] have been offered for establishing a scale of atomic electronegativities; the most widely used scale is that of Pauling, which is based on thermochemical data.[2] Let us briefly examine this method as well as several of the other more successful ones.

(i) Pauling's thermochemical method. It is reasonable to expect the energy of a bond A—B to be the arithmetic mean of the bond energies of the symmetrical molecules A—A and B—B. That is, if the atoms A and B are quite similar,

$$E_{AB} = \tfrac{1}{2}(E_{AA} + E_{BB}) \tag{2.1}$$

When the electronegativities of A and B are different, the electron density of the covalent bond will not be symmetrical, but higher near the atom of greater electronegativity. This produces a partial negative charge at this atom and an equivalent positive charge at the other atom.

$$\overset{\delta+}{A} \quad \overset{\delta-}{:B}$$

Thus, the covalent bond develops an ionic character, and the Coulombic attraction between the opposite charges makes the bond stronger than if it were purely covalent. Hence, the observed bond energy E_{AB} will be greater than the arithmetic mean of the bond energies of A_2 and B_2, and Pauling used this difference, defined by Eq. (2.2),

$$\Delta_{AB} = E_{AB} - \tfrac{1}{2}(E_{AA} + E_{BB}) \tag{2.2}$$

to set up a scale of relative electronegativities. Notice that Δ_{AB} is equivalent to the heat liberated in the reaction

$$\tfrac{1}{2}A_2 + \tfrac{1}{2}B_2 \longrightarrow A—B \tag{2.3}$$

when the substances are all in the gaseous state.

As defined by Eq. (2.2), Δ is the extra ionic energy of a covalent bond A—B and should always be positive. However, in some cases–for example, the alkali hydrides–the computed Δ values are negative. Pauling noted that if the algebraic mean of the bond energies is replaced by the geometric mean, as defined by Eq. (2.4),

$$\Delta'_{AB} = E_{AB} - \sqrt{E_{AA} \cdot E_{BB}} \tag{2.4}$$

then the Δ' values are positive for all cases.[3] Nevertheless, Pauling used the arithmetic means in setting up his scale of electronegativities because Δ is the energy change in reaction (2.3) and can be determined from heats

[1]H. O. Pritchard and H. A. Skinner, *Chem. Revs.,* **55**, 745 (1955).

[2]L. Pauling, *Nature of the Chemical Bond* (3rd ed.; Ithaca, N. Y.: Cornell U. P., 1960), pp. 88 ff.

[3]T. L. Allen, *J. Chem. Phys.,* **27**, 810 (1957), proposed the use of the reciprocal mean.

of reaction, whereas prior knowledge of individual bond energies is required for the geometric means.

Since Δ_{AB} arises from electronegativity differences of A and B, it is reasonable to equate the Δ_{AB} to some function of the difference in electronegativities.[4] Pauling found a suitable relationship between the electronegativity difference $X_A - X_B$ and Δ_{AB} according to Eq. (2.5)

$$X_A - X_B = \sqrt{\Delta_{AB}} \qquad (2.5)$$

and in terms of bond energies, this will give (2.6)

$$(X_A - X_B) = \sqrt{\frac{E_{AB} - \frac{1}{2}(E_{AA} + E_{BB})}{23}} \qquad (2.6)$$

where the bond energies are expressed in electron-volts. Now, if one element, say hydrogen, is chosen as a reference, the relative electronegativities of most other elements may be determined. Pauling did this, first setting $X_H = 0$. For instance, if $X_H = 0$, then $X_A = \Delta_{HA}^{1/2}$. Also, X_A could be determined from the sum $\Delta_{HB}^{1/2} + \Delta_{BA}^{1/2}$. The two values thus derived for X_A should be the same, but usually there is a small difference. On the other hand, X_B could be calculated from Δ_{BA} and the value of X_B as determined from Δ_{HB}. Thus, a great deal of juggling can be done to reach a set of electronegativities which shows the best self-consistency. For many metals whose M—M bond energy is not known, values were determined from the heat of formation of MX_n by the equation.

$$\Delta = \frac{-\Delta H_f}{n}.$$

For his final scale (Table 2.1), Pauling shifted his reference point from $X_H = 0$ to $X_H = 2.1$, which merely raised all values. An inspection of Table 2.1 shows that, in general, electronegativities increase as one goes up and to the right on the periodic table.

Table 2.1. RELATIVE ATOMIC ELECTRONEGATIVITIES FOR SOME ELEMENTS ACCORDING TO PAULING[2]

H	B	C	N	O	F
2.1	2.0	2.5	3.0	3.5	4.0
	Al	Si	P	S	Cl
	1.5	1.8	2.1	2.5	3.0
	Sc	Ge	As	Se	Br
	1.3	1.8	2.0	2.4	2.8
	Y	Sn	Sb	Te	I
	1.2	1.8	1.9	2.1	2.5

[4]R. Ferreira, *J. Phys. Chem.*, **63**, 745 (1959).

By using new enthalpy data and revised bond energy values, electronegativities were recently recalculated by Pauling's procedure.[5] These values are given in Table 2.2. The major difference between Pauling's table and the revised table is the alternation in values for certain groups. For example, there is a fluctuation of values for B, Al, Ga, In, Tl, for C, Si, Ge, Sn, Pb, and N, P, As, Sb, whereas there is a monotonic decrease for the alkali metals, the alkaline earth metals, and the halogens. Rochow,[10] and earlier, Sanderson,[14] showed that a large number of observations which otherwise would be anomalous are consistent with this variation of electronegativity. For example, ϕ_3C—H and ϕ_3Ge—H react with ϕLi to form ϕ_3CLi and ϕ_3GeLi, respectively, whereas ϕ_3Si—H and ϕ_3Sn—H yield ϕ_4Si and ϕ_4Sn, respectively. This implies that the C—H and Ge—H bonds are more polar than the Si—H and Sn—H bonds with the H positive, and this would be expected if the electronegativities of C and Ge are greater than those of Si and Sn. Similarly, SiH_4 is hydrolyzed and oxidized much more readily than are CH_4 and GeH_4. Also, R_3C—Br and R_3Ge—Br compounds are readily reduced by zinc in concentrated hydrochloric acid to the corresponding hydrocarbons, whereas the corresponding Si and Sn compounds do not react.

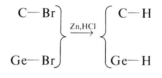

but

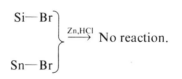

Rochow[10] has shown also that there is a similar alternation in the heats of formation of analogous compounds of this group of elements. For instance, the heats of formation in kcal/mole of the MO and MCl_4 compounds, where M is one of the group IVB elements, are:

	C	Si	Ge	Sn	Pb
MO	−26.4	−26.7	−22.8	−68.4	−52.4
MCl_4	−33.3	−153.0	−130.0	−130.3	−78.9

The alternation of electronegativities is partially attributable to the transition and lanthanide contractions.[5] These contractions lead to a greater force of attraction between the nucleus and boundary electrons. In

[5]A. L. Allred, *J. Inorg. Nucl. Chem.,* **17,** 215 (1961).

building up the fourth row of the periodic table, increasing nuclear charge accompanies the filling of the $3d$ subshell and causes Ga and Ge to be more compact (but not smaller) than Al and Si. Similarly for the sixth row, an increase in nuclear charge is balanced by electrons entering the $4f$ shell. Thus, elements to the right of Hf are more compact and more electronegative than the elements in the corresponding groups in the fifth row. This effect is less pronounced when the ultimate s and p subshells are being filled. More and more experimental evidence is being found in support of the alternation in electronegativities for Groups III, IV, and V.[13] Although Pauling's table does not show this alternation, its use in organic chemistry has not been affected, because few organic compounds involve elements beyond those in the first two rows and the halogens, for which there is no alternation.

(ii) Mulliken's electroaffinity scale. Mulliken[6] proposed that the average of the ionization potential (I_A) and the electron affinity (E_A) should give a good measure of the electroaffinity or electronegativity of an atom.[7]

$$A = A_{gas}^{+} + e^{-}, \qquad \Delta E = I_A$$

$$A + e^{-} = A^{-}, \qquad \Delta E = E_A$$

$$X_A = \tfrac{1}{2}(I_A + E_A)$$

However, there was and still is little experimental data on electron affinities of elements,[8] so that it is difficult to set up an extensive scale of electronegativities by this method. Nevertheless, the values that were obtained parallel to a fair degree the values of Pauling.

(iii) Gordy's covalent boundary potential scale. Gordy[9] identified electronegativity "for a neutral atom in a stable molecule as the potential at a distance r (covalent radius) from its nucleus which is caused by the nuclear charge effective at that distance." In estimating the effective nuclear charge, he assumed that electrons in closed shells exert full screening power and each valence electron has 0.5 screening effect. Thus, the potential at the covalent boundary is given as

$$F = \frac{e[n - 0.5(n - 1)]}{r} = \frac{0.5e(n + 1)}{r}$$

[6]R. S. Mulliken, *J. Chem. Phys.*, **2**, 782 (1934); compare J. Hinze and H. H. Jaffe, *J. Am. Chem. Soc.*, **84**, 540 (1962).

[7]M. A. Fineman, *J. Chem. Educ.*, **33**, 478 (1956).

[8]Cf. A. P. Ginsberg and J. M. Miller, *J. Inorg. Nucl. Chem.*, **7**, 351 (1958) for empirical method of estimating electron affinities.

[9]W. Gordy, *Phys. Rev.*, **69**, 604 (1946).

To give values in agreement with Pauling's values, the constants were changed and electronegativities calculated from Eq. (2.7).

$$X = \frac{0.31(n + 1)}{r} + 0.5 \qquad (2.7)$$

where X is the electronegativity, n is the number of electrons in the valence shell, and r is the single-bond covalent radius of the atom in angstrom units. Gordy's scale of electronegativities is quite close to that of Pauling.

(iv) Rochow's electrostatic method. Rochow[10] calculated the force of attraction between the nucleus of an atom A and an electron from a bonded atom at the covalent boundary, r, of A:

$$\text{force} = \frac{e^2 Z_{\text{eff}}}{r^2} \qquad (2.8)$$

The effective nuclear charge Z_{eff} is less than the actual charge Z owing to the screening by the electrons in the atom. Rochow assumed that the force of attraction given by Eq. (2.8) is an approximate measure of the extent to which an atom in a molecule attracts electrons to itself, which he therefore calls the *absolute electronegativity* of the atom.

The quantity Z_{eff}/r^2 was calculated using Pauling's covalent radii and Slater's[11] method of calculating effective nuclear charges. When the results from Eq. (2.8) were plotted against Pauling's electronegativity values, a straight line was obtained, which gives the relationship between Pauling's relative electronegativities and Rochow's "absolute" electronegativities:

$$X = 0.359 \frac{Z_{\text{eff}}}{r^2} + 0.744 \qquad (2.9)$$

A complete table of electronegativities of the elements has been published based on Eq. (2.9).[12] This table is reproduced in Table 2.2.

(v) Sanderson's stability ratio scale. Sanderson raised the question: what is it about the atomic structures of the inert elements that makes them chemically inert? It is not the number of electrons in the outer orbit, for chloride ion and argon have the same number, but Cl$^-$ is far from being unreactive. Whatever property is responsible, Sanderson[14] reasoned that there is an optimum condition which is reached at the inert element of each row of the

[10] E. G. Rochow and A. L. Allred, *J. Inorg. Nucl. Chem.*, **5**, 264, 269 (1958).

[11] J. C. Slater, *Phys. Rev.*, **36**, 57 (1930).

[12] E. J. Little, Jr., and M. M. Jones, *J. Chem. Educ.*, **37**, 231 (1960).

[13] A. W. Laubengayer, *et al.*, *J. Am. Chem. Soc.*, **81**, 3826 (1959).

[14] (a) R. T. Sanderson, *Science*, **114**, 670 (1951); *J. Chem. Educ.*, **29**, 539 (1952); (b) R. T. Sanderson, *J. Am. Chem. Soc.*, **74**, 4792 (1952); *J. Inorg. Nucl. Chem.*, **7**, 157 (1958).

Table 2.2* Electronegativity Values for the Elements[5,12]

1	2	3	4	5	6	7	8	9	10	11	12	13	14	15	16	17
H 2.1/2.20																
Li 0.97/0.98	Be 1.47/1.57											B 2.01/2.04	C 2.50/2.55	N 3.07/3.04	O 3.50/3.44	F 4.10/3.98
Na 1.01/0.93	Mg 1.23/1.31											Al 1.47/1.61	Si 1.74/1.90	P 2.06/2.19	S 2.44/2.58	Cl 2.83/3.16
K 0.91/0.82	Ca 1.04/1.00	Sc 1.20/1.36	Ti 1.32/1.54	V 1.45/1.63	Cr 1.56/1.66	Mn 1.60/1.55	Fe 1.64/1.83	Co 1.70/1.88	Ni 1.75/1.91	Cu 1.75/1.90	Zn 1.66/1.65	Ga 1.82/1.81	Ge 2.02/2.01	As 2.20/2.18	Se 2.48/2.55	Br 2.74/2.96
Rb 0.89/0.82	Sr 0.99/0.95	Y 1.11/1.22	Zr 1.22/1.33	Nb 1.23/··	Mo 1.30/2.16	Tc 1.36/··	Ru 1.42/··	Rh 1.45/2.28	Pd 1.35/2.20	Ag 1.42/1.93	Cd 1.46/1.69	In 1.49/1.78	Sn 1.72/1.96	Sb 1.82/2.05	Te 2.01/··	I 2.21/2.66
Cs 0.86/0.79	Ba 0.97/0.89	†	Hf 1.23/··	Ta 1.33/··	W 1.40/2.36	Re 1.46/··	Os 1.52/··	Ir 1.55/2.20	Pt 1.44/2.28	Au 1.42/2.54	Hg 1.44/2.00	Tl 1.44/2.04	Pb 1.55/2.33	Bi 1.67/2.02	Po 1.76/··	At 1.90/··
Fr	Ra	‡														

† | La 1.08/1.10 | Ce 1.08/1.12 | Pr 1.07/1.13 | Nd 1.07/1.14 | Pm 1.07/·· | Sm 1.07/1.17 | Eu 1.01/·· | Gd 1.11/1.20 | Tb 1.10/·· | Dy 1.10/1.22 | Ho 1.10/1.23 | Er 1.11/1.24 | Tm 1.11/1.25 | Yb 1.06/·· | Lu 1.14/1.27 |

†	La	Ce	Pr	Nd	Pm	Sm	Eu	Gd	Tb	Dy	Ho	Er	Tm	Yb	Lu
	1.08/1.10	1.08/1.12	1.07/1.13	1.07/1.14	1.07/··	1.07/1.17	1.01/··	1.11/1.20	1.10/··	1.10/1.22	1.10/1.23	1.11/1.24	1.11/1.25	1.06/··	1.14/1.27

‡	Ac	Th	Pa	U	Np	Pu
	1.00/··	1.11/··	1.14/··	1.22/1.38	1.22/1.36	1.22/1.28

*Upper set based on electrostatics, lower set based on thermochemistry.

periodic table with respect to charge, compactness, distribution, etc., among the electrons, neutrons, and other atomic particles. Sanderson identified this factor with the electron density (ED) of the atoms, and the ED_i for the inert element of each row represents a maximum stability. Then, the ratio of the ED for the elements in a given row to that of the inert element of that row gives the stability ratio (SR) of the elements in that row.

$$\frac{ED}{ED_i} = SR$$

The ED is essentially the charge per unit volume

$$ED = \frac{Z}{4.19r^3} \tag{2.10}$$

where r is the covalent radius (or ionic radius for ions) and Z is the atomic number, i.e., number of orbital electrons. Although Sanderson does not regard his SR values to be electronegativities of elements, the two are quite parallel and their use leads to the same conclusions.

(vi) Other scales.[15] Other empirical scales of electronegativities have been proposed. Gordy[15(b)] proposed a scale based on several bond parameters according to the equation

$$k = aN \left(\frac{X_a X_b}{d^2} \right)^{3/4} + b \tag{2.11}$$

where k is the force constant of the bond A—B, N the bond order, d the bond distance, a and b are constants, and X_a and X_b are the electronegativities of atoms A and B. Gordy[16] also pointed out that there is a reasonably good linear relationship between the work function W and the electronegativity of the element

$$W = 2.27X + 0.34 \text{ volts}$$

where X is the electronegativity. Previous to Gordy's covalent boundary potential equation (2.7) for computing electronegativities, several other similar equations had been proposed[17] based on the number of valence electrons, the atomic number, and/or the covalent radius. In general, all of these methods give electronegativity values in fair agreement with those of Pauling.

[15](a) J. K. Wilmshurst, *Can. J. Chem.*, **38**, 467 (1960); (b) W. Gordy, *Phys. Rev.*, **69**, 604 (1946); (c) R. L. Williams, *J. Phys. Chem.*, **60**, 1016 (1956); (d) S. T. Li, *Chem. Abstracts*, **52**, 14315 (1958); R. D. Kross and V. A. Fassel, *J. Am. Chem. Soc.*, **77**, 5858 (1955).

[16]W. Gordy and W. J. O. Thomas, *J. Chem. Phys.*, **24**, 439 (1956).

[17]T. H. Liu, *J. Chinese Chem. Soc.*, **9**, 119 (1942); *Chem. Abs.*, **37**, 6187 (1943); S. Li, *J. Chinese Chem. Soc.*, **10**, 167, 169 (1943); *Chem. Abs.*, **38**, 3193 (1944); C. E. Sun, *J. Chinese Chem. Soc.*, **10**, 77 (1943); *Chem. Abs.*, **38**, 4480 (1944).

There have been, too, several modifications of the Pauling method of calculating electronegativities from thermochemical data.[18] Little improvement is gained by the much more complex equations used, although some alternation in values appears in some of the results.

It can be seen that there are some significant differences in the two sets of electronegativity values given in Table 2.2. Neither set can be preferred exclusively over the other. On the one hand, the electrostatic set (upper values) includes more elements and shows the variation for N, P, As, Sb, for which there is some experimental justification.[14] On the other hand, the thermochemical set (lower values) has some values which are more realistic, such as the relative values for C and I. The electronegativity scale based on electrostatic force (and on stability ratio) predicts the electronegativity of trivalent arsenic to be greater than that of phosphorus whereas several scales predict the opposite order. We have already seen [Sec. 1.2.9(d)] that the electronegativity of an atom is affected by the types of other atoms attached to it (compare C in $CHCl_3$ with C in CH_4) and by the state of hybridization (compare C in CH_3—CH_3 with C in $HC\equiv CH$). Also, the electronegativity of an atom varies with its state of oxidation. Along this line, it is interesting to note that only when oxygen, fluorine, or the CF_3 group is attached to sulfur can sulfur give a stable compound in the $+6$ state, i.e., $SO_4^=$, SF_6, etc. Consequently, a completely accurate table of electronegativities would have to list the values for an element in all of its compounds. This, of course, is absurd.

The selection of a "best" electronegativity value is somewhat arbitrary, then. Electronegativity is not an invariant property. Values calculated from electrostatics, work functions, and stability ratios are invariant for each element, whereas values obtained by thermochemical and n.m.r. measurements vary according to the oxidation states of elements but are rather insensitive to degree of hybridization of elements.[19] In view of the arbitrariness in the choice of an electronegativity value for an element and the fact that physical and chemical properties are influenced by other factors such as bond order and π bonding, it is to be expected that there will not always be observed a smooth correlation of all properties with the electronegativity of a series of elements. For this reason, group electronegativities are sometimes used to an advantage. This approach, however, is entirely qualitative.

It has been pointed out that the units of electronegativity differ as expressed by the various methods.[20] For example, the units of some of the

[18] M. A. Fineman and R. Daignault, *J. Inorg. Nucl. Chem.*, **10**, 205 (1959); J. Belluque and R. Daudel, *Rev. sci.*, **84**, 541 (1946).

[19] A. L. Allred and A. L. Hensley, Jr., *J. Inorg. Nucl. Chem.*, **17**, 43 (1961).

[20] R. P. Iczkowski and J. L. Margrave, *J. Am. Chem. Soc.*, **83**, 3547 (1961).

methods are as follows:

Pauling's thermochemical:	$(energy)^{1/2}$
Mulliken's electroaffinity:	energy
Rochow's electrostatic:	force
Gordy's boundary potential:	energy/electron
Sanderson's stability ratio:	dimensionless

Consequently, most scales of electronegativity are indirect or secondary measures of electronegativity.

It is to be realized that an alternative to the use of electronegativity in the modern structural theory is to adopt the concept of orbital hybridization, which equally well accounts for many bond properties such as bond contraction [Sec. 1.2.9(d)], polarity,[21] and force constants.

2.2 Relative group electronegativities

(i) Cleavage of organomercurials. One of the earliest reported series of relative electronegativities of groups was that of Kharasch.[22] He assumed that an organomercurial R—Hg—R' ionizes to a small extent in aqueous HCl and that the ratio of R⁻ to R'⁻ is proportional to their relative electronegativities.

$$R-Hg-R' \rightleftharpoons R-Hg^+ + R'^- \xrightarrow{HCl} RHgCl + R'-H \quad (2.12)$$

Then, the R' quickly reacts with H⁺ to yield R'H. Thus, by the cleavage of unsymmetrical R—Hg—R' compounds with HCl and by measuring the relative amounts of RH and R'H produced, Kharasch set up a table of relative electronegativities of various aromatic and aliphatic groups. Since then, others have used this method to expand the list of groups to almost 50.[23]

Kharasch's sequence for some groups of interest is

$$CH_3O-\underset{}{\bigcirc}- > CH_3-\underset{}{\bigcirc}- > \underset{}{\bigcirc}- > Cl-\underset{}{\bigcirc}- >$$

$$CH_3- > CH_3CH_2- > \phi CH_2- > (CH_3)_3C- > \phi_3C-$$

One comforting aspect of his work is that his results are very self-consistent. That is, when measuring the relative electronegativity of A against B and of B against C and it is found that A > B and B > C, then when A is measured against C, it is found that A > C.

---

[21]W. Moffitt, *Proc. Roy. Soc. (London)*, **202A**, 548 (1950).

[22]M. S. Kharasch, *et al.*, *J. Am. Chem. Soc.*, **48**, 3130 (1926); *J. Org. Chem.*, **3**, 405 (1938) and earlier papers.

[23]See Table 7 in reference 1.

(ii) **From dipole moments.** Brown[24] showed that a series of organic groups, when arranged in order of the carbon-chlorine bond moments in the $R-Cl$ derivatives, is identical with the electronegativity series of Kharasch. On this basis, Brown assigned positions to groups not studied by Kharasch. Apparently, then, the same order of relative electronegativities of groups is obtained from a physical as well as a chemical method. As a selected series, we have the following order of decreasing electronegativities:

$$\phi-C\equiv C- \;>\; \phi-CH=CH- \;>\; CH_3CH=CH- \;>\; CH_2=CH- \;>$$

$$CH_3O-\!\!\left\langle\bigcirc\right\rangle\!\!- \;>\; CH_3-\!\!\left\langle\bigcirc\right\rangle\!\!- \;>\; \left\langle\bigcirc\right\rangle\!\!- \;>$$

$$Cl-\!\!\left\langle\bigcirc\right\rangle\!\!- \;>\; H- \;>\; CH_3- \;>\; CH_3CH_2- \;>\; (CH_3)_2CH- \;>$$

$$CH_2\!\!\begin{array}{c} \diagup CH_2-CH_2 \diagdown \\ \diagdown CH_2-CH_2 \diagup \end{array}\!\!CH- \;>$$

$$CH_2=CHCH_2- \;>\; \phi-CH_2- \;>\; (CH_3)_3C- \;>\; \phi_3C-$$

(iii) **From acid dissociation constants.** In a neutral molecule such as that of 1-chloropropane,

$$\begin{array}{c} H\;\;H\;\;H \\ |\;\;\;|\;\;\;| \\ H:C:C:C:Cl \\ |\;\;\;|\;\;\;| \\ H\;\;H\;\;H \end{array}$$

the greater electronegativity of chlorine over that of carbon gives the chlorine a fractional negative charge and the carbon a fractional positive charge. The withdrawal of electrons from the carbon atom increases its thirst for electrons; that is, it acquires a greater electronegativity than that of the β carbon atom. This brings about a small displacement of the electron pair between the α and β carbon atoms towards the α carbon atom, which thereby decreases the electron density about the β carbon atom to produce there a smaller fractional positive charge. In the same fashion a still smaller partial positive charge develops on the γ carbon atom. This situation can be described in different words by saying that the chlorine atom induces a positive charge on the α carbon atom, which induces a smaller positive charge on the β carbon atom, and which in turn induces a still smaller positive charge on the γ carbon atom.

This transmission of induced charges along a chain of bonded atoms is called *chain induction.* The British school gives it the symbol I_s, in which

[24]H. C. Brown, *J. Am. Chem. Soc.,* **61,** 1483 (1939).

the subscript from the word "static" conveys the idea of a polarization effect in the ground state or normal state of a molecule. When the electron attracting power of a group is greater than that of the hydrogen atom, I_s for the group has a negative sign.

$$+I_s \qquad\qquad -I_s$$

$$-\overset{-}{N}R > -\overset{-}{O} > -\overset{-}{S} > -Se^- \qquad -\overset{+}{O}R_2 > -\overset{+}{N}R_3 > NO_2$$
$$-F > -OR > -NR_2 > -CR_3$$
$$-F > -Cl > -Br > -I$$
$$=O > =NR > =CR_2$$

G. N. Lewis first used the effect of chain induction to explain the relatively high acid strengths of the chloroacetic acids.

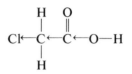

In chloroacetic acid, the chlorine atom pulls the electron pair towards itself and thereby induces a partial positive charge on the carbon atom. In turn, progressively smaller positive charges are induced on the carboxylic carbon atom and the hydroxyl oxygen atom. The hydroxyl oxygen atom of chloroacetic acid is, therefore, more positive than that of unsubstituted acetic acid, and this facilitates dissociation of the proton. As a result, chloroacetic acid is a stronger acid than is acetic acid. Moreover, the more chlorine atoms there are on the α carbon atom, the greater will be the induced positive charge on the hydroxyl oxygen atom. Accordingly, dichloroacetic acid should be stronger than monochloroacetic acid, and the trichloroacid should be still stronger. This is actually the case, with trichloroacetic acid being a strong acid. The same sequence is found for the fluoroacetic acids (Table 2.3).

Table 2.3. DISSOCIATION CONSTANTS ($\times 10^3$) OF SOME HALOACETIC ACIDS

X	XCH_2-COOH	$X_2CH-COOH$	$X_3C-COOH$
Cl	1.4	50	130
F	2.1	57	500

This inductive effect on the strengths of substituted acetic acids decreases rapidly with distance, as shown by the order of decreasing acid strengths of α-, β-, and γ-substituted chlorobutyric acids and by the data in Table 2.4.

$$10^5 K_a$$

$$CH_3\!-\!CH_2\!-\!\underset{\underset{\displaystyle Cl}{|}}{CH}\!-\!COOH \qquad 139$$

$$CH_3\!-\!\underset{\underset{\displaystyle Cl}{|}}{CH}\!-\!CH_2\!-\!COOH \qquad 8.9$$

$$\underset{\underset{\displaystyle Cl}{|}}{CH_2}\!-\!CH_2\!-\!CH_2\!-\!COOH \qquad 3$$

Table 2.4. DISSOCIATION CONSTANTS ($\times 10^5$) OF SOME CARBOXYLIC ACIDS[25]

X	$XCH_2\!-\!COOH$	$X(CH_2)_2\!-\!COOH$	$X(CH_2)_3\!-\!COOH$
H	1.75	1.34	1.50
I	71	9.0	2.3
CF_3	100	7	
Br	138	9.8	2.6
Cl	140	10.1	3.0
COOH	149	6.4	4.5
F	213		
CN	342	10.2	3.7

Since the acid-strengthening effect of the substituents in these acetic acids arises chiefly from the relative electronegativity of the substituent, it is reasonable to use the K_a of the acids $R\!-\!CH_2COOH$ as an approximate measure of the relative electronegativities of the R groups. This has been done to give the sequence shown in Table 2.5, where the groups are listed downward in decreasing order of K_a. This is essentially the same as Kharasch's order except for the simple alkyl groups, which usually have the

Table 2.5. DISSOCIATION CONSTANTS OF SOME MONOSUBSTITUTED ACETIC ACIDS $X\!-\!CH_2COOH$

X	$10^5 K_a$	X	$10^5 K_a$
CN	342	H	1.75
F	213	D	$H > D$[28]
Cl	140	$(CH_3)_2CH$	1.55
Br	138	CH_3CH_2	1.51
I	71	CH_3	1.34
CH_3O	30	$(CH_3)_3C$	0.89
C_6H_5	4.88	$(CH_3)_3Si$	0.6

[25] D. J. G. Ives and K. Sames, *J. Chem. Soc.*, 513 (1943) A. L. Henne and C. J. Fox, *J. Am. Chem. Soc.*, **73**, 2323 (1951).

order methyl > ethyl > isopropyl > t-butyl. Similar comparisons have been made for substituted benzoic acids or for acids of the type X—COOH, where X is the group for comparison. In these and other series there is frequently a resonance effect; therefore the series offers a poorer measure of the inductive effect. It should be emphasized that in all series there is a solvation effect, and this may disrupt a good correlation between the electronegativity of groups and the ionization constants of a series of acids (See Sec. 3.4). For example, solvation of glycolic acid is strong and produces a positive heat of ionization, which gives the OH group an anomalous position.[26]

(iv) **Polar substituent constants.** Taft[27] used the differences in rates of hydrolysis of esters in acid and base as a measure of the polar effect of groups. As will be taken up in Sec. 4.11.4, the transition states for hydrolysis of typical esters in acid and in basic media are believed to have the structures

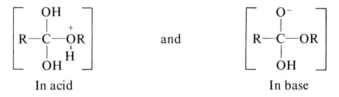

In acid   In base

Other than two protons, the two species have the same steric requirements, so that the steric effect of R on the rates of hydrolysis should be insignificant. Also, since the acid carbon is saturated, there should be no resonance interaction between the C and the R group. Consequently, the principal effect of R on the stability of these two transition states, and therefore on the rates of hydrolysis, is the inductive effect of R. Taft expressed this inductive effect by the equation

$$\sigma^* = \frac{1}{2.5}\left[\left(\log \frac{k}{k_0}\right)_b - \left(\log \frac{k}{k_0}\right)_a\right] \qquad (2.13)$$

where k and k_0 are the reaction rate constants for a substituted ethyl ester, R—CO_2Et, and a reference ethyl ester, R_0CO_2Et; the subscripts outside of the parentheses refer to the relative rates in base and in acid, and σ^* is the polar constant for a given group R. Taft chose $R_0 = CH_3$ for a

[26]E. J. King, *J. Am. Chem. Soc.*, **82**, 3575 (1960).

[27]R. W. Taft, Jr., in *Steric Effects in Organic Chemistry*, ed. M. S. Newman (New York: Wiley, 1956), chap. 13.

[28]Dissociation constants of deutero acids and phenols [E. A. Halevi, *Tetrahedron*, **1**, 174 (1957); R. P. Bell and M. B. Jensen, *Proc. Chem. Soc. (London)*, 307 (1960)], and rates of solvolysis of deuterated benzhydryl chlorides [H. S. Klein and A. Streitwieser, Jr., *Chem. and Ind. (London)*, 180 (1961)] indicate that hydrogen is more electronegative than deuterium.

Table 2.6. SOME POLAR SUBSTITUENT CONSTANTS[27]

Group	σ^*	Group	σ^*
$(CH_3)_3\overset{+}{N}CH_2-$	$+1.90$	C_6H_5-	$+0.600$
O_2NCH_2-	1.40	$H-$	0.490
$NC-CH_2-$	1.30	ϕCH_2-	0.215
FCH_2-	1.10	CH_3-	0.000
$ClCH_2-$	1.05	C_2H_5-	-0.100
$BrCH_2$	1.00	$(CH_3)_2CH-$	-0.190
ICH_2-	0.85	$(CH_3)_3C-$	-0.300

reference group and set $\sigma^* = 1$ for CH_3. He then calculated σ^* for a large number of groups, some of which are given in Table 2.6.

Taft demonstrated that σ^* can be used as a measure of the electronegativity of groups. For illustration, dipole moments of alkyl halides, RX, and of other classes of compounds may be computed with high accuracy from σ^*.

Again, the order of the electronegativity of groups when determined from σ^* is quite similar to that of Kharasch. However, semiquantitative comparisons can be made from σ^*. For example, σ^* values show that the inductive effect decreases about one-third across each single bond.

group: CF_3- CF_3CH_2- $CF_3CH_2CH_2-$ $CF_3-(CH_2)_3-$
σ^*:   2.7   0.92   0.32   0.12

This percentage decrease of the inductive effect across each $C-C$ bond was pointed out earlier by Branch and Calvin[29] on the basis of acid dissociation constants.

(v) From infrared absorption intensities. The frequency of absorption by a given bond in the infrared region of the spectrum is related to the bond force constant, and the intensity of the absorption is a function of the change in dipole moment of the bond during excitation. Thus, the intensity is related to the polar character of the bond, and the polar character, of course, is affected by the electronegativities of the groups attached to the two bonded atoms. Accordingly, the relative intensities of the ν_{O-H} band for various $R-OH$ compounds can be used as a measure of the relative electronegativities of the R groups.[30] Similarly, the relative intensities of $\nu_{P=O}$ bands in phosphonic acids have been used for establishing the rela-

---

[29]G. E. K. Branch and M. Calvin, *The Theory of Organic Chemistry* (Englewood Cliffs, N.J.: Prentice-Hall, 1941), p. 218.

[30]T. L. Brown and M. T. Rogers, *J. Am. Chem. Soc.*, **79**, 577 (1957); *J. Phys. Chem.*, **61**, 820 (1957).

tive electronegativities of groups.[31] This method, too, gives results that are highly self-consistent and is useful for ascertaining relative electronegativities for a multitude of groups. Actually, integrated intensities are used rather than intensity maxima.[32] Again, the selected series of groups roughly parallels that found by previous methods for their relative electronegativities. The larger the A value, the greater is the electronegativity of the R group.

Group	A^{30}
CCl_3—CH_2—	0.92
$ClCH_2$—CH_2—CH_2—	0.74
$HC{\equiv}C$—CH_2—	0.69
ϕ—CH_2—	0.66
$CH_2{=}CH$—CH_2—	0.58
CH_3—	0.54
CH_3—CH_2—CH_2—	0.52
CH_3—CH_2—CH— $\\ \quad\quad\quad\quad |$ $\\ \quad\quad\quad\quad CH_3$	0.46
Cyclohexyl—	0.44
$(CH_3)_3C$—	0.39

(vi) From infrared absorption frequencies. Walsh[33] attempted to determine atomic electronegativities of atoms from the stretching force constants of the diatomic molecules H—X (k_{HX}), but his values did not agree with the usually accepted Pauling values. Later, Wilmshurst[34] showed that the square root of the H—X force constant rather than the first power of k_{HX} is linearly related to the electronegativity of X by the equation

$$\chi_X = 1.104 \times 10^{-3} \left(1 + \frac{M_H}{M_X}\right)^{-\frac{1}{2}} \nu_{HX} - 0.24 \qquad (2.14)$$

where χ_X is the electronegativity of atom X, M_H and M_X are the masses of H and X to correct for anharmonicity, and ν_{HX} is the H—X infrared absorption frequency. Since the absorption frequency is directly related to the bond force constant and the latter is affected by the electronegativity of X, then the frequency is a function of the electronegativity, related by Eq. (2.14). From Wilmshurst's table of group electronegativities, the order for

[31]J. V. Bell, J. Heisler, H. Tannenbaum, and J. Goldenson, *J. Am. Chem. Soc.,* **76,** 5185 (1954).

[32]For comments on methods of determining A, see A. Cabana and C. Sandorfy, *Spectrochim. Acta,* 335 (1960).

[33]A. D. Walsh, *Proc. Roy. Soc. (London),* **A207,** 13 (1951).

[34]J. K. Wilmshurst, *J. Chem. Phys.,* **28,** 733 (1958). See also R. D. Kross and V. A. Fassel, *J. Am. Chem. Soc.,* **77,** 5858 (1955).

some groups of interest is

$$HO— > CH_3O— > H_2N— > HC\equiv C— > NC— > \phi— > Cl_3C— >$$
$$CH_2\!\!=\!\!CH— > HS—$$

This sequence is consistent with that from the previously discussed methods except for the —CN and —CCl₃ groups, whose positions here appear to be way out of order. Wilmshurst[35] also set up a scale of relative electronegativities based on the C—H bending frequencies in substituted methanes, which order was essentially the same as that from the H—X stretching frequencies.[36] Although Wilmshurst claims that his methods for determining group electronegativities are adjusted for the effects of orbital hybridization and bonding to other atoms, there is no compelling argument[38] for accepting his order in preference to the order commonly observed from the other methods of determination.

Other attempts have been made to correlate infrared frequencies with group electronegativities. For instance, the effects of substituents on the multiple bond stretching frequencies in phosphoryl derivatives $(R_1R_2R_3P\!\!=\!\!O)$,[39] in carbonyl derivatives $(R_1R_2C\!\!=\!\!O)$,[40,41] and in nitriles[42] have been used as measures of the relative electronegativities of the R groups. A sequence based on the frequency shifts in phosphoryl compounds, for example, is[39]

$$F— > NC— > Cl— > H_3CO— > Br— > cyclohexyl— > \phi— >$$
$$HO— > CH_3— > H_2N—$$

and a sequence from carbonyl frequency shifts is[40]

$$CF_3— > CCl_3— > CBr_3— > CHCl_2— > CHBr_2— >$$
$$CH_2Cl— > CH_2Br—$$

Again, there is general agreement with the Kharasch order, although certain prominent divergences appear. This does not mean that the Kharasch

[35]J. K. Wilmshurst, *J. Chem. Phys.*, **26**, 426 (1957); *Can. J. Chem.*, **35**, 937 (1957).

[36]Wilmshurst[37] also attempted to calculate the electronegativity of a group with an equation similar to Gordy's covalent boundary potential (Eq. 2.7) in which reasonable assumptions are made for computing n, the number of valence electrons of the group, and r, the covalent radius of the bonding atom of the group. Again, his order is essentially the same as that which he obtained from infrared frequencies.

[37]J. K. Wilmshurst, *J. Chem. Phys.*, **27**, 1129 (1957).

[38]J. K. Wilmshurst, *J. Phys. Chem.*, **62**, 631 (1958).

[39]J. V. Bell, J. Heisler, H. Tannenbaum, and J. Goldenson, *J. Am. Chem. Soc.*, **76**, 5185 (1954).

[40]R. E. Kagarise, *J. Am. Chem. Soc.*, **77**, 1377 (1955).

[41]E. T. McBee and D. L. Christman, *J. Am. Chem. Soc.*, **77**, 755 (1955) and references cited therein.

[42]R. K. Sheline, *J. Inorg. Nucl. Chem.*, **6**, 187 (1958).

scale is the correct one; it is cited merely as a common reference scale for comparison.

(vii) From nuclear magnetic resonance shielding parameters. It was stated in Sec. 1.2.13 that nuclei spin like tops and, when placed in a magnetic field, they precess as a slowly spinning top does owing to the force of gravity. The interaction of the magnetic field with the orbital electrons induces a small magnetic field within the atoms in opposite direction to the applied field. As a result, the net magnetic field at the nucleus is less than that on the macroscopic sample, or in other words, the nucleus has been partially shielded from the external magnetic field. The magnitude of the shielding effect depends upon the particular type of atom, i.e., which element, and on how its electron cloud has been affected by other attached atoms.

If an additional alternating magnetic field is imposed on the stationary field, an absorption of energy will occur when the alternating frequency corresponds to the frequency of precession of the atom. In other words, the stationary field gets all of the atoms to precessing in unison, whereas the alternating field causes them to wabble in rhythm, which accounts for the term nuclear magnetic resonance (n.m.r.).

Only certain atoms exhibit resonance absorption, and most studies have been on hydrogen, fluorine, or phosphorus atoms. If the field strength is varied until absorption shows up by a given atom in a reference compound, say F in HF, then when a group is substituted for H, a different field strength will be required to get absorption again. This change in field strength is called a *chemical shift* or the *shielding parameter* δ, and is calculated from the relationship

$$\delta = \frac{10^6(H_r - H_c)}{H_r}$$

where H_r and H_c are the applied magnetic field strengths for the reference compound and the modified compound, respectively. The magnitude of δ is affected by the electronegativity of R, because the less R pulls the electrons away from the measured atom (H, F, or P), the more the orbital electrons shield the atom.

Several persons have determined relative electronegativities of groups by this method and, again, the results are in substantial agreement with those by the previously discussed methods.[43,45]

[43] B. P. Dailey and J. N. Shoolery, *J. Am. Chem. Soc.*, 77, 3977 (1955). Certain reservations must be made regarding these results because they were measured in 50 per cent benzene solution, and it is known that weak solute-solvent interactions occur with some of the compounds.

[44] J. R. Cavanaugh and B. P. Dailey, *J. Chem. Phys.*, 34, 1099 (1961).

[45] (a) H. S. Gutowsky, *et al.*, *J. Am. Chem. Soc.*, 74, 4809 (1952); (b) A. L. Allred and E. G. Rochow, *J. Am. Chem. Soc.*, 79, 5361 (1957).

A small modification of this method is to measure the nuclear quadrupole coupling constant. In the magnetic field with the superimposed alternating field, dipole-dipole interactions cause certain *coupled* motions to occur which are related to the ionic character of a specific bond, and the ionic character is in turn a function of the electronegativity difference of the bonded atoms. Measurements of the nuclear quadrupole coupling have been made to evaluate the relative electronegativities of a few groups.[46] The method offers an improvement over Pauling's method for highly ionic compounds.

Other properties of substances have been used in attempts to set up a scale of relative group electronegativities, ·such as bond dissociation energies of R—H or R—Cl,[47] heats of reactions,[1] the mean of ionization potential and electron affinity,[1] dipole moments, or other properties.[48] These methods either do not have sufficient data for an extended series or else measure effects other than just electronegativities.

For comparison, the relative electronegativities of a selected series of groups as determined by different methods are given in Table 2.7. A "generally expected" order for the groups and the halogens is given in the last column. The application of this table will become evident as relative electronegativities are used to assess the inductive effects of groups in accounting for or predicting the chemical and physical properties of molecules. For illustration, on the basis of relative electronegativities, one would predict that $CHBr_2COOH$ is a stronger acid than is $CH_2ClCOOH$, or that CF_3—O—CF_3 is an extremely weak base and could not serve as a solvent for the formation of a Grignard, or knowing the relative ease of oxidation of alkyl groups by nitric acid one would predict that the oxidation of *p*-isopropyl-*sec*-butylbenzene would give *p*-isopropylbenzoic acid rather than *p*-*sec*-butylbenzoic acid.[49] The effect of electronegativities on bond distances was pointed out in Sec. 1.2.9(d).

2.3 Ionic character of covalent molecules

If a bond A—B were purely covalent, it would be expected to have not more than a very small dipole moment, whereas if the bond were an ion-pair A^+B^-, its dipole moment would be approximately the product of an electric charge and the internuclear distance. Pauling[50] took the ratio of the actual moment of A—B to the moment for an ionic structure as a measure of the ionic character of the bond. Based on the dipole moments and bond

[46] B. P. Dailey and C. H. Townes, *J. Chem. Phys.*, **23**, 118 (1955).
[47] M. A. Fineman, *J. Phys. Chem.*, **62**, 947 (1958).
[48] A. F. Clifford, *J. Phys. Chem.*, **63**, 1227 (1959).
[49] L. N. Ferguson and A. I. Wims, *J. Org. Chem.*, **25**, 668 (1960).
[50] Page 98 of reference 2.

Table 2.7. RELATIVE ELECTRONEGATIVITIES OF SOME COMMON GROUPS AS DETERMINED BY DIFFERENT METHODS

Hydrolysis of R—Hg—R'[22]	Dipole moments of RCl[24]	K_a of R—CH$_2$COOH
—CN		—CN
CH_3O—⟨C$_6$H$_4$⟩—	CH_3O—⟨C$_6$H$_4$⟩—	F—
CH_3—⟨C$_6$H$_4$⟩—	CH_3—⟨C$_6$H$_4$⟩—	Cl—
⟨C$_6$H$_5$⟩—	⟨C$_6$H$_5$⟩—	Br—
Cl—⟨C$_6$H$_4$⟩—	Cl—⟨C$_6$H$_4$⟩—	I—
CH_3—	CH_3—	CH_3O—
C_2H_5—	C_2H_5—	⟨C$_6$H$_5$⟩—
ϕ—CH_2—	ϕ—CH_2—	H—
$(CH_3)_3C$—	$(CH_3)_3C$—	$(CH_3)_2CH$—
ϕ_3C—	ϕ_3C—	CH_3CH_2—
		CH_3—
		$(CH_3)_3C$—

Polar substituent constants[27]	Infrared absorption intensities[30,31]	NMR shielding parameters[43-45]	Generally expected order
FCH_2-	$HC{\equiv}C-CH_2-$	$F-$	$-CN$
$ClCH_2-$	$\phi-CH_2-$	$HO-$	$F-$
$BrCH_2-$	$CH_2{=}CH-CH_2-$	$Cl-$	$Cl-$
ICH_2-	CH_3-	$Br-$	$Br-$
⬡—	$CH_3-CH_2-CH_2-$	H_2N-	F_3C-
$H-$		⬡—	Cl_3C-
$\phi-CH_2-$	$CH_2{\scriptstyle\diagdown}{\atop}{CH_2-CH_2 \atop CH_2-CH_2}{\atop}{\scriptstyle\diagup}CH-$	$-CHO$	Br_3C-
CH_3-	$(CH_3)_3C-$	$I-$	Cl_2CH-
C_2H_5-		$-COOH$	Br_2CH-
$(CH_3)_2CH-$		$-CN$	$ClCH_2-$
$(CH_3)_3C-$		$-SH$	$HC{\equiv}C-$
			C_6H_5-
			$CH_2{=}CH-$
			$H-$
			$D-$
			CH_3-
			C_2H_5-
			⬡S—
			$(CH_3)_3C-$
			ϕ_3C-
			ϕ_3Si-

distances of the hydrogen halides, H—X, Pauling developed an equation relating their ionic character to the electronegativity differences of the atoms in HX. This equation has been revised using more accurate dipole moment data to the form[51]

$$\text{per cent ionic character} = 0.16(X_A - X_B) + 0.035(X_A - X_B)^2 \quad (2.15)$$

where X_A and X_B are the electronegativities of atoms A and B. Table 2.8 gives the per cent ionic character for some bond electronegativity differences. Although the table gives semiquantitative figures for various differences in electronegativity, this procedure should not be used more than to say that a bond is primarily ionic or chiefly covalent. Thus, Eq. (2.15)

Table 2.8. PER CENT IONIC CHARACTER FOR BOND
ELECTRONEGATIVITY DIFFERENCES[51]

$X_A - X_B$	Per cent ionic character	$X_A - X_B$	Per cent ionic character
0.2	3	1.8	40
0.4	7	2.0	46
0.6	11	2.2	52
0.8	15	2.4	59
1.0	20	2.6	65
1.2	24	2.8	72
1.4	29	3.0	80
1.6	35	3.2	87

correctly predicts that CsF, which has the largest electronegativity difference of any pair of elements, is primarily ionic; it predicts that the metal-oxygen bond in alkali metal oxides and alkaline earth metal oxides is largely ionic; and that NaI has a fairly large covalent character. On the other hand, the bonds in SiF_4 and SnF_4 are computed from Tables 2.2 and 2.8 to have approximately the same ionic character, but according to their boiling points, SiF_4 (b.p. $-90°$) is essentially covalent and SnF_4 (b.p. 705°) is primarily ionic. Apparently the small difference in ionic radii of silicon and tin is large enough to give the tetrafluorides different degrees of ionic character. Thus, too many other parameters affect the observed ionic character of substances to use this method of estimating ionic character of a molecule.[52] However, it is useful when considering binary compounds.

[51] N. B. Hannay and C. P. Smyth, *J. Am. Chem. Soc.*, **68**, 171 (1946); R. A. Oriani and C. P. Smyth, *J. Chem. Phys.*, **16**, 1167 (1948).

[52] Cf. some of the criticisms and countercriticisms of Pauling's method in the literature: D. Z. Robinson, *J. Chem. Phys.*, **17**, 1022 (1949); P. N. Schatz, *J. Chem. Phys.*, **22**, 695 (1954); W. J. Gordy, *J. Chem. Phys.*, **22**, 1470 (1954).

It is noteworthy that Fajans and Pauling attempted to assess the covalent or ionic character of a compound from opposite directions. Fajans
considered the factors that tend to make an ionic bond more covalent and
Pauling attempted to find the ionic character of a covalent bond. To illustrate Fajans' approach, he postulated that in the presence of a cation, the
electron cloud of the anion is deformed by the attractive force of the positively charged cation.[53] Thus, the fluoride ion has a smaller polarizability

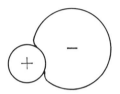

Fig. 2.1. Anion, polarized by a cation.

than the iodide ion, and the observed internuclear distance of the LiF molecule is close to the sum of the Li^+ and F^- ionic radii. However, the internuclear distance of the LiI molecule is less than that of the sum of its ionic
radii because the iodide ion in LiI is considerably polarized.

	$d_{internuclear(obs.)}$	$r^+ + r^-(calc.)$
LiF	2.01 Å	2.01Å
LiCl	2.49	2.57
LiBr	2.64	2.75
LiI	2.87	3.02

The extreme limit of this polarization would be for the outer electrons of
the anion to fall into the valence orbital of the cation, i.e., to form a covalent bond. Fajans named three factors that lead to covalency: (1) high
cationic charge, (2) small cationic radius, and (3) large anionic radius. The
greater is the cationic charge, the greater is the attractive force for the anion
electron cloud. The smaller is the cation, the more dense is its charge and
the greater is its polarizing force. Also, its nucleus gets closer to the anion
electron cloud. Finally, the larger is the anion radius, the farther from its
nucleus are its valence electrons and the weaker is the attractive force between the electrons and the nucleus; hence, the electrons can be displaced
more easily. The effects of these factors are illustrated by the data in
Table 2.9. For example, factor (1) explains the greater covalent character
of $SnCl_4$ over that of $SnCl_2$, factor (2) accounts for SiF_4 being more covalent than SnF_4, and factor (3) predicts that $AlCl_3$ would be more covalent
than AlF_3. The boiling point has been selected as the criterion for assessing

[53] K. Fajans, *Naturwissenschaften,* **11,** 165 (1923).

Table **2.9** ILLUSTRATIONS OF FAJAN'S RULES OF COVALENCY

Influencing factor	Covalent compounds	Ionic compounds
Cationic charge	$SnCl_4$ (b.p. 114°)	$SnCl_2$ (b.p. 623°)
	$FeCl_3$ (b.p. 315°)	$FeCl_2$ (b.p. 1000°)
	$PbCl_4$ (liq.; dec. 105°)	$PbCl_2$ (b.p. 954°)
Cation radius	SiF_4 (b.p. −90°)	SnF_4 (b.p. 705°)
Anion radius	$AlCl_3$ (b.p. 183°)	AlF_3 (b.p. 800°)
	$SnCl_4$ (b.p. 114°)	SnF_4 (b.p. 705°)

the essentially covalent or essentially ionic nature of these compounds, but it is to be realized that this is not a perfect criterion.

2.3.1 PERMANENT AND INDUCED DIPOLE MOMENTS[54]

When a body contains positive and negative charges, so that points A and B are the centers of negative and positive charge, respectively, it behaves in an electric field like a body with a single negative pole at A and a single positive pole at B. It would tend to rotate clockwise as shown in the drawing

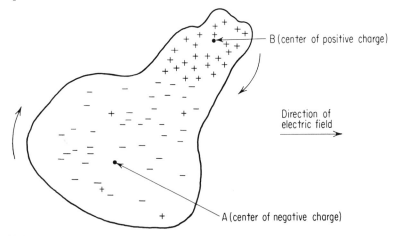

B (center of positive charge)

Direction of electric field

A (center of negative charge)

until the line joining points A and B lies parallel to the field. The product of the distance d, between the two points A and B, and the resultant negative charge e at A gives the magnitude m of the dipole.

$$m = de$$

Since molecular distances are in units of 10^{-8} cm, and the charge of an electron is of the order of 10^{-10} esu, dipole moments will have an order of

[54]C. P. Smyth in *Techniques of Organic Chemistry*, vol. 1, pt. 3, ed. A. Weissberger (3rd ed.; New York: Interscience, 1960), chap. 39; L. E. Sutton in *Determination of Organic Structures by Physical Methods*, ed. E. A. Braude and F. C. Nachod (New York: Academic, 1953), chap. 9; J. W. Smith, *Electric Dipole Moments* (London: Butterworths, 1955).

magnitude of 10^{-18} esu; this unit is called a *debye*. Thus, dipole moments are given in debyes. The situation described above is for a neutral body. It is seen that the moment arises not from the net charge but from the separation of charge. Hence, if points A and B coincide, there is no moment. Ions are polarizable, but are not considered dipoles.[55]

A bond dipole in an asymmetrical molecule will give to the molecule a permanent dipole, equal to the product of the negative charge (which equals the positive charge with a change of sign) and the distance between the two centers of charge. When a molecule, polar or nonpolar, is placed in an electric field, the electrons are attracted away from their normal positions by the external positive pole,[56] and thus a dipole is set up within the molecule, called an *induced dipole*. The magnitude of the induced dipole, μ_{ind}, depends upon the field strength F and the polarizability α, i.e., the displaceability of the electric centers by the external electric field. The induced dipole moment will last only as long as the external field is present.

When molecules with a permanent dipole moment μ and a polarizability α are placed in an electric field, they will rotate to align their permanent dipoles parallel with the field. Also, their electrons will be displaced towards the positive pole. Then, the total molar polarization of the medium due to the presence of the molecules will be that induced by the field plus that from the alignment of the permanent dipoles.[56]

$$P = P_{induced} + P_{permanent} = P_\alpha + P_\mu$$

From classical theory, it is found that the total polarization can be expressed by Eq. 2.16, where N is Avogadro's number, k is Boltzmann's constant, and T is the absolute temperature. From this equation it is seen that

$$P = \frac{4\pi N}{3}\alpha + \frac{4\pi N}{3} \cdot \frac{\mu^2}{3kT} \tag{2.16}$$

P_α is independent of the temperature, whereas P_μ varies inversely with the temperature. Polarization from the permanent dipole moment decreases with increasing temperature because with a rise in temperature, the molecules possess more kinetic energy and offer greater resistance to alignment by the external field.

The experimental determination of α and μ is commonly made by measuring dielectric constants.[57] The dielectric constant is simply the ratio of

[55]Cf. K. Mysels, *J. Chem. Phys.*, **21**, 201 (1953).

[56]This is neglecting the opposite displacement of the positive centers (nuclei), but since their masses are so much greater than that of the electrons, the atomic polarization in a rapidly oscillating field is small enough to be neglected usually.

[57]P. Bender has described the assembly of electrical components for the measurement of dipole moments, *J. Chem. Educ.*, **23**, 179 (1946). Dipolemeters are commercially available from the Kahl Scientific Instrument Corp., El Cajon, California.

the capacitance of a capacitor with the substance as dielectric to that when air (or a vacuum) is the dielectric.

$$e = \frac{C_x}{C_{air}}$$

Then, from the dielectric constant, the total polarization may be calculated from Eq. (2.17), where e is the dielectric constant, ρ is the density, and M is the molecular weight of the substance.

$$P = \frac{e-1}{e+2} \cdot \frac{M}{\rho} \tag{2.17}$$

In order to determine α and μ from P, one of several general techniques may be used.

(1) The most accurate procedure is to measure P at a series of temperatures and plot it against the reciprocal of the absolute temperature. From Eq. (2.16), it is seen that the first derivative of P with respect to $1/T$ equals $4\pi N\mu^2/9k$. That is, the slope of the line obtained when P is plotted against $1/T$ will give $4\pi N\mu^2/9k$, from which μ can be calculated. The intercept at $1/T = 0$ gives the constant $4\pi N\alpha/3$, which permits a calculation of α.

(2) An alternative technique is to measure the index of refraction n of the substance, and use light of various frequencies.[58] Light has a rapidly oscillating electric field which can induce polarization of the molecules. Obviously, the polarization by light of infinite frequency will be solely that due to induction. Therefore, a plot of the index of refraction against frequency and an extrapolation to infinite frequency is made. It has been shown from classical theory that $e = n^2$, so that substitution of n^2 for e in Eq. (2.17) gives Eq. (2.18).

$$P = \frac{n^2-1}{n^2+2} \cdot \frac{M}{\rho} \tag{2.18}$$

Hence, at infinite frequency, P of Eq. (2.18) will equal P_α. Again P_μ is calculated from the relationship $P_\mu = P - P_\alpha$, where P is determined by a single measurement.

(3) A third possible technique is to measure the dielectric constant in an alternating field. The induced polarization is due to a shifting of electrons, which will oscillate instantaneously with the field, whereas the polarization resulting from the permanent dipole moment involves migration and rotation of molecules. Rotation of the molecules will be sluggish, and with increasing alternating frequency of the external field, rotation of the molecules will lag more and more behind the field oscillation. Hence, the total polarization will diminish to that from induction alone; that is, P will approach P_α as a limit. Again, P is plotted against the field oscillation fre-

[58] I. F. Halverstadt and W. D. Kumler, *J. Am. Chem. Soc.,* **64,** 2988 (1942).

quency and extrapolated to infinite frequency. This will give a value for $P_\alpha = 4\pi N\alpha/3$, from which α may be computed from the relationship $P_\mu = P - P_\alpha$ when P is measured at any specific frequency. However, the high frequencies required for this procedure make the method difficult to use.[59] Measurements of dielectric constants or indexes of refraction are made on vapors or solutions. Usually in very dilute solutions the equation $P = N_1 P_1 + N_2 P_2$ will hold as a first approximation, where P is the measured polarization of the solution, N_1 and N_2 are the mole fractions of the solvent and solute, and P_1 and P_2 are the corresponding molar polarizations. If it is desired, measurements can be made at several concentrations and an extrapolation made to infinite dilution. Of course, the solvent should be one that does not interact with the solute.

Table 2.10. Some Polarizabilities[60]

Li^+	0.03	F^-	0.81	F	0.38	O (hydroxyl)	0.59
Na^+	0.24	Cl^-	2.98	Cl	2.28	O (ether)	0.64
K^+	1.00	Br^-	4.24	Br	3.34	O (carbonyl)	0.84
NH_4^+	1.65	I^-	6.45	I	5.11	N (1°)	0.87
Ag^+	1.90	OH^-	1.89	CN	2.12	N (2°)	0.93
Be^{+2}	0.01	O^{-2}	3.00	H	0.42	N (3°)	1.03
Mg^{+2}	0.10			C	0.93	Double bond	0.58 extra
Ca^{+2}	0.60			CH_2	1.77	Triple bond	0.86 extra
						C_6H_5	9.38

2.3.2 VECTOR ADDITION OF DIPOLE MOMENTS

It was shown in Sec. 2.1 that differences in electronegativity of atoms A and B in the bond A—B give rise to a dipole in the bond; in fact, one of the earliest attempts to develop a scale of electronegativities was based on bond dipole moments. Later, Smyth[61] calculated dipole moments for several bonds from an equation formulated by Mulliken[62] relating the electronegativity difference of the atoms forming the bond, the bond length, the bond moment, and any secondary moment from induction of nonbonding electrons. From the H—C bond moment, for example, and the dipole moment of CH_3Cl, Smyth calculated the C—Cl bond moment. For illustration, if the tetrahedral bond angles in CH_3—Cl are undistorted, the sum of the three H—C bond moments projected along the C—Cl axis is equivalent to

[59] Nevertheless, good values are obtainable from the dielectric loss (cf. M. Davies, *Quart. Revs.*, **8**, 250 (1954).

[60] J. A. A. Ketelaar, *Chemical Constitution* [Princeton, N.J.: (Elsevier) Van Nostrand, 1953], p. 90.

[61] C. P. Smyth, *J. Chem. Phys.*, **4**, 209 (1937).

[62] R. S. Mulliken, *J. Chem. Phys.*, **3**, 573 (1935).

one H—C moment along this axis (since H_3C—H has no moment). Thus, the dipole moment of the methyl chloride molecule is taken as the vector sum of the H—C moment plus the C—Cl moment, and the C—Cl moment is the observed CH_3Cl dipole moment less the H—C moment. Similarly, the C—O bond moment was calculated from the H_3C group moment and the dipole moment of methyl ether. In this fashion, Smyth set up a table of bond moments (Table 2.11). A few bond moments have also been determined from measurements of infrared absorption intensities[63] as well as other empirical approaches.[64]

Table 2.11. SOME BOND DIPOLE MOMENTS[61]

Bond (+ −)	Bond moment	Bond (+ −)	Bond moment
H—C_{sp^3}	0.30	C—I	1.29
H—N	1.31	C—N	0.40
H—O	1.53	C=N	0.90
H—F	1.98	C≡N	3.60
H—Cl	1.03	C—O	0.86
H—Br	0.78	C=O	2.40
H—I	0.38	C—S	2.95
H—S	0.68	C=S	2.80
C—F	1.51	N—O	0.30
C—Cl	1.56	N→O	3.20
C—Cl (2 Cl)	1.20	N=O	2.00
C—Cl (3 Cl)	0.85	S→O	2.50
C—Br	1.48		

As an illustration of their use, one could estimate the dipole moment of methyl alcohol.[68]

[63]W. L. G. Gent, *Quart. Revs.*, **2**, 383 (1948); A. M. Thorndike, A. J. Wells, and E. B. Wilson, Jr., *J. Chem. Phys.*, **15**, 157 (1947); J. W. Straley, *J. Chem. Phys.*, **23**, 2183 (1955); I. C. Hesatsune and D. F. Eggers, Jr., *J. Chem. Phys.*, **23**, 487 (1955); T. L. Brown, *Chem. Rev.*, **58**, 581 (1958); this method gives a "dynamic" dipole which is not necessarily, but is usually assumed to be, the same as the "static" dipole moment.
[64]B. Lakatos, *Z. Elektrochem.*, **61**, 944 (1957).

The dipole moment is computed on a basis of the geometry of the molecule and the bond moments. Using the law of cosines for the parallelogram, one has

$$\mu_{\text{resultant}} = \sqrt{(0.3 + 0.86)^2 + (1.53)^2 + (2 \times 1.16 \times 1.53) \cos 108°}$$
$$= \sqrt{1.35 + 2.34 + 5.38(-0.309)}$$
$$= \sqrt{2.03} = 1.64 \text{ D}$$

$$\mu_{\text{observed}} = 1.67 \text{ D}$$

Thus, the calculated and observed dipole moments for methyl alcohol agree quite well.

The magnitude and direction of the C—H bond moment has long been a matter of dispute.[65] It was shown in Sec. 1.2.9(d) that the state of hybridization of carbon affects its bond characteristics, which were attributed to corresponding changes in the electronegativity of carbon. The value of the C—H bond moment would also be expected to vary with the hybridization of carbon, and expectation has been confirmed. The bond moment has been determined from infrared dispersion measurements[66] and the results are included in Table 2.12.

Table 2.12. BOND CHARACTERISTICS OF THE C—H BOND

Molecular species	Hybridization of carbon	Force constant dynes/cm $\times 10^5$	Bond distance (Å)	Bond energy kcal/mole	Bond moment C^-—H^+
CH	p	4.1	1.12	80	
CH_4	sp^3	5.0	1.094	104	0.31
$H_2C{=}CH_2$	sp^2	5.1	1.087	106	0.63
$HC{\equiv}CH$	sp	5.9	1.058	121	1.05

Similarly, the C—C bond moment should be affected by the hybridized state of the carbon atoms. The following values, determined by an empirical method, have been proposed.[67]

[65] W. L. Gent, *Quart. Revs.*, **2**, 383 (1948); C. A. Coulson, *Valence* (London: Oxford, 1952), p. 207; A. D. Walsh, *Disc. Faraday Soc.*, **2**, 18 (1947); C. R. Mueller and H. Eyring, *J. Chem. Phys.*, **19**, 193 (1951).

[66] R. Rollefson, *et al.*, *J. Chem. Phys.*, **19**, 1595 (1951); *Phys. Rev.*, **57**, 710 (1940); C. F. Hammer, thesis, University of Wisconsin, 1948.

[67] A. J. Petro, *J. Am. Chem. Soc.*, **80**, 4230 (1958).

[68] For tables of dipole moments see L. G. Wesson, *Tables of Electric Dipole Moments*, (Cambridge, Mass.: Technology Press, 1948); C. H. Townes and A. L. Schawlow, *Microwave Spectroscopy* (New York: McGraw-Hill, 1955); A. A. Maryott and F. Buckley, National Bureau of Standards Circular 537 (1953).

$$\overset{+}{C}_{sp^3}-\overset{-}{C}_{sp^2} \qquad 0.68 \text{ D}$$

$$\overset{+}{C}_{sp^2}-\overset{-}{C}_{sp} \qquad 1.15$$

$$\overset{+}{C}_{sp^3}-\overset{-}{C}_{sp} \qquad 1.48$$

In the case of aromatic molecules more use is made of group moments. Vector addition of the H—C bond moments in benzene, each one of which has an equal but oppositely oriented H—C moment, gives a resultant dipole moment of zero for the molecule, which is in agreement with observation. When two atoms or groups A and B are substituted *para* to each other, the dipole moment of the derivative should be close to the algebraic sum of the C_1—A and B—C_4 bond moments.

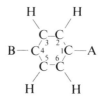

For example, one might expect the dipole moment of *p*-chloronitrobenzene to be the approximate sum or difference of the moments of chlorobenzene and nitrobenzene. The use of the sum or difference depends on the directions of the moments of ϕ—Cl and ϕ—NO_2 relative to the aromatic nucleus. As shown below, it turns out to be the difference.

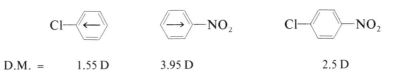

D.M. =   1.55 D   3.95 D   2.5 D

This is to be expected, because the greater electronegativity of chlorine in one case, and of nitrogen and oxygen in the other, over that of carbon directs the C—Cl and C—NO_2 bond moments away from the ring.[69] Hence, in each case the moments of ϕ—Cl and ϕ—NO_2 are directed away from the ring, so that in *p*—Cl—C_6H_4—NO_2 the two dipoles oppose each other.

Conversely, this procedure can be used as a means of determining the direction of the moment in a monosubstituted benzene. For illustration, the direction of the dipole of toluene might not be readily predictable. The direction can be determined from the moment of a *p*-substituted toluene and the knowledge of the direction of the moment of the *p*-substituent.

[69] The direction of a dipole is conventionally taken as that from the positive pole towards the negative pole.

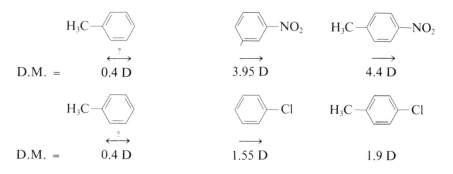

D.M. =   0.4 D   3.95 D   4.4 D

D.M. =   0.4 D   1.55 D   1.9 D

In these two cases, the moment of the *p*-disubstituted benzene is approximately the sum of the moments of the respective monosubstituted benzenes, which indicates that the moment of toluene must be directed towards the ring. From the direction of the ϕ—CH_3 dipole moment one can say that a hydrogen atom is more electronegative than a methyl group. That is, the bond moment in the C_4—H bond is thought to be directed towards the C_4 atom owing to the greater electronegativity of sp^2—hybridized carbon over that of hydrogen. Since the overall moment for the molecule is towards the ring, there is a greater moment in the C_1—CH_3 bond than in the C_4—H bond. The difference in electronegativities between C_1 and the CH_3 group is greater, therefore, than the difference between C_4 and H; in other words, carbon can attract the shared pair of electrons from the CH_3 group more than from the hydrogen atom. It follows, then, that the hydrogen atom is more electronegative than a CH_3 group. These are the same relative electronegativities as obtained from the several methods discussed in Sec. 2.2. It should be pointed out, however, that the direction of the dipole moment of ϕ—CH_3 can also be explained in terms of hyperconjugation (see Sec. 4.5).

Since the OCH_3 group may rotate about the C—O axis, its group moment may not be coplanar with the ring.

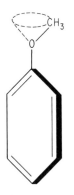

From the dipole moments of anisole, bromobenzene, and *p*-bromoanisole, the moment angle of the methoxyl group is calculated to be 72°. Based on this moment angle, the agreement between calculated and observed moments of substituted anisoles indicates that the OCH_3 group is held fairly rigidly in the plane of the ring (presumably the result of resonance energy). The moment of hydroquinone dimethyl ether (1.730) indicates that the two OCH_3 groups have the orientation

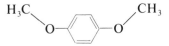

The approximate moment of a *meta* or *ortho* disubstituted benzene also can be obtained by vector addition of the moments of the respective monosubstituted compounds. If μ_1 and μ_2 are the moments associated with the substituents of the monosubstituted benzenes, their vector addition can be made according to the law of cosines, where ϕ is 60° for the *ortho* isomer and 120° for the *meta* isomer.

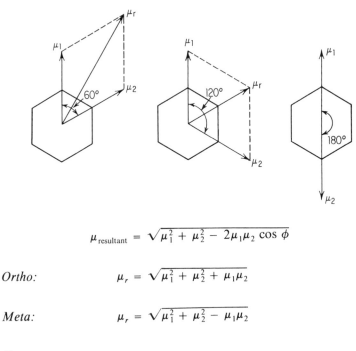

$$\mu_{resultant} = \sqrt{\mu_1^2 + \mu_2^2 - 2\mu_1\mu_2 \cos \phi}$$

Ortho: $$\mu_r = \sqrt{\mu_1^2 + \mu_2^2 + \mu_1\mu_2}$$

Meta: $$\mu_r = \sqrt{\mu_1^2 + \mu_2^2 - \mu_1\mu_2}$$

Para: $$\mu_r = \mu_2 - \mu_1$$

As an illustration, the values calculated from these equations for the chlorotoluenes are in satisfactory agreement with the observed values.

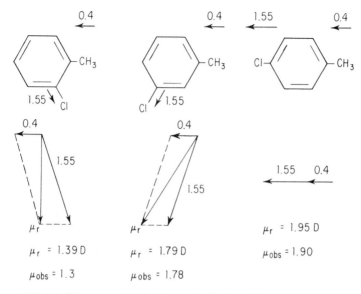

Branch and Calvin[70] have made similar calculations for a number of disubstituted benzenes, and their results are listed in Table 2.13. The discrepancies between calculated and observed values are largest for the *ortho* position with large substituents. The reason is, steric repulsion between the *ortho* substituents spreads the groups apart and makes the actual angles larger than the assumed 60°. For example, the bromine atoms in *o*-dibromobenzene actually form angles of 15° with the ring, thus increasing ϕ, whereas they are planar with the ring in the *para* isomer.

Table 2.13. CALCULATED AND OBSERVED MOMENTS (IN DEBYES) OF
SOME DISUBSTITUTED BENZENES[70]

X	Moment of C_6H_5X	Y	Moment of C_6H_5Y	Ortho Obs.	Ortho Calc.	Meta Obs.	Meta Calc.	Para Obs.	Para Calc.
CH_3	0.4	CH_3	0.4	0.5	0.7	0.4	0.4	0	0
F	1.43	F	1.43	2.4	2.48				
Cl	1.55	Cl	1.55	2.3	2.67	1.48	1.55	0	0
Br	1.52	Br	1.52	2.0	2.63	1.5	1.52	0	0
I	1.3	I	1.3	1.7	2.25	1.3	1.30	0	0
NO_2	3.95	NO_2	3.95	6.0	6.83	3.79	3.95	0	0
CH_3	0.4	Cl	1.55	1.3	1.39	1.78	1.79	1.90	1.95
CH_3	0.4	NO_2	3.95	3.66	3.76	4.17	4.16	4.4	4.35
Cl	1.55	NO_2	3.95	4.3	4.91	3.4	3.44	2.5	2.4
Cl	1.55	Br	1.52	2.2	2.67	1.5	1.54	0	0.03

[70]G. E. K. Branch and M. Calvin, *The Theory of Organic Chemistry*, p. 135.

As an example of a non-benzene system, unusually good results were obtained in the calculation of the moment of camphorquinone. From the dipole moment of camphor, 3.05 D, and the computed angle between carbonyl dipoles in camphorquinone (76°), one may calculate the moment of the latter compound:

$$\mu_r = \sqrt{(3.05)^2 + (3.05)^2 + 2 \cdot 3.05 \cdot 3.05 \cos 76°}$$

$$= 4.82 \text{ D}$$

This agrees better than should be expected with the measured value of 4.81 D.[71]

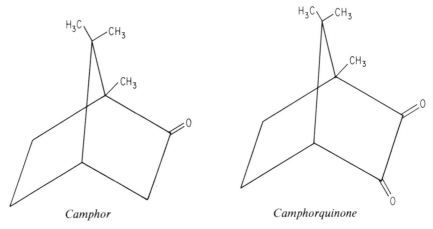

Camphor   *Camphorquinone*

The above procedure must be modified when the group moment of the substituted benzene is not in the plane of the ring. For illustration, the angle between the resultant dipole moment of aniline and the axis of maximum polarization is about 70°.[72] Since the axis of maximum polarizability lies in the plane of the benzene ring, this means that the N—H bonds are at some wide angle to the ring. That is, nitrogen still has an appreciable pyramidal structure.

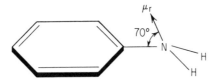

The dipole moment of such compounds, where the group is not coplanar with the ring, may be closely estimated by use of Eq. (2.19).[73]

[71] W. D. Kumler and J. Meinwald, *J. Am. Chem. Soc.*, **83**, 4591 (1961).

[72] W. D. Kumler and I. F. Halverstadt, *J. Am. Chem. Soc.*, **63**, 2182 (1941).

[73] O. Fuchs, *Z. Physik. Chem.*, **14B**, 339 (1930).

$$\mu_r = \sqrt{\mu_1^2 + \mu_2^2 + 2\mu_1\mu_2 \cos \phi \cos C_1 \cos C_2} \qquad (2.19)$$

where μ_r = resultant moment of the disubstituted benzene,

μ_1, μ_2 = moments of the respective monosubstituted benzenes,

ϕ = angle between axes of rotation of the groups in the disubstituted benzene (= 180° for the *para* isomer, 120° for the *meta* isomer, and 60° for the *ortho* isomer).

C_1, C_2 = angles which the group moments make with their axes of rotation.

On the basis of this equation, it was proposed that the C—Hg—Cl bond in some phenylmercurials is not 180° as expected for *sp* hybridization. Best agreement was obtained between calculated and observed dipole moments of chloromercurianisoles on the basis that the C—Hg—Cl bond forms an angle of 130–150°.[74]

The fact that symmetrical molecules such as Br_2, N_2, BCl_3, CF_4, C_6H_6, p—Cl—C_6H_4—Cl, and p—O_2N—C_6H_4—NO_2 do not have dipole moments, whereas unsymmetrical molecules do, provides some support for the notion that bond moments are principally responsible for molecules having permanent dipole moments. However, molecular dipole moments arise from other factors. The principal factor is the asymmetry of charge in the bonding electrons arising from differences in electronegativity of the bonded atoms. A second major factor is the polarization of nonbonding electrons. For example,[75] the $\overset{+}{H}$—$\overset{-}{N}$ bond dipoles and the dipole from the lone-pair electrons on the nitrogen atom are in the same direction, giving the molecule an appreciable dipole moment (1.59 D). In contrast, the direction of the $\overset{-}{F}$—$\overset{+}{N}$ bond dipoles is opposed to the dipole of the lone-pair electrons on the nitrogen, which gives the molecule a small dipole moment (0.2 D). Thus, the dipole moment of water is due not only to the H—O bond moments, but also to the moments arising from the lone-pair electrons on the oxygen atom. Similarly, the C—I and C—S bond moments are larger than expected from electronegativity differences, and this can be attributed to the nonbonding electrons on the iodine and sulfur atoms. Nevertheless, the empirical method of computing bond dipole moments includes effects of nonbonding electrons, which explains the agreement between observed and calculated dipole moments from vector addition of bond moments. Coulson[76] has pointed out that two other factors that contribute to the dipole moments of molecules are the homopolar dipole arising from inequality of the size of the bonded atoms and the possible asymmetry of the atomic orbitals involved in the bonds. The contribution of

[74] J. C. Sipos, J. Sawatzky, and G. F. Wright, *J. Am. Chem. Soc.*, **77**, 2759 (1955).

[75] V. Schomaker and C. Lu, *J. Am. Chem. Soc.*, **72**, 1182 (1950).

[76] C. A. Coulson, *Valence* (Fair Lawn, N.J.: Oxford U. P., 1952), p. 147.

each of the four factors has not been assessed, but each is believed to be significant.

2.3.3 APPLICATIONS OF ELECTRIC DIPOLE MOMENT DATA

It was shown in Sec. 2.3.2 that agreement between observed dipole moments and moments calculated by the vector addition of bond dipoles is used for confirmation of molecular structures. An early application of dipole moments was in the distinguishment of *cis* and *trans* isomers. It was easy to show that normal azobenzene, having no dipole moment, is the *trans* isomer, and that the labile form, having a moment of 3.00 D, must be the *cis* isomer. Section 1.6.2 discussed the degree of association of carboxylic acids and other compounds as determined from dipole moment measurements. In Sec. 3.3.1 mention will be made of the use of dipole moments in studying different conformations of molecules, and in Sec. 4.7 extensive use will be made of dipole moments to provide evidence of the contributions of ionic forms to the resonance hybrids of molecules.

An excellent discussion of the application of dipole moments to the solution of chemical problems is given by Sutton.[54]

STUDY QUESTIONS

1. What is the essential difference between the methods of Rochow and of Gordy for determining the force of the nucleus upon an electron at the boundary of the covalent radius of an atom?

2. What various properties of elements are used as bases for determining relative atomic electronegativities?

3. In which compound does phosphorus have the greater electronegativity, PCl_3 or $POCl_3$?

4. What arguments can be given that in the cleavage of R—Hg—R′ with HCl, the relative amounts of RH and R′H produced are a measure of the equilibrium amounts of R^- and $R′$ in solution rather than a measure of the relative rates of cleavage of the R—Hg and Hg—R′ bonds?

5. Offer an explanation for the smaller pK_a of formic acid than acetic acid.

6. Predict which compound will have the greater acid strength: CCl_3CH_2OH or CF_3CH_2OH.[77]

7. Is the boiling point of TeF_6 ($-35°$) consistent with the ionic character calculated

[77] F. A. Long, *J. Am. Chem. Soc.*, **81**, 1050, (1959).

for it from Table 2.9? Offer an explanation for its apparently large covalent character.

8. Offer an explanation for the weakness of HF as an acid in comparison with the other hydrogen halides in terms of electronegativities.[78]

9. The C—H bond distances in methane, ethane, ethylene, acetylene, and benzene are, in Å, 1.095, 1.102, 1.071, 1.058, and 1.084, respectively. On the basis of bond lengths what is the relative electronegativity of the methyl, ethyl, vinyl, ethynyl, and phenyl groups, and how does your order compare with that in Table 2.7? What can be said about the relative s character of the hybrid carbon orbitals of the C—H bonds? [Cf. Sec. 1.2.9(d).]

10. Offer an explanation for the relative acid strengths of the following pairs of acids:

Acid	$10^5 K_a$	Acid	$10^5 K_a$
CH_2=CH—CH_2—$COOH$	4.62	Phenylacetic acid	4.88
$CH_3CH_2CH_2$—$COOH$	1.50	Cyclohexylacetic acid	2.36
CH_2=CH—CH_2—$COOH$	4.62	ϕ—CH_2—$COOH$	4.88
CH_2=CH—CH_2CH_2—$COOH$	2.11	ϕ—CH_2CH_2—$COOH$	2.19
CH_2=CH—CH_2CH_2—$COOH$	2.11		
$CH_3CH_2CH_2CH_2$—$COOH$	1.38		

11. If H is more electronegative than alkyl or cycloalkyl groups, how would you account for the dipole moments of aliphatic and cycloaliphatic amines decreasing in the order $RNH_2 > R_2NH > R_3N$?[79]

12. $HCCl_3$ forms a stronger H bond with phosphoryl compounds than does $HCCl_2$—CCl_3.[80] Predict which acid should be associated to the larger degree, CCl_3—CH_2—$COOH$ or $ClCH_2$—$COOH$.

13. What orientation would you predict for the OCH_3 group in o-bromoanisole? Compare your prediction with that calculated from its dipole moment (2.47 D). Assume the dipole moment of ϕBr and ϕ—OCH_3 are 1.5 and 1.23 D, respectively.

14. In the presence of each other, why is the anion polarized more than the cation?

15. Would you expect the C—Br bond moment to increase or decrease with an increasing number of chlorine atoms attached to the carbon atom?

16. Predict the relative order of increasing dissociation constants for the carboxylic acids of cyclopropane, cyclobutane, and cyclohexane, and give the basis for your prediction.[81]

---

[78] L. Pauling, *J. Chem. Educ.*, **33**, 16 (1956).

[79] E.g., the moments of mono-, di-, and tricyclohexylamine are 1.32 D, 1.06 D, and 0.42 D.

[80] M. W. Hansen and J. B. Bouck, *J. Am. Chem. Soc.*, **79**, 5631 (1957).

[81] Cf. J. D. Roberts and V. C. Chambers, *J. Am. Chem. Soc.*, **73**, 5030 (1951); M. Kilpatrick and J. G. Morse, *J. Am. Chem. Soc.*, **75**, 1854 (1953).

17. What factors will you consider in predicting the relative acid strengths of phenol, *m*-nitro-trifluoromethylcarbinol, phenyl-trifluoromethylcarbinol, and α-phenylethanol?[82]

18. Make the following predictions and in each case give the basis for your prediction:

    (a) the relative dipole moments of vinyl bromide, allyl bromide, ethyl bromide, and methyl bromide.

    (b) The relative ionization potentials of NH_3, CH_3NH_2, $(CH_3)_2NH$, $(C_2H_5)NH_2$, $(CH_3)_3N$, and $(n\text{-}C_3H_7)_3N$.[83]

    (c) the relative acid strengths of C_6H_5OH and C_6D_5OH.[84]

19. For which system would you predict the larger dipole moment, a five-membered cyclic imide, e.g., succinimide, or a six-membered cyclic imide, e.g., glutarimide?[85]

[82] R. Stewart and R. Van der Linden, *Can. J. Chem.*, **38**, 399 (1960).

[83] K. Watanabe and J. R. Mottl, *J. Chem. Phys.*, **26**, 1773 (1957).

[84] H. S. Klein and A. Streitwieser, Jr., *Chem. and Ind. (London)*, 180 (1961).

[85] Cf. C. M. Lee and W. D. Kumler, *J. Am. Chem. Soc.*, **83**, 4586 (1961).

CHAPTER *III*

3.1 Van der Waals radii

When atoms closely approach one another and their valence shells do not coalesce to form a bond, large repulsive forces arise between the kernels of the atoms.[1] Thus, each atom or neutral atomic grouping has a definite volume within which it resists penetration by other atoms. Pauling[2] has estimated the radii of these volumes, called *van der Waals* radii, for a number of atoms and groups, and some values are given in Table 3.1. Pauling's data are taken from diffraction measurements on crystals. A few values have also been determined from measurements on liquids, and these radii usually are a little smaller than the Pauling values. For example,[3] the radii

---

[1]D. F. Heath and J. W. Linnett, *J. Chem. Phys.*, **18**, 147 (1950).

[2]L. Pauling, *Nature of the Chemical Bond* (3rd ed.; Ithaca, N.Y.: Cornell U. P., 1960), pp. 260, 263.

[3]C. P. Smyth and K. B. McAlpine, *J. Am. Chem. Soc.*, **57**, 979 (1935); C. P. Smyth and W. S. Walls, *J. Chem. Phys.*, **1**, 200 (1935).

INTRAMOLECULAR FORCES

found from crystalline compounds and the liquid state are 1.8 and 1.65 Å for chlorine, and 1.95 and 1.8 Å for bromine. Because of this differential, Pauling's values are sometimes reduced 10 per cent in their application. Furthermore, van der Waals radii give a poor measure of intramolecular nonbonding distances because the van der Waals radii are determined from *interatomic* distances in crystals. On the other hand, covalent radii would be too small, so that some intermediate values between covalent and van der Waals radii are frequently chosen.[4]

Pauling has called attention to the point that the van der Waals radii in Table 3.1 are 0.75 to 0.83 Å greater than the corresponding single-bond covalent radii, and to within its limit of reliability a van der Waals radius could be taken as equal to the covalent radius plus 0.80 Å.

We have already seen that atoms and molecules have short-range non-

[4] E. A. Braude and E. S. Waight, *Progress in Stereochemistry*, vol. I, ed. W. Klyne (New York: Academic, 1954), p. 145; E. Heilbronner and R. Gerdil, *Helv. Chim. Acta,* **39,** 1996 (1956).

Table 3.1. VAN DER WAALS RADII OF SOME ATOMS[2] (Å)

H	1.2				
N	1.5	O	1.4	F	1.35
P	1.9	S	1.85	Cl	1.80
As	2.0	Se	2.0	Br	1.95
Sb	2.2	Te	2.2	I	2.15
CH_3	2.0	Half thickness of benzene nucleus = 1.70			

bonding attractive forces referred to as van der Waals forces (Sec. 13.3), dipolar Coulombic forces, and London dispersion forces. These are attractive forces and increase with decreasing interatomic distances up to the van der Waals radius, when the repulsive forces suddenly increase rapidly with any further close approach of the atoms. The question might arise, why are only the *attractive* van der Waals and dispersion forces considered? This question can be answered in the following way. The forces are dipolar in character and one can expect that like-charged poles have as much of a statistical chance of meeting and producing repulsive forces as unlike-charged poles have of meeting to produce attractive forces. However, when the like-charged poles meet and repel each other, they tend to separate and thereby decrease the interatomic repulsion, whereas the unlike-charged poles tend to get closer to each other and thereby increase the attraction. Also, when the dipoles approach each other with like-charged poles together, they tend to depolarize each other, i.e., decrease the separation of charge in each dipole, whereas when oriented with unlike-charged poles together, each dipole tends to increase the charge separation in the other dipole. Consequently, these two effects make the repulsive forces self-diminishing and the attractive forces self-increasing. Furthermore, the orientation of molecules with opposite charges as nearest neighbors gives a more stable system than one having dipoles oriented with like charges nearest to each other. Since molecules tend to assume the state of greatest stability, the former orientation predominates. These two factors then, polarization and orientation, are the reasons that only the attractive intermolecular van der Waals forces are considered.

As already stated, when nonbonding atoms begin to approach one another closer than van der Waals radii, a marked repulsion sets in which rapidly increases in magnitude with small decreases in interatomic distances. Thus, intramolecular crowding can distort normal bond angles or stretch normal bond lengths. For this reason, the substituents in polysubstituted benzenes frequently are twisted from the theoretical bond angle of 120° with the ring and planar groups are rotated out of the plane of the ring. For examples, in *o*-chlorobenzoic acid, the carboxyl carbon atom and the chlorine atom form angles of 122.5 and 124.7 degrees with the ring, respectively, the COOH group is rotated 13.7° out of the plane of the ring, and the two groups bend about 0.04 Å in opposite directions out of the plane of the ring.[5] The two bromine atoms in *o*-dibromobenzene are bent 15° in opposite directions out of the plane of the ring, whereas they are planar in the *para* isomer. Even in *m*-dinitrobenzene, the repulsion between the nitro groups and the hydrogen atom between the two groups forces the nitro groups to rotate 11° out of the plane of the ring.[6]

3.2. Stereochemistry

In the last score years, there has been an increasing awareness of the three-dimensional geometry of molecules, or what is called *stereochemistry*. This has led organic chemists to make some giant strides in unraveling the complexities of natural products. Some of the most significant of these advances have been (1) the quantitative measurements of the *steric effect*; (2) the determination of the absolute configuration of some optically active molecules; (3) the development of methods for asymmetric induction; (4) the synthesis of highly strained molecules; (5) the synthesis of molecules with new types of molecular asymmetry; (6) the development of methods for conformational analysis; and (7) the elucidation of the stereochemical courses of certain chemical transformations. These developments form the basis of a series of volumes;[7] an extensive discussion here would be beyond the scope of this book.

It is recognized that molecules have certain spatial requirements because of the rigidity of covalent bonds and the repulsive forces arising when atoms are crowded together within van der Waals radii. Any infringement on these spatial demands can markedly alter the characteristic physical or chemical properties of a given molecule. Such modifications in molecular properties, resulting from a spatial crowding within the periphery of van der Waals radii, is referred to as the *steric effect*.

The steric effect was first recognized by Hofmann in 1872 when he found that tertiary amines with large alkyl groups will not form quaternary ammonium salts. Later, he found that *sym*-tetramethylbenzonitrile cannot be hydrolyzed in the usual manner as used, for example, in the hydrolysis of benzonitrile. The idea of attributing these anomalies to a mechanical obstruction of atoms was first brought forward by Kehrmann,[8] and the term *steric hindrance* was suggested by V. Meyer.[9] However, as will be shown,

[5] G. Ferguson and G. A. Sim, *Acta Cryst.,* **14,** 1262 (1961).

[6] J. Trotter, *Acta Cryst.,* **14,** 244 (1961).

[7] *Progress in Stereochemistry,* vol. 1, ed. W. Klyne, (New York: Academic Press, 1954); vol. 2 (1958) and vol. 3 (1962) ed. W. Klyne and P. B. D. de la Mare; see also D. J. Cram, *J. Chem. Educ.,* **37,** 317 (1960).

[8] F. Kehrmann, *Ber.,* **22,** 3315 (1888).

[9] V. Meyer, *Ber.,* **27,** 510 (1894).

the steric effect does not always hinder a reaction; it may also facilitate a given reaction.

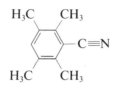

sym-tetramethyl-benzonitrile

It is well established now that the steric effect may have a pronounced influence on the physical properties and the chemical behavior of molecules. For illustration, some of the properties markedly affected by steric requirements may be listed as:

1. Internal rotations.
2. Polar character.
3. Bond distances.
4. Complex stability (CT complexes, inclusion compounds, chelates, etc.).
5. Chromatographic separations.[10]
6. Hydrogen bonding.
7. Molecular spectra (cf. Chap. 5).
8. Magnetic susceptibility (resulting from free radical stabilization).
9. Chemical reactivities and equilibria.
   (a) Acid and base strengths.
   (b) Additions to double bonds.
   (c) *Ortho* substitution.
   (d) Polarographic oxidations and reductions.[11]
   (e) Oxidation of hindered phenols.
   (f) Elimination reactions.

A discussion of all these effects alone could fill a book.[12] In the present textbook, the influence of steric effects on most of these properties is woven into the discussion of the property itself, e.g., spectra, resonance, hydrogen bonding, etc. Furthermore, some of the effects, e.g. polar character and bond distances, are indirect and arise through the influence of steric requirements on resonance. Therefore, only a few selected properties will be discussed in this chapter, and others are integrated into the discussion elsewhere.

[10] L. H. Klemm, *et al., J. Org. Chem.,* **24**, 1468 (1959), and earlier papers; J. K. Carlton and W. C. Bradbury, *J. Am. Chem. Soc.,* **78**, 1069 (1956); E. A. Johnson, *Steric Effects in Conjugated Systems*, ed. G. W. Gray (London: Butterworths, 1958), pp. 174 ff.

[11] L. H. Klemm, C. D. Lind, and J. T. Spence, *J. Org. Chem.,* **25**, 611 (1960); F. L. Lambert and K. Kobayashi, *J. Am. Chem. Soc.,* **82**, 5324 (1960).

[12] *Steric Effects in Organic Chemistry*, ed. M. S. Newman (New York: Wiley, 1956).

3.3. Steric hindrance to internal rotations.

3.3.1 CONFORMATIONAL ANALYSIS [13,14]

The crudeness of early experimental techniques prevented the isolation or detection of more than one isomer in substances like 1,2-dichloroethane. This gave rise to the concept of *free rotation* about single bonds. The powerful techniques of modern chemistry, such as the several diffraction methods (electron, X-ray, neutron) and the many forms of spectroscopy (infrared, Raman, microwave, ultraviolet, nuclear magnetic resonance, electron spin resonance, and optical rotatory dispersion) have revealed that certain preferred configurations are energetically favored and have a finite existence. For example, three distinct conformations of the 1,2-dichloroethane molecule are shown in Fig. 3.1. The term *conformation*, first used

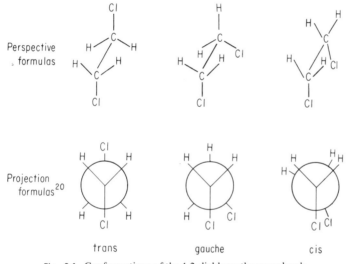

Fig. 3.1. Conformations of the 1,2-dichloroethane molecule.

by W. N. Haworth in 1929, refers to the various configurations of a molecule which differ in space by a rotation of two atoms about a single bond and are capable of finite existence. Less widely used terms are "constellation" in the German and Swiss literature, and "rotational isomers" from chemical physics. Isomers having different conformations are commonly called *conformers*. By conformational analysis, then, is meant the analysis of the physical and chemical properties of a compound in relation to its geometry and population of its conformers.

[13](a) E. L. Eliel, *Stereochemistry of Carbon Compounds* (New York: McGraw-Hill, 1962); (b) for other reviews, see E. L. Eliel, *J. Chem. Educ.*, **37**, 126 (1960); W. G. Dauben and K. S. Pitzer in *Steric Effects in Organic Chemistry*, ed. M. S. Newman, (New York: Wiley, 1956), chap. 1; D. H. R. Barton and R. C. Cookson, *Quart. Revs.*, **10**, 44 (1956).

[14] H. H. Lau, *Angew. Chem.*, **73**, 423 (1961).

It is often difficult or almost impossible to visualize the spatial relationships in molecules from their projections on a plane, in which case one must turn to the use of models. There are two general types of models in common use, the so called "ball and stick" models[15] and the scale models.[16] Fortunately, several schemes have been devised for representing the three-dimensional structures of molecules on a plane. For example, the Haworth and the Fischer diagrams are commonly used for indicating the configurations of a molecule but cannot be used well for showing different conformations. The Hermans[17] and the Newman[18] projection formulas are quite good for demonstrating conformations. If one rotates the grouping A—C—C—B about the C—C bond, there are six positions of particular interest. These are shown below with the use of Newman projection formulas.

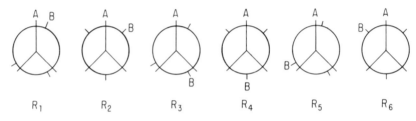

R_1 R_2 R_3 R_4 R_5 R_6

As one might expect, several terms are used in the literature in referring to these different conformations; the most prevalent are listed in Table 3.2.

Table 3.2. COMMON TERMS FOR DISTINGUISHING DIFFERENT

CONFORMATIONS OF $\overset{A}{\diagdown}C\!-\!C\overset{B}{\diagup}$

Symbol in text	German terms	American and British terms	Klyne-Prelog terms[19]
R_1	ekliptisch, verdeckt, planar-syn	fully eclipsed, *cis*, *s-cis* (or *cisoid*)	$\pm$ syn-periplanar ($\pm$ sp)
R_2	windschief, syn, schief-syn	*gauche*, skew	+ syn-clinal (+ sc)
R_3	teilweise verdeckt, schief-anti	partially eclipsed	+ anti-clinal (+ ac)
R_4	gestalt, planar-anti, auf Lücke	fully staggered, anti, *trans, s-trans* (or *transoid*)	$\pm$ anti-periplanar ($\pm$ ap)
R_5	teilweise verdeckt, schief-anti	partially eclipsed	− anti-clinal (− ac)
R_6	windschief, syn, schief-syn	*gauche*, skew	− syn-clinal (− sc)

The *s-cis* and *s-trans* terms have usually referred to conformations about a single bond having a significant double-bond character (cf. p. 227). It is to be noted that only the Klyne-Prelog scheme distinguishes R_2 from R_6, or R_3 from R_5. However, in many cases the terms *gauche*, *cis*, and *trans* can be used without ambiguity. Thus, the three conformations shown in Fig. 3.1 are commonly called the *trans*, *gauche*, and *cis* conformations.[21]   The Klyne-Prelog system for designating angles of rotation about a single bond is the result of dividing a circle in three different ways.

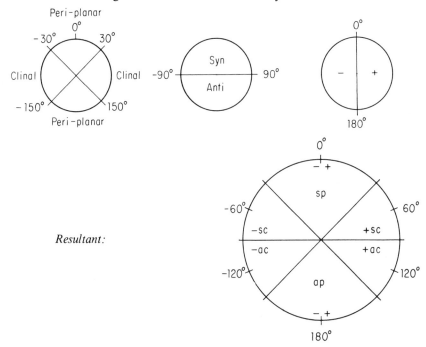

[15]The first and most common in the United States are the Brode models. Barton models (D. H. R. Barton, *Chem. and Ind.*, 1136 (1956)) are more recent. Petersen models (*Chem. Eng. News*, Oct. 12, 1959, p. 108) are made of neoprene to simulate the bending of chemical bonds. Dreiding models (A. S. Dreiding, *Helv. Chem. Acta*, **42**, 1339 (1959)), purchaseable from Fa. W. Büchi, Flawil, Switzerland, are quite effective for cyclic compounds.

[16]There are a host of scale models commercially available, most of which are fairly expensive. Some of the most prominent are the Hirschfelder-Taylor models, the Stuart-Briegleb models, and the Courtauld atomic models.

[17]P. H. Hermans, *Z. physik. Chem.*, **113**, 351 (1924).

[18]M. S. Newman, *J. Chem. Educ.*, **32**, 344 (1955).

[19]W. Klyne and V. Prelog, *Experientia*, **16**, 521 (1960).

[20]M. S. Newman, *J. Chem. Educ.*, **32**, 344 (1955).

[21]It is recognized that in a sense each molecule with an infinitesimal difference in angle of rotation about the C—C bond might be considered as a different conformer. This would mean that there are an infinite number of such conformers. For practical reasons, then, reference is made only to those conformations which have a possible finite existence.

For the grouping A—C—C—B, then, the conformation in which the angle formed by the A—C—C and C—C—B planes is 60° is designated +sc.

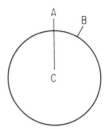

On this basis, as one looks along the axes of each C—C bond in cyclohexane, the partial conformations of each CH_2—CH_2 grouping are +sc, −sc, +sc, −sc, +sc, −sc for the chair conformer, +sc, −sc, +sp, +sc, −sc, +sp for the boat form, and +sp, +sp, −sc, +sp, +sp, −sc for the twist form.

In the transformation of 1,2-dichloroethane from one conformation to another, rotation takes place about the C—C bond and the atoms of one CH_2Cl group must approach and pass the atoms of the other CH_2Cl group. As rotation takes place, the repulsive forces increase[22]–forces between the bond dipoles, bonding electrons, and van der Waals repulsions–reach a maximum for the *cis* conformation, and then diminish. Simultaneously, the thermodynamic stability or potential energy of the molecules varies inversely with these interatomic repulsions, so that the *trans* isomer is the most stable and the *cis* isomer the least stable. Their relative stabilities can be represented by the diagram in Fig. 3.2, where the potential energy of the molecule is plotted against the angle ϕ between the Cl—C—C planes. A similar curve can be drawn for ethane in which the three valleys (minima) would be of equal depth.

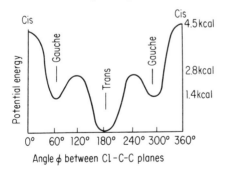

Fig. 3.2. Potential energy curve for rotation about the C—C bond of 1,2-dichloroethane.[24]

[22]The exact nature of these forces has not been clearly defined and several hypotheses have been offered. Cf. H. Eyring, D. M. Grant, and H. Hecht, *J. Chem. Educ.*, **39**, 466 (1962).

[23]E. B. Wilson, Jr., *Adv. Chem. Phys.*, **2**, 367 (1959).

[24](a) W. D. Gwinn and K. S. Pitzer, *J. Chem. Phys.*, **16**, 303 (1948); (b) H. J. Bernstein, *J. Chem. Phys.*, **17**, 262 (1949).

The thermodynamic properties of molecules can be calculated through statistical mechanics in which the contributions from translation, rotation, and vibrations are considered.[25] Such calculations are in good agreement with experimental measurements when applied to rigid molecules. Based on the concept of free rotation about single bonds, the application of the statistical method gave results in poor agreement with experimental values. It was first shown by Kemp and Pitzer[26] that the discrepancies can be attributed to the existence of a barrier to rotation about single bonds. The height of the barrier can be determined from the difference between the entropy calculated from heat capacity measurements and that computed by statistical mechanics (which assumes free internal rotation). The shape of the potential energy curve is obtained by developing a potential energy function which best reproduces the thermodynamic data.[25] This was done for 1,2-dichloroethane to give a barrier of 1.4 kcal/mole between the *trans* and *gauche* conformations.[26]

It can easily be seen with scale models of *cis*-1,2-dichloroethane that the two chlorine atoms would overlap if the normal bond distances and angles were maintained. The chlorine-chlorine distance has been calculated as a function of the angle ϕ between the Cl—C—C planes ($\phi = 180°$ for the *trans* conformation and $0°$ for the *cis*), and it was estimated that the two Cl atoms would be in contact at an angle of $\phi = 50°$.[24(a),27] This would make the energy barrier between the *gauche* and *cis* conformations approach infinity. However, the repulsion is relieved by the Cl atoms' bending back (widening the Cl—C—C bond angle) and by other bond deformations. These distortions require some energy, but the van der Waals repulsions decrease rapidly with small increases in interatomic distances, and the total potential energy of the molecule is minimized. For example, the difference in potential energy of the *cis* and *trans* conformations has been estimated to be 4.5 kcal/mole.[24(b)]

The thermodynamic method just discussed provided the first convincing evidence of the existence of energy barriers to internal rotations. The appearance of the several powerful physical methods for structure determination, such as the diffraction and spectroscopic techniques, has made a variety of experimental techniques available for quantitative measurements of these energy barriers. These methods have been summarized and reviewed recently.[23] Unfortunately, the reliability of some of these methods leaves much to be desired, and considerable refinement is necessary before a satis-

[25] J. G. Aston in *Determination of Organic Structures by Physical Methods*, ed. E. A. Braude and F. C. Nachod (New York: Academic, 1955), chap. 13.

[26] J. D. Kemp and K. S. Pitzer, *J. Chem. Phys.*, **4**, 749 (1936); *J. Am. Chem. Soc.*, **59**, 276 (1937).

[27] It has been found experimentally that the chlorine-chlorine distance is 4.4 Å for the *trans* isomer and 3.2 Å for the *gauche* isomer (W. Edgell and G. Glockler, *J. Chem. Phys.*, **9**, 376 (1941)).

factory theory of the origin of potential energy barriers may evolve or be rigorously tested.

The *energy differences* between conformations also have been measured by several methods. The average energy of a gas collision at room temperature is RT, or about 0.6 kcal. Consequently, at room temperature most of the molecules of 1,2-dichloroethane will have the *trans* configuration, while a small fraction of the molecules which happen to make unusually favorable collisions will have the *gauche* form. There is an equilibrium between the two isomers at any given temperature which will change with temperature; the proportion of the less stable *gauche* conformation increases with an elevation in temperature. The different conformations are characterized by having different infrared and Raman frequencies and different dipole moments, diffraction patterns,[28] and other properties. The relative amounts of light absorption by the two conformations, for example, are directly proportional to their relative amounts present. Hence, for the equilibrium between the *trans* and *gauche* conformations, the equilibrium constant, K, and the heat of isomerization, i.e. the difference in potential energies of the two conformers, can be determined from the absorbance of the characteristic absorption bands at two or more temperatures (see Sec. 5.5.1).

$$trans \rightleftharpoons gauche$$

$$K = \frac{C_g}{C_t} \tag{3-1}$$

$$A = C\epsilon \tag{3.2}$$

In Eq. (3-2), A is the absorbance, C is the molar concentration, and ϵ is the absorptivity. If one assumes that the change in the ratio of absorptivities with temperature change is insignificant, then the left side of the van 't Hoff equation

$$\frac{d(\ln K)}{d(1/T)} = \frac{-\Delta H}{RT}$$

can be replaced by the expression

$$\frac{d(\ln A_g/A_t)}{d(1/T)}$$

The slope of the line when the ratio of absorbances is plotted against

[28] J. D. McCullough, *J. Am. Chem. Soc.*, **62**, 480 (1940); D. P. Stevenson and V. Schomaker, *J. Am. Chem. Soc.*, **61**, 3173 (1939); J. Y. Beach and K. Y. Palmer, *J. Chem. Phys.*, **6**, 639 (1938).

$1/T$ will permit a calculation of ΔH, and the intercept of $1/T = 0$ will lead to a value for K.[29]

By an equivalent method, the variation with temperature of the dipole moment[30] or optical rotation[31] of a mixture of *trans* and *gauche* conformations will yield the isomerization energy ΔH. The results of several methods are listed in Table 3.3. It can be seen there that the energy difference between *trans* and *gauche* 1,2-dichloroethane in the liquid state is much

Table 3.3. ENERGY DIFFERENCES FOR THE *Trans* AND *Gauche* CONFORMATIONS OF 1,2-DICHLOROETHANE

Energy difference (kcal/mole)	Method
1.03, 1.32	Infrared, gas
1.48	Infrared, solution
1.21	Raman, and dipole moment
1.40	Heat capacity, gas
0	Raman, liquid

lower than the values for the gaseous state or in solution. An explanation for this difference has been offered by Mizushima[32] based on a hypothesis of Onsager[33] that a rigid dipole may induce dipoles in a closely packed medium which, in turn, affects the original dipole. As a result, the potential energy of a polar molecule will change when the molecule is placed in a more closely packed medium, and Onsager showed that the energy change can be estimated by

$$E = \frac{2(e - 1)}{2e + 1} \frac{\mu^2}{a^3} \tag{3.3}$$

[29] Cf. Y. Morino, K. Kuratani, and M. Katayama, *J. Chem. Phys.*, **18**, 754 (1950); H. J. Bernstein, *J. Chem. Phys.*, **18**, 897 (1950); **17**, 256 (1949); J. Powling and H. J. Bernstein, *J. Am. Chem. Soc.*, **73**, 1820 (1951); D. H. Rank, R. E. Kagarise, and D. W. E. Axford, *J. Chem. Phys.*, **17**, 1354 (1949); G. J. Szasz, N. Sheppard, and D. H. Rank, *J. Chem. Phys.*, **16**, 704 (1950).

[30] J. R. Thomas and W. D. Gwinn, *J. Am. Chem. Soc.*, **71**, 2785 (1949); C. T. Zahn, *Phys. Rev.*, **38**, 521 (1931); H. Gerding and P. G. Meerman, *Rec. trav. chim.*, **61**, 525 (1942).

[31] For the special case of rotation about an asymmetric carbon atom, the rotational isomerization energy can be determined by making measurements of optical activity at different temperatures. For example, H. J. Bernstein and E. E. Pederson (*J. Chem. Phys.*, **17**, 885 (1949)) found the energy barrier to rotation about the C_2—C_3 bond in *d-sec*-butyl alcohol to be 0.8 kcal/mole, and also determined the concentrations of the three isomers at 20°C to be 42.3 per cent, 42.3 per cent, and 15.3 per cent, respectively.

[32] Y. Morino, S. Mizushima, K. Kuratani, and M. Katayama, *J. Chem. Phys.*, **18**, 754 (1950).

[33] L. Onsager, *J. Am. Chem. Soc.*, **58**, 1486 (1936). Compare with a similar equation proposed by K. Higasi (*Sci. Papers Inst. Phys. Chem. Research, Tokyo*, **28**, 284 (1936)).

where e is the dielectric constant of the medium, μ is the dipole moment of the substance, and a is the molecular volume. Since *trans*-1,2-dichloroethane has no dipole moment, it does not undergo an energy change in the condensation. However, the *gauche* conformation has a moment and consequently becomes more stable in the liquid than in the gaseous state. This net stabilization of the *gauche* form with respect to the *trans* upon liquefaction has been estimated to be 1 kcal/mole.[32] This is in good agreement with the 1 to 1.4 kcal difference found for the gaseous state and the zero kcal difference found for the liquid state.[34] The energy differences between conformations of some other compounds are listed in Table 3.4.

Table 3.4. ENERGY DIFFERENCES BETWEEN *Gauche* AND *Trans* CONFORMATIONS OF SOME SUBSTITUTED ETHANES

Compound	ΔE (kcal/mole)
$FCH_2\!-\!CH_2F$	1.03–1.48
$ClCH_2\!-\!CH_2Br$	1.43–1.85
$BrCH_2\!-\!CH_2Br$	1.4 –2.0
$BrCH_2\!-\!CF_2Br$	0.7
$CH_3CH_2\!-\!CH_2CH_3$	.77
$CH_3CH_2\!-\!CH_2Cl$	−.05
$CH_3CH_2\!-\!CH_2Br$	−.1

It is to be realized that the procedures just discussed give energy differences between conformations, i.e., differences between potential energy minima on a chart like Figure 3.2. On the other hand, the statistical mechanical method gives the height of the energy barrier between conformations. When potential functions restricting rotation can be developed, energy barriers may also be determined from other properties such as dipole moments.[35] The statistical mechanical method offers the advantage of being applicable to compounds such as ethane where the rotation does not produce distinguishable conformations.

Nuclear magnetic resonance has been a valuable addition to the methods used in determining energy differences between conformations in equilibrium as well as energy barriers restricting rotations. The application of this technique is discussed in Sections 3.3.3 and 5.5.6.

In general, the *erytho* isomer is found to be more stable than the *threo* isomer of diastereoisomeric pairs in which differences in potential energy primarily are due to compression energy (i.e., van der Waals rather than dipole-dipole forces). The terms erythro and threo stem from a relationship to the sugars erythrose and threose:

[34] H. Gerding and P. G. Meerman, *Rec. trav. chim.*, **61**, 525 (1942); D. H. Rank, R. E. Kagarise, and D. W. E. Axford, *J. Chem. Phys.*, **17**, 1354 (1949).

[35] Cf. E. Rutner and S. H. Bauer, *J. Am. Chem. Soc.*, **82**, 298 (1960).

Erythrose   Threose

Both diastereoisomers have an eclipsed orientation but at least two sets of

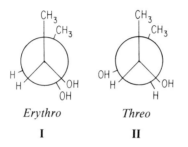

Erythro   Threo
I   II

similar substituents are side-by-side in the erythro isomer. Cram and
Elhafez[36] have tabulated the products of reduction of ketones (III) and
oximes (IV) with sodium in alcohol or with sodium amalgam, reagents that
are accepted as producing the more stable epimer,[37] and the erythro isomers (V and VI) are formed in the greater amounts.

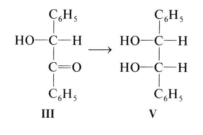

III   V

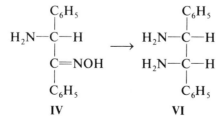

IV   VI

[36] D. J. Cram and F. A. A. Elhafez, *J. Am. Chem. Soc.*, **74**, 5828 (1952).
[37] D. H. R. Barton and R. Robinson, *J. Chem. Soc.*, 2045 (1954).

Similarly, equilibration of the *threo* acids (VII) gives the more stable *erythro* acids (VIII).

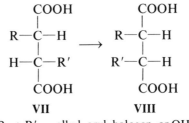

VII   VIII

R ≠ R′ = alkyl, aryl, halogen, or OH

The energy barriers restricting internal rotations within a number of molecules as measured by various procedures are listed in Table 3.5. It is

Table 3.5. ENERGY BARRIERS RESTRICTING INTERNAL ROTATIONS[38]

Compound	Barrier kcal/mole	Compound	Barrier kcal/mole
CH_3—CH_3[39]	3.04	Cl_3C—CCl_3	12.0
CH_3—CF_3[40]	3.45	Cl_3Si—$SiCl_3$	0
CF_3—CF_3[47]	4.35	CH_2Br—CH_2Br[45]	1.4–1.77
CH_3—SiF_3	1.2	$(CH_3)_2CHOH$	3.4
CH_3—CH_2OH[41]	3.0 (for CH_3)	$(CH_3)_2CO$	1.0
	1.0 (for OH)	$(CH_3)_2O$	3.1
CH_3OH	3.4	$(CH_3)_2S$	2.0
CH_3SH	1.5	$(CH_3)_2NH$	3.5
CH_3NH_2	3.0	C_6H_5—$CH{=}CH_2$	2.2
$(CH_3)_2Zn$	0	$CH_2{=}CH$—$CH{=}CH_2$[46]	5.0
$(CH_3)_4C$	4.3	C_2H_5—C_2H_5[48]	3.3
$(CH_3)_4Si$[42]	1.3		

interesting to note that there is essentially free rotation in dimethyl acetylene because the methyl groups are remote from each other. However, the table shows that rotations in most compounds will not be free nor com-

[38] K. S. Pitzer, *Chem. Revs.*, **27**, 39 (1940).

[39] D. R. Lide, Jr., *J. Chem. Phys.*, **29**, 1426 (1958).

[40] H. S. Gutowsky and H. B. Levine, *J. Chem. Phys.*, **18**, 1297 (1950).

[41] J. O. Halford, *J. Chem. Phys.*, **18**, 365 (1950).

[42] Y. Morino and M. Iwasaki, *J. Chem. Phys.*, **17**, 216 (1949).

[43] W. B. Smith and J. L. Massingill, *J. Am. Chem. Soc.*, **83**, 4301 (1961).

[44] The terms *s-trans* and *s-cis* refer to geometric isomerism about a single bond.

[45] H. J. Bernstein, *J. Chem. Phys.*, **18**, 897 (1950).

[46] J. G. Aston, G. J. Szasz, H. W. Wooley, and F. G. Brickwedde, *J. Chem. Phys.*, **14**, 67 (1946).

[47] E. L. Pace and J. G. Aston, *J. Am. Chem. Soc.*, **70**, 566 (1948).

[48] K. S. Pitzer, *J. Chem. Phys.*, **8**, 711 (1940).

pletely blocked, but restricted. The larger barrier in butadiene over that in butane can be attributed to the double-bond character of the central bond in butadiene.

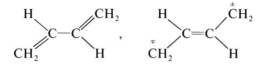

The compound consists of 96 per cent *s-trans* at room temperature,[43] and this conformer is more stable than the *s-cis* form by 2.3 kcal/mole.[44] This measurement is supported not only by quantum mechanical calculations,[49] but also by Raman data,[50] electron diffraction measurements,[51] and thermodynamic measurements.[46,48]

The same predominance of the *s-trans* form at room temperature has been found for conjugated aldehydes and ketones, except where there are opposing steric effects. For example, from diffraction studies,[52] glyoxal and dimethylglyoxal were found to exist primarily in the *s-trans* form. Electron diffraction data[53] have provided strong evidence that acrylaldehyde and crotonaldehyde each coexist in planar *s-cis* and *s-trans* conformations in ratios of 1:3 for the former at 35°C and 1:1 for crotonaldehyde at 70°C. On the other hand, steric requirements in phorone and mesityloxide cause the *s-cis* conformations to be the more stable at room temperature.[54]

Unusually strong intramolecular forces may sometimes increase the barrier to internal rotation in favor of one conformer. For examples, ethylene glycol and 2-aminoethanol exist largely in the *gauche* conformation owing to the presence of an intramolecular H bond. 2-Chloroethanol also has the *gauche* conformation but in this case the conformer is not stabilized by an intramolecular H bond as shown by its infrared spectrum.[56] Apparently, some intramolecular dipole forces favor the *gauche* conformation.

The butane molecule is an important one for later discussions. As with 1,2-dichloroethane, the only conformations to consider are the *trans* (IX) and two equivalent *gauche* conformations (X and XI). It has been estimated that the energy difference between the *trans* and *gauche* forms is 0.8

[49] R. S. Mulliken, *Revs. Mod. Phys.*, **14**, 265 (1942).

[50] K. Bradacs and L. Kahovec, *Z. physik. Chem.*, **B48**, 63 (1940); R. S. Rasmussen, D. D. Tunnicliff, and R. R. Brattain, *J. Chem. Phys.*, **11**, 432 (1943).

[51] V. Schomaker and L. Pauling, *J. Am. Chem. Soc.*, **61**, 1769 (1939).

[52] J. E. LuValle and V. Schomaker, *J. Am. Chem. Soc.*, **61**, 3520 (1939).

[53] H. Mackle and L. E. Sutton, *Trans. Faraday Soc.*, **47**, 695 (1951).

[54] J. B. Bentley, K. B. Evarard, R. J. B. Marsden, and L. E. Sutton, *J. Chem. Soc.*, 2957 (1949).

[55] D. Y. Curtin, *Rec. Chem. Progress*, **15**, 111 (1954).

[56] M. Kuhn, W. Lüttke, and R. Mecke, *Z. Anal. Chem.*, **170**, 106 (1959).

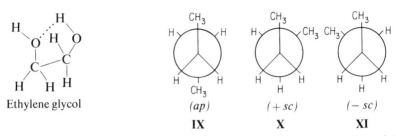

Ethylene glycol	*(ap)*	*(+sc)*	*(−sc)*
	IX	**X**	**XI**

kcal/mole, with the *trans* form predominating at room temperature and the *cis* conformation about 5 kcal/mole less stable than the *gauche.*[13(b)]

In addition to providing information about the relative stabilities of conformations, these foregoing concepts are of value in understanding and predicting the courses of certain reactions.[55] For illustration, in the dehalogenation of a *vic*-dihalide, the reaction goes easiest when the two carbon atoms and the two halogen atoms are coplanar, and the C-halogen bonds antiparallel, i.e., a *trans* elimination.[57] The conformation of the *meso* isomer of 2,3-dibromobutane which meets this requirement is XII, and XIII for the *dl* isomers. In XII there are two steric interactions, i.e., repulsions between groups larger than H, whereas in XIII there are three (two methyl-

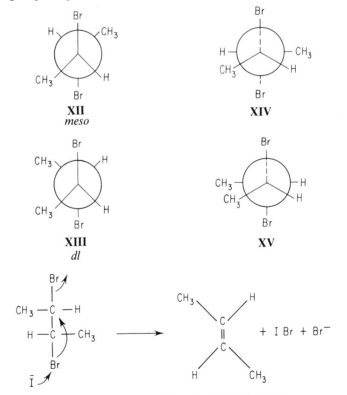

XII	**XIV**
meso	

XIII	**XV**
dl	

[57]D. H. R. Barton and E. Miller, *J. Am. Chem. Soc.*, **72**, 1066 (1950).

bromine and one methyl-methyl interaction). Hence, XIII should be less stable than XII. Furthermore, in the transition states of these isomers, that from XII has the CH_3 groups opposed to H atoms while the transition state from the *dl* isomers has two CH_3 groups opposed. This should make XV of higher energy than XIV. As a result, the energy difference between XII and XIV is smaller than that between XIII and XV, and having a smaller activation energy, XII should react the faster. This expectation is confirmed by the observation[58] that XII reacts twice as fast as XIII to give the *trans* 1,2 dimethylethylene. The *dl* forms, on the other hand, give the *cis* olefin.

Similarly, ring closures proceeding through an approximately planar transition state will, in general, be faster for the diastereoisomer reacting through the transition state where small groups are eclipsed than for the isomer where larger groups are eclipsed. That is, the reaction of XVI via XVII will be faster than that of XVIII via XIX, where S and L stand for

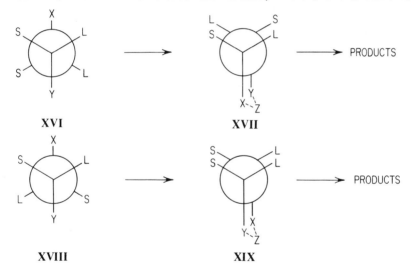

small and large groups, respectively. For example, acetone condenses with racemic dihydrobenzoin XX at a faster rate than with the *meso* isomer XXI.[59]

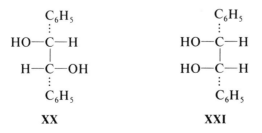

[58] W. G. Young, D. Pressman, and C. D. Coryell, *J. Am. Chem. Soc.*, **61**, 1640 (1939).
[59] P. H. Hermans, *Z. phys. Chem.*, **113**, 337 (1924).

3.3.2 ALICYCLIC SYSTEMS

The first explanation of the olefinic character of cyclopropane and of the differences in stability of the cycloalkanes with respect to ring size was offered by von Baeyer. He proposed that all rings are planar and that a ring strain arises from the distortion of the C—C—C bond angles from the normal tetrahedral angle.[60] He expressed this *bond angle strain* in terms of the angle deviation d according to the relationship:

$$d = \tfrac{1}{2}\left(109°28' - \overset{\displaystyle C \diagdown \diagup C}{\underset{\displaystyle C}{}} \text{ angle}\right).$$

Thus, assuming the rings to be regular polygons, d for the lower cycloalkanes would be:

	d		d
C_3	24°44′	C_5	0°44′
C_4	9°44′	C_6	−5°16′
		C_7	−9°33′

At least Baeyer's proposal accounts for the well-known olefinic character of cyclopropyl derivatives (see Sect. 4.5) such as their tendency to add halogens, undergo a Diels-Alder reaction, and exhibit conjugation with attached C=C or C=O bonds. However, Baeyer's notion does not explain the lack of strain in cyclohexane nor the much greater stability of cycloheptane over that of cyclobutane.

We saw in Figure 1.20 that of two similar compounds, the more stable compound has the smaller heat of combustion. Accordingly, the total strain in the cycloalkane molecules should be reflected in their heats of combustion. The heats of combustion per CH_2 for n-alkanes is 157.4 kcal/mole, whereas for the cycloalkanes it is as shown in Table 3.6.[61] From these data one may calculate the total strain in the cycloalkane rings as shown in the table. It can be seen that the ring strain varies considerably as it passes through a minimum with the normal size rings, through a maximum with the medium-size rings, and falls off again with the large rings.[62] Apparently, there are marked differences in intramolecular forces within the molecules to affect their relative stabilities.

[60]For a compilation of bond angles and interatomic distances in small ring molecules, see E. Goldish, *J. Chem. Educ.*, **36**, 408 (1959).

[61]J. Coops, H. van Kamp, W. A. Lambregets, J. Visser, and H. Dekker, *Rec. trav. Chim.*, **79**, 1226 (1960).

[62]Rings are classified according to the number of atoms in the ring as follows: *small* = 3-4 atoms, *normal* = 5-7, *medium* = 8-11, and *large* = 12 or more. The original proposal

Since the C_5 ring appears to have only a small bond angle strain, some of its instability relative to C_6 must be due to a different source. As to be discussed presently, cyclohexane exists in a *chair* conformation in which each CH_2 has an sc (staggered) orientation with respect to the two adjacent methylene groups. Thus, there is a minimum repulsive interaction between

Table 3.6   HEATS OF COMBUSTION PER CH_2 AND
TOTAL STRAIN FOR CYCLOALKANES[61]

n	H_c/n	Total strain $n \cdot (H_c/n - 157.4)$
3	166.6	27.6 kcal/mole
4	164	26.2
5	158.7	6.5
6	157.4	0
7	158.3	6.3
8	158.6	9.6
9	158.8	12.6
10	158.6	12.0
11	158.4	11.0
12	157.7	3.6
13	157.8	5.2
14	157.4	0
15	157.5	1.5
16	157.5	1.6
17	157.2	−3.4

n = number of carbon atoms in ring.
H_c = heat of combustion in kcal/mole.

adjacent CH_2 groups. Inasmuch as each group is also free of Baeyer strain, cyclohexane has the lowest potential energy of the lower alkanes. If cyclopentane were to have a planar structure, each CH_2 would be eclipsed with the two adjacent methylene groups. This would produce considerable repulsive interaction similar to that present in fully eclipsed ethane (Pitzer strain). This Pitzer strain could be relieved by a puckering of the ring which would be attended by an increase in the Baeyer strain. The net result is that the ring puckers slightly to the extent that the total strain is a minimum.[63] However, the puckering does not produce a fixed nonplanar ring. There is

of this terminology (V. Prelog and H. C. Brown, *J. Am. Chem. Soc.*, **73**, 212 (1950)) designated 8–12 member rings as medium-size but in view of the subsequent finding that C_{12} rings do not exhibit transannular effects, the term medium ring is reserved for the 8–11 membered rings.

[63] J. G. Aston, S. C. Schumann, H. L. Fink, and P. M. Doty, *J. Am. Chem. Soc.*, **63**, 2029 (1941).

a "pseudo rotation" in which the puckering rotates around the ring and no one or two carbon atoms are exclusively out of the plane of the others.[64]

Two nonplanar configurations of the C_5 ring are the envelope and the half-chair forms. The half-chair is formed by C_3 and C_4 twisting above and

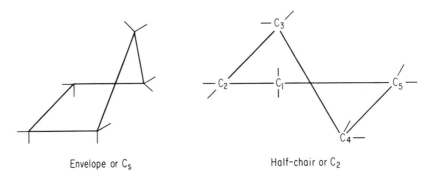

Envelope or C_s Half-chair or C_2

below the plane of the C_2—C_1—C_5 carbons, respectively. These configurations have no finite existence for cyclopentane, but some of its derivatives have one or the other conformation. For example, sucrose and bicyclo-[1,3] hexane are reported to have the envelope structure and cyclopentanone and 1,2-O-isopropylidene furanose derivatives have the half-chair form.[65]

The C_6 ring could conceivably have several shapes.

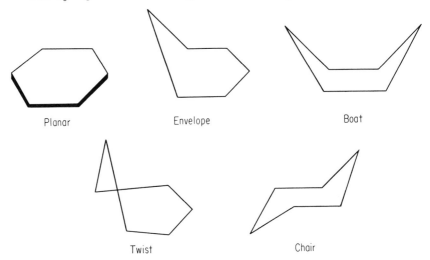

Planar   Envelope   Boat

Twist   Chair

[64] K. S. Pitzer and W. E. Donath, *J. Am. Chem. Soc.,* **81,** 3213 (1959); J. P. McCullough, R. E. Pennington, J. C. Smith, I. A. Hossenlopp, and G. Waddington, *J. Am. Chem. Soc.,* **81,** 5880 (1959).

[65] F. V. Brutcher, Jr., T. Roberts, S. J. Barr, and N. Pearson, *J. Am. Chem. Soc.,* **81,** 4915 (1959), and references cited therein; R. J. Abraham, K. A. McLauchlan, L. D. Hall, and L. Hough, *Chem. and Ind. (London),* 213 (1962).

Spectral,[66] electron diffraction,[67] and thermodynamic considerations convincingly support the premise that the chair form is the most stable of these five configurations, and at room temperature, cyclohexane exists entirely in the chair conformation.[67,68] The boat, twist, and chair forms are each free of bond angle strain but the chair form possesses the least Pitzer strain. Several approaches have been used to esimate the energy difference between the chair and the boat conformations; values range from 1.31 to 10.6 kcal/mole.[69] A simple view, for example, is to consider the boat form as having two C—C bonds of the *cis*-ethane structure. The Pitzer strain is then at least twice the internal rotational barrier of ethane or approximately 6.0 kcal/mole. This calculation, however, neglects the nonbonded repulsion between the abutting H's on the bow and stern C atoms, which are extremely close together. The best experimental value for the difference is

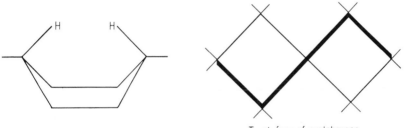

Twist form of cyclohexane

about 5.5 kcal/mole.[70] Even so, it seems likely that the twist conformation is energetically favored over the boat conformation because not only is it bond-angle strainless (as is also the boat conformation) but it does not have the bow-stern abutting hydrogen repulsion and there is some decrease in eclipsed ethane-type interactions.[70] Thus, when cyclohexane or its derivatives assume what is commonly considered to be the boat conformation, the molecules may actually have the more stable twist conformation. One example has been found for substituted *cis*-1,4-cyclohexanediols.[71] Examination of models of 1,4-cyclohexanediols indicates that intramolecular H bonding can occur only when the OH groups are *cis* and then only if the ring has a non-chair conformation. Spectral data on 2,5-di-*t*-butyl-1,4-cyclohexanediol reveal the presence of two or more conformations, with

[66] K. W. F. Kohlrausch, *et al.*, *Z. physik. Chem.*, **B48**, 177 (1941); R. S. Rasmussen, *J. Chem. Phys.*, **11**, 249 (1943).

[67] O. Hässel and H. Viervoll, *Acta Chem. Scand.*, **1**, 929 (1947); *Research*, **3**, 504 (1950).

[68] P. Hazebroek and L. J. Oosterhoff, *Disc. Faraday Soc.*, **10**, 87 (1951).

[69] R. B. Turner, *J. Am. Chem. Soc.*, **74**, 2118 (1952); K. Ito, *J. Am. Chem. Soc.*, **75**, 2430 (1953).

[70] W. S. Johnson, V. J. Bauer, J. L. Margrave, M. A. Frisch, L. H. Dreger, and W. N. Hubbard, *J. Am. Chem. Soc.*, **83**, 606 (1961).

[71] R. D. Stolow, *J. Am. Chem. Soc.*, **83**, 2592 (1961).

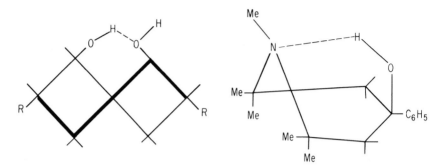

at least one having an intramolecular H bonded twist conformation. Also, the ring of 4-hydroxy-1,2,2,6,6-pentamethyl-4-phenylpiperdine may have a twist rather than a boat conformation as reported on the basis of intramolecular H bonding.[72]

The chair conformation of cyclohexane has a six-fold axis of symmetry which divides the twelve C—H bonds into two types. Six parallel the axis as in **XXII** and are called *axial* (symbolized *a*), while six radiate outward at angles of 109.5° to the axis as shown in **XXIII** and are called *equatorial* (symbolized *e*).[73] The cyclohexane ring is quite flexible and the chair conformation may invert from one chair (**XXIV**) into another chair form (**XXV**).[74] The energy barrier to this transformation is approximately 10

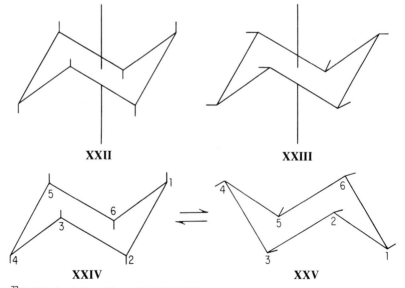

XXII   **XXIII**

XXIV   **XXV**

[72] R. E. Lyle, *J. Org. Chem.*, **22**, 1280 (1957).

[73] D. H. R. Barton, O. Hässel, K. S. Pitzer, and V. Prelog, *Science*, **119**, 49 (1954).

[74] For a review of the stereochemistry of six-member ring systems, see H. D. Orloff, *Chem. Revs.*, **54**, 426 (1954); W. Klyne, *Progress in Stereochemistry*, vol. 1 (New York: Academic, 1954), chap. 2; D. H. R. Barton, *J. Chem. Soc.*, 1027 (1953).

kcal/mole.[75] All bonds which were axial in **XXIV** are equatorial in **XXV** and those which were equatorial in **XXIV** are axial in **XXV**. This may be visualized by the use of Newman projection formulas **XXVI** and **XXVII**, in which the carbon atoms are numbered. The two forms are perfectly equivalent and indistinguishable when all atoms on carbon are identical.

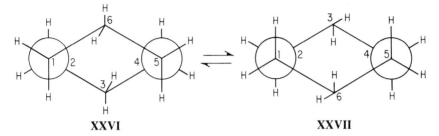

XXVI   **XXVII**

    In a monosubstituted cyclohexane, the substituent may occupy an axial or an equatorial position as in **XXVIII** or **XXIX**. A study of scale models shows that the axial CH_3 is closer to the axial H's on the same side of the ring (1 : 3 interactions) than the equatorial CH_3 is to the adjacent equatorial or axial H's (1 : 2 interactions). In **XXVIII**, there are two $CH_3 : CH_2$ interactions comparable to the $CH_3 : CH_3$ interactions in *gauche-n*-butane and

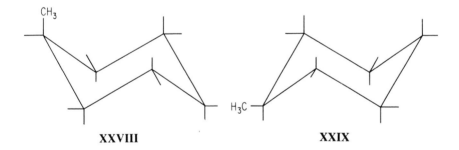

XXVIII   **XXIX**

none in **XXIX**. Accordingly, **XXIX** should be more stable than **XXVIII** by twice the *gauche-trans* energy difference for *n*-butane or about 1.6 kcal/ mole. This compares well with the value of 1.8 kcal estimated from thermodynamic data.[76] Electron diffraction measurements also provide evidence that the equatorial conformation of a monosubstituted cyclohexane is the more stable.[77] However, in most monosubstituted cyclohexanes the ring is very flexible, i.e., the energy barrier between the two chair conformations is small, and both forms exist in appreciable proportions. For example, cyclohexanol in CS_2 solution exists about 65 per cent in the equatorial

[75] R. K. Harris and N. Sheppard, *Proc. Chem. Soc. (London)*, 419 (1961); F. R. Jensen, D. S. Noyce, C. H. Sederholm, and A. J. Berlin, *J. Am. Chem. Soc.*, **82**, 1256 (1960).

[76] C. W. Beckett, K. S. Pitzer, and R. Spitzer, *J. Am. Chem. Soc.*, **69**, 977, 2488 (1947).

[77] O. Hässel, *Research*, **3**, 504 (1950).

conformation[78] and cyclohexyl bromide in CCl_4 solution has an 80 per cent equatorial content.[79]

As a consequence of the stronger 1:3 diaxial repulsive forces, mono- and disubstituted cyclohexanes will preferably assume the following con- formations:

Monosubstituted: XXX rather than XXXI.
trans-1,2-Disubstituted: XXXII rather than XXXIII.
cis-1,3-Disubstituted: XXXIV rather than XXXV.
trans-1,4-disubstituted: XXXVI rather than XXXVII.

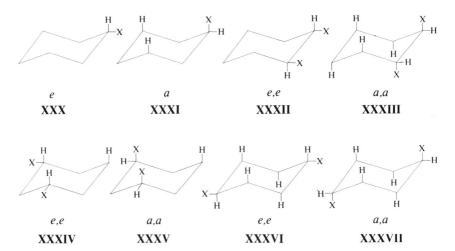

e	*a*	*e,e*	*a,a*
XXX	**XXXI**	**XXXII**	**XXXIII**

e,e	*a,a*	*e,e*	*a,a*
XXXIV	**XXXV**	**XXXVI**	**XXXVII**

These expectations are confirmed through the extensive studies of Hässel and coworkers on the electron diffraction of cyclohexane derivatives in the vapor phase,[80] and by other types of physical studies.

With more than two groups on the cyclohexane ring, the all-equatorial isomer becomes increasingly the more stable conformation because it places the groups the farthest apart.[81] For example, menthol exists almost en- tirely in the all-equatorial form (XXXVIII). An all-axial 1,3,5-trisub- stituted cyclohexane is unknown to the author.

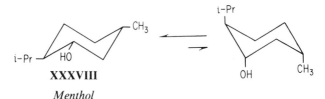

XXXVIII

Menthol

[78]R. A. Pickering and C. C. Price, *J. Am. Chem. Soc.*, **80**, 4931 (1958).
[79]G. G. LeFevre, *et al.*, *Proc. Chem. Soc. (London)*, 117 (1960).
[80]Cf. O. Hässel, *Quart. Revs.*, **7**, 221 (1953).
[81]N. L. Allinger and M. A. Miller, *J. Am. Chem. Soc.*, **83**, 2145 (1961).

It is possible, of course, that strong polar forces or H bonding may preferentially stabilize the diaxial over the diequatorial conformation. For example, electrostatic repulsion forces the dianion of cyclohexane-1,2-dicarboxylic acid to assume the diaxial (XXIX) rather than the diequatorial (XL) conformation,[83] and *trans*-1,2-dihalocyclohexanes exist as mixtures of the *e,e* and *a,a* conformations.[82] Also, H bonding, as confirmed by infrared spectral data, holds the *cis*-1,3-cyclohexanediol in a diaxial (XLI) conformation in preference to the diequatorial form.

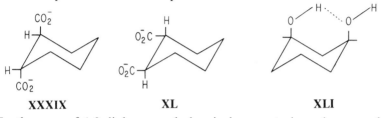

| XXXIX | XL | XLI |

In the case of 1,2-diols, several chemical reagents have been used to distinguish *cis* and *trans* orientations. However, it has been shown that even lead tetraacetate, which has been studied the most widely, does not provide a reliable measure of the proximity of adjacent OH groups. In dilute carbon tetrachloride, cyclic 1,2-diols exhibit two hydroxyl infrared bands, one for the free OH and one for the H-bonded OH. The closer the OH groups are, the stronger is the H-bond and the larger the difference $\Delta \nu$ between the infrared frequencies. An empirically drawn relationship between $\Delta \nu$ and the H$\cdots$O distance of the O—H$\cdots$O bond was developed[85] which serves as a good index of the distance between hydroxyl groups of 1,2-diols.[84] For example, the $\Delta \nu$ values for *cis* and *trans* cyclohexanediol reveal that *a,e* OH groups of the *cis* isomer are closer together than the *e,e* OH groups of the *trans* isomer.

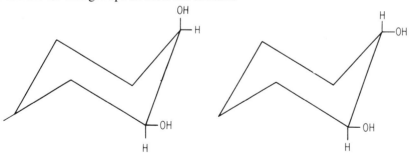

[82] K. Kozima and T. Yoshino, *J. Am. Chem. Soc.,* **75,** 166 (1953); M. Kilpatrick and J. G. Morse, *J. Am. Chem. Soc.,* **75,** 1846 (1953); H. D. Smith and F. P. Byrne, *J. Am. Chem. Soc.,* **72,** 4406 (1950).

[83] R. Gane and C. K. Ingold, *J. Chem. Soc.,* 2153, 2179 (1931).

[84] H. Kwart and W. G. Vosburgh, *J. Am. Chem. Soc.,* **76,** 5400 (1954).

[85] L. P. Kuhn, *J. Am. Chem. Soc.,* **74,** 2492 (1952); S. Julia, D. Varech, Th. Bürer, and H. H. Günthard, *Helv. Chim. Acta,* **43,** 1623 (1960).

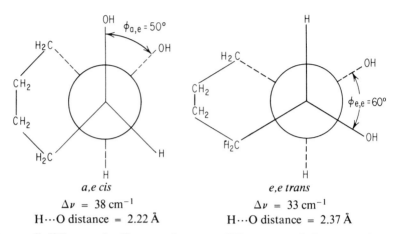

a,e cis
$\Delta\nu = 38\ \text{cm}^{-1}$
H···O distance = 2.22 Å

e,e trans
$\Delta\nu = 33\ \text{cm}^{-1}$
H···O distance = 2.37 Å

The small difference in distances between OH groups of the *cis* and *trans* isomers is critical enough to prevent the *trans* isomer from forming an acetonide, although the *cis* isomer does.

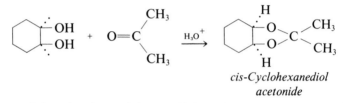

cis-Cyclohexanediol
acetonide

The spectral data for the cyclohexanediols and several others are given in Table 3.7. It is noteworthy that the H···O distance in 1,2-cyclopentanediol is longer than that in the bicycloheptane ring, where the two OH groups are forced to be eclipsed, and this substantiates the premise reached from heats of combustion (p. 231) that the cyclopentane ring is slightly puckered.

Although the equatorial conformer of a substituted cyclohexane is thermodynamically more stable than the axial form, the molecule may react in either conformation since the isomerization barrier is much less than the activation energies for most reactions. Thus, complete kinetics for reactions of flexible ring compounds must be in terms of the rates of reaction of the equatorial and axial conformations,

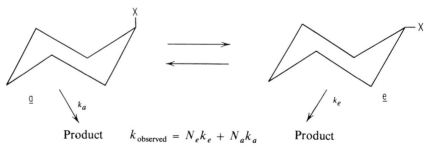

Product $k_{\text{observed}} = N_e k_e + N_a k_a$ Product

Table 3.7.   INFRARED SPECTRAL DATA ON SOME 1,2-DIOLS[85]

| Compound | ν_{OH} (cm^{-1}) | | $\Delta\nu_{OH}$ (cm^{-1}) | Calc'd H$\cdots$O distance, Å |
	Free	H-bonded		
	3634	3602	32	2.36
	3626	3587	39	2.22
	3633	3572	61	1.84
	3633	3531	102	1.42
	3632	3539	103	1.41

where N and k are the respective mole fractions and rate constants of the equatorial and axial conformations. The general kinetics for such a system were independently worked out by Winstein and Holness[87] and Eliel and Ro.[88] The equations developed by either group may be used to determine the equilibrium ratio K of the equatorial and axial conformations when the mixture cannot be resolved, and also specific rate constants for each conformation. By studying the variation of these constants with temperature, one may obtain the free energy difference between the e and a conformations, which is commonly designated the A value.[87] Since the two forms have discrete infrared absorption bands, a measurement of the change of intensity of the absorption bands as a function of temperature will give the enthalpy (not free energy) difference between the two conformers.[89] Proton resonance,[90] complexation,[91] and other equilibration methods[92] have been used to determine A values. Although the results show considerable variations, the approximate values for a few groups are as follows:[92]

Group	A value (kcal/mole)
CH_3	1.8
C_2H_5	1.86
OH	0.4–0.96
OCH_3	0.74
OC_2H_5	0.98
COOH	1.6–1.9

An ingenious technique for obtaining conformational homogeneity was developed by Winstein and Holness by introducing a t-butyl group into the ring.[87] The large, bulky t-butyl group retains the *cis*- (XLII) or *trans*-substituted t-butyl-cyclohexane (XLIII) in a fixed conformation.

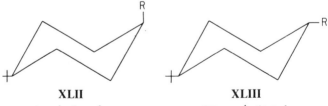

XLII	XLIII
cis-substituted	*trans-substituted*
t-butylcyclohexane	*t-butylcyclohexane*

[86]L. P. Kuhn, *J. Am. Chem. Soc.*, **74**, 2492 (1952).

[87]S. Winstein and N. J. Holness, *J. Am. Chem. Soc.*, **77**, 5562 (1955).

[88]E. L. Eliel and R. S. Ro, *Chem. and Ind. (London)*, 251 (1956); *J. Am. Chem. Soc.*, **79**, 5992 (1957).

[89]E. L. Eliel, *J. Chem. Educ.*, **37**, 126 (1960).

[90]L. W. Reeves and K. O. Strömme, *Can. J. Chem.*, **38**, 1241 (1960); A. J. Berlin and F. R. Jensen, *Chem. and Ind. (London)*, 998 (1960).

[91]S. J. Angyal and D. J. McHugh, *Chem. and Ind. (London)*, 1147 (1956).

[92]D. S. Noyce and L. J. Dolby, *J. Org. Chem.*, **26**, 3619 (1961); N. L. Allinger and S-E. Hu, *J. Am. Chem. Soc.*, **84**, 370 (1962).

Cyclohexanone, too, has a flexible chair configuration, and a substituent in the α position may occupy an axial or equatorial position. With a polar substituent in the α position, dipole-dipole forces operate in addition to van der Waals forces and the former may be the greater. At a given temperature, there is an equilibrium between the equatorial (XLIV) and the

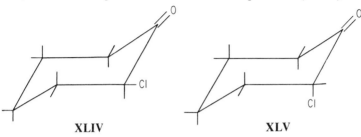

XLIV   XLV

axial (XLV) conformations with (XLV) being the more stable. This equilibrium is not only temperature dependent but is also affected by the solvent and the concentration. The tendency of a halogen to take an equatorial conformation when α to a carbonyl group decreases in the order F, Cl, Br. That is, the fluorine atom can most easily be forced into the e conformation. This is the order to be expected on a basis of size of the halogen atoms (van der Waals forces) and opposite to the order predicted on a basis of polar effects.[94] Since XLV has the smaller dipole moment and potential energy, an increase in solvent polarity or an increase in temperature shifts the equilibrium towards the equatorial conformation (XLIV).[93]

Inasmuch as an α halogen atom of cyclohexanone prefers to be axial and a β-methyl group prefers to be equatorial, the two forces oppose one another in *trans*-2-bromo-5-methylcyclohexanone and the compound can be expected to exist in solution as a mixture of XLVI t,e and XLVI t,a. The *cis*-isomer too could exist as XLVI c,a and XLVI c,e, where the first italic letter denotes configuration (c = cis, t = trans) and the second refers to the orientation of the halogen atom (a = axial, e = equatorial). Experimental analyses of the conformational composition of XLVI t indicate an e/a ratio of about 60 : 40 in heptane solution, which increases to 80 : 20 in more

[93] N. L. Allinger, J. Allinger, *et al.*, *J. Am. Chem. Soc.*, **82**, 5876 (1960).

[94] An alternative suggestion was made that XLV' makes a significant contribution to the resonant hybrid (E. J. Corey and H. J. Burke, *J. Am. Chem. Soc.*, **77**, 5418 (1955)). Since

such resonance would decrease in the order Br, Cl, F, and could best occur when the halogen is axial, the effect of the resonance would be to shift the XLIV $\rightleftharpoons$ XLV equilibrium to the right to the greatest degree for the bromo derivative and the least for the fluoro compound. This order of contribution from XLV' would parallel the order for the content of the equatorial conformation in the equilibrium mixtures.

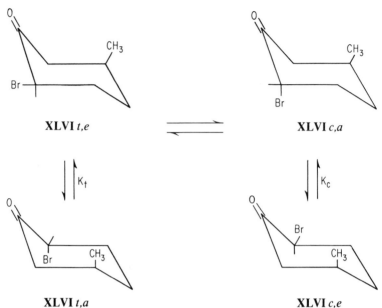

polar solvents.[95] In the 3,3-dimethyl-2-bromocyclohexanone, dipolar repulsion outweighs the steric effect and the compound exists predominantly with an axial bromine. On the other hand, 1,3-diaxial repulsion exceeds the dipolar forces in the 4,4-dimethyl isomer and the compound exists

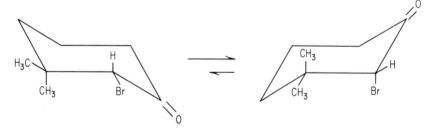

chiefly with an equatorial bromine atom. Similarly, 1,3-diaxial forces in 2,6-dibromocyclohexanones outweigh bromine-carbonyl dipolar forces and the bromines have diequatorial orientations as in XLVII.[96]

It can be seen, then, that Pitzer and Baeyer strains have a profound influence on the conformations and properties of C_5 and C_6 ring compounds. Of course, Baeyer strain accounts for much of the strain in C_3 and C_4 compounds. Nevertheless, the C—C bond distances are unusually long

[95] N. L. Allinger, et al., J. Org. Chem., 25, 6 (1960).
[96] C. Djerassi, N. Finch, R. C. Cookson, and C. W. Bird, J. Am. Chem. Soc., 82, 5488 (1960).

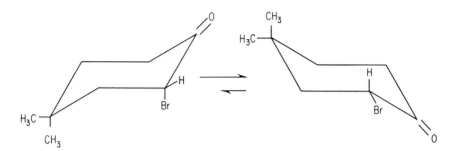

(> 1.56 Å) in cyclobutane and many of its derivatives, and the rings are nonplanar.[97] This has been attributed to Pitzer strain.

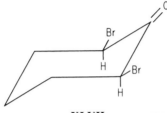

XLVII

In contrast to the acyclic compounds, whose properties usually change smoothly with chain length, most of the properties of the alicyclic compounds pass through a maximum or minimum in the range of the medium-size rings.[98] For example, in addition to the aforementioned strain energy reaching a maximum at C_9, it has been observed that the density and refractive index of the cycloalkanol acetates are a maximum at C_9. The rate of solvolysis of the p-toluenesulfonates of the cyclanols is a maximum at C_{10}; the dissociation constants of the $(CH_2)_n NH_2^+$ salts reach a maximum in the medium-size ring range; the refractive indices and ultraviolet λ_{max} values for the 1,3-cycloalkadienes pass through a minimum at the C_9 diene; the rates of reduction of cyclanones with sodium borohydride are the slowest with the C_{10} ketone.[99] Whereas cyclohexanone cyanohydrin hardly dissociates at all, cyclodecanone does not add HCN to form the cyanohydrin. These and many other unusual properties of the medium-size ring compounds can be attributed to the shapes of their rings.[100] In cyciodecane (XLVIII), for example, the ring has a very rigid conformation with some

[97] J. D. Dunitz and V. Schomaker, *J. Chem. Phys.*, **20**, 1703 (1952); H. P. Lemaire and R. L. Livingston, *J. Am. Chem. Soc.*, **74**, 5732 (1952); A. Almennigen, O. Bastiansen, et al, *Acta Chem. Scand.* **15**, 711 (1961).

[98] V. Prelog, *J. Chem. Soc.*, 420 (1950); *Angew. Chem.*, **70**, 145 (1958).

[99] H. C. Brown and K. Ichikawa, *Tetrahedron*, **1**, 221 (1957).

[100] J. D. Dunitz and V. Prelog, *Angew. Chem.*, **72**, 896 (1960).

C—C—C bond angles larger than the tetrahedral angle and with some transannular hydrogen atoms (on $C_1 + C_4 + C_7$ and $C_2 + C_6 + C_9$) closer

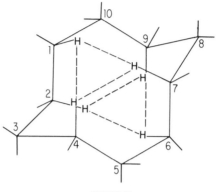

XLVIII

together (1.83 to 2.10 Å) than van der Waals distances (2.8 Å).[101] This proximity of the atoms across the ring in the medium-size rings is also revealed by some of their chemical and physical properties.[107] For instance, transannular hydride shifts, electrophilic attack, and nucleophilic substitution occur in numerous ring systems. Several examples are given below.

(i) **Hydride shifts.** Transannular hydride shifts were first demonstrated simultaneously by V. Prelog[104] and A. C. Cope[105] and their coworkers. For

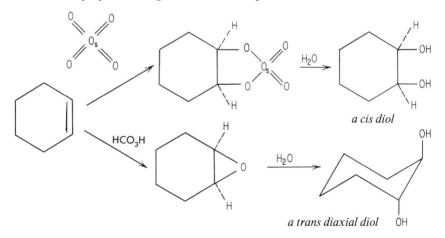

a cis diol

a trans diaxial diol

[101]J. D. Dunitz and H. M. M. Shearer, *Helv. Chim. Acta,* **43,** 18 (1960).

[102]J. Sicher, J. Zavada, and M. Svoboda, *Proc. Chem. Soc. (London),* 199 (1961).

[103](a). V. Prelog, *et al., Helv. Chim. Acta,* **36,** 341 (1953); (b): K. Schenker and V. Prelog, *ibid.,* **36,** 896 (1953).

[104]V. Prelog and K. Schenker, *Helv. Chim. Acta,* **35,** 2044 (1952).

[105]A. C. Cope, S. W. Fenton, and C. F. Spencer, *J. Am. Chem. Soc.,* **74,** 5884 (1952).

illustration, most cyclic alkenes react with osmium tetroxide to produce a *cis* diol and with performic acid to yield a *trans* diaxial diol. The C_6, C_7, and C_{12} cycloalkenes react in this manner but C_8–C_{11} give a mixture of products some of which arise by transannular hydride shifts. Thus, solvolysis of *trans*-cyclodecene oxide gives 1,6-cyclodecanediol rather than the 1,2-diol.[103a]

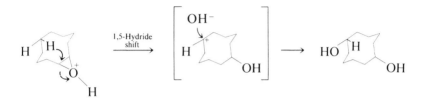

Similarly, the addition of bromine to *cis* and *trans*-cyclodecene gives *cis*- and *trans*-1,6-dibromocyclodecane, respectively, instead of the normal 1,2-dibromo addition product.[102]

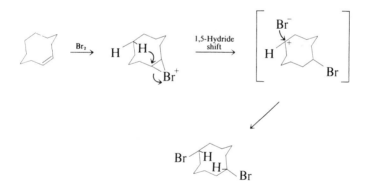

In the C_8 ring, for example, the solvolysis of *cis*-cyclooctene oxide (XLIX) with formic acid followed by alkaline hydrolysis of the monoformate yields *cis*-1,4-cyclooctanediol (L), 3-cyclooctene-1-ol (LI), 4-cyclooctene-1-ol (LII), the expected *trans*-1,2-cyclooctanediol (LIII), and other minor products.[106(a)]

[106](a) A. C. Cope, G. A. Berchtold, P. E. Peterson, and S. H. Sharman, *J. Am. Chem. Soc.*, **82**, 6366 (1960); (b) A. C. Cope, R. J. Cotter, and G. G. Roller, *J. Am. Chem. Soc.*, **77**, 3590, 3594 (1955); (c) A. C. Cope, D. C. McLean, and N. A. Nelson, *J. Am. Chem. Soc.*, **77**, 1628 (1955); (d) N. L. Allinger, *et al., J. Am. Chem. Soc.*, **83**, 1974 (1961).

[107]Cf. J. Sicher, "The Stereochemistry of Many Membered Rings," in *Progress in Stereochemistry*, vol. 3, ed. W. Klyne and P. B. D. de la Mare (New York: Academic, 1962), chap. 6. For a concise survey of transannular effects, see R. A. Raphael, *Proc. Chem. Soc. (London)*, 97 (1962).

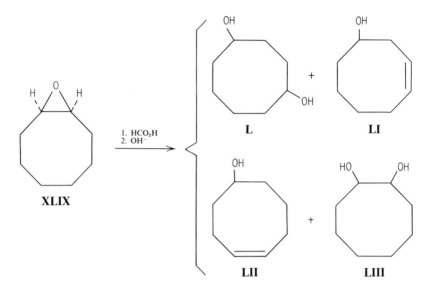

L   LI

XLIX

LII   LIII

Formation of the transannular products L–LII involves rearrangement of the oxonium ion LIV to the carbonium ion LV by a 1,3-hydride shift or to LVI by a 1,5-hydride shift.

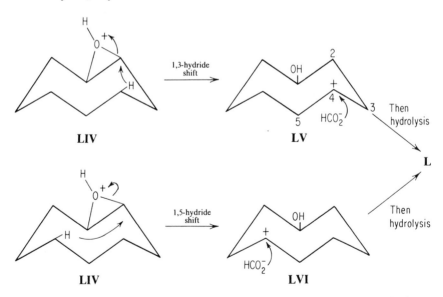

LIV   LV

LIV   LVI

L

Then, attack of a solvent molecule at C_4 of LV or at C_6 of LVI would form the ester of L. On the other hand, elimination of a proton from C_3 of LV or from C_7 of LVI would produce LI, and elimination of a proton from C_5 of LV or LVI would give LII. For example:

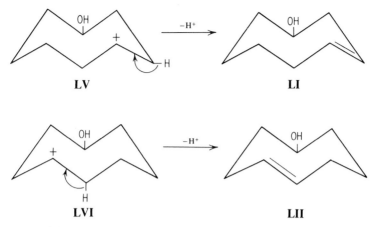

The course of the reaction was elucidated by the use of deuterium labeling at the C_5 and C_6 positions.[106] Thus, with *cis*-cyclooctene-5,6-D_2 oxide, the labeled products would be as shown on page 248. The 1,4-glycol (L) arises through a 1,3-hydride shift to yield (LIX) and a 1,5-hydride or 1,5-deuteride shift to produce (LXI) and (LXIII), respectively. Likewise, the 3-cyclo-octene-1-ol (LI) arises by a 1,3-hydride shift to (LVIII) or as (LX) by a 1,5-hydride shift and as (LXII) by a 1,5-deuteride shift. By degradation and analysis of the deuterated products, it was deduced that the 1,4-diol (L) is formed in a ratio of 61 per cent by a 1,5-hydride shift and 39 per cent by a 1,3-hydride shift, and the 3-cyclooctene-1-ol (LI) is formed in a ratio of 94 per cent by a 1,5-hydride shift and 6 per cent by a 1,3-hydride shift.

ii. Electrophilic substitution. When *trans*-5-cyclodecene-1-yl p-toluenesulfon-ate is heated with diethylaniline it produces a mixture of *cis*-1,2-octalin and 1,9-octalin.[106b]

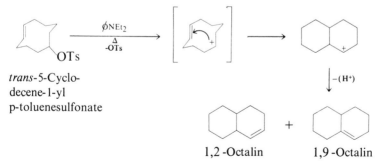

trans-5-Cyclo-
decene-1-yl
p-toluenesulfonate

1,2 -Octalin   +   1,9 -Octalin

The reaction is thought to proceed as formulated, in which the C_1 car-bonium carbon attacks the π bond to form a transannular bond. Another example is the acid-catalyzed isomerization of *trans*-cyclodecene to *cis*-

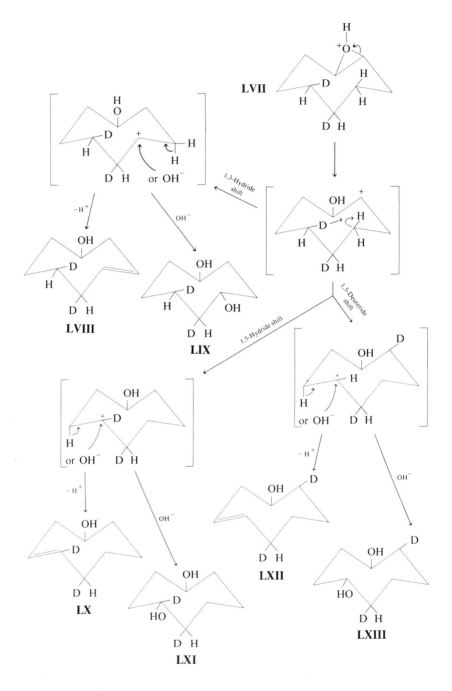

cyclodecene in which there is also formed a small amount of the *cis-* and *trans*-decalins.[106c]

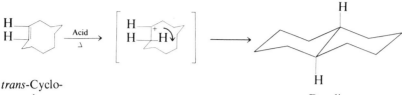

trans-Cyclo-
decene

Decalin

An unusual transannular reaction, possibly involving a transannular electrophilic substitution, is found in the nitration of [2.2]metacyclophane to yield tetrahydronitropyrene: [106d]

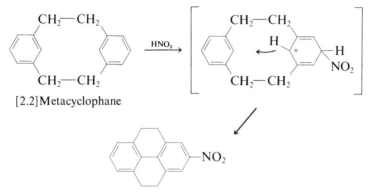

[2.2]Metacyclophane

Tetrahydronitropyrene

iii. Nucleophilic substitution.   Reduction of 6-hydroxycyclodecanone oxime with sodium in n-butanol gives a mixture of the expected 6-aminocyclodecanol plus the bicycl-11-aza-bicyclo[4.4.1]undecene: [106b]

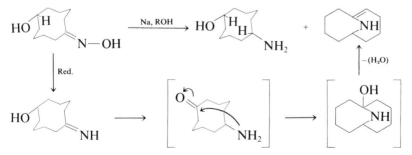

It was proposed that the reaction proceeds as shown. In another example of transannular nucleophilic substitution, it was found that dibromination of cyclodecanone with N-bromosuccinimide and heating the crude product with base produces $\Delta^{9,10}$-octalone-1: [103b]

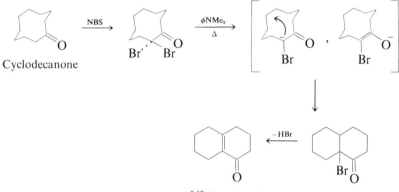

$\Delta^{9,10}$-Octalone-1

Weaker electron-donating transannular interactions have been observed too. For example, as *m* and *n* get smaller in the paracyclophanes (LXIV), there is greater interaction between the parallel π-electron clouds of the two benzene rings.[109]   This is shown by the fact that the rate of monoacetylation of the paracyclophanes increases as *m* and *n* decrease but the rate of introducing an acetyl group into the second ring decreases.

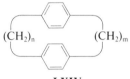

LXIV

Thus, the proximity of the second ring increases the availability of electrons for electrophilic substitution into the first ring but the electron-withdrawing acetyl group in the first ring decreases the electron density not only in that ring but in the neighboring second ring too.   The stabilizing transannular interactions in the charge-transfer complexes of paracyclophanes were mentioned on page 107.

In the cyclic aminoketones (LXV) there is a strong interaction between the carbonyl carbon atom and the nitrogen atom.[110,111]   This was revealed by a study of their dipole moments, infrared and ultraviolet spectra,[112] and their rotatory dispersion curves.[113]   The perchlorate salt of (LXV), for

[108]Cf. R. Pauncz and D. Ginsburg, *Tetrahedron,* **9,** 40 (1960); G. Chiwzcloglu, Th. Doehaerd, and B. Tursch, *Bull. soc. chim. France,* 1322 (1960); V. Prelog, *Angew. Chem.,* **23,** 896 (1960); N. L. Allinger and S. Greenburg, *J. Am. Chem. Soc.,* **81,** 5733 (1959).

[109]D. J. Cram, *Rec. Chem. Progress,* **20,** 71 (1959).

[110]N. J. Leonard, *et al., J. Am. Chem. Soc.,* **82,** 4075 (1960) and earlier publications.

[111]N. J. Leonard, *Record Chem. Progr.,* **17,** 243 (1956).

[112]N. J. Leonard, D. F. Morrow, and M. T. Rogers, *J. Am. Chem. Soc.,* **79,** 5476 (1957).

[113]N. J. Leonard, J. A. Adamcik, C. Djerassi, and O. Halpern, *J. Am. Chem. Soc.,* **80,** 4858 (1958).

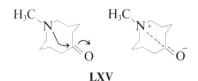

LXV

example, is probably best represented as a bicyclic ring because it exhibits
no carbonyl absorption in the infrared:

It can be seen that the close proximity of certain atoms across medium-
size rings can markedly affect their properties. Some transannular effects
on ultraviolet, infrared, and nuclear magnetic resonance spectra are discussed in Sec. 5.4.2. The medium-size and large rings may have considerable flexibility; often the compounds exist as a mixture of conformations.[108] For example, cycloalkenes lower than C_8 cannot form the *trans*
configuration, consequently these olefins consist of all *cis* isomer. However, the medium-size rings can form *trans* as well as *cis* double bonds,
and pyrolysis of cyclooctyltrimethylammonium hydroxide produces a
60:40 *trans-cis* mixture of cyclooctene. Cyclooctene is the smallest cyclo-
alkene isolable in the *trans* form. The *cis* isomers of C_8–C_{10} are still more
stable than the corresponding *trans* isomers. The changeover point is C_{11},
for which, like the acyclic alkenes, the *trans* isomer is the more stable. The
trans C_8 and C_9 cycloalkenes undergo addition reactions more rapidly than
the *cis* isomers, which can be taken as further evidence for the greater
strain in the *trans* isomers.

Transannular effects in cyclohexene and bicycloheptene systems are
less clearly defined.[114]

The conformations of the medium-size and large rings not only bring
about transannular effects but can alter the typical properties of functional
group substituents. For example, the 1,2-benzo-cyclen-3-one *p*-nitro-
phenylhydrazones

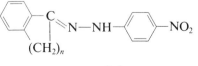

$n = 2$–5

[114]Cf. H. Kwart and L. J. Millar, *J. Am. Chem. Soc.*, **83**, 4552 (1961), and references
cited therein.

decrease in color depth from orange (n = 2) to a pale yellow (n = 5).[115] The ultraviolet spectrum of the member n = 5 is similar to that of cyclo-hexanone-p-nitrophenylhydrazone, which can be attributed to a twisting of the Schiff base grouping out of the plane of the benzene ring. The compound is thus a cycloaliphatic rather than an aromatic Schiff base.

The conformational concepts applied to the cyclohexyl ring[116] may be extended to heterocyclic and to polycyclic compounds. Decalin, for instance, consists of two fused cyclohexyl rings in which each ring may assume a chair or boat configuration and the H's on the two juncture carbon atoms may be *cis* or *trans*. Two isomeric decalins were first isolated by Hückel in 1925,[117] and have been assigned the *trans* structure LXVI and the chair-chair *cis* structure LXVII.[118] The boat-boat *cis* structure LXVIII is of less stability than LXVII because of considerable Pitzer strain between

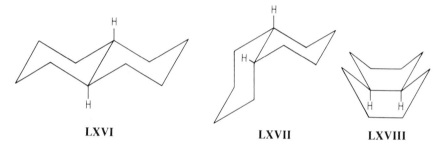

| LXVI | LXVII | LXVIII |

several axial hydrogen atoms in LXVIII. The ring juncture of *trans*-decalin has the two carbon atoms occupying equatorial positions. This forces a certain rigidity on the molecule because, although either ring could flip to a boat form, the entire molecule cannot invert to make all former equatorial bonds become axial, and vice versa, as does cyclohexane. This means that a substituent in the ring can be assigned a definite axial or equatorial position since the $e \rightleftharpoons a$ equilibrium does not occur. Hence, there could be two *trans*-2-methyldecalins, and the isomer with the least diaxial repulsion (LXIX) should be the more stable.

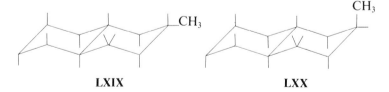

| LXIX | LXX |

[115]R. Huisgen, W. Rapp, I. Ugi, H. Walz, and E. Mergenthaler, *Ann.*, **586**, 1 (1954).
[116]H. D. Orloff, *Chem. Revs.*, **54**, 347 (1954).
[117]W. Hückel, *Ann.*, **441**, 1 (1925).
[118]O. Bastiansen and O. Hässel, *Nature*, **157**, 765 (1946). Considerable chemical evidence also supports this conformation for *cis*-decalin.

This ring rigidity, of course, exists in the sterols too. On the other hand, the *cis*-decalin is an *e,a* configuration and allows some ring flexibility. Thus, conformational analyses made on cyclohexane rings must also be applied to the *cis*-decalin structure. In general, the most stable conformations of the polycylic compounds will be those with the larger number of chair rings.

The significance of conformational analysis was largely recognized after the pioneering paper of Barton appeared in 1950.[119] Since then, many reviews have been published.[13,120] The earliest useful applications of conformational analysis concerned polycyclic molecules, such as the steroids and triterpenes, whose structures remain in rather rigid conformations. Later, extensive attention was given to the cyclohexanes which present a more complex problem owing to the flexibility of the ring. An equally

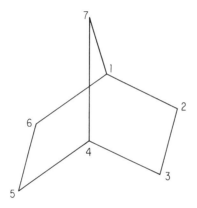

small molecule with a rigid structure is the bicyclo [2.2.1] heptane ring which may be regarded as a cyclohexane in which C_1 and C_4 have been tied together by a CH_2 bridge (C_7). Because several important natural products, such as camphor and borneol, incorporate the bicyclo [2.2.1] heptane nucleus in their structures, the chemistry of this ring has been studied extensively. The early work concerned structure determination and synthesis whereas the more recent work involves reaction mechanisms and stereochemistry. For example, much of the current theory on nonclassical carbonium ions (Sec. 4.12) has been developed from studies in this area.

As a finale to this section, some examples of the use of physical methods for conformational analysis and of the effects of conformational relationships on chemical reactivities will be given.

[119]D. H. R. Barton, *Experientia,* **6,** 316 (1950).

[120]D. H. R. Barton and R. C. Cookson, *Quart. Revs.,* **10,** 44 (1956); R. C. Cookson, *Ann. Repts. Chem. Soc.,* **44,** 170 (1957); S. J. Angyal and J. A. Mills, *Revs. Pure and Applied Chem.,* **2,** 185 (1952).

A. PHYSICAL PROPERTIES[121]

1. **Infrared spectra.** This physical property has been especially helpful for the elucidation of molecular conformation. Most often, but not rigidly so, infrared stretching frequencies for C—X bonds are higher for equatorial than for axial X. Some examples for the cyclohexane ring are given in Table 3.8. The C—OH[122] frequency of sterols[123] is in the narrow range 1030–1040 cm^{-1} for an equatorial OH and 1000–1010 cm^{-1} for an axial OH.[124] In steroidal systems,[125,126] the introduction of a halogen alpha to a carbonyl group increases ν_{CO} by 18 cm^{-1} or less if the halogen is axial and 16–31 cm^{-1} if the halogen is equatorial. On the basis of these empirical relationships, for example, it was deduced that the cyclopentanone ring has the half-chair conformation.[128] Also, infrared spectroscopy has been used to measure equilibrium constants between conformers.[129]

Table 3.8. INFRARED STRETCHING FREQUENCIES OF SOME CYCLOHEXYL CONFORMERS

X in $C_6H_{11}X$	Bond	Infrared frequency (cm^{-1}) Equatorial	Axial	Ref.
D	C—D	2174	2146	127(a),(b)
F	C—F	1062	1129	127(a)
Cl	C—Cl	743	688	127(a)
Br	C—Br	685	658	127(a)
Br	C—Br	709	685	127(c)
I	C—I	654	638	127(a)

[121]H. H. Lau, *Angew. Chem.,* **73,** 423 (1961); H. W. Thompson, *The Chemistry of Natural Products* (London: Butterworths, 1961), pp. 439 ff.

[122]There is disagreement on whether the band is related to the C—O bond or to the O—H bond. Cf. L. J. Bellamy, *The Infrared Spectra of Complex Molecules* (2nd ed.; New York: Wiley, 1958), p. 110.

[123]A. Furst, H. H. Kuhn, R. Scotoni, and H. H. Günthard, *Helv. Chim. Acta,* **35,** 951 (1952); H. Rosenkrantz, A. T. Milhorat, and M. Farber, *J. Biol. Chem.,* **195,** 509 (1950); R. N. Jones, *et al., J. Am. Chem. Soc.,* **73,** 3215 (1951), and earlier papers.

[124]This generalization does not apply to all types of cyclanols. Cf. W. G. Dauben, E. Hoerger, and N. K. Freeman, *J. Am. Chem. Soc.,* **74,** 5206 (1952).

[125]R. N. Jones, D. A. Ramsay, F. Herling, and K. Dobriner, *J. Am. Chem. Soc.,* **74,** 2828 (1952); D. H. R. Barton, J. F. Page, and C. W. Shoppee, *J. Chem. Soc.,* 331 (1936).

[126]E. G. Cummins and J. E. Page, *J. Chem. Soc.,* 3847 (1957); E. J. Corey and H. J. Burke, *J. Am. Chem. Soc.,* **77,** 5418 (1955).

[127](a). M. Larnaudie, *Compt. rendu. acad. sci.,* **235,** 154 (1952); (b). E. J. Corey, M. G. Howell, A. Boston, R. L. Young, and R. A. Sneen, *J. Am. Chem. Soc.,* **78,** 5036 (1956); (c). E. L. Eliel, *Chem. and Ind. (London),* 568 (1959).

[128]F. V. Brutcher, Jr., T. Roberts, S. J. Barr, and N. Pearson, *J. Am. Chem. Soc.,* **81,** 4915 (1959).

[129]R. A. Pickering and C. C. Prier, *J. Am. Chem. Soc.,* **80,** 4931 (1958); W. Hückel and Y. Riad, *Ann.,* **637,** 33 (1960).

2. Raman spectra. The usual techniques of Raman spectroscopy can be applied to gain information about the population of conformers in a mixture. By this method, for instance, it was shown that *trans*-1,4-dihalocyclohexanes have only the diequatorial conformation in the solid state but exist in solution as an equilibrium mixture of the diequatorial and diaxial forms.[130] By measuring the relative intensities of the characteristic Raman lines, differences in the energies of the isomeric pairs were determined.

3. Microwave spectra. The accuracy of the microwave spectroscopic measurements of potential barriers to internal rotations is relatively high,[23] and it offers an extremely valuable addition to the family of methods used in making conformational analyses. The value determined for ethyl chloride, for instance, 3.560 ± 0.012 kcal/mole, is what might be expected on the basis of the value for ethane (3.04 kcal/mole[131]).

4. Ultraviolet spectra. An axial substituent generally produces a bathochromic shift in the ultraviolet spectra of substituted cyclohexanones whereas an equatorial group exerts a hypsochromic shift:[132]

	$\Delta\lambda_{max}$ of the 280-mu band of	
	α-substituted cyclohexanones	
α-Substituent	Axial	Equatorial
Cl	22 mu	-7 mu
Br	28	-5
OH	17	-12
OAc	10	-5

5. Nuclear magnetic resonance spectra. Nuclear magnetic resonance spectroscopy has taken its place among the variety of physical techniques now used to study hindered internal rotations and for conformational analysis. If the n.m.r. spectra of the various conformations of a compound differ, its spectrum will be temperature dependent, and the temperature coefficient may be used to estimate the energy difference between two major conformations. When the rate of interconversion is rapid, the spectrum is a time-averaged spectrum of the mixture of conformations. On the other hand, if the spectrum is independent of temperature changes over a reasonable range, either the energy difference between conformers is so small that temperature changes do not alter appreciably the relative populations or rotation is highly hindered and essentially only one isomer is present. On this basis, it was shown that 1-chloro-2-bromethane undergoes rapid rotation

[130]K. Kozima and T. Yoshino, *J. Am. Chem. Soc.*, **75**, 166 (1953).

[131]D. R. Lide, Jr., *J. Chem. Phys.*, **30**, 37 (1959).

[132]R. C. Cookson, *et al.*, *J. Chem. Soc.*, 282 (1954); 352 (1955).

[133]K. B. Wiberg and B. J. Nist, *J. Am. Chem. Soc.*, **83**, 1226 (1961).

about the C—C bond,[134] whereas 1,1-difluoro-1,2-dibromo-2,2-dichloro-ethane exists only in the *meso* conformation at room temperature.[135]

It has been found that axial protons in six-membered rings exhibit resonance absorption at higher fields than equatorial protons.[136b] Two examples are the following:

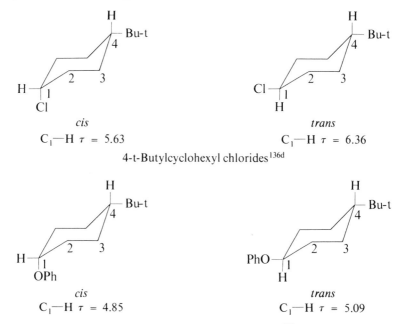

C_1—H τ = 5.63 C_1—H τ = 6.36

4-t-Butylcyclohexyl chlorides[136d]

C_1—H τ = 4.85 C_1—H τ = 5.09

4-t-Butylcyclohexyl acid phthalates[136e]

Similarly, the chemical shift for axial protons in the 3-position of steroids is 22–25 c.p.s. higher than for equatorial protons. Also, the coupling constants between axial H's on adjacent carbon atoms are 5–8.5 c.p.s. whereas between *a* and *e* or between *e* and *e* pairs the coupling constants are only

---

[134] J. A. Pople, W. G. Schneider, and H. J. Bernstein, *Can. J. Chem.,* **35**, 1060 (1957).

[135] P. M. Nair and J. D. Roberts, *J. Am. Chem. Soc.,* **79**, 4565 (1957).

[136] (a). R. R. Fraser, *Can. J. Chem.,* **40**, 78 (1962); (b). R. U. Lemiuex, R. K. Kullnig, H. J. Bernstein, and W. G. Schneider, *J. Am. Chem. Soc.,* **80**, 6098 (1958); (c). A. H. Kewin and S. Winstein, *J. Am. Chem. Soc.,* **84**, 2464 (1962); (d). F. D. Greene, C. Chu, and J. Walia, *J. Am. Chem. Soc.,* **84**, 2464 (1962); (e). N. L. Allinger and S. Greenberg, *J. Am. Chem. Soc.,* **84**, 2394 (1962).

2-3.5 c.p.s. These generalizations have been used for making conformational analyses. For example, the conformations of cyclohexene,[132] of aldopyranoses,[136a] and of bicycloheptanes[136b] have been assigned on a basis of spin-spin coupling constants.

As discussed in Sect. 5.5.6, simple cyclohexanes undergo rapid chair-chair interconversions.   At room temperature the CXH proton of X—C_6H_{11} gives a single peak at an average position for the axial and equatorial protons. Their characteristic chemical shifts δ_a and δ_e can be determined by either of two procedures: (1) make measurements at sufficiently low temperature where the rate of interconversion is very slow or (2) use 4-t-butyl substituted derivatives in which this group holds the molecules in a fixed conformation. Under the first method, for example, the CXH signal in chloro- or bromocyclohexane is a single peak at room temperature which broadens at $-40°$ and splits into two peaks at $-55°$. From the variation of the broad peak with temperature changes, the energy barrier resisting interconversion was found to be 10.8 kcal/mole. In the second method, the peaks are broad and care must be taken in assigning δ_a and δ_e values. Nevertheless, the method readily provides A values for various groups in good accord with other methods, and some recently determined values as (compare page 240):

Group	A value (in CCl_4)[136c]
i-Pr.	2.28 kcal/mole
Et	1.74
Me	1.74
OH	0.78

6. X-Ray diffraction.   Through the use of X-ray diffraction analysis, the surprising discovery was made that the cyclodecane ring does not have the crown structure, which is easily constructed from the regular molecular models, but has a conformation with C_{2h} symmetry.[138]   As shown in the annexed diagram three hydrogen atoms above the XY plane and three below are closer together than normal van der Waals distances (ca. 2.8 A). This forces some of the C—C—C bond angles to assume values considerably larger than the tetrahedral angle. Thus, bond angle strain and transannular repulsion accounts for the large ring strain in the medium-size rings listed in Table 3.6. Also, the unusual bond angles and transannular interference prevents the construction of this conformation of cyclodecane with the regular molecular models. In spite of the obvious ring strain, this con-

[137]R. A. Bonham and L. S. Bartell, *J. Am. Chem. Soc.*, **81**, 3491 (1959); Y. Morino and K. Kuchitsu, *J. Chem. Phys.*, **28**, 175 (1958).

[138]J. D. Dunitz, *et al.*, *Helv. Chim. Acta*, **43**, 760 (1960) and earlier papers in the series: W. Nowacki and M. H. Mladeck, *Chimia*, **15**, 531 (1961).

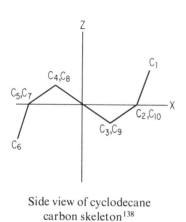

Side view of cyclodecane
carbon skeleton[138]

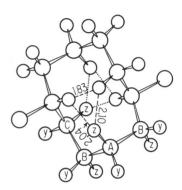

Top view of cyclodecane[138]

formation must lie in a deep potential energy well because it has been found by X-ray analysis in four derivatives of cyclodecane.[138]

7. Electron diffraction. Much of the information about the conformations of C_6 rings is based on the electron diffraction work of the Scandinavian workers.[77,80] For one example, it was shown that *trans*-1,4-dichlorocyclohexane exists in almost equal amounts of the diaxial and diequatorial conformations.[139] In another case, it was found that n-butane exists as 60 per cent *trans*, 40 per cent *gauche*, whereas surprisingly, the *gauche* conformer is the predominant one in n-propyl chloride.[137] Also, electron and X-ray diffraction measurements have shown that simple cyclobutanes are nonplanar with unusually long C—C bond distances.[60,97]

8. Dipole moments. Mention has already been made of the use of dipole moments for the study of axial and equatorial α-halocyclohexanones.[93] The general procedure is to calculate the per cent of the two conformers from the observed dipole moment by use of the equation

$$\mu^2 = \mu_1^2 N_1 + \mu_2^2 N_2$$

where μ = observed moment.
        μ_1 and μ_2 = moments of the two components, either estimated or measured.
        N_1 and N_2 = mole fractions of the two components.

As a rule, the results are in substantial agreement with those from other methods as shown by the comparison made at the end of the discussion of optical rotatory dispersion.

[139] V. A. Atkinson and O. Hässel, *Acta Chem. Scand.*, **13**, 1737 (1959).

9. Thermochemical measurements. The initial proposal leading to the present views on hindered internal rotations about single bonds grew out of the thermodynamic calculations based on thermochemical measurements.[26] This has already been discussed. When different conformations can be isolated, individual heats of combustion may be measured. Thus, it was early recognized that the *trans*-2-alkylcyclohexanols, which have a diequatorial conformation, are less stable than the *cis* conformers (which are *e,a*).[140]

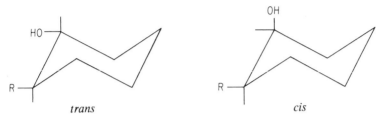

trans   cis

10. Optical rotation.[141] Although the theory of optical rotatory dispersion (ORD) has not been included in this text, any discussion on stereochemical analysis by physical methods would be obsolete if it failed to mention this modern technique. ORD refers to the change in optical rotation with a change in wavelength of light source. This means, of course, that the method can be applied only to optically active compounds. Since many polycyclic and natural substances have asymmetric centers, the method finds its greatest use in these areas. Normally, measurements are made in the ultraviolet-visible range where a functional group of the compound under study has an absorption band with a small extinction coefficient. This makes the carbonyl group ideal, and a vast majority of studies have been with ketones. Two principal types of curves are produced. One is a simple curve where there is a smooth increase in rotation (positive or negative) with decreasing wavelength. These plain curves are only of limited use and occur when the sample has no optically active absorption band in this region. Anomalous curves are those in which there is a *peak* and *trough* as shown in Fig. 3.3. The type with the peak first as one goes to shorter wavelengths reflects a *positive* Cotton effect, the other is the result of a *negative* Cotton effect.

Following the pioneering work of Carl Djerassi, several valuable empirical correlations between stereo structure and ORD have been formulated. One of the highly useful correlations is called the octant rule.[143] To apply this rule, one uses three mutually perpendicular planes (Fig. 3.4): a vertical

[140]A. Skita and W. Faust, *Ber.,* **64,** 2878 (1931).

[141]C. Djerassi, *Optical Rotatory Dispersion* (New York: McGraw-Hill, 1960); *Science,* **134,** 649 (1961).

[142]Taken from *Chem. Eng. News,* August 21, 1961, p. 91.

[143]W. Moffitt, R. B. Woodward, A. Moscowitz, W. Klyne, and C. Djerassi, *J. Am. Chem. Soc.,* **83,** 4013 (1961).

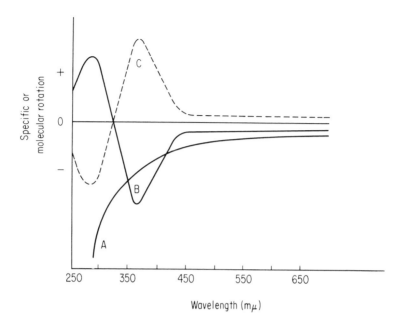

Fig. 3.3. Plain and anomalous ORD curves.[142]   The two principal kinds of ORD curves are plain (*A*) and anomalous (*B* and *C*). A plain curve can also slope upward into the area of positive rotation. Curve *B* shows a negative Cotton effect–the trough occurs first in going to shorter wave lengths. Curve *C*, with the peak coming first, shows a positive Cotton effect.

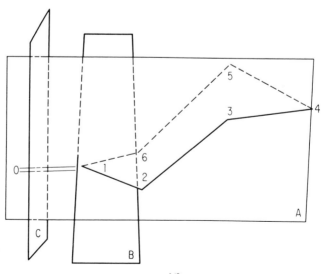

Fig. 3.4 [142]

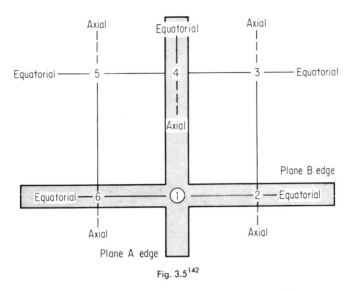

Fig. 3.5[142]

plane A through C_1 and C_4, a horizontal plane B through C_1, C_2, and C_6, and a second vertical plane C perpendicular to the other two and through the carbonyl bond. There are, then, four *octants* to the left of plane C and four to the right. Looking along the C$=$O axis toward C_4, one sees the four octants to the right of plane C as diagrammed in Fig. 3.5. The substituents at C_4 lie in plane A, and planar equatorial substituents at C_2 and C_6 lie in plane B.

The operation of the octant rule can be summarized by Fig. 3.6. Groups that lie in plane A or B do not contribute to the Cotton effect.

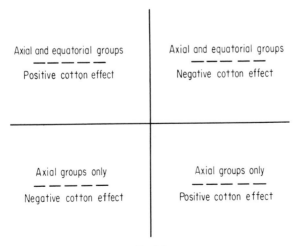

Fig. 3.6.

Groups in the upper left octant and axial groups in the lower right contribute to a positive Cotton effect, and groups in the upper right and axial groups in the lower left contribute to a negative Cotton effect. This rule makes it possible to deduce conformations, or if the conformation is known, to determine the absolute configuration of a molecule.

For illustration, β-methylcyclohexanone can exist in two chair conformations LXXI and LXXII. According to the octant diagrams, con-

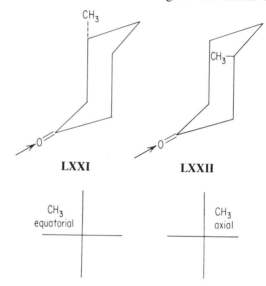

LXXI   LXXII

CH₃
equatorial

CH₃
axial

former LXXI with the equatorial CH_3 will exhibit a positive Cotton effect and the other, with an axial CH_3, will show a negative Cotton effect. Since the experimental ORD curve exhibits a positive Cotton effect, the compound must exist in the equatorial conformation. This deduction is in agreement with conclusions derived from other physical data.

In view of the octant rule it is easy to understand the "axial halo-ketone" generalization, which states:[146] The introduction of an equatorial halogen in either α position of a cyclohexanone does not alter the sign of the Cotton effect of the halogen-free ketone, whereas the introduction of an axial Cl or Br into the α position may affect the sign of the Cotton effect of the parent ketone. When one looks along the $O{=}C$ axis as indicated by the arrow, if the halogen is on the left there will be a negative Cotton effect and a positive Cotton effect if the halogen is to the right.

[144] A. Moscowitz, E. Charney, U. Weiss and H. Ziffer, *J. Am. Chem. Soc.,* **83,** 4660, 4661 (1961); for similar effects pertaining to the α,β-enone system, see C. Djerassi, R. Records, E. Bunnenberg, K. Mislow, and A. Moscowitz, *J. Am. Chem. Soc.,* **84,** 870 (1962).

[145] Cf. J. B. Hendrickson, *J. Am. Chem. Soc.,* **83,** 4537 (1961), for pertinent references.

[146] C. Djerassi and W. Klyne, *J. Am. Chem. Soc.,* **79,** 1506 (1957); C. Djerassi, L. E. Geller, and E. J. Eisenbraun, *J. Org. Chem.,* **25,** 1 (1960).

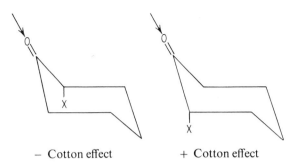

    − Cotton effect   + Cotton effect

Another useful correlation between conformation and ORD involves a skewed butadiene system. Butadiene would be asymmetric in any of its nonplanar conformations, and if the diene system had one of these conformations as part of a rigid ring, the dissymmetric group would impart optical activity to the ring. Such a condition has been found responsible for a Cotton effect in the ORD curves of certain 1,3-cyclohexadiene rings.[144] In addition, it has been derived theoretically and demonstrated experimentally that the direction of the Cotton effect so produced depends upon the helical direction of the skewed diene. The left-handed twist produces a negative Cotton effect, and a positive Cotton effect results from a right-handed twist. On the basis of this rule, the conformations of a number of steroid and other ring compounds have been confirmed or newly established.[144]

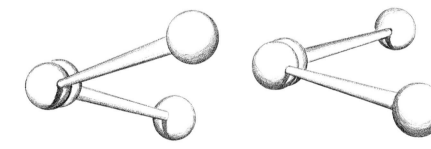

    Right-handed helical   Left-handed
        twist   helical twist

[147] N. L. Allinger, J. Allinger, L. E. Geller, and C. Djerassi, *J. Org. Chem.*, **25**, 6 (1960); *J. Org. Chem.*, **26**, 3521 (1961).

[148] K. Savard, *J. Biol. Chem.*, **202**, 457 (1953); see also G. H. Alt and D. H. R. Barton, *J. Chem. Soc.*, 4284 (1954).

[149] K. von Auwers, *Ann.*, **420**, 84 (1920); A. Skita, *Ber.*, **56**, 1014 (1923); N. L. Allinger, *Experientia*, **10**, 328 (1954); R. B. Kelly, *Can. J. Chem.*, **35**, 149 (1957).

[150] A. E. van Arkel, *Rec. trav. chim.*, **51**, 1081 (1932); **53**, 246 (1934); H. V. Bekkum, A. V. Veen, P. E. Verkade, and B. M. Wepster, *Rec. trav. chim.*, **80**, 1310 (1961).

Several other useful empirical rules have been developed to relate molecular rotation and absolute configuration.[151] As an example of one, it has been found that for two epimeric ketones

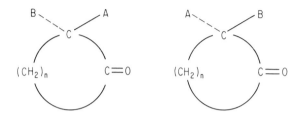

if B is the bulkier of the two exocyclic substituents A and B, then the ketone on the left should be the more dextrorotatory.[151(a)]

Thus, it can be seen that ORD is a powerful supplement to the other physical methods used for stereochemical analysis. It is gratifying that several of the techniques discussed in this section lead to comparable results when applied to the same compound. For illustration, the percentages of *axial* halogen in the bromo and chloro derivatives of *trans*-2-halo-5-methyl-cyclohexanone as determined by five different methods are as follows:[147]

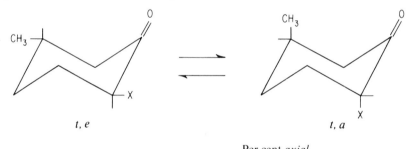

	Per cent *axial*	
	X = Br *(in dioxane)*	X = Cl *(in dioxane)*
Infrared spectroscopy	26	22
Ultraviolet spectroscopy	18	12
Dipole moments	19	5 (in benzene)
Energy calculations	21	8
ORD	20	0

The conformation ratios differ for different solvents; they are larger for less polar solvents.

Finally, it should be added that attempts have been made to calculate the energy of a given conformation.[145] The general scheme is to select some function which relates energy to geometric parameters of the various pos-

---

[151] (a) A. K. Bose, *Tetrahedron Letters,* no. 14, 461 (1961); (b) J. H. Brewster, *Tetrahedron,* **13,** 106 (1961), and earlier papers.

sible molecular conformations and which usually makes use of empirical or thermodynamic data. Then, one calculates the sum of energies related to the various geometrical parameters of a specific conformation and minimizes this sum with respect to the independent variations of each of the parameters. As a means of reducing this formidable task, assumptions are made regarding the constancy of some of the parameters, or some of the energy functions are ignored. In spite of the overwhelming complexity of this approach, a fair degree of success has been achieved in some instances.[145]

11. **Miscellaneous physical properties.** Other limited or qualitative relations between conformation and physical property have been observed. For example, equatorial cyclanols have been found to be chromatographically adsorbed more strongly on paper than their axial epimers.[148] The von Auwers-Skita rule and its modification, the conformational rule,[149] in their most general form state that alicyclic isomers having fully equatorial conformations will have a larger molecular volume and lower boiling point, density, and refractive index than those isomers having partially axial conformations. The van Arkel or dipole rule,[150] which applies to geometrically isomeric olefins, states that the isomer of higher dipole moment will have the higher boiling point, refractive index, and density. These and other similar rules[151] can provide confirming evidence for a proposed structure but they are not without exceptions.[152] Conformations can sometimes be deduced from dissociation constants. For example, it is not surprising to find a significant difference in ΔpK_a for *cis* and *trans*-cyclohexane dicarboxylic acids, where ΔpK_a is the difference between the pK_a's of the first and second dissociation constants:[83]

	ΔpK_a	
	cis	*trans*
1,2-cyclohexanedicarboxylic acids	1.80	1.15
1,3-cyclohexanedicarboxylic acids	0.76	0.82

The smaller ΔpK_a value for the *trans*-1,2 acid, for example, is due to greater separation between the charged carboxylate groups in the dianion, which, owing to electrostatic repulsion, assumes the diaxial (LXXIII) rather than the diequatorial conformation (LXXIV). In the dianion of the 1,3-acid (LXXV), for which there is only one chair structure possible, the CO_2^- groups are farther apart, and thereby the CO_2^- from the first dissociation has a smaller affect on the second dissociation to give a smaller ΔpK_a. Other conformation-physical property relationships have involved molar *Kerr* constants[153] and melting points.[154]

[152] E. L. Eliel and R. G. Haber, *J. Org. Chem.*, **23**, 2041 (1958).

[153] C. G. LeFevre and R. J. W. LeFevre, *J. Chem. Soc.*, 3458 (1957).

[154] R. T. Arnold, G. Peirce, and R. A. Barnes, *J. Am. Chem. Soc.*, **72**, 1627 (1950).

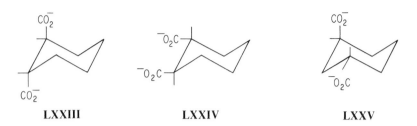

LXXIII   **LXXIV**   **LXXV**

With cyclic systems of relatively fixed conformation, such as with the 2-halo-4-t-butylcyclohexanones, the epimer with the axial halogen is reduced more easily. This has been tentatively explained in terms of a *trans*-type elimination mechanism:[155]

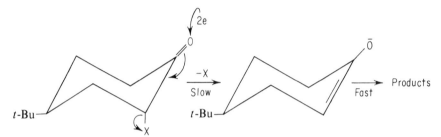

The generalization can be of use in ascertaining the conformation of an α-halogen in systems where the spectral or other physical methods may be indecisive.

B. CHEMICAL PROPERTIES

In view of the foregoing discussion on the relationships between conformation and physical properties, it is not surprising to find that the conformations of molecules have also a marked effect upon their chemical properties. Some examples in acyclic systems were discussed in Sec. 3.3.2; now a few reaction-types with alicyclic compounds can be presented. Intramolecular steric conditions may affect the rates of all reactions, and only the influence of conformational factors will be taken up here. The effects of steric hindrance on chemical reactivity in general will be discussed in Sec. 3.5.

(i) **Eliminations.** As stated in Sec. 3.3.2, a planar four-center transition state is preferred in a 1,2-ionic elimination reaction. As a consequence, the reactions proceed more rapidly when 1,2-*trans* substituents occupy two axial positions. For example, dehydration of a 7α-hydroxy steroid eliminates a β hydrogen atom.

[155] A. M. Wilson and N. L. Allinger, *J. Am. Chem. Soc.*, **83**, 1999 (1961).

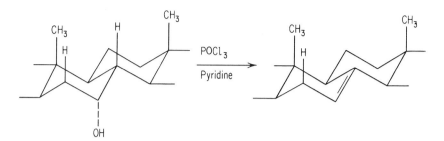

The βC_8—H bond is broken rather than the βC_6—H because the former elimination produces a tertiary carbonium ion. (In order to produce the $\Delta^{6,7}$ double bond, one may esterify the alcohol group and pyrolyze the ester, in which case one gets *cis* elimination. See below.) Similarly, dehydrohalogenation of menthyl chloride gives only 2-menthene, since there is no *trans* proton on C_4, whereas neomenthyl chloride gives 2- and 3-menthene.[157]

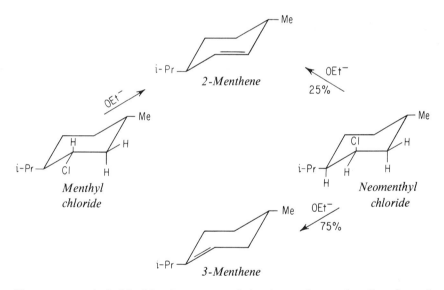

Since neomenthyl chloride gives more of the 3-menthene, the direction of dehydrohalogenation of menthyl chloride is not due to the methylene C_2 atom's being more reactive than the tertiary C_4 carbon atom. Furthermore, neomenthyl chloride reacts about 200 times as fast as menthyl chloride, which can be attributed to the fact that the H and Cl atoms are *trans* but not diaxial in menthyl chloride. The molecule perhaps inverts to the other chair form in which the substituents are *trans*, and since this conformation is very unfavorable, the rate of reaction is slow.

[156]C. H. DePuy and R. W. King, *Chem. Revs.*, **60**, 431 (1960).

[157]W. Hückel, W. Tappe, and G. Legutke, *Ann.*, **543**, 191 (1940).

In pyrolytic eliminations, on the other hand, olefin formation takes place via a planar cyclic transition state.[156] This condition is most easily met in a cyclohexane ring when the groups have an equatorial-axial *cis* arrangement. Other configurations develop larger van der Waals repulsion and bond angle strains in order to achieve the coplanarity. Thus, when a 7α-acetoxy steroid is pyrolyzed, one gets cleavage of the αC_6—H bond.

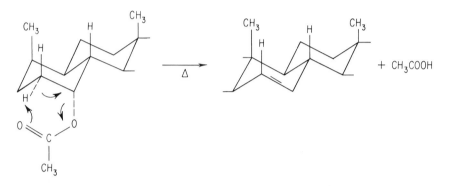

Similarly, when menthol xanthate (equatorial ester group) is pyrolyzed, 3-menthene is the principal product, whereas pyrolysis of neomenthyl xanthate (axial ester group) yields 2-menthene as the major product.[157]

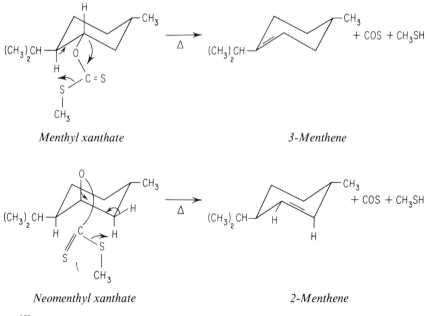

Menthyl xanthate   *3-Menthene*

Neomenthyl xanthate   *2-Menthene*

[158] F. S. Fawcett, *Chem. Revs.*, **47**, 219 (1950).

When the elimination takes place by a neighboring group displacement, the rate of reaction of a 1,2-disubstituted cyclohexane is much faster when the substituents are *trans* diaxial than when *cis* or diequatorial. For example, *trans*-2-acetoxycyclohexyl brosylate (LXXVI) reacts 630 times as fast as the *cis* isomer.[159] This difference in reactivity can be ascribed to a back-side approach of the acetate to facilitate the departure of the brosylate ion.

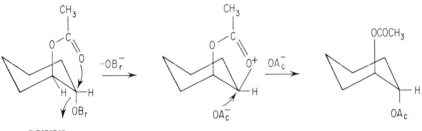

LXXVI

As a generalization then, we can say that 1,2-ionic eliminations and neighboring group displacements are favored by diaxial *trans* orientations, whereas uncatalyzed pyrolytic eliminations occur when the groups have axial-equatorial conformations.

(ii) Solvolysis. Rates of solvolysis are clearly dependent upon conformation. For example, the relative rates of solvolysis of some cyclic chlorides in aqueous ethanol are as follows:[160]

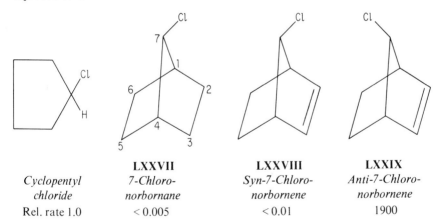

	LXXVII	**LXXVIII**	**LXXIX**
Cyclopentyl chloride	*7-Chloro-norbornane*	*Syn-7-Chloro-norbornene*	*Anti-7-Chloro-norbornene*
Rel. rate 1.0	< 0.005	< 0.01	1900

These reactivities can be explained in terms of relative stabilities of transition states. A carbonium ion at C_7 is less stable than an acyclic secondary

[159] S. Winstein, E. Grunwald, and L. L. Ingraham, *J. Am. Chem. Soc.,* **70**, 821 (1948).
[160] W. G. Woods, R. A. Carboni, and J. D. Roberts, *J. Am. Chem. Soc.,* **78**, 5653 (1956).

carbonium ion because it is not stabilized by hyperconjugation. Hyperconjugation would involve a double bond to one of the bridgehead carbon
atoms in violation of Bredt's empirical rule (see below).

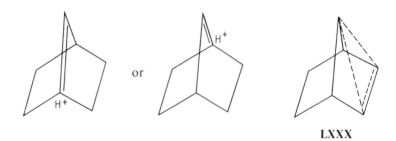

LXXX

Consequently, chlorides LXXVII and LXXVIII are solvolyzed much more
slowly than cyclopentyl chloride. However, the double bond in LXXIX
facilitates ionization of the chlorine atom by a C=C neighboring group
participation to yield the nonclassical carbonium ion LXXX (see Sec. 4.12).
This increases the rate of solvolysis by a factor of 10^5. It is in order to add
here that Bredt's rule, which states in effect that bridged rings cannot form
a double bond at the bridge-head carbon atom, has been used frequently to
explain the failure of certain reactions of bridged-ring derivatives and as a
guide in making a choice between alternative structures for a given molecule.[158]   For illustration, 1-chlorocamphene and 1-bromotriptycene are inert
towards nucleophilic reagents such as alcoholic KOH or silver nitrate. This

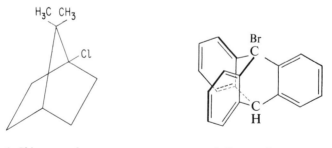

1-*Chlorocamphene*   1-*Bromotriptycene*

can be attributed to the failure of the tertiary carbon atom to form a carbonium ion; and in turn, the carbonium ion does not form because of the
absence of any resonance stabilization which would require a double bond
to the bridge-head carbon atom. Likewise, α-halocamphoric acid anhydrides do not undergo dehydrohalogenation, which would produce a
double bond at the bridge-head.

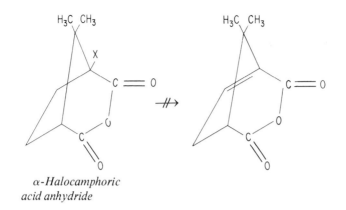

α-Halocamphoric
acid anhydride

On the other hand, the acid readily suffers dehydrohalogenation, but now,

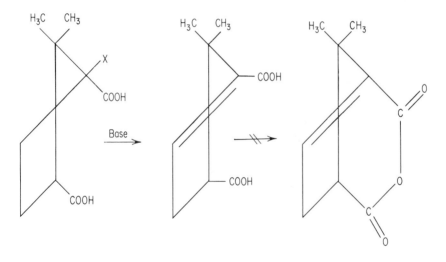

the unsaturated acid will not form the anhydride.

Bredt's rule does not apply to larger rings (beginning at about C_8, possibly C_7 in some systems), and many larger ring compounds have been isolated containing bridge-head double bonds, e.g.,[98, 106(b)]

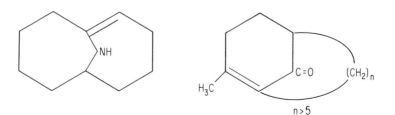

(iii) Esterifications. Two isomers of 4-*t*-butylcyclohexanol have been prepared, one with the OH axial (LXXXI) and the other with an equatorial OH (LXXXII). Not only is the *trans* isomer (LXXXII) more stable, since it has less Pitzer strain, but its equatorial OH group is less shielded and is esterified more rapidly. In fact, almost without exception, equatorial OH groups are esterified more rapidly and equatorial ester groups are hydrolyzed more rapidly than axial groups.

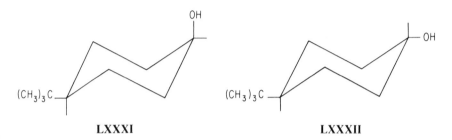

LXXXI   LXXXII

(iv) Reduction of cyclanones. As a generality, the reduction of unhindered ketones with lithium aluminum hydride produces an equatorial OH group, whereas the use of aluminum alkoxides yields an axial OH group. The reagent approaches the ketone from the side which adds a proton to produce some sort of organometallic intermediate. It has been shown that most of the experimental data can be interpreted when two factors are considered:[161] (1) *steric approach control*—the relative ease of formation of the initial intermediate in the reaction, and (2) *product development control*—the relative ease of formation of the products. In most cases, one or the other factor is the dominant one, and this accounts for the success of previous authors in correlating data for a given series of compounds. For illustration, in the reduction of menthone,

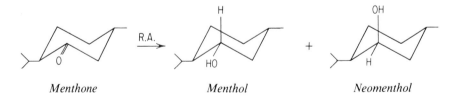

Menthone   *Menthol*   *Neomenthol*

a small reducing agent can approach the carbonyl group equally as well from either side so that the reduction is under the influence of product development control to give mostly the more stable equatorial hydroxy product. As the reducing agent gets larger, steric approach control grows in importance and eventually becomes the dominant factor:

[161] W. G. Dauben, G. J. Fonken, and D. S. Noyce, *J. Am. Chem. Soc.*, **78**, 2579 (1956).

Reducing agent	Per cent equatorial OH
$LiAlH_4$	71
$NaBH_4$	49
$Al(OPr\text{-}i)_3$	30

In another example,[162] the proportion of equatorial alcohol produced in the reduction of a bicyclo [3.1] hexanone decreases as the size of the reducing agent gets larger.

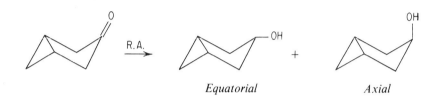

Equatorial   Axial

Reducing agent	Per cent equatorial in product
$LiAlH_4$	89
$NaBH_4$	64
$Al(OPr\text{-}i)_3$	40

(v) Oxidations. The rates of oxidation of secondary alicyclic alcohols with chromic acid are well correlated in terms of 1,3-diaxial interactions.[163, 164] The conversion of a tetrahedral hydroxylated carbon to a trigonal carbonyl carbon removes any 1,3-diaxial repulsive interactions, and the greater this relief in strain the faster the alcohol will undergo oxidation, i.e., the rate determining step is speeded up.

$$R_2CHOH + HCrO_4^- + H^+ \rightleftharpoons R_2CHOCrO_3H + H_2O$$

$$R_2C\underset{\underset{H}{|}}{-}OCrO_3H + H_2O \xrightarrow{slow} R_2C{=}O + HCrO_3^- + H_3O^+$$

For illustration, cholestane-3a-ol has two 1,3-diaxial OH : H interactions whereas there are none in the 3β isomer. The 3α isomer is oxidized three times as fast as the 3β isomer.

[162] S. Winstein and J. Sonnenberg, *J. Am. Chem. Soc.*, **83**, 3235 (1961).

[163] J. Schreiber and A. Eschenmoser, *Helv. Chim. Acta*, **38**, 1529 (1955).

[164] See also J. C. Richer, L. A. Pilato, and E. L. Eliel, *Chem. and Ind. (London)*, 2007 (1961).

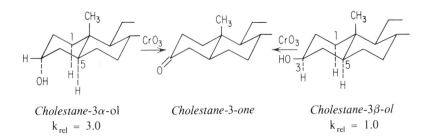

Cholestane-3α-ol   Cholestane-3-one   Cholestane-3β-ol
$k_{rel} = 3.0$ $k_{rel} = 1.0$

The relative rates of oxidation of other cholestanols are in accord with this view.

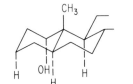

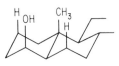

1 α-ol	2β-ol	4β-ol
3 OH : H interactions	OH : CH$_3$, OH : H	2 OH : H, OH : CH$_3$
$k_{rel} = 13$	$k_{rel} = 20$	$k_{rel} = 35$

| | Relative rate of CrO$_3$ oxidation in | |
| Cholestane | 91% acetic acid at 20° [163] | |
	β	α
1-Hydroxy	9.7	13
2-Hydroxy	20	1.3
3-Hydroxy	1.0	3.0
4-Hydroxy	35	2.0
6-Hydroxy	36	2.0
7-Hydroxy	3.7	12.3

3.3.3. ISOMERISM AND HINDERED ROTATIONS

It was demonstrated in the two previous sections that steric requirements may hinder internal rotations and that the resulting conformations may have different physical properties and chemical reactivities. In some acyclic systems the barrier to rotation is sufficiently large to prevent the easy inter-conversion of the conformations and permit the isolation of the different isomers. One such system which has received considerable attention is biphenyl. Rotation of the phenyl rings about the 1,1′-carbon-carbon bond is hindered by the repulsion of atoms or groups in the *ortho* positions. The repulsion is at a minimum when the planes of the rings are perpendicular

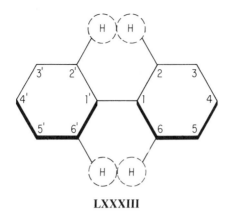

LXXXIII

to each other, for then the *ortho* groups are at a maximum distance apart. As a result of van der Waals repulsion, then, the two phenyl rings tend to form an angle of 90°. Opposing this tendency to be perpendicular is a resonance effect involving electronic interactions between the two rings. In addition to all of the Kekulé and ionic forms of benzene which occur in each ring independently, there are the ionic forms involving both rings:

In all of these polar forms, the two rings are almost coplanar and the inter-ring bond is a double bond. This brings the four *ortho* groups closer together and increases the nonbonding repulsion. Thus, the molecule will assume the configuration which has a minimum potential energy for the sum of the opposing effects of steric repulsion and resonance stabilization. With only hydrogen atoms in the *ortho* positions, the resonance effect predominates and the molecule is planar.[165] Actually, the molecule is planar in the solid state[166] but in solution[167] or in the vapor state there is approximately a 45-degree angle between planes.[168] When larger groups are substituted for hydrogen in the *ortho* positions, the van der Waals repulsion increases and this steric hindrance outweighs the resonance effect and forces the rings to assume nonplanar orientations.

---

[165] J. Guy (*J. chim. phys.*, **46**, 469 (1949)) has calculated the per cent of maximum resonance energy occurring for various angles between phenyl rings to be: 100% for o°; 90% for 12°; 19% for 45°; 10% for 61°; and zero for 90°.

[166] G. L. Clark and L. W. Pickett, *J. Am. Chem. Soc.*, **53**, 167 (1931); J. Trotter, *Acta Cryst.*, **14**, 1135 (1961).

[167] E. Merkel and Ch. Wiegand, *Z. Naturforsch.*, **3b**, 93 (1948).

[168] O. Bastiansen, *Acta Chem. Scand.*, **3**, 348 (149).

Consider a substituted biphenyl in which the *ortho* repulsions force the two rings to be almost perpendicular to each other and let neither ring be symmetrically substituted, although the rings may have similar substituents. In the coplanar position, the *ortho* groups would overlap if they maintained their normal bond angles and distances, and this would create a large barrier to rotation about the 1,1' bond. Under this condition the relative

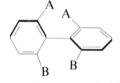

orientations of the two rings are frozen, and either one of two conformations is possible. This is illustrated in Fig. 3.7, where it can be seen that two mirror-image nonsuperposable isomers are possible. Since neither structure has an element of symmetry,[169] the two isomers are optically active. Thus,

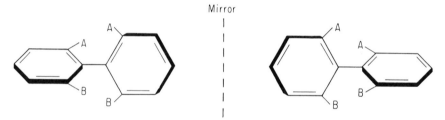

Fig. 3.7. Sketch of a biphenyl derivative and its conformational mirror image.

optical isomerism here is the result of steric hindrance to an internal rotation. It is noteworthy that if either ring is symmetrical, the two mirror-image conformations are superposable (Fig. 3.8) and optical activity will not be observed. A plane of symmetry coincides with the plane of the unsymmetrically substituted ring.

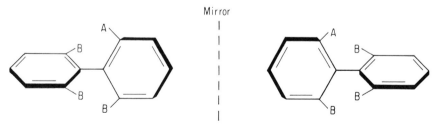

Fig. 3.8. Sketch of a biphenyl derivative and its superposable mirror image.

Often it is not possible to isolate the optical isomers of an unsymmetrically substituted biphenyl because the *ortho* repulsive forces merely

[169] H. B. Thompson, *J. Chem. Educ.*, **37**, 530 (1960).

hinder rotation about the 1,1' bond rather than block rotation completely. A reversible rotation may take place in solution until there is an equal molar ratio of the two mirror-image molecules and only a racemic mixture is recovered. Nevertheless, it is possible to use the rate of this racemization as a measure of the kinetic barrier to rotation of the phenyl rings. The kinetics of the racemization have been studied, and it was found to be a reversible first-order reaction.[170] The activation energies for racemization of a variety of optically active biphenyls have been found to be in the range of 18 to 25 kcal/mole, but the data are not sufficiently accurate to be used as a quantitative measure of the relative stabilities of the respective conformations.[171, 172]

As a qualitative guide for predicting the resolvability of substituted biphenyls, it has been suggested[172] that when the sum of certain derived atomic or group radii (see Table 3.9) of A and B in Fig. 3.7 is appreciably greater than 2.90 Å, the biphenyl will be resolvable; when the sum is considerably less than 2.90 Å, the groups will not greatly hinder rotation and the biphenyl will not be resolvable; and when the sum is close to 2.90 Å,

Table 3.9. Derived Atomic and Group Radii Used for Predicting Resolvability of *o*-Substituted Biphenyls[173]

Group	Radius (Å)
H	0.94
F	1.39
OH	1.45
CO_2H	1.56
NH_2	1.56
CH_3	1.73
Cl	1.89
NO_2	1.92
Br	2.11
I	2.20

these will be borderline cases. For example, the sums of the radii of the *ortho* groups of the following compounds are indicated and it is observed that the empirical rule would accurately predict the degree of interference of the *ortho* groups. That is, in either planar conformation, the sum of the radii of (A) is significantly greater than 2.90 Å and it is observed that the compound is readily resolvable and that the optical isomers do not racemize. For (B), the intermediate sum (if F and F are together, then the two COOH groups are together so there is more interference than when F is opposite COOH) is close to 2.90 Å and it is found experimentally that (B) can be resolved but racemizes easily. In (C), the sums are less than 2.90 Å

[170] G. B. Kistiakowsky and W. R. Smith, *J. Am. Chem. Soc.,* **58**, 1043 (1936).

[171] C. C. Li and R. Adams, *J. Am. Chem. Soc.,* **57**, 1565 (1935).

[172] R. Adams, *Rec. Chem. Progress,* Summer issue, **91**, (1949), and earlier papers.

[173] M. S. Leslie and E. E. Turner, *J. Chem. Soc.,* 1588 (1933).

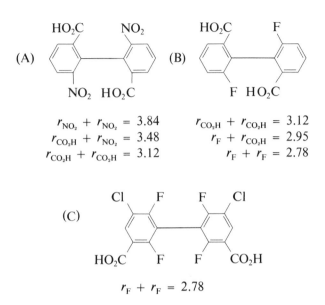

$$r_{NO_2} + r_{NO_2} = 3.84$$
$$r_{CO_2H} + r_{NO_2} = 3.48$$
$$r_{CO_2H} + r_{CO_2H} = 3.12$$

$$r_{CO_2H} + r_{CO_2H} = 3.12$$
$$r_F + r_{CO_2H} = 2.95$$
$$r_F + r_F = 2.78$$

$$r_F + r_F = 2.78$$

and the compound cannot be resolved. It is noteworthy that (C) is not resolvable in spite of the buttressing effect that exists in the compound. With a sufficiently large group, such as the $\overset{+}{As}(CH_3)_3$ group, a biphenyl can be resolved with only the single group.[173]

Hindered rotation about the 1,1′ bond in biphenyls has been detected by methods other than the actual isolation of the conformers. A very sensitive tool is ultraviolet spectroscopy. Essentially, biphenyl derivatives which have approximately coplanar rings have spectra similar to biphenyl, whereas the derivatives which are sterically hindered from being coplanar have spectra resembling those of correspondingly substituted benzenes (see Sec. 5.4.2). Also, a chemical test has been devised to detect hindered rotation in biphenyls.[174] This test is based on the formation of colored products when substituted benzidenes are oxidized.

$$H_2N \text{—} \langle \text{—} \rangle \text{—} \langle \text{—} \rangle \text{—} NH_2 \xrightarrow{oxid} HN = \langle \text{—} \rangle \langle \text{—} \rangle = NH \longrightarrow \text{colored products}$$

In this reaction, a coplanar quinone-imine is produced. However, if *ortho* repulsions hinder the two rings from lying in the same plane, the reaction is inhibited and decreases the formation of the colored products. Thus, the intensity of color produced upon oxidation of substituted benzidines was used as a measure of the steric hindrance between the *ortho* substituents.

[174] A. J. Bilbo and G. Wyman, *J. Am. Chem. Soc.*, **75**, 5313 (1953).

Other types of molecules are resolvable into optical isomers owing to a barrier to rotation about a single bond, notably substituted styrenes (LXXXIV) and amines (LXXXV to LXXXVII).

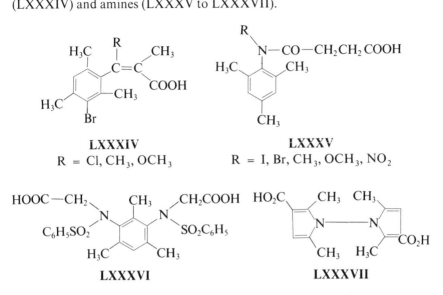

LXXXIV
R = Cl, CH$_3$, OCH$_3$

LXXXV
R = I, Br, CH$_3$, OCH$_3$, NO$_2$

LXXXVI

LXXXVII

On the other hand, hindered phenyl ethers (LXXXVIII) are extremely difficult to resolve.[175]

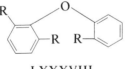

LXXXVIII

Some interesting systems recently resolved are LXXXIX–XCI. In all of these cases, optical activity is the result of hindered rotation about single bonds.

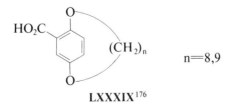

n=8,9

LXXXIX[176]

[175] M. Allen and R. Y. Moir, *Can. J. Chem.*, **37**, 1799 (1959).
[176] A. Lüttringhaus and G. Eyring, *Ann.*, **604**, 111 (1957).

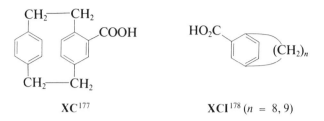

XC[177]   XCI[178] $(n = 8, 9)$

It was early recognized that the effectiveness of groups in hindering rotation is not the same in all systems. For example, an order was found for increasing rates of racemization, i.e., decreasing barrier to rotation about the crowded bond, in several series of compounds:

Series LXXXIV: $R = Cl > CH_3 > OCH_3$
Series LXXXV: $R = I > CH_3 > Br > OCH_3 > NO_2$
Series XCII:[179] $R = SO_3H, I > Br > CH_3 > Cl > NO_2 > COOH$
                      $OCH_3 > NH_2 > F.$

It is noticeable that these orders do not parallel the van der Waals radii of the groups nor are the sequences the same, e.g., compare OCH_3 with NO_2 in LXXXV and XCII, or CH_3 with Cl in LXXXIV and XCII, or CH_3 with Br in LXXXV and.XCII. Therefore, factors other than the relative sizes of the groups are involved.

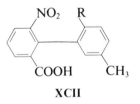

XCII

It was proposed almost simultaneously in two different laboratories[180, 181] that the preferred conformation of molecules may be determined by setting up a potential energy function for the molecule and mimimizing it with respect to van der Waals repulsions and strain energies from bond distortions. For illustration,[182] it can be reasoned that racemization of an optically active biphenyl molecule involves passage from the twisted configuration through a planar orientation. This planar configuration can be

[177] D. J. Cram, W. J. Wechter, and R. W. Kierstead, *J. Am. Chem. Soc.,* **80,** 3126 (1958).
[178] A. T. Blomquist, R. E. Stahl, Y. C. Meinwald, and B. H. Smith, *J. Org. Chem.,* **26,** 1687 (1961).
[179] R. Adams and J. B. Hale, *J. Am. Chem. Soc.,* **61,** 2825 (1939).
[180] T. L. Hill, *J. Chem. Phys.,* **14,** 465 (1946).
[181] F. H. Westheimer and J. E. Mayer, *J. Chem. Phys.,* **14,** 733 (1946).
[182] F. H. Westheimer in *Steric Effects in Organic Chemistry,* ed. M. S. Newman (New York: Wiley 1956), chap. 12.

regarded as the activated complex for racemization; the energy of activation, then, is the energy required to produce the planar form from the twisted form. In the planar form of XCIII, the *ortho* bromine and hydrogen atoms are crowded together to a distance less than the sum of their

Br H

HOOC—COOH

H Br

XCIII

van der Waals radii. This steric repulsion is relieved by several bond deformations, among which Westheimer and Mayer assumed the following to be most significant (in XCIII):

(1) stretching of the 1,1' carbon-carbon bond;
(2) deformation of the angles b;
(3) deformation of the angles a;
(4) stretching of the C—H$_{ortho}$ bonds;
(5) stretching of the C—Br bonds;
(6) deformation of the rings;
(7) deformation of the angles c.

Energy is required to bring about any of these distortions but they diminish the van der Waals repulsion and take place to just the extent necessary to minimize the energy of the planar form of XCIII. If E is the energy difference between the twisted and coplanar forms of XCIII, it can be obtained from the equation

$$E = \Sigma \; \tfrac{1}{2} a_2 q_i^2 + V(q_1, q_2, q_3, \cdots, q_N) \qquad (3\text{-}4)$$

where q_i are the displacements of the various coordinates of the molecule (such as the distance of the 1,1' C—C bond), the constants a_i are the force constants for these displacements, and the term for V represents the van der Waals interactions of the *ortho* hydrogen and bromine atoms. The van der Waals repulsion depends upon the distance between the nonbonded ortho hydrogen and bromine atoms, and is thus a function of the amount of the displacements q_i. The minimum value of E is the activation energy. Westheimer used literature values for the various force constants a_i, or estimated those not known, and approximated a van der Waals potential for use in Eq. (3-4). This led to a calculated energy of activation for XCIII of 18 kcal/mole. This estimate compares well with the experimental value of 19 kcal/mole.[183a]

[183](a) M. M. Harris, *Proc. Chem. Soc.* (London), 367 (1959); (b) K. Mislow, et al., *J. Am. Chem. Soc.,* **84,** 1455 (1962).

Westheimer and Mayer's calculations showed that the activation energy is made up of the following components:

van der Waals repulsion   6 kcal
deflection of the C—Br bonds   7.2
ring deformations   2.5
other deformations   2.5

Thus, bending back the *ortho* substituents constitutes the largest single contributor to the activation energy. It was calculated that the C—Br bond is deflected back about 12 degrees in the activated complex of XCIII. It should be pointed out that surprisingly, 2,2'-dihalo-, 2,2'-dimethyl- and 2,2'-dinitro-biphenyls have a *cis* rather than *trans* conformation as shown by dipole moment, electron diffraction, n.m.r., and ORD measurements.[183b] Apparently some attractive van der Waals or dispersion forces are of significant magnitude in these molecular environments.

The introduction of substituents into the biphenyl molecule may alter the activation energy of racemization. This can be the result of two different effects. One is resonance, which affects the length and force constant of the 1,1' carbon-carbon bond, and a second is a steric effect from groups in the *meta* positions which hinder bending back the *ortho* substituents. For illustration, Adams[172] and his students measured the rates of racemization of optically active biphenyls derived from XCIV; the data are listed in

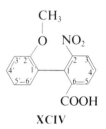

XCIV

Table 3.10. It can be seen that groups in the 3' position have a marked effect of slowing down the racemization process. This is due to their blocking or "buttressing" the methoxyl group from bending back to permit rotation

Table 3.10. HALF-LIVES FOR THE RACEMIZATION OF SOME BIPHENYLS[172]

Substituent in XCIV	Position in XCIV		
	3'	4'	5'
H	9.4 min.	9.4 min.	9.4 min.
OCH_3	98.1	2.6	10.8
CH_3	332	3.6	11.5
Cl	711	12	31
Br	827	25	32
NO_2	1905	115	35.4

about the 1,1' bond. Westheimer termed this the *buttressing* effect. It is much smaller in the 5' position where it is buttressing the smaller hydrogen atom. A more pronounced buttressing effect was observed for compound XCV, which was found to racemize approximately 10^{-5} times as fast as XCVI.[184] The difference between their activation energies or racemization is about 7 kcal/mole, which is an indication of the magnitude of the buttressing effect of the meta iodine atoms.

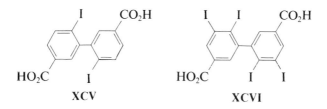

The effects of substituents in the 4' position are not as clearly understood. It is observed that the electron-donating groups CH_3 and OCH_3 facilitate racemization. This may be attributable to a resonance stabilization of the planar activated state by forms such as XCVII (b) and (c). On the other hand, it has been proposed[185] that the reason that XCVIII is resolvable while XCIX is not, is that resonance forms of type XCVIII (b) shorten the 1,1' bond and bring the *ortho* groups closer together to increase the van der Waals repulsion and thereby hinder racemization.

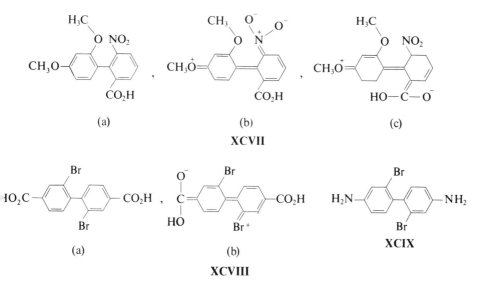

[184] M. Rieger and F. H. Westheimer, *J. Am. Chem. Soc.*, **72**, 19 (1950).
[185] M. Calvin, *J. Org. Chem.*, **4**, 256 (1939).

The buttressing effect shows up in a number of ways. For example, association of di-ortho-substituted phenols is markedly reduced because the ortho substituents hinder intermolecular H-bonding (Sec. 5.4.3). However, the association is further diminished when groups are also in the meta positions of the di-ortho-substituted phenols because the meta substituents prevent the ortho groups from bending back to allow association.[186] The buttressing effect also causes groups in substituted benzenes to rotate out of the plane of the ring. For illustration, benzoic acid is planar in the solid state whereas the COOH group is rotated 13.7° in o-chlorobenzoic acid and 23° in 5-nitro-2-chlorobenzoic acid.[286b]

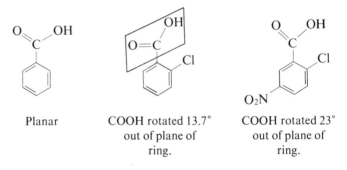

Planar   COOH rotated 13.7°   COOH rotated 23°
                      out of plane of   out of plane of
                      ring.   ring.

The o-chlorine atom forces the rotation of the COOH group in the center compound, and in the nitro acid, the nitro group buttresses the 6-hydrogen atom to prevent its bending back out of the way of the COOH group. Likewise, nitrobenzene and p-dinitrobenzene are planar in the solid state but the nitro group is rotated 11° in m-dinitrobenzene and 15° in 2,4-dinitrochlorobenzene. In nitrobenzene, the ortho hydrogen atoms can bend back a little to allow the nitro group to be planar with the ring but in the *m*-dinitro compound, the second nitro group buttresses the intervening hydrogen atom and forces the other nitro group to rotate some out of the plane of the ring. Other examples of the buttressing effect will be shown spectroscopically in Chapter 5.

3.4. Steric effects and chemical equilibria

One of the first attempts to obtain a quantitative measure of the magnitude of steric effects in the absence of the resonance effect was initiated by H. C. Brown in 1940. He studied the stabilities of Lewis-type salts.

Brown's[187] thesis was that in a salt of an amine, such as C, steric repulsions between the R groups on the nitrogen atom and the R' groups on

[186] W. C. Sears and L. J. Kitchen, *J. Am. Chem. Soc.,* **71**, 4110 (1949).

[187] H. C. Brown, M. D. Taylor, M. Gerstein, and H. Bartholomay, *J. Am. Chem. Soc.,* **66**, 431 (1944); **69**, 1332 (1947); *Science,* **103**, 385 (1946).

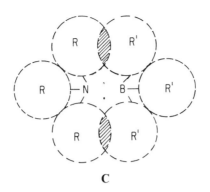

C

the boron decrease the stability of the salt and thereby decrease the apparent base strength of the amine. Brown referred to this steric repulsion at the interface as *F-strain* for *face* or *frontal* strain. For illustration, trimethylamine is a stronger base than is pyridine when the reference acid is one of small volume, but when the acid becomes one of significant size, F-strain in the salt of the trimethylamine is sufficient to cause an inversion of relative base strengths:

$$(CH_3)_3N: + C_5H_5N:HCl \quad \rightleftharpoons \quad (CH_3)_3N:HCl \quad + C_5H_5N:$$

$$(CH_3)_3N: + C_5H_5N:BH_3 \quad \rightleftharpoons \quad (CH_3)_3N:BH_3 \quad + C_5H_5N:$$

$$(CH_3)_3N: + C_5H_5N:BF_3 \quad \rightleftharpoons \quad (CH_3)_3N:BF_3 \quad + C_5H_5N:$$

but

$$(CH_3)_3N: + C_5H_5N:B(CH_3)_3 \quad \rightleftharpoons \quad (CH_3)_3N:B(CH_3)_3 + C_5H_5N:$$

Similarly, lutidine is a stronger base than is pyridine when the reference acid is HCl, but toward larger acids, such as BF_3, F-strain renders lutidine the weaker base.

This view is also supported quantitatively by the data in Tables 3.11 and 3.12. It can be seen from the second and third columns of Table 3.11 that an alkyl group increases the basicity of the nitrogen toward protonic acids, and that 2-*t*-butylpyridine is only a slightly weaker base than 2-picoline. With BF_3 as the acid, the F-strain in the picoline salts is still negligible, but it becomes appreciable in salts of 2,6-lutidine and amounts to over 10 kcal in the salt of 2-*t*-butylpyridine. Finally, with $B(CH_3)_3$, the F-strain amounts to approximately 7 kcal even in 2-picoline and is at least 17 kcal in 2,6-lutidine and 2-*t*-butylpyridine.

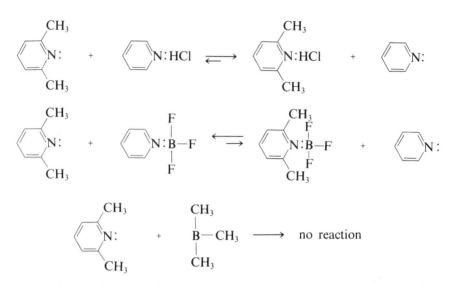

Table 3.11. RELATIVE BASE STRENGTHS OF SOME PYRIDINE DERIVATIVES[188]

Base	pK_a	Heat of reaction (kcal/mole)		
		CH_3SO_3H	BF_3'	$B(CH_3)_3$
Pyridine	5.17	17.1	25	15.3
4-Picoline	6.02	18.8	25.5	17.6
3-Picoline	5.68	..	25.3	17.6
2-Picoline	5.97	18.3	23.3	10
2,6-Lutidine	6.58	19.5	17.5	< 0
2-t-Butylpyridine	5.76	17.3	14.8	< 0

Table 3.12. ENERGY RELATIONSHIPS FOR SOME PYRIDINE BASES[189]

RC_5H_4N R	Heat of reaction (kcal/mole) $RC_5H_4N + BF_3$	Activation energy (kcal) of RC_5H_4N plus		
		CH_3I	C_2H_5I	$(CH_3)_2CHI$
H	25.0	13.9	16.0	17.7
3-CH_3	25.3	13.6	15.5	17.4
4-CH_3	25.5	13.6	15.7	17.3
2-CH_3	23.3	14.0	16.5	19.2
2-CH_3CH_2	22.7	14.2	16.6	
2-$(CH_3)_2CH$	21.7	14.8	17.1	
2-$(CH_3)_3C$	14.8	17.5		

[188]H. C. Brown, presented at the Howard University Chemistry Lecture Series, October 18, 1951; *J. Chem. Educ.*, **36**, 424 (1959).

[189]M. J. S. Dewar, *Electronic Theory of Organic Chemistry* (Oxford: Clarendon Press, 1950), p. 62.

The effects of F-strain are observable also in displacement reactions. If the transition state for the reaction between CH_3X and pyridine is represented as CI,[189] then as the steric requirements of the alkyl group become

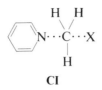

CI

larger, the stability of the activated complex should decrease. This would increase the activation energy and reduce the rate of reaction. This notion is substantiated by the data in Table 3.12, where it can be seen that as the basicities of the pyridine bases towards BF_3 decrease, the energies of activation for quarternary salt formation increase. It is noteworthy, also, that the activation energies increase for a given base as the sizes of the alkyl iodides increase.

It can be shown that these effects must arise from steric rather than inductive effects. In a salt $Me_3B:NMe_3$, replacement of methyl groups on either the nitrogen or boron atom by larger groups uniformly leads to a decrease in the stability of the salts.

$$Me_3N:BMe_3 > R_3N:BMe_3, \qquad R = Et, i\text{-Pr}, t\text{-Bu}$$

$$Me_3N:BMe_3 > Me_3N:BR_3$$

If the effect were polar, a group that increased the basicity of the amine should decrease the acidity of the boron acid. For instance, replacing the methyl groups on nitrogen by halogen atoms decreases the base strength of the amine and increases the acid strength of the boron.[190] Furthermore, the neutrality of 2,6-lutidine toward boron trimethyl is due to F-strain outweighing the base-strengthening electrical effect of the methyl groups, since mesitonitrile, in which there is no steric hindrance, is a slightly stronger base than benzonitrile towards BF_3.[191]

The demonstration of the existence of F-strain emphasizes the importance of stating the reference acid when comparing the base strength of two or more bases, as was pointed out by Lewis and later by Brown. Toward a proton, the order of decreasing base strength of methyl- or ethylamines is: secondary, primary, tertiary, and ammonia. If the reference acid is changed, F-strain may increase to make the secondary amine weaker then the primary amine. Finally, with increasing F-strain, the order of decreasing base strength can reach the sequence: NH_3, RNH_2, R_2NH, R_3N. In an extensive study of the relative base strengths of aliphatic amines

[190]A. B. Burg and A. A. Green, *J. Am. Chem. Soc.*, **65**, 1838 (1943); N. E. Miller, *Diss. Abstr.*, **18**, 1972 (1958).

[191]H. C. Brown and R. B. Johannesen, *J. Am. Chem. Soc.*, **72**, 2934 (1950).

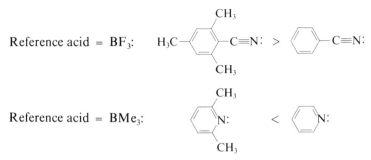

toward various acids, Brown and his coworkers[187] observed several sequences given in Fig. 3.9. Curve A is the order anticipated on the basis of polar effects only; that is, $NH_3 < RNH_2 < R_2NH < R_3N$. Curve C illustrates the result when F-strain in the salt causes the basicity of the

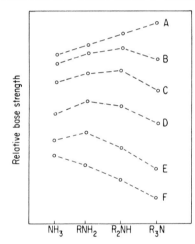

Fig. 3.9. Possible sequences of the relative base strengths of ammonia and aliphatic amines against various reference acids.

tertiary amine to drop below that of ammonia, giving the order $R_3N < NH_3 < RNH_2 < R_2NH$. Curves D, E, and F represent sequences in which the strain steadily increases until finally all of the amines become weaker than NH_3. In the experimental studies of Brown's group, all but the sequences A and C were observed, and specific examples are listed in Table 3.13.

$$A = NH_3 < RNH_2 < R_2NH < R_3N$$
$$B = NH_3 < R_3N < RNH_2 < R_2NH$$
$$C = R_3N < NH_3 < RNH_2 < R_2NH$$
$$D = R_3N < NH_3 < R_2NH < RNH_2$$
$$E = R_3N < R_2NH < NH_3 < RNH_2$$
$$F = R_3N < R_2NH < RNH_2 < NH_3$$

It is observed in Table 3.13 that the relative base strength of the methylamines towards protonic acids in aqueous solution is also B. One would

Table 3.13. RELATIVE BASE STRENGTHS OF ALIPHATIC AMINES[187]
(Designated according to the curves in Fig. 3.9)

R in amine	$H_3O^+_{aq.}$	$B(Me)_3$	$B(Et)_3$	$B(i\text{-}Pr)_3$	$B(t\text{-}Bu)_3$	$Ag^+_{aq.}$
				Reference acid		
Methyl	B	B	D	D	E	
Ethyl	B	D	E	E	F	E
Isopropyl	B	E	E	F	F	
tert.-Butyl		F	F	F	F	

not expect any appreciable F-strain between the methyl groups on the nitrogen atom and a proton in the salt to make the tertiary amine anomalously weak. Brown attributed this unexpected order to what he called *back* or B-strain.[187] This is a repulsion between the methyl groups on the nitrogen which develops at the "back" of the amine fragment of the salt. Brown assumed that the nitrogen bonds in a trimethylamine salt have a tetrahedral configuration and in the free base the C—N—C bond angles are greater than the tetrahedral angle. This crowds the methyl groups together in the salt and reduces its stability. This B-strain may exist in the base as well as in the salt, but greater strain in the salt inhibits salt formation and effectively decreases the apparent base strength of the amine.

In support of his proposal, Brown offered the additional observation that the order of base strengths of the methylphosphines toward protonic acids and boron-trimethyl is that which would be expected in the absence of B- and F-strain.

$$PH_3 < CH_3PH_2 < (CH_3)_2PH < (CH_3)_3P$$

When attached to the larger atom of phosphorus, the methyl groups are farther apart and develop little B-strain.

The occurrence of B-strain manifests itself also in the reactivity of compounds where the transition state affords a decrease in strain. For illustration, Brown and his coworkers found the rates of hydrolysis of *t*-alkyl

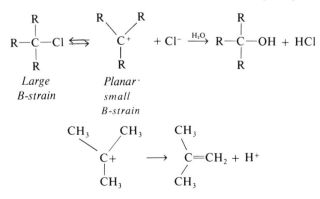

*Large
B-strain*

*Planar·
small
B-strain*

chlorides to increase with increasing bulkiness of the alkyl groups. B-strain in the *t*-alkyl halide is relieved when the planar transient carbonium ion is formed; hence the greater the B-strain in the alkyl halide, the greater is the driving force to produce the transition state. The carbonium ion can also eliminate a proton to produce an olefin. The B-strain that would again exist in the carbinol is avoided by olefin formation. Consequently, the greater the bulkiness of the alkyl groups, the greater should be the proportion of olefin in the hydrolysis products of t-alkyl halides. This is observed to be the case according to the data in Table 3.14 where differences between (i) and (ii), (iii) and (iv), and (v) and (vi) demonstrate that B-strain facilitates olefin formation.

Table 3.14. PERCENTAGES OF OLEFIN IN THE HYDROLYSIS
PRODUCTS OF *t*-ALKYL HALIDES

Carbonium ion	*Per cent olefin*
(i) Me_3C^+	16
(ii) $t\text{-}BuMe_2C^+$	61
(iii) Et_3C^+	40
(iv) $t\text{-}BuEt_2C^+$	90
(v) $MeCH_2Me_2C^+$	34
(vi) $t\text{-}BuCH_2Me_2C^+$	65

R. Spitzer and K. S. Pitzer[192] challenged Brown's adoption of B-strain to account for the base weakness of trimethylamine. They calculated the energy required to deform the C—N—C bond angles of trimethylamine from the extreme angle of 112° to the tetrahedral angle, including the energy to compress the methyl groups against van der Waals and electrostatic repulsion. A total value of 0.5 kcal was obtained. In contrast to this, the total strain in $(CH_3)_3N:B(CH_3)_3$ is estimated from heats of dissociation to be 3–8 kcal/mole. Spitzer and Pitzer concluded therefore that the magnitude of the B-strain in trimethylamine is far too small to account for its anomalous weakness. They point out, however, that B-strain may exist in amines containing larger alkyl groups. Later, the C—N—C bond angles of trimethylamine were found to be 109° ± 2°, so that salt formation causes only a small decrease in bond angles. It would appear, then, that B-strain alone cannot account for the small base strength of trimethylamine. Brown has demonstrated unequivocally the existence of F- and B-strain in molecules; however, it is evident that F- and B-strain do not provide a completely satisfactory explanation for the relative base strengths of aliphatic amines and ammonia in aqueous media towards protonic acids.

It has been shown that an important factor is solvation.[193] For illustra-

[192]R. Spitzer and K. S. Pitzer, *J. Am. Chem. Soc.*, **70**, 1261 (1948).

[193]H. K. Hall, *J. Am. Chem. Soc.*, **79**, 5441, 5444 (1957); L. Sacconi and G. Lomarbo, *J. Am. Chem. Soc.*, **82**, 6266 (1960).

tion, in nonaqueous solvents such as chloroform[194] or acetonitrile,[195] the order of base strengths of n-alkyl amines toward protonic acids is[196]

$$R_3N \gg R_2NH > RNH_2.$$

Thus, they follow the order expected from the inductive effect of the alkyl groups. In an aqueous medium, several types of solvation effects occur, the principal one of which is hydrogen bonding. For example, there is (i) $N\!-\!H\cdots OH_2$ bonding between the free base and water, which was shown in Sec. 1.6.2 to increase water solubility of primary and secondary amines over that of corresponding tertiary amines. Also, (ii) $HO\!-\!H\cdots N$ hydrogen bonding can occur, which, because of steric hindrance between the alkyl groups and the aggregated solvent molecules, takes place with NH_3 to the largest extent.[197] Hydrogen bonding of types (i) and (ii) stabilizes the free base of the nitrogen compounds in the order $NH_3 > RNH_2 > R_2NH > R_3N$, and would tend, in the absence of other effects, to give an order of decreasing base strengths $R_3N > R_2NH > RNH_2 > NH_3$. However, in the salts, type (i) becomes (iii) $\overset{+}{N}\!-\!H\ldots OH_2$ and the hydrogen bonds are stronger owing to the greater electronegativity of the nitrogen. Since this occurs to the greatest extent for the NH_4^+ ion, the order of base strengths would be (in the absence of other effects) $NH_3 > RNH_2 > R_2NH > R_3N$. Hence, hydrogen bonding in the free base gives an opposite order from hydrogen bonding in the ion, and the net effect, combined with the inductive effects, turns out to be $R_2NH > RNH_2 > R_3N > NH_3$.

---

[194]R. G. Pearson and F. V. Williams, *J. Am. Chem. Soc.*, **76**, 258 (1954).

[195]E. J. Forman and D. N. Hume, *J. Phys. Chem.*, **63**, 1949 (1959).

[196]However, it has been found that this order is not preserved in all nonaqueous solvents. (J. W. Bayles and A. F. Taylor, *J. Chem. Soc.*, 417 (1961)).

[197]It is probable that the relative order of inherent strength of the $N\cdots HO_2$ bond is just the reverse, i.e., strongest with Me_3N. Some support for this notion comes from the observation that in the absence of the steric hindering solvation effect of water, the $N\cdots H$ bond appears to be stronger in $Cl_3CH:N(C_2H_5)_3$ than in $Cl_3CH:NH_3$. (Cf. M. E. Emerson, E. Grunwald, M. L. Kaplan, and R. A. Kromhout, *J. Am. Chem. Soc.*, **82**, 6312 (1960)).

[198]Incidentally, this order has also been explained in terms of hyperconjugation (D. H. McDaniel, *Science*, **125**, 545 (1957). The salts of the alkyl phosphines are stabilized by resonance among such forms as

$$H_3C\!-\!\overset{\overset{\displaystyle CH_3}{|}}{\underset{\underset{\displaystyle CH_3}{|}}{P^\pm}}\!-\!H, \qquad H_3C\!-\!\overset{\overset{\displaystyle \overset{+}{H}CH_2}{\|}}{\underset{\underset{\displaystyle CH_3}{|}}{P^-}}\!-\!H$$

9 eq. forms

Thus, resonance stabilization is greatest for the tertiary phosphine and does not occur with $^+PH_4$. On this basis, the order of base strengths expected would be in accord with that observed. Such resonance stabilization cannot occur for the amines because nitrogen does not expand its valence shell to accommodate ten electrons.

Pearson[137] has pointed out that in the case of the methyl phosphines, $\overset{+}{P}$—$H\cdots OH_2$ hydrogen bonding is not strong enough to upset the order produced by the inductive effect, namely, $R_3P > R_2PH > RPH_2 > PH_3$.[198]

Another factor affecting base strengths is the effect of steric hindrance to solvation.[199] The larger the groups about the nitrogen in the amine cation (aqueous solvation of the uncharged amine can be neglected), the lower is the solvation energy and the smaller will be the apparent base strength of the amine. This will be brought out in greater detail when the effect of steric hindrance to resonance is taken up (Sec. 4.7.5).

In summation, then, it can be said that (1) towards a small acid such as a protonic acid, the inherent relative base strengths of the aliphatic amines follow the order expected from the inductive effect: $R_3N >> R_2NH > RNH_2$. This will be the case in nonaqueous solvents and in the vapor state. (2) In an aqueous medium, solvation effects alter the above order to give an apparent order of $R_2NH > RNH_2 > R_3N$. (3) Towards larger acids, F- and B-strain may alter the observed base strengths of the amines to give an order lying anywhere between the two extremes of $R_3N > R_2NH > RNH_2 > NH_3$ and $NH_3 > RNH_2 > R_2NH > R_3N$.

Also, the dissociation constants of acids are affected by steric effects.[200] For instance, the dissociation constant of methyl-t-butylneopentylacetic acid is $1/25$ of that of acetic acid[201] and the ionization of 2,6-di-t-butylphenols is about $1/1000$ that of the corresponding phenols.[202,203] An examination of the dissociation constants of other trialkylacetic acids shows that the major factor responsible for the reduction in acid strength is a steric hindrance to solvation. The large groups prevent solvation of the anion and thereby decrease its stability. This would have the effect of diminishing ionization of the acid. This view is strengthened by the observation[202] that 2,6-di-t-butylphenols of type CII will not dissolve in aqueous alkali or give other phenolic tests whereas 2,6-di-t-butylphenols of type

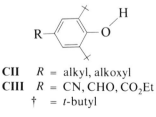

CII	R = alkyl, alkoxyl
CIII	R = CN, CHO, CO_2Et
†	= t-butyl

[199]B. M. Wepster, *Rec. trav. chim.*, **76**, 357 (1957).
[200]G. S. Hammond in *Steric Effects in Organic Chemistry*, ed. M. S. Newman (New York: Wiley, 1956), chap. 9.
[201]G. S. Hammond and D. H. Hogle, *J. Am. Chem. Soc.*, **77**, 338 (1955); *J. Am. Chem. Soc.*, **72**, 4297 (1950).
[202]L. A. Cohen, *J. Org. Chem.*, **22**, 1333 (1955).
[203]G. H. Stillson, D. W. Sawyer, and C. K. Hunt, *J. Am. Chem. Soc.*, **67**, 303 (1945).

CIII are soluble in aqueous alkali. Phenols of type CIII will not react with diazomethane or sodium metal in boiling ligroin, so the OH group is still highly shielded. However, in CIII the anionic negative charge may be delocalized to the *para* substituent. That is, the anion of the formyl derivative CIV, for example, is a resonance hybrid of forms (a) and (b) in

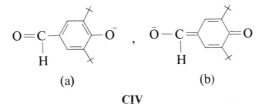

(a)   (b)

CIV

which the quinoidal form makes an unusually large contribution. This fact was verified by infrared spectroscopic data which showed that the carbonyl group in CIV has a larger single-bond character than in CV. Ultraviolet spectral data also corroborated this view. The larger distribution of charge in the ions of CIII over that in the ions of CII permits a solvation of the anion and accounts for the solubility of CIII in aqueous alkali.

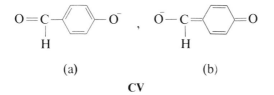

(a)   (b)

CV

There is evidence of anionic charge at the *para* position even in unsubstituted 2,6-di-*t*-butylphenols. For instance, alkyl halides react with hindered phenols in alcoholic KOH to give C-alkyl and O-alkyl products.[204]

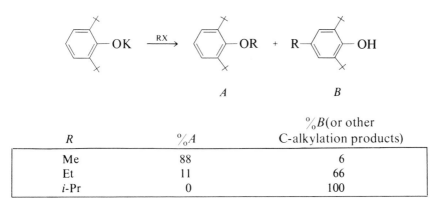

A   *B*

R	%A	%B(or other C-alkylation products)
Me	88	6
Et	11	66
i-Pr	0	100

[204]N. Kornblum and R. Seltzer, *J. Am. Chem. Soc.*, **83**, 3668 (1961).

It can be seen that, with increasing size of the alkyl group, less ether is produced and that the isopropyl group yields no ether.

The 2,6-di-*t*-butylphenols of type CIII are soluble in alkali but still ionize to a much smaller degree than the respective nonhindered phenols (Table 3.15). This indicates that the weakness of the hindered phenols, and probably the hindered acetic acids, is not due completely to hindrance to solvation of the anions.[205] It is possible that the hydrocarbon groups lower the effective dielectric constant about the carboxy group which increases the electrostatic free energy of the anion and, hence, decreases the ionization constant.[201]

Table 3.15. DISSOCIATION CONSTANTS OF SOME PHENOLS
IN 50% AQUEOUS ETHANOL[202]

Substituent	Phenol pK_a	Di-*t*-butylphenol pK_a
p-CHO	8.81	11.3
p-CN	9.10	11.4
p-CO$_2$Et	9.61	11.8

It should be pointed out here that the steric effect operates not only through hindering solvation (including the spatial blocking of solvent molecules and the effect of changing the dielectric constant) but through a hindrance to resonance and possibly through the increase of internal strains after protonation of an amine. This latter effect will be discussed in Sec. 4.8.1.

3.5. Chemical properties and steric requirements

Steric requirements have varying influences on the courses of almost all organic reactions.[206] Consequently, volumes could be written on this subject, and only a few reaction-types selected by chance interest of the author will be taken up here.

3.5.1. ESTERIFICATIONS.[207]

One of the first reaction-types in which steric effects were investigated was esterification. For illustration,[208] alcohols and acids which are highly substituted about their reaction centers are esterified very slowly, if at all,

---

[205]For example, the larger solvation of the ion of glycolic acid gives the acid an unusually large dissociation constant (E. J. King, *J. Am. Chem. Soc.*, **82**, 3575 (1960)).

[206]C. K. Ingold, *Quart. Revs.*, **11**, 1 (1957).

[207]M. S. Newman, ed., *Steric Effects in Organic Chemistry*, chap. 4.

[208]J. J. Sudborough and L. L. Lloyd, *J. Chem. Soc.*, 467 (1899); 4308 (1908); H. Goldschmidt, *Ber.*, **28**, 3218 (1895); M. S. Newman, *J. Am. Chem. Soc.*, **72**, 4783 (1950).

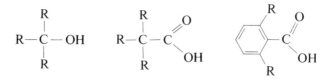

under the usual conditions of alcohol, acid, and hydrogen chloride. Instead, the hindered acids such as mesitylenecarboxylic acid are esterified with alcohols only in a strong acid solvent such as concentrated sulfuric acid or trifluoroacetic acid.[209] The difference in behavior can be attributed to a difference in reaction mechanism.[210] The unhindered acid forms a planar carbonium ion intermediate (CVI). The hindered acid has difficulty in forming such an ion because of steric repulsion from the R groups, and as a result, it is esterified only very slowly, if at all. On the other hand, in a strongly acidic medium, the hindered acid may react by forming the less crowded intermediate ion CVII.

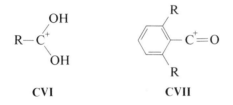

CVI   CVII

Along a similar line, the complete haloform reaction is hindered by groups shielding the carbonyl group. For example, acetophenone reacts with alkaline hypochlorite to give chloroform plus benzoate ion,

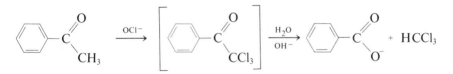

whereas 2,6-dimethyl-acetophenone gives only the trichlorinated product.[211]

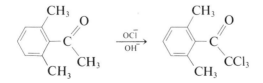

[209] M. S. Newman, *Rec. Chem. Progress,* Spring issue, 1 (1948); A. Bradley, and M. E. Hill, *J. Am. Chem. Soc.,* **77,** 1575, 2888 (1955).

[210] P. D. Bartlett, *J. Chem. Educ.,* **30,** 22 (1953).

[211] R. T. Arnold and E. Rondestvedt, *J. Am. Chem. Soc.,* **67,** 1265 (1945).

Apparently, the ortho methyl groups block the approach of the nucleophilic reagent (H_2O or OH^- ion) from attacking the carbonyl carbon atom for subsequent cleavage of the C—CCl_3 bond.

3.5.2. ADDITIONS TO MULTIPLE BONDS.[207]

Various types of additions to C=C bonds are blocked by steric hindrance. For illustration, 2,6-disubstituted styrenes resist polymerization almost completely, whereas styrenes substituted in other positions polymerize readily.[212] Another example is found in the series CVIII, CIX, and CX.[213] Tetraphenylethylene (CVIII) adds H_2, and Cl_2 slowly, but does not add Br_2.[214] Tetra-α-napthylethylene (CIX) adds H_2 but not Cl_2 or Br_2.[215]

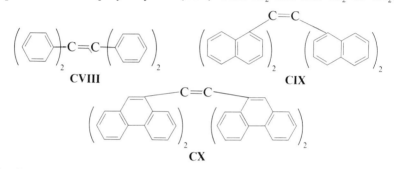

CVIII   CIX

CX

Finally, tetra-9-phenanthrylethylene (CX) does not even add H_2.[216] Thus, as the groups get larger about the olefinic carbon atoms, they gradually block out smaller and smaller molecules from attacking the olefinic carbon atoms. In Sec. 4.8.3 it will be shown that resonance has a small role in this reaction which is far outweighed by the steric hindrance.

Reactions involving additions to carbonyl groups are also quite sensitive to steric conditions. For instance, highly hindered ketones such as isopropyl ketone do not add Grignard reagents containing bulky groups, e.g., isopropyl magnesium chloride. Similarly, only aldehydes and methyl ketones form insoluble sodium bisulfite addition compounds, because with two large groups, the bisulfite ion cannot approach the shielded carbonyl carbon atom. Highly hindered ketones form Schiff bases only under "forcing conditions."[217]

[212]T. Alfrey, Jr., and W. H. Ebelke, *J. Am. Chem. Soc.*, **71**, 3235 (1949); F. M. Lewis and F. R. Mayo, *J. Am. Chem. Soc.*, **70**, 1533 (1948); E. T. McBee and R. A. Sanford, *J. Am. Chem. Soc.*, **72**, 5574 (1950); F. R. Buck, *et al.*, *Nature*, **162**, 103 (1948).

[213]The author is indebted to Mr. Naoya Nakagawa of Tokyo University for calling this sequence to his attention.

[214]W. H. Zartman and H. Adkins, *J. Am. Chem. Soc.*, **54**, 1168 (1932); H. Finkelstein, *Ber.*, **43**, 1533 (1910).

[215]L. Pauling and J. Sherman, *J. Chem. Phys.*, **1**, 679 (1933).

[216]F. Bergmann and S. Israelashwile, *J. Am. Chem. Soc.*, **67**, 1951 (1945).

[217]D. E. Pearson and F. Greer, *J. Am. Chem. Soc.*, **77**, 1294 (1955).

3.5.3 AROMATIC SUBSTITUTION.[218]

Among the several factors which affect the isomeric composition of di-substituted products from electrophilic reactions of monosubstituted ben-zenes is the steric factor.[218(a)] Spatial requirements do not change an *o,p*-directing group to an *m*-orienting group or vice versa, but have a pronounced effect upon the *o,p* ratio of products. For instance, in Table 3.16 it can be seen that the size of the substituent in the monosubstituted

Table 3.16.[224] ILLUSTRATION OF THE STERIC FACTOR
IN AROMATIC SUBSTITUTION

A. Orientation in monoalkylation of toluene			
Entering group	*Per cent ortho substitution*	*Per cent meta substitution*	*Per cent para substitution*
Me	53.8	17.3	28.8
Et	45	30	25
i-Pr	37.5	29.8	32.7
t-Bu	0	7	93
B . Isomer composition in mononitration of the alkylbenzenes			
Compound	*Per cent ortho*	*Per cent meta*	*Per cent para*
C_6H_5Me	58.45	4.4	37.15
C_6H_5Et	45	6.5	48.5
C_6H_5-*i*-Pr	30	7.7	62.3
C_6H_5-*t*-Bu	15.8	11.5	72.7

benzene as well as the size of the entering group can decrease *ortho* sub-stitution essentially to zero.

There is also qualitative evidence of the steric factor in aromatic sub-stitution. For example, mesitylene will react with a methyl halide but not with a *t*-butyl halide in a Friedel-Crafts reaction:

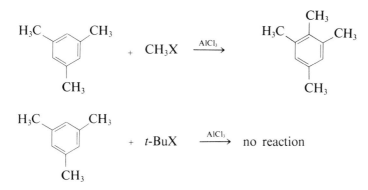

[218](a) G. S. Hammond and M. F. Hawthorne, *Steric Effects in Organic Chemistry,* chap. 3; (b) W. W. Kaeding, *J. Org. Chem.,* **26,** 4851 (1961).

The failure to react can be attributed to steric hindrance because a *t*-BuX will react with an open ring such as toluene, and mesitylene will react with a smaller alkyl halide such as methyl halide. Similarly, chlorine will react with *m*-*t*-butylphenol at the 2-, 4-, and 6-positions; bromine will substitute

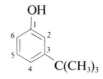

at the 4- and 6-positions but not the 2-position; and iodine will enter position 6 but not the 2- or 4-positions.[218(b)] The critical spatial requirements for reaction on two adjacent groups are vividly illustrated by the observation that one cannot substitute a Cl atom for the α hydrogen atom in compound CXI, but it can be done in CXII.

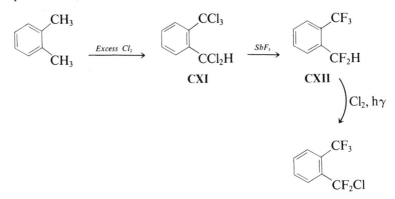

The foregoing reveals steric hindrance to nuclear and side-chain substitution, and led to the conclusion[219] that it is unlikely that *o*-di-*t*-butylbenzene could be prepared by a Friedel-Crafts reaction although it might be made by an indirect method. This is the case, for the only successful preparation of the compound so far has been by the reaction of $Co_2(CO)_6 \cdot t$—Bu—C≡C—Bu—*t* with acetylene.[220] By a similar reaction, 1,2,4-tri-*t*-butyl- and 1,2,4,5-tetra-*t*-butylbenzene were also prepared.[221] Other derivatives of *o*-di-*t*-butylbenzene, such as *o*-phenylene-di-isobutyric acid[222] and alcohol[223] have been prepared by oxidations of certain side-chain ring compounds.

[219]H. C. Brown, *et al.*, *J. Am. Chem. Soc.*, **75**, 1 (1953).

[220]C. Hoogzand and W. Hübel, *Angew. Chem.*, **73**, 680 (1961); E. M. Arnett and M. E. Strem, *Chem. and Ind. (London)*, 2008 (1961).

[221]W. Hübel, and C. Hoogzand, *Chem. Ber.*, **93**, 103 (1960).

[222]H. A. Bruson, F. W. Grant, and E. Bobko, *J. Am. Chem. Soc.*, **80**, 3633 (1958).

[223]L. R. C. Barclay, N. D. Hall, and J. W. MacLean, *Tetrahedron Letters*, no. 7, 243 (1961).

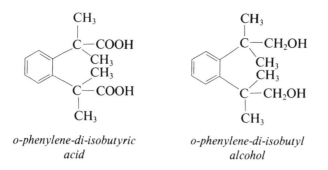

o-phenylene-di-isobutyric   o-phenylene-di-isobutyl
          acid   alcohol

3.5.4. 2,6-Di-t-BUTYLPHENOLS.

Steric hindrance produces some very interesting effects on the properties of 2,6-di-t-butylphenols, such as an obliteration of typical phenolic properties and the formation of stable free radicals. The unusually low acid strength of these phenols was discussed in Sec. 3.4.

Mention was made on page 151 that 2,6-di-t-alkylphenols are monomeric rather than associated because of steric hindrance to inter-molecular H bonding. Just how shielded the phenolic OH is in a 2,6-di-t-butylphenol (CXIII) is revealed by the fact that when R is any alkyl or

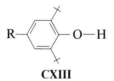

CXIII

† = t-butyl group

alkoxyl group, the phenol is insoluble in alkali and even in alcoholic KOH, gives no color with ferric chloride solution, and reacts only slowly if at all with sodium metal, methyl magnesium bromide, or diazomethane.[225] As stated previously, the steric effect also decreases the ionization about a thousandfold.

Phenols of type CXIII, in which there are no α hydrogen atoms on R, can be oxidized in the absence of oxygen to give deep-blue, paramagnetic stable free radicals.[226]

[224]H. C. Brown and W. H. Bonner, *J. Am. Chem. Soc.,* **76,** 605 (1954), and earlier papers; See also G. A. Olah and S. J. Kuhn, *J. Am. Chem. Soc.,* **84,** 3684 (1962) for steric effects of the solvent.

[225]C. D. Cook, *et al., J. Chem. Educ.,* **32,** 312 (1955).

[226] C. D. Cook, *et al., J. Org. Chem.,* **25,** 1429 (1960), and earlier papers in this series; E. Müller, *et al., Chem. Ber.,* **92,** 474 (1959).

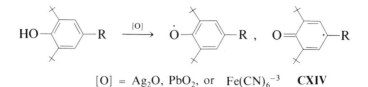

$$[O] = Ag_2O, \, PbO_2, \, \text{or} \quad Fe(CN)_6^{-3} \quad \textbf{CXIV}$$

Steric hindrance prevents the free radical from dimerizing. Nevertheless, it slowly reacts with molecular oxygen (which has two unpaired electrons) in a way that reveals the odd-electron character of the *para* carbon atom.

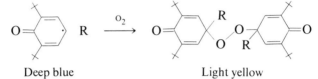

Deep blue   Light yellow

An interesting compound is the condensation product of 2,6-di-*t*-butyl-phenol with formaldehyde.[227]

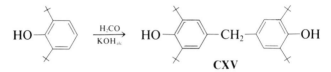

CXV

When CXV is oxidized with alkaline ferricyanide in the absence of oxygen, the stable free radical CXVI is obtained.

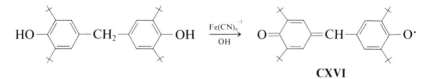

CXVI

The free radical CXVI can be recrystallized from ethanol in the form of blue needles which are paramagnetic.

STUDY QUESTIONS

1. Why is the energy barrier restricting internal rotation smaller in Cl_3Si—$SiCl_3$ than in Cl_3C—CCl_3?

2. Why is the barrier restricting internal rotation about the C—C single bond as measured in styrene (2.2 kcal/mole) smaller than might be expected?

3. How should the barriers to C—C and C—O rotations compare in ethylene chlorohydrin and ethanol?

[227] M. S. Kharasch and B. S. Joshi, *J. Org. Chem.*, **22**, 1435, 1439 (1957).

4. Offer an explanation for the observation that 4,4'-dihydroxy-2,3,5,6-2',3',5',6'-octamethylbiphenyl has not been oxidized to the corresponding quinone.

5. Draw the *cis* and *trans* isomers of 1,2-, 1,3-, and 1,4-methylcyclohexanols, and predict which conformation should be the more stable one for each pair of position isomers.[228]

6. The pK_a of cyclohexanecarboxylic acid in aqueous dimethylformamide is 7.82 and that of *trans*-4-*t*-butylcyclohexanecarboxylic acid is 7.79. What can be said about the polar effect of the *t*-butyl group on the ionization of the COOH group in the latter compound?

7. Offer an explanation for the following facts:
   (a) The barrier to rotation of the NO_2 group in nitromethane is essentially zero (13.8 cal/mole). Would your argument apply to the acetate ion too?
   (b) Vinyl halides and chlorobenzene form Grignards in tetrahydrofuran but not in ethyl ether.
   (c) Dioxane is soluble in water but ethyl ether is not.
   (d) *trans*-Cyclooctene is fairly soluble in aqueous silver nitrate while the *cis* isomer is not.
   (e) The barrier to rotation of the CH_3 group in ethane is lower than that of the CF_3 group in perfluoroethane, but the barrier to rotation of the CF_3 group is larger in $C_6H_5CF_3$ than the barrier is for the CH_3 group in $C_6H_5CH_3$.[229]
   (f) Towards BMe_3, $EtMe_2N$ is a weaker base than Me_3N whereas $EtMe_2P$ is a stronger base than Me_3P.[230]

8. Predict the following, and give the basis for each prediction:
   (a) The relative rates of debromination of stilbene dibromide for the meso and the racemic isomers.[231]
   (b) The relative stabilities of the following pairs:[232]
   Cl_3P—$N(C_2H_5)_3$ and Cl_3P—$N(CH_3)_3$,
   Cl_3P—$N(CH_3)_3$ and Br_3P—$N(CH_3)_3$,
   $(CH_3)_3P$—$N(CH_3)_3$ and Cl_3P—$N(CH_3)_3$,
   Cl_3P—$As(CH_3)_3$ and Cl_3P—$N(CH_3)_3$,
   $(CH_3)_2O$—$B(CH_3)_3$ and $(CH_3)_2S$—$B(CH_3)_3$,
   $(C_2H_5)_3P$—$B(CH_3)_3$ and $(CH_3)_3P$—$B(CH_3)_3$.

9. Which should have the larger diequatorial conformation content, *trans*-1,2-dichloro- or *trans*-1,2-dibromocyclohexane?[233]

[228] Cf. D. S. Noyce and D. B. Denney, *J. Am. Chem. Soc.,* **74,** 5912 (1952); S. Siegel, *J. Am. Chem. Soc.,* **75,** 1317 (1953); H. L. Goering and C. Serres, *J. Am. Chem. Soc.,* **74,** 5908 (1952).

[229] For data, see D. W. Scott, *et al., J. Am. Chem. Soc.,* **81,** 1015 (1959).

[230] H. D. Kaesz and F. D. A. Stone, *J. Am. Chem. Soc.,* **82,** 6213 (1960).

[231] Cf. W. G. Young, D. Pressman, and C. Coryell, *J. Am. Chem. Soc.,* **61,** 1640 (1939).

[232] R. R. Holmes, *J. Am. Chem. Soc.,* **82,** 5285 (1960); H. D. Kaesz and F. G. A. Stone, *J. Am. Chem. Soc.,* **82,** 6213 (1960); W. A. G. Graham and F. G. A. Stone, *J. Inorg. Nucl. Chem.,* **3,** 164 (1956).

[233] P. Bender, D. L. Flowers, and H. L. Goering, *J. Am. Chem. Soc.,* **77,** 3463 (1955).

10. Which conformation should exhibit the greater dipole-dipole association in solution, axial or equatorial α-chlorocyclohexanone?

11. Assign conformational structures to two samples of 2-chloro-4-t-butylcyclohexanone, one of m.p. 59° and dipole moment 4.29 D, and the other of m.p. -15° and dipole moment 3.17 D.

12. It has been proposed that geminal dialkyl groups strikingly increase the rate of ring closure of 4-bromobutylamine because geminal substituents increase the per cent of comformations having a coiled configuration rather than an extended conformation. If this is true, why would 2,2-substituents be more effective than 3,3-substituents?[234]

13. Predict the relative acid strengths of R—CO—CH$_2$—CO—R where R = Me, i-Pr, and t-Bu.[235]

14. Should 1,3,5-triphenylbenzene be a planar molecule?[236]

15. Predict the relative stabilities of the *cis* and *trans* isomers of the 1,2-, the 1,3-, and the 1,4-dimethylcyclohexanes.[237]

16. Comment on the opposite trends in m.p.'s of the following 2-substituted biphenyls:[238]

Substituent	2-Isomer	4-Isomer
H	69°	69°
F	71	74
Cl	34	76
Br	-20	89
I	liq.	113

17. Offer an explanation for the much smaller O—H infrared absorption frequency for 1,1,2,2-tetra-t-butylethane-1,2-diol than for ethyleneglycol.[239]

18. *Trans*-1-methylcyclohexane-1,2-diol has O—H infrared absorption bands at 3618 and 3597 cm^{-1} whereas *trans*-1-isopropylcyclohexane-1,2-diol has a single peak at 3625 cm^{-1}. What can be said about the conformations of these two compounds on the basis of these spectral data?

19. The only 2,2'-dimethylbiphenyl found reported in the literature to be optically active is 2,2',3,3'-tetramethylbiphenyl. How can you account for the optical activity of this latter compound?[240]

20. How would you interpret the change with temperature of the dipole moment of α-chlorocyclohexanone in benzene solution:[241] 3.96 D at 27.4° and 3.66 D at 52.0°.

[234]R. F. Brown and N. M. van Gulick, *J. Org. Chem.*, **21**, 1046 (1956).

[235]For data, cf. G. S. Hammond, W. G. Borduin, and G. A. Guter, *J. Am. Chem. Soc.*, **81**, 4682 (1959).

[236]For an answer, cf. O. Bastiansen, *Acta Chem. Scand.*, **6**, 205 (1952).

[237]Cf. P. D. Bartlett, *J. Chem. Educ.*, **30**, 22 (1953).

[238]S. Brownstein, *J. Am. Chem. Soc.*, **80**, 2300 (1958).

[239]L. Kuhn, *J. Am. Chem. Soc.*, **80**, 5950 (1958).

[240]W. Theilacker and R. Hopp, *Chem. Ber.*, **92**, 2293 (1959).

[241]S. Yaroslavsky and E. D. Bergmann, *J. Chem. Phys.*, **33**, 635 (1960).

21. (+)-3-Methylcyclopentanone exhibits a positive Cotton effect in its ORD curve. Predict the sign of the Cotton effect for (−)-3-isopropenylcyclopentanone.[242]

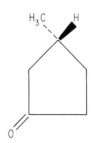

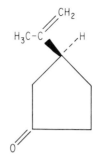

(+)-3-Methylcyclopentanone   *(−)-3-Isopropenylcyclopentanone*

22. Predict which hydroxylic carbon would be oxidized the fastest to a carbonyl group by chromic acid in acetic acid in the steroid cholestane-3β,5α,6β-triol.

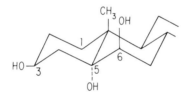

23. On what basis would you predict a (C_1 or C_4) bridge-head carbonium ion in the norbornane ring to be unstable?

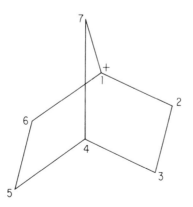

[242]Cf. C. Djerassi and B. Tursch, *J. Am. Chem. Soc.*, **83**, 4611 (1961).

24. Predict which alcohol will be oxidized the faster by chromic acid in acetic acid,

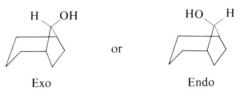

Exo   Endo

25. Which would you predict to be the major alcohol produced by the reduction of the following ketone with NaBH$_4$ in pyridine, the endo or exo isomer?

CHAPTER *IV*

4.1. The Modern Structural Theory of Organic Chemistry

The *structural theory* of organic chemistry was developed in the nineteenth century as a means of describing organic molecules to facilitate both an interpretation of their properties and the prediction of new properties. A. Kekulé and A. S. Couper independently devised the system of using symbols of elements joined by dashes as a method of representing the structures of molecules. From a study of chemical properties, organic compounds were classified on a basis of common functional groups, and the members of each class were expected to have the same qualitative chemical properties with perhaps small differences in degree of reactivity. Slowly it was realized, however, that when certain functional groups are close to one another, the characteristic properties of each group are markedly altered. For example, the neutral OH group becomes acidic when attached to a carbonyl group (giving the COOH group) and the carbonyl group no longer undergoes the typical carbonyl addition reactions. As another example,

CHARGE DISTRIBUTION

AND MOLECULAR PROPERTIES

n-pentyl chloride is easily hydrolyzed in hot aqueous alkali while neopentyl chloride is not. Also, allyl and benzyl halides hydrolyze readily at moderate temperatures while vinyl and aryl halides do not. In order to account for these differences in behavior within a given class, which are not explicable by the original structural theory, the theory has been frequently modified to include concepts such as tautomerism, resonance, induction, steric hindrance, and orbital hybridization. These concepts are used together in a judicious manner, and this multi-effect approach can be called the *modern structural theory* of organic chemistry.

As the electronic theory of matter developed, chemists have increasingly interpreted the behavior of molecules in terms of the distribution of charges in the molecules.[1] Several methods (Sec. 4.11) or models have been used to designate charge distributions in molecules, including free valences, molecular orbitals, the free-electron model, the charge-cloud model, and

[1] Cf. symposium on "Theory and Experiments on the Problem of Chemical Bonding," *Z. Elektrochem.*, **61**, 859–1120 (June, 1957).

resonance theory. The latter method has been particularly fruitful and widely employed because it is based on the use of structural formulas which are familiar to all chemists. Therefore, we will devote the major portion of this chapter to resonance theory, and say just a little about other methods of approximating charge distributions. It is important to realize that resonance theory is not necessarily the best method and that in some cases one or more of the other methods offer an advantage for describing the charge distribution in a given molecular system.[2]

The reader should be mindful of the fact that this chapter deals with resonance of molecules in the ground state. In the chapter on spectroscopy, resonance in excited states will also be considered, for which there is a difference in relative contributions of polar and nonpolar structures.

4.2. The Concept of Resonance

The concept of resonance was introduced by Heisenberg through quantum mechanics in the 1920's and was generalized by Pauling in the early 1930's. During the same period, similar ideas were advanced by Arndt and his co-workers in Germany and by Robinson and Ingold in England. They used the terms *zwischenstufen* and *mesomerism*, respectively. Each group proposed that the actual electron distributions of certain molecules are not identical to those designated by a conventional valence-bond (VB) structure.[3]

It is easy to understand why the early successes of the structural theory led to the practice of representing the structures of molecules by structural formulas. These formulas are gross representations of the charge distributions of molecules. As we know from our elementary organic course, there are some molecules for which no single VB structure is consistent with all of their properties. In these cases, the concept of resonance is adopted, in which several conceivable structures are written and the molecule is regarded as having a fixed structure which is a composite of all of those written. Thus, the molecule will have properties approaching but not identical to each of the structural formulas written.

It is to be emphasized that when resonance is proposed for a molecule, the structure of the molecule is a fixed composite (the term used is *resonance hybrid*) of all VB structures written. The molecule does not assume each

[2] H. A. Bent (*Chem. Revs.*, **61**, 275 (1961)) has developed a completely empirical rule regarding the amount of *s* character of hybrid *s-p* bonds, by which he is able to account for a variety of physical properties of molecules. The method is useful in that it uses a single approach or concept to explain such properties as bond angles, lengths and force constants, dipole moments, ionization potentials, and heats of addition to multiple bonds.

[3] Kekulé, of course, proposed the dynamic structure of benzene in 1865, and A. Lapworth (*J. Chem. Soc.*, **79**, 1265 (1901)) conceived the possibility of electron shifts as early as 1901.

structure part of the time, nor do some of the molecules have one of the contributing structures while other molecules have others. For illustration, the carboxylate ion is a resonance hybrid of two equivalent structures

$$R-C\diagdown_{O^-}^{\diagup O} \quad \text{and} \quad R-C\diagdown_{O}^{\diagup O^-}$$

and the two carbon-oxygen bonds are of equal lengths rather than unequal as would be the case for either structure alone. Furthermore, the C=O bond of the carboxyl group loses its identity in the ion, for the latter no longer exhibits the typical COOH group Raman frequency near 1700 cm^{-1}. For these reasons, the structure of a carboxylate ion is sometimes written

$$R-C\diagdown_{O}^{\diagup O} \; -$$

This implies that the two C—O bonds are identical. Many other examples will be given in the rest of the text.

A fair analogy of the concept of resonance is found in the consideration of the pedigree of a dog.[4] For illustration, if one of the parents of a given dog A is a full-breed dachshund and the other is a full-breed collie, then A is exactly a half-breed of each and will resemble each parent in certain details. If now A has an offspring B, whose other parent is again a collie, then B is 3/4 collie and 1/4 dachshund. It now resembles a collie more than a dachshund. Furthermore, a dog could be a descendent of more than two breeds—say, for example, 1/16 collie, 3/16 dachshund, 1/8 greyhound, 3/8 airedale, and 1/4 bloodhound. The mongrel would probably have some features resembling those of each full-breed. However, it would have a distinct identity, and not be a full-breed collie 1/16 of the time, full-breed dachshund 3/16 of the time, and so forth. In a similar sense, the actual structure of a molecule may be a resonance hybrid of two or more forms from which equal or unequal contributions may be made.

Professor J. D. Roberts has pointed out one weakness of the above analogy. When a molecule is a resonance hybrid of several structures, its structure is not actually any one of the forms, it merely has some resemblance to the contributing forms. Therefore, the structures of the contributing forms have no physical existence. That is, there are no stable molecules with either Kekulé structure. Such systems of atoms are much less stable with respect to the actual structure of benzene and would change into it. Structures written as contributing to a resonance hybrid, then, are fictitious. On the other hand, the full-breed dogs mentioned above are real and have a definite existence; for this reason the analogy is not quite complete. A

[4] G. W. Wheland, *Advanced Organic Chemistry* (2nd ed.; New York: Wiley, 1950), p. 404.

closer analogy would be to describe a rhinoceros as intermediate between a dragon and a unicorn. Everyone knows what these look like although they are not living creatures. If a person had never seen a rhinoceros, he could get a good mental picture of one in terms of the features of a dragon and a unicorn.

Resonance differs from tautomerism in two important features. First, as just pointed out, the written structures contribuuring to a resonance hybrid have no real existence, whereas tautomers usually coexist in solution and in some cases the two may be isolated. Resonance, on the other hand, conveys the idea of a single fixed structure, at least for a certain time interval of about 10^{-13} seconds.[5] Secondly, the position of a proton in tautomers will differ by several angstrom units whereas the positions of the nuclei in resonating forms differ by no more than 0.3 Å. For example, a bond between two adjacent carbon atoms of the Kekulé forms is a single bond in one form and a double bond in the other. If it were a double bond it would have a length of 1.33 Å, and of 1.54 Å if a single bond. The two extremes differ by 0.21 Å. Similarly, the two extremes for the carbon-oxygen bond in the carboxylate ion differ by only 0.20 Å (C—O, 1.41 Å, C=O, 1.21 Å).

4.3. Resonance Structures

There are several guiding principles for writing VB resonance structures and for qualitatively assessing their relative importance:[6, 7]

(i) *Resonance structures are interconvertible by one or a series of short electron-shifts.*

Usually, one can write a good approximate structural formula for a compound, and then several others may be derived from this first structure as needed to be consistent with all observed properties. For illustration, the covalences of the elements in vinyl chloride, its molecular formula, and the principles of classical organic chemistry would lead to I(a) as a fairly good structural formula for the compound. However, in order to account for the C—Cl bond distance's being much shorter than that in simple alkyl chlorides (1.78 Å), for the smaller dipole moment (1.44 D) than that of

---

[5] This period is obtained from the *uncertainty principle* which states, in effect, that the product of the minimum resolution in energy and time is equal to, or greater than, Planck's constant, h.

$$\Delta E \cdot \Delta T \geq h$$

Accordingly, if it is assumed that the potential energies of molecules are known to within 1 kcal, or 7×10^{-14} erg/mole, the time interval within which a given molecule will assume an assigned structure is $h/7 \times 10^{-14} = 10^{-13}$ sec.

[6] G. W. Wheland, *Resonance in Organic Chemistry* (New York: Wiley, 1955), pp. 12 ff.

[7] R. S. Mulliken, *Conference on Hyperconjugation* (New York: Pergamon, 1959), pp. 96 ff.

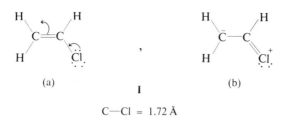

(a)   (b)

I

C—Cl = 1.72 Å

ethyl chloride (2.05 D), and for its inertness towards nucleophilic groups, form I(b) is regarded as making a significant contribution to the resonance hybrid structure of vinyl chloride. It is derived from I(a) by the two short electron-shifts involving lone-pair and π electrons. Other examples of resonating forms[8] can be given for which it can be seen that they are inter-convertible by a series of short electron-displacements.

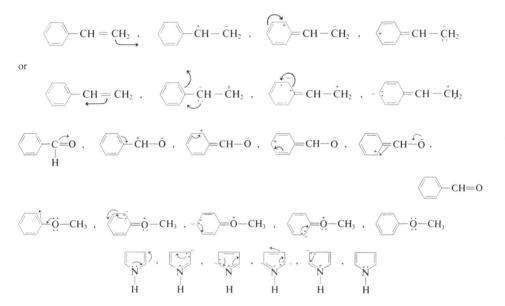

Thus, resonance between substituents and the benzene ring increases or decreases the electronic charge at the *ortho* and *para* positions. In the

----

[8] The expressions *resonance forms* and *resonating structures* refer to the structures contributing to a resonance hybrid, and does not denote action or oscillating structures such as Kekulé proposed for benzene. The terms are used to avoid awkward or lengthy expressions which would be needed if always one had to say "the structures contributing to the resonance hybrid." It is conventional to use double-headed arrows ⟷ between resonating structures, but this author always uses commas between the resonance forms. This practice avoids the possible inference that there is a dynamic reversible oscillation between the structures. Rather, the implication is that the substance has a structure which is a smeared-out or mental com-posite electron structure of the various structures given.

pyrrole ring, each carbon atom acquires an increased electron density which is consistent with its marked ease of reaction with electrophilic reagents.

(ii) *Resonating structures must have the same number of unpaired electrons.*

It is obvious that if two structures have a different total number of electrons, they represent different molecular species and cannot be resonance contributors to the same resonance hybrid. There is the possibility, however, that two or more structures may possess the same number of electrons but have different numbers of *unpaired* electrons, e.g., II, III, and IV.

$$CH_2{=}CH{-}CH{=}\overset{..}{\underset{..}{O}}: \qquad CH_2{=}CH{-}\overset{.}{CH}{-}\overset{.}{\underset{..}{O}}: \qquad \overset{.}{CH_2}{-}CH{=}CH{-}\overset{.}{\underset{..}{O}}:$$

$$\textbf{II} \qquad\qquad \textbf{III} \qquad\qquad \textbf{IV}$$

If the unpaired electrons in III had antiparallel spins, then they would pair up to form a covalent bond and thus III would be equivalent to II. If the spins were antiparallel in IV, again, short electron-shifts would bring about a pairing up of the electrons to give II, and effectively, IV would be equivalent to II. However, if the electrons in III and IV had parallel spins, then the structures would have a different *multiplicity* than II and could not be resonance contributors to the same molecular species as II.

(iii) *The resonance structures that follow the rule of two[9] are the most stable.*

Two-, four-, or six-electron covalent bonds are much more stable than are one- or three-electron bonds. The carbon-carbon bond distances and force constants of benzene are all the same and intermediate between the values for the two-electron and four-electron bonds in ethane and ethylene, respectively. One might immediately think, therefore, that the bonds in benzene are three-electron bonds. However, three-electron bonds are far too weak (ca. 60 kcal/mole) to exist in the stable aromatic ring. Any structure in which hydrogen has more than two electrons in its valence shell ($1s$) or in which any atom of the second row of the periodic table has more than eight electrons in its valence shell is too unstable to contribute to the resonance of a molecule under normal conditions. In fact, the elements in the second row strive to have eight valence electrons, and the principle is referred to as the *Lewis octet rule*.[10] The elements in the third row may use $3s$, $3p$, or $3d$ orbitals and it is not uncommon for these elements to accommodate more than eight electrons in their valence shell, e.g. sulfur and

---

[9]W. R. Luder and S. Zuffanti, *The Electronic Theory of Acids and Bases* (New York: Wiley, 1946).

[10]Compare J. W. Linnett's modification of this rule (*J. Am. Chem. Soc.*, **83**, 2643 (1961)).

phosphorus compounds,

$$R-O-\overset{\overset{\displaystyle O^-}{|}}{\underset{\underset{\displaystyle O^-}{|}}{S}}^{\pm\pm}O-H, \quad R-O-\overset{\overset{\displaystyle O}{\|}}{\underset{\underset{\displaystyle O}{\|}}{S}}-OH \qquad R-\overset{\overset{\displaystyle R}{|}}{\underset{\underset{\displaystyle R}{|}}{P}}^{\cdot}-O^-, \quad R-\overset{\overset{\displaystyle R}{|}}{\underset{\underset{\displaystyle R}{|}}{P}}=O$$

where R is any carbon-attached group.

(iv) *The more covalent bonds there are in a VB structure, the greater is its stability.*

When atoms approach one another to within covalent bond distances, either their valence orbitals will coalesce to form bonding molecular orbitals or the atoms will repel each other strongly, and separate. Since each bond will add about 50–100 kcal/mole to the stability of the system, while the *differences* in stability of resonating forms are only a fraction of this amount, the resonance structure with the greater number of bonds will usually be the more stable.

(v) *Dipolar VB structures will in general be less stable than nonpolar structures.*

Unless one atom is electropositive, in which case an ionic bond tends to be formed, the stability of a dipolar structure is diminished by an amount of energy required to prevent coalescence or mutual annihilation of the opposite charges. Hence, the two resonance structures of a carboxylic acid (V) have the same number of bonds but V(b) is the less stable because of *charge-separation.*

$$\underset{\text{(a)}}{R-C\overset{\displaystyle \nearrow O}{\underset{\displaystyle \searrow O-H}{}}} \text{,} \qquad \underset{\text{(b)}}{R-C\overset{\displaystyle \nearrow O^-}{\underset{\displaystyle \searrow O^{\pm}H}{}}}$$

V

The farther apart the unlike charges are, the less stable is the resonance form. Therefore, of the ionic resonance forms of butadiene (VI), forms VI(d) are the least stable and VI(b) the most stable. Of course, the non-polar form VI(a) is the most stable of all of the forms and makes the greatest contribution to the resonance hybrid. That is to say, the structure of the normal molecule most nearly resembles VI(a).

$$\underset{\text{(a)}}{CH_2{=}CH{-}CH{=}CH_2,} \quad CH_2{=}CH{-}\overset{-}{CH}{-}\overset{+}{CH_2},$$

$$\underset{\text{(c)}}{\overset{+}{CH_2}{-}CH{=}CH{-}\overset{-}{CH_2},} \quad \underset{\text{(d)}}{\overset{-}{CH_2}{-}\overset{+}{CH}{-}\overset{+}{CH}{-}\overset{-}{CH_2}}$$

VI

(vi) *Structures involving formal charges are the most stable when the negative charge resides on the most electronegative atom and the positive charge on the least electronegative atom.*

This rule indicates that for a ketone, ionic form VII(b) is more stable than VII(c), and this view is substantiated experimentally by the dipole moments and chemical properties of ketones. Thus, when "carbonyl reagents" add to the double bond of a ketone, the positive fragment of the addendum always adds to the oxygen atom.

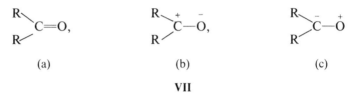

| (a) | (b) | (c) |

VII

(vii) *The closer the stabilities of resonance structures, the greater is the degree of resonance.*

Those systems which involve equivalent VB structures have a large degree of resonance. The species may be charged or neutral. Some examples follow.

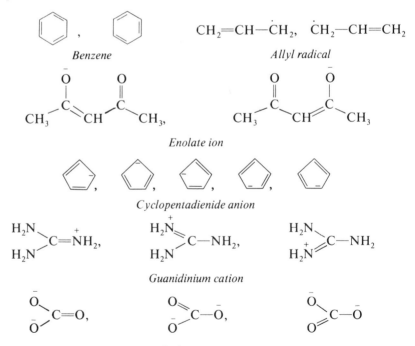

Those cases in which charge is moved around have the effect of spreading out the charge and avoid the accumulation of excess charge on a single atom. This *electroneutrality principle* of Pauling is found to have a stabilizing effect.

Resonance of forms having the same number of bonds is severalfold greater than when the contributing structures have different numbers of bonds. The former is referred to as *isovalent resonance*.[11] Thus, the cases shown above are of the isovalent type and each is known to correspond to a large resonance energy.

(viii) *Resonance can occur only between structures that correspond to very nearly the same relative positions of all atomic nuclei.*

This, of course, precludes resonance between isomers. Furthermore, isomers are real and isolable whereas resonance structures are hypothetical and only approach real structures.

Resonance occurs to a much smaller extent for most open-chain conjugated systems than for completely conjugated ring systems because of unequal bond distances in the former. For instance, the carbon-carbon bonds are all of equal length in benzene and, accordingly, resonance between the two Kekulé structures is substantial. However, in a molecule like butadiene, the carbon-carbon bonds are of unequal length. It would take too much energy to compress the C_2—C_3 bond to a distance equal to that of the end carbon-carbon bonds and, as a consequence, resonance for the butadiene system is small compared to that of the aromatic ring. This factor has been discussed by Lennard-Jones[12] and by Coulson[12] in terms of *compression energies*.[13]

$$1.483 \text{ Å}$$
$$CH_2\text{=}CH\text{—}CH\text{=}CH_2$$
$$1.337 \text{ Å}$$

Discussion. These rules are only qualitative guides, and sometimes they conflict. For example, the principal ionic resonance structures of aryl and vinyl halides, aniline, and phenol are at variance with generalization (vi).

Fluorobenzene   Phenol

In another case, rules (iv) and (v) are in conflict regarding the relative stability of the ionic and nonpolar resonance forms of boron triflouride.

---

[11] R. S. Mulliken, *Tetrahedron,* **6,** 68 (1959).

[12] J. E. Lennard-Jones, *Proc. Roy. Soc.,* **A158,** 280 (1937); C. A. Coulson, *Valence* (Oxford: The Clarendon Press, 1952).

[13] See also R. Breslow and H. W. Chang, *J. Am. Chem. Soc.,* **83,** 2371 (1961).

(three equivalent forms)

Pauling[14] has calculated the per cent double-bond character in the boron trihalides and found it to decrease from 33 per cent for F to 6 per cent for I. Thus, the ionic structures make a substantial contribution to the resonance hybrid of BF_3, so that the volatility, solubility and other covalent properties of BF_3 must be attributed to the near equality in opposite charges arising on the B and F atoms from electronegativity differences and resonance. That is to say, electronegativity differences increase the negative charge on the F whereas resonance among the ionic structures has the opposite effect. As another example of the occasional conflict between the generalizations given above, consider phenylisocyanide. The major resonating structures, not involving the benzene ring, are VIII(a) and (b). Form VIII(b) is expected to be the more stable according to rules (iii) and (iv), while it is also expected to be the less stable based on rules (v) and (vi). One

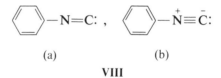

    (a)   (b)

VIII

has to examine its properties to determine which structure makes the greater contribution, i.e., which one the more nearly resembles the actual structure of phenylisocyanide. From dipole moments (3.5 D, directed toward carbon) and infrared absorption frequencies ($N\equiv C$ absorption in the triple-bond range), it is concluded that VIII(b) is the more important structure.

The actual structure of a molecule most closely resembles that of the most stable VB resonance structure. That is, the relative contributions of resonance structures to the resonance hybrid are in direct ratio to their relative stabilities. For illustration, of the nonpolar and ionic resonance structures of benzene, the two Kekulé forms make the major contribution to the ground-state resonance hybrid. The ionic forms make a much larger contribution to the excited-state resonance hybrid. The more nearly equal in stability two or more resonance structures are, the less the actual structure resembles either equivalent form and the more it becomes an exact composite of the equivalent forms.

[14] L. Pauling, *Nature of the Chemical Bond* (3rd ed.; Ithaca, N. Y.: Cornell U. P., 1960), p. 318.

4.4. Resonance Energies

The resonance energy of a molecule is defined as the difference between the actual or experimental heat of formation of a compound and that calculated from tabulated bond energies for its most stable VB structure. For example, from the bond energies listed in Table 1.10, p. 48, the calculated heat of formation of one of the Kekulé structures of benzene is

$$\Delta H_{calc} = 6(C—H) + 3(C—C) + 3(C=C)$$
$$= 6(98.8) + 3(83.1) + 3(145) = 1277 \text{ kcal}$$

The experimental heat of combustion of benzene is 789.1 kcal/mole, so that from the equation

$$C_6H_6 + 7\tfrac{1}{2} O_2 = 6 CO_2 + 3 H_2O + 789.1 \text{ kcal}$$

the heat of formation of benzene is computed to be

$$6(410.7) + 3(244.9) - 7\tfrac{1}{2}(146.2) - 789.1 = 1313.3 \text{ kcal}$$

The difference, $1313.3 - 1277 = 36.3$ kcal/mole, is the resonance energy of benzene.

This method of determining resonance energies from heats of combustion data is not as accurate as one would like, because the resonance energy is the difference between two large numbers and any errors in the large numbers accumulate in the value of the resonance energy. For illustration, if the error in the heat of combustion data is 0.15 per cent or about 1 kcal, the error in the resonance energy of benzene would be 1/36 or 2.8 per cent. An error of 1 kcal is a much larger per cent error for resonance energies smaller than that of benzene.

An alternative method of determining resonance energies has been to use heats of hydrogenation.[15] The heat of hydrogenation of an olefin is the heat liberated in the reaction

$$R_2C=CR_2 + H_2 \longrightarrow R_2C—CR_2$$
$$\qquad\qquad\qquad\qquad\quad | \quad |$$
$$\qquad\qquad\qquad\qquad\ H \ \ H$$

in which one H—H bond and a C=C π bond are broken, and two C—H bonds are formed. The heat of the reaction should therefore be

$$\Delta H = 2E_{C-H} - E_{C\pi C} - E_{H-H}$$

where E_{C-H}, E_{H-H}, and $E_{C\pi C}$ are the energies of the C—H bond, the H—H bond, and the carbon-carbon π bond, respectively. The latter is the difference between the C=C and C—C bond energies, or $145 - 80 = 65$ kcal. It might be supposed that the heat of hydrogenation of all isolated

---

[15] J. B. Conant and G. B. Kistiakowsky, *Chem. Revs.*, **20**, 181 (1937).

(unconjugated) olefinic bonds would be the same. If the double bond were conjugated with another multiple bond, the molecule would be stabilized by a certain amount of resonance energy which would be lost in the hydrogenation. The heat of hydrogenation would then be

$$\Delta H = 2E_{C-H} - E_{C\pi C} - E_{H-H} - E_R$$

where E_R is the resonance energy. It can be seen that the heat of hydrogenation is smaller than that of a similar unconjugated olefin by an amount equal to the resonance energy of the conjugated molecule. This conclusion is also reached from Fig. 1.20, p. 50. This provides a method, then, of determining the resonance energies of molecules. In order that other effects, such as steric and entropy changes, may cancel, comparisons need to be made with similarly conjugated C=C bonds. For illustration, the heat of hydrogenation of 1-pentene (30.3 kcal) as listed in Table 4.1 differs from that of 2-pentene (28 kcal). Since the two double bonds of 1,4 pentadiene are identical to that in 1-pentene, the heat of complete hydrogenation of 1,4-pentadiene should be twice that of 1-pentene, which is actually observed. In the absence of resonance, the value to be expected for 1,3-pentadiene would be 30.3 kcal for the terminal double bond plus 28 kcal for the inner double bond, or a total of 58.3 kcal. The observed value is 54.1. Therefore, the resonance energy of 1,3-pentadiene is 58.3 − 54.1 = 4.2 kcal/mole. By the same procedure, the resonance energy of 1,3-cyclohexadiene is found to be 2(28.6) − 55.4 = 1.8 kcal, and that of benzene is 3(28.6) − 49.8 = 36 kcal. It might be noted here that in the addition of only one mole of hydrogen, benzene is converted to cyclohexadiene, and thereby the ring loses 36 − 1.8 = 34.2 kcal of resonance energy. Hydrogenation of an olefinic bond releases no more than 32.8 kcal, so that in order to hydrogenate benzene to cyclohexadiene, heat must be supplied, whereas heat is released in the hydrogenation of any of the other compounds of Table 4.1.

Resonance energies have also been calculated through empirical[16] and

Table 4.1. HEATS OF HYDROGENATION OF SOME HYDROCARBONS[15]

Substance	ΔH kcal/mole	Substance	ΔH kcal/mole
Ethylene	32.8	1,3-Pentadiene	54.1
Propene	30.1	1,5-Hexadiene	60.6
1-Pentene	30.3	Cyclohexene	28.6
2-Pentene	28	1,3-Cyclohexadiene	55.4
1,4-Pentadiene	60.6	Benzene	49.8

[16] J. L. Franklin, *J. Am. Chem. Soc.,* **72,** 4278 (1950); F. Klages, *Chem. Ber.* **82,** 358 (1949).

quantum mechanical methods,[17] and the results are in reasonable agreement with the values listed in Table 4.2. The values are far from being absolute. For instance, values for simple compounds such as phenol and anisole as listed in several authoritative reference books differ by 2 or more kcal[6, 20, 21] and values for pyrrole range from 17.4 to 30.9 kcal/mole.[22]

Table 4.2. SOME RESONANCE ENERGIES

Substance	Resonance energy kcal/mole	Substance	Resonance energy kcal/mole
Benzene	36	Carbon monoxide	58
Naphthalene	61	Carbon dioxide	33
Anthracene	84	Carbon disulfide	29
Biphenyl	71	Phenol	50
trans-Stilbene	77	Aniline	51
Styrene	51	Anisole	52
1,3,5-Cycloheptatriene	6.7	Benzaldehyde	47
Azulene	46	Acetophenone	54
Cyclooctatetraene	4.8[18]	Benzophenone	93
Pyridine	37	Propionic acid	24
Pyrrole	24	Ethyl propionate	24
Tropolone	36[19]	Benzoic acid	67
Acetamide	25	Ethyl benzoate	79
Benzamide	74	Benzoquinone	16
Urea	41		

An important point to make at this time is that resonance is not a primary force. When we speak of resonance energies it is not implied that the resonance energy *produces* or brings about the observed effect. To the contrary, resonance is merely used as a device to interpret the observation in terms of structural formulas. Although the expression is commonly used that "the molecule or structure is stabilized by resonance," the actual meaning is not according to the literal wording. It is merely stated this way to avoid a cumbersome sentence.

[17] G. W. Wheland, *Resonance in Organic Chemistry,* p. 665.

[18] H. D. Springall, T. R. White, and R. C. Cass, *Trans. Faraday Soc.,* **50,** 815 (1954); R. B. Turner, *et al., J. Am. Chem. Soc.,* **79,** 4127 (1957).

[19] W. N. Hubbard, C. Katz, G. B. Guthrie, G. Waddington, *J. Am. Chem. Soc.,* **74,** 4456 (1952).

[20] J. G. Aston, *Determination of Organic Structures by Physical Methods,* ed. E. A. Braude and F. C. Nachod (New York: Academic, 1955), p. 560.

[21] L. Pauling, *Nature of the Chemical Bond,* p. 197.

[22] H. Zimmermann and H. Geisenfelder, *Z. Elektrochem.,* **65,** 369 (1961).

4.5. Hyperconjugation[23, 24]

In the foregoing pages, resonance structures have differed in the positions of π and lone-pair electrons. In certain cases, resonance structures may also involve σ electrons. For illustration, when C—H bonds are alpha to a multiple bond, resonance forms may be written involving a "no bond" between the α C and H atoms.

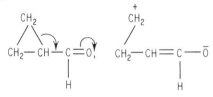

In a sense, the C—H bond is conjugated with the double bond. Similarly, with three-membered rings, a shift of σ electrons and a "conjugated" multiple bond may occur.

There is one fundamental difference between ethylenic and cyclopropyl carbon atoms. In the former, carbon uses sp^2 hybrid orbitals while in the latter it uses sp^3 hybrid orbitals. There is much less orbital overlap of the C_3 orbitals, but because of bond-angle strain, the bond angles are spread apart some. This also allows slightly less orbital overlap. The bonds have been referred to as "banana" bonds. The arc lines between carbon atoms form 60-degree angles but the bonds are not directed along this line.

$$\overset{\displaystyle CH_2}{\underset{\displaystyle CH_2 \qquad CH_2}{\diagup \diagdown}}$$

Since σ electrons are much more localized and less polarizable than π electrons, the contribution of these ionic forms involving σ bonds is much less than that from ionic forms involving π or lone-pair electrons.

It has been observed for decades that the cyclopropane ring has an olefinic character.[25] Not only does cyclopropane undergo addition re-

[23] *Conference on Hyperconjugation*, Indiana University, June, 1958 (New York: Pergamon, 1959).

[24] J. W. Baker, *Hyperconjugation* (Fair Lawn, N.J.: Oxford U. P., 1952); V. A. Crawford, *Quart. Revs.*, **3**, 226 (1949).

[25] R. Robinson, *J. Chem. Soc.*, 1042 (1916).

actions but the cyclopropyl group is able to conjugate with multiple bonds. Thus, cyclopropylcarbonyl compounds and α,β-enone systems behave similarly towards bases, HBr, and reducing agents,[26(a)] and vinylcyclo-propane undergoes a Diels-Alder reaction.[26(b)] It was early recognized that cyclopropyl derivatives exhibit molecular refraction exaltations[27(a)] and absorb ultraviolet light in regions between those characteristic of the corresponding ethylenic and saturated alkyl compounds.[27(b)] In recent years, many data have been collected to demonstrate the ability of the cyclopropyl group to transmit electronic charge.[28] It was suggested in 1935 that the mobility of a σ electron pair may indeed be a small fraction of that of a multiple bond. Thus, to explain the order of the rates of reaction of alkyl-substituted benzyl halides with pyridine, Baker and Nathan[29] proposed that an α C—H bond of an alkyl group has a small ability to release electrons as does an unsaturated group. The rate of the reaction

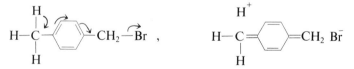

with various alkyl groups for R was found to be in the order $CH_3 >$ $CH_3CH_2 > (CH_3)_2CH > (CH_3)_3C$. Inasmuch as a methyl group is more electronegative than a t-butyl group, this is just the opposite order to that expected on the basis of the activating inductive effect of these groups, because the reaction is one that is facilitated by electron accession toward the halogen. Instead, the order parallels the relative number of α C—H bonds in the alkyl group, and can be attributed to the corresponding electron-release of σ electrons.

$$\begin{array}{cc}
\overset{\displaystyle H}{\underset{\displaystyle H}{H-C}} \!\!\! \underset{}{\bigcirc} \!\! -CH_2-Br \ , & \overset{\displaystyle \overset{+}{H}}{\underset{\displaystyle H}{H-C}} \!\! = \!\! \underset{}{\bigcirc} \!\! = CH_2 \ \overset{-}{Br}
\end{array}$$

This general conjugative ability of alkyl groups and three-membered cyclic rings is called *hyperconjugation*.[30] Like resonance, it is a device used to interpret molecular properties in terms of structural formulas. Since the magnitude of the effect is much smaller than that of resonance, hyper-conjugation can be regarded as a second-order resonance. Consequently,

[26] (a) E. P. Kohler and J. B. Conant, *J. Am. Chem. Soc.,* **39**, 1409 (1917); (b) S. Sarel and E. Breuer, *J. Am. Chem. Soc.,* **81**, 6522 (1959).

[27] (a) J. W. Bruhl, *Ber.,* **32**, 1222 (1899); T. Tschugaeff, *Ber.,* **33**, 3122 (1900); N. Zelin-sky and J. Zelokow, *Ber.,* **34**, 2867 (1901); (b) E. P. Carr and C. P. Burt, *J. Am. Chem. Soc.,* **40**, 1590 (1918).

[28] Cf. R. Fuchs, C. A. Kaplan, J. J. Bloomfield, and L. F. Hatch, *J. Org. Chem.,* **27**, 733 (1962).

[29] J. W. Baker and W. S. Nathan, *J. Chem. Soc.,* 1844 (1935).

[30] This name was suggested by W. G. Brown, *J. Am. Chem. Soc.,* **63**, 41 (1941).

an interpretation of several types of properties in terms of hyperconjugation will be discussed here, and thereafter, hyperconjugation will be used right along with resonance.

(i) **Heats of Hydrogenation.** It was shown in Sec. 1.2.12 that for compounds of similar structure, the smaller the heat of hydrogenation or heat of combustion is, the more stable is the compound. The heats of hydrogenation of ethylene and 1-pentene are 32.8 and 30.3 kcal/mole, respectively. The difference, 2.3 kcal, can be attributed to a stabilization of 1-pentene through hyperconjugation of the α C—H bonds.

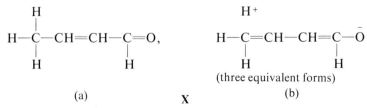

Thus, the structure of 1-pentene can be regarded as a resonance hybrid of forms IX(a)–(c), and the energy of hyperconjugation is measured as it would be for a conjugated diene. It is evident from its heat of hydrogenation, 28 kcal/mole, that 2-pentene is stabilized by an additional 2.3 kcal, which can be attributed to the larger number of α C—H bonds and, hence, greater hyperconjugation.

$$CH_3-\overset{\overset{\displaystyle H}{|}}{\underset{\underset{\displaystyle H}{|}}{C}}-CH=CH-\overset{\overset{\displaystyle H}{|}}{\underset{\underset{\displaystyle H}{|}}{C}}-H, \quad CH_3-\overset{\overset{\displaystyle H^+}{|}}{\underset{\underset{\displaystyle H}{|}}{C}}=CH-\overset{-}{CH}-\overset{\overset{\displaystyle H}{|}}{\underset{\underset{\displaystyle H}{|}}{C}}-H,$$

(two equiv. forms)

$$CH_3-\overset{\overset{\displaystyle H}{|}}{\underset{\underset{\displaystyle H}{|}}{C}}-\overset{-}{CH}-CH=\overset{\overset{\displaystyle H^+}{|}}{\underset{\underset{\displaystyle H}{|}}{C}}-H, \text{ etc.}$$

(three equiv. forms)

The heat of hydrogenation of the ethylenic bond in crotonaldehyde is only 25 kcal/mole.[31] Thus, the hyperconjugation is increased by the conjugated C=O bond.

$$H-\overset{\overset{\displaystyle H}{|}}{\underset{\underset{\displaystyle H}{|}}{C}}-CH=CH-\overset{\overset{\displaystyle H}{|}}{\underset{\underset{\displaystyle H}{|}}{C}}=O, \qquad H-\overset{\overset{\displaystyle H^+}{|}}{\underset{\underset{\displaystyle H}{|}}{C}}=CH-CH=\overset{-}{\underset{\underset{\displaystyle H}{|}}{C}}-\overset{-}{O}$$

(three equivalent forms)

(a)   **X**   (b)

[31] G. B. Kistiakowsky, *J. Am. Chem. Soc.*, **60**, 440 (1938).

(ii) Ionization potentials. Since hyperconjugation increases the electron-density on olefinic carbon atoms, it can be expected that ionization potentials of olefins decrease as hyperconjugation increases. This expectation is confirmed by the data listed in Table 4.3. It can be seen there that hyperconjugation provides a good account of the heats of hydrogenation and ionization potentials of the methylated ethylenes.

Table 4.3. IONIZATION POTENTIALS AND HEATS OF HYDROGENATION
OF SOME OLEFINS

Compound	I. P.[32] volts	Heat of hydrogenation kcal/mole
$H_2C\!=\!CH_2$	10.62	32.8
$CH_3\!-\!CH\!=\!CH_2$	9.76*	30.1
cis-$CH_3\!-\!CH\!=\!CH\!-\!CH_3$	9.34	28.6
trans-$CH_3\!-\!CH\!=\!CH\!-\!CH_3$	9.27	27.6
$(CH_3)_2C\!=\!CH_2$	9.26	28.4
$(CH_3)_2C\!=\!CH\!-\!CH_3$	8.89	26.9
$(CH_3)_2C\!=\!C(CH_3)_2$	8.53	26.6

*Value for 1-butene

The heats of hydrogenation of propene, 1-butene, isopropylethylene, and t-butylethylene are virtually the same.

$$CH_3\!-\!CH\!=\!CH_2 \quad 30.1 \text{ kcal/mole}$$
$$CH_3CH_2CH\!=\!CH_2 \quad 30.3$$
$$(CH_3)_2CH\!-\!CH\!=\!CH_2 \quad 30.3$$
$$(CH_3)_3C\!-\!CH\!=\!CH_2 \quad 30.3$$

At first glance this appears to be inconsistent with the notion of C—H hyperconjugation. However, steric strain in the olefin will produce an increased heat of hydrogenation while Pitzer strain in the product will lower the heat of reaction for the hydrogenation process. Thus, a smaller heat of hydrogenation can indicate a stabilization of the reactant or a destabilization of the product.[33] Apparently with the monoalkylethylenes, as the alkyl group gets larger, it produces a larger Pitzer strain in the hydrogenation product, and the opposing effects of decreased hyperconjugation and increased Pitzer strain result in the heat of hydrogenation of these compounds being the same.

Hyperconjugation also accounts for the drop in ionization potential of the $H_2C\!=\!O$ group of formaldehyde as the H's are replaced by alkyl groups.[34]

[32] J. Collin and F. P. Lossing, *J. Am. Chem. Soc.,* **81**, 2064 (1959).
[33] R. B. Turner, *Conference on Hyperconjugation, op. cit.,* p. 1.
[34] K. Higasi, I. Omura, and H. Baba, *Nature,* **178**, 652 (1956).

$$H_2C{=}O \qquad CH_3{-}CH{=}O \qquad \underset{\underset{\displaystyle CH_3}{|}}{CH_3CH_2{-}C{=}O}$$

I.P. = 10.88   10.26   9.74 volts

(iii) **Electric Dipole Moments.** The electric dipole moments of some aldehydes are listed in Table 4.4. If the marked difference between the moments of $H_2C{=}O$ and $CH_3{-}CH{=}O$ were due to the difference in electronega-

Table 4.4. DIPOLE MOMENTS OF SOME ALDEHYDES

Compound	Dipole moment
H_2CO	2.27 D
CH_3CHO	2.72
CH_3CH_2CHO	2.73
$CH_3CH_2CH_2CHO$	2.72
$CH_3{-}CH{=}CH{-}CHO$	3.67

tivities of the H atom and the CH_3 group, then there would be significant differences between the moments of the other saturated aldehydes, because there are differences in the electronegativities of the respective alkyl groups. The fact that the saturated aldehydes have the same moment gives support to the notion that hyperconjugation among such forms as XI accounts for the larger polar character of the saturated C_2-C_4 aldehydes in the table. Furthermore, the $C{-}C_{C=O}$ bond is shorter than a regular $C{-}C$ bond by 0.04 Å. Thus, a contribution from form XI(b) also accounts for the double-bond character of the $C{-}C_{C=O}$ bond. The much larger moment of crotonaldehyde can be attributed to the greater separation in charge in the ionic forms X(b).

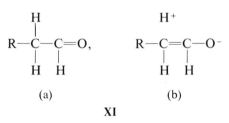

(a)   (b)

XI

The dipole moments of isopropyl and cyclopentyl chlorides are almost the same.

2.04 D   2.08 D

These moments arise from the greater electronegativity of the Cl atom, and are directed along the C—Cl bond. On the basis of induction, one might expect the moment of cyclopropyl chloride to be about the same; however, the moment (1.76 D) is 0.3 D less. This can be explained in terms of the hyperconjugation among such forms as

$$
\begin{array}{ccc}
CH_2 & H_2C^- & H_2C \\
|\ \ \ \rangle CH-Cl, & |\quad CH=\overset{+}{Cl}, & |\ \ \rangle CH=\overset{+}{Cl} \\
CH_2 & H_2C & H_2C^-
\end{array}
$$

In the ionic forms, the dipole is directed opposite to that from induction to give a smaller net moment.

   This hyperconjugation, which does not take place to any significant degree with the larger cyclic rings, is facilitated by the weak C—C bonds of the cyclopropyl ring. The C—C—C bond angles are only a little more than 60°, which permits less overlap of the hybrid sp^3 atomic orbitals, and consequently the usually strong C—C bonds cannot be formed. The decrease in bond energy is about 50 kcal/mole.[35]

   As stated previously, the conjugative ability of a three-membered ring is less than that of a multiple bond. For example, the dipole moments of cyclopropyl ketones are between those of alkyl and vinyl ketones.[36]

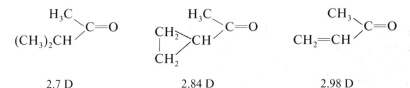

| 2.7 D | 2.84 D | 2.98 D |

The dipoles of the ionic forms of the resonance hybrid of the vinyl ketone

and of the cyclopropyl ketone

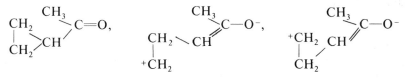

for which there are no analogous forms[37] for the isopropyl ketone, are oriented to supplement the induction moments. The intermediate moment

---

[35] R. A. Ogg and W. J. Priest, *J. Chem. Phys.,* **7**, 736 (1939).

[36] M. T. Rogers, *J. Am. Chem. Soc.,* **69**, 2544 (1947).

[37] Hyperconjugation structures involving the CH_3 and C=O group occur for the three ketones and would produce no significant difference in their moments.

of the cyclopropyl ketone indicates that its hyperconjugation is less important than the resonance of the vinyl ketone.

Based on dipole moments, the hyperconjugation effect of a cyclopropyl group is slightly larger than that of a methyl group. For illustration, the moments of toluene and cyclopropylbenzene are 0.37 and 0.5 D, respectively, which can be attributed partially to hyperconjugation among forms such as

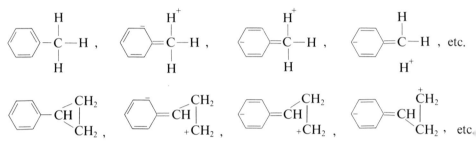

The partial resemblance of the cyclopropyl group to the ethylenic bond is apparent, and it can be seen that there is some conjugation in the $C{=}C{-}C{-}C$ system. Cyclopropane even forms charge-transfer com-
$$\begin{smallmatrix}\backslash\;/\\C\end{smallmatrix}$$
plexes.[38] However, the cyclopropyl group can only be the terminal group in a conjugated system. For illustration, XII is a three-unit conjugated system but in XIII the cyclopropyl group breaks the conjugation between the $C{=}C$ and $C{=}O$ bonds.[39] That is, resonance structures which uphold the

covalences of the atoms cannot be written for XIII involving the extended three-unit chain.

(iv) Bond distances. One of the earliest arguments offered in support of the concept of hyperconjugation was bond distance data. For example, the $C{-}C$ bond length in propene[40] is 1.488 Å in contrast to 1.543 Å in ethane, and the $C{=}C$ bond is 1.353 Å compared to 1.334 Å in ethylene. These bond distances can be explained in terms of the double-bond character of the $C_2{-}C_3$ bond and the single-bond character of the $C_1{-}C_2$ bond owing to the contribution of XIV(b) to the resonance hybrid.

[38] C. F. H. Tipper, *J. Chem. Soc.,* 2045 (1955).
[39] R. H. Eastman and S. K. Freeman, *J. Am. Chem. Soc.,* **77,** 6642 (1955).
[40] D. R. Lide, Jr., and D. E. Mann, *J. Chem. Phys.,* **27,** 868 (1957).

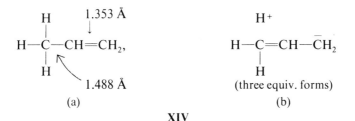

XIV

Similarly, hyperconjugation can account for the C—C bond shortening in acetaldehyde.[41]

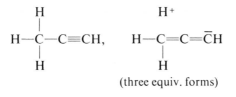

In contrast to acetaldehyde, the C—C bond in perfluoroacetaldehyde (1.54 Å) is essentially the same length as in ethane.[42] The C—C bond contraction in methyl acetylenes can also be attributed partially to hyperconjugation.

$$H-\overset{\displaystyle H}{\underset{\displaystyle H}{\overset{|}{\underset{|}{C}}}}-C\equiv CH, \qquad H-\overset{\displaystyle H^+}{\underset{\displaystyle H}{\overset{|}{\underset{|}{C}}}}=C=\bar{C}H$$

(three equiv. forms)

The following data show that contrary to earlier reports, the C_{sp^3}—C_{sp} bond in the methyl compounds is distinctly shorter than that in the *t*-butyl compounds.[43]

	Me—C≡CH	*t*-Bu—C≡CH	Me—C≡N	*t*-Bu—C≡N
C—C distance:	1.459 Å	1.495	1.458	1.495

This supports the concept of C—H hyperconjugation in the methyl derivatives. Incidentally, several authors have presented evidence for C—C[44] and C—F[45] hyperconjugation. The magnitude of C—C hyperconjugation is less than that of C—H hyperconjugation but the inductive effect of the *t*-butyl group augments the effect of C—C hyperconjugation and sometimes the

---

[41] R. W. Kelb, C. C. Lin, and E. B. Wilson, Jr., *J. Chem. Phys.*, **26**, 1695 (1957).

[42] L. E. Sutton, *Conference on Hyperconjugation, op. cit.*, pp. 74 ff.

[43] L. J. Nugent, D. E. Mann, and D. R. Lide, Jr., *J. Chem. Phys.*, **36**, 965 (1962).

[44] R. W. Taft, Jr., and I. C. Lewis, *Conference on Hyperconjugation, op. cit.*, p. 24; E. Berliner and F. J. Bondhus, *J. Am. Chem. Soc.*, **70**, 854 (1948); H. C. Brown, *et al.*, *J. Am. Chem. Soc.*, **79**, 1897 (1957); P. D. Bartlett, *J. Chem. Educ.*, **30**, 22 (1953).

[45] J. Bornstein, *et al.*, *J. Am. Chem. Soc.*, **79**, 1745 (1957).

two can give the *t*-butyl group as much electron-donating power as does the CH_3 group through C—H hyperconjugation (see Sec. 4.10). For example, the carbonium ions formed by the addition of a proton to a ring carbon atom of 1,3,5-trialkylbenzenes are stabilized by hyperconjugation and induction. The mesitylene cation is more stable than the toluene cation by a factor of 280,000 and more stable than the other trimethylbenzenes by a factor of 70. This is the result of the greater C—H hyperconjugation for mesitylene over that in toluene (more α C—H bonds), and to the fact that of the trimethylbenzenes, only in mesitylene are all of the α C—H's conjugated with the protonated carbon atom.

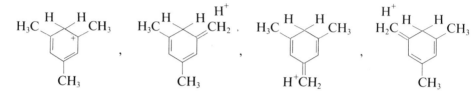

What is surprising, the 1,3,5-trialkylbenzenes show no change in basicity toward a protonic acid as the alkyl groups vary from methyl, ethyl, isopropyl to *t*-butyl.[46] Apparently the loss in α C—H hyperconjugation for this series is counterbalanced by a gain in C—C hyperconjugation plus inductive and polarizability effects of the alkyl groups. This same view can be applied to the C—C_{CN} bond distance in *t*-butyl cyanide.

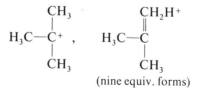

(v) Carbonium ion stability. It has been well established that the decreasing order of stability of carbonium ions is tertiary > secondary > primary. This is commonly attributed to a decrease in hyperconjugation stabilization in the same order.

$$H_3C-\overset{\underset{\textstyle CH_3}{|}}{\overset{\textstyle CH_3}{|}}{C^+} \;,\quad H_3C-\overset{\underset{\textstyle CH_3}{|}}{C}{\overset{\textstyle CH_2H^+}{\|}}$$

(nine equiv. forms)

The greater the number of hydrogen atoms attached to α carbon atoms, the more forms can be written and the greater is the stability of the carbonium ion. Thus, tertiary carbons undergo solvolysis and other reactions involv-

[46] D. A. McCaulay and A. P. Lien, *Conference on Hyperconjugation, op. cit.,* p. 118.

ing carbonium ion intermediates or transition states faster than secondary carbons, which in turn react faster than primary carbon atoms.

(vi) An alternative view. Now, although examples have been presented in this section to show how the concept of hyperconjugation may be used to explain certain properties of molecules, it must be pointed out that most of these same properties can also be explained in terms of orbital hybridization.[52] In particular, ground-state properties such as bond distances, dipole moments, and heats of combustion are greatly affected by orbital hybridization. For illustration, it was discussed in Sec. 1.2.9(d) that in examining the effects of resonance or other factors upon bond distances, one should not use the ethane C—C bond length as a reference for single bonds in which either carbon atom is sp^2 or sp hybridized, but use the sum of the natural hybridized covalent radii. Thus, the C_2—C_3 bond length in butadiene is not expected to be 1.54 Å as it is in ethane but in the range 1.46–1.49 Å, depending upon the method used to determine the natural C_{sp^2}—C_{sp^2} length (see Table 1.8). This value is very close to the measured length (1.483 Å) and hence, there is little bond contraction from resonance. Similarly, the bond contractions attributed to hyperconjugation in this section can be attributed largely to orbital hybridization.

Further, the bond energies of bonds formed by sp^2 carbon must be greater than those of analogous bonds formed by sp^3 carbon. Hence, resonance energies (and hyperconjugation energies) computed from heats of hydrogenation or combustion should be revised to account for the changes in bond energies accompanying changes in orbital hybridization.

Also, it is shown in several places in this text [e.g., Secs. 1.2.9(d), 5.4.4] that the electronegativity of carbon increases with increasing s character of its bonding orbital. Hence, toluene is expected to have a small dipole moment owing to the difference in electronegativities of the sp^3 methyl carbon and the sp^2 phenyl carbon atoms. Too, the s character of cycloalkyl carbon atoms increases with increasing bond-angle strain, such that a cyclopropyl carbon atom is more electronegative than an n-propyl carbon atom. It is expected, then, that the dipole moment of cyclopropyl chloride should be less than that of n-propyl chloride.

(vii) Summary. It is generally agreed that at least four factors may affect bond lengths: (1) electron delocalization, (2) orbital hybridization changes of the bonded atoms, (3) electronegativity of attached atoms, and (4) steric interactions between nonbonded atoms. The debatable point at this time is the relative contributions of factors (1) and (2).[48] It appears that the consensus of opinion is the following: (i) Hybridization is the major factor responsible for contraction of the C—C bond adjacent to C=C or C≡C bonds, and covalent radii for hybridized carbon atoms serve well for predicting such bond lengths. The other three factors play a minor role but can not be neglected. For example, hybridization does not account for the planarity of butadiene. Other bond properties such as dipole moments and ionization potentials may be more sensitive to hyperconjugation in which case hyperconjugation makes a larger contribution to these properties than to bond lengths. (ii) When carbon is attached to atoms with one-pair electrons, delocalization has a larger effect on bond distances and can be shown to produce some bond contraction. For illustration, if the contraction of C_{sp^3} to $C_{sp^2} = 0.025$ A° and from C_{sp^3} to $C_{sp} = 0.067$ A° is subtracted from the total bond shortening observed in the following C—X bonds, the residual bond contraction is found to be as follows:[49]

X	Type of carbon	C—X bond length	Residual bond contraction
N	C_{sp^3}	1.47 A°	
	C_{sp^2}	1.36	0.08 A°
	C_{sp}	1.35	.05
O	C_{sp^3}	1.43	
	C_{sp^2}	1.34	.07
F	C_{sp^3}	1.384	
	C_{sp^2}	1.347	.01
	C_{sp}	1.27	.05
Cl	C_{sp^3}	1.781	
	C_{sp^2}	1.726	.03
	C_{sp}	1.631	.08

Thus, the residual bond contraction values indicate there is some bond shortening in these bonds beyond that from hybridization changes of carbon. (iii) The concept of hyperconjugation is extremely useful for interpreting a wide variety of experimental data.[47] Although it may be a minor factor with respect to ground states of some molecules, it is certainly a dominant factor in stabilizing excited and transition states of molecular species.

4.6. Resonance and spatial configuration

A brief illustration has been given of the use of hyperconjugation for accounting for certain properties of molecules. Now, the same approach will be taken for resonance on a broader scope.

[47] M. M. Kreevoy, *Conference on Hyperconjugation,* op. cit., p. 47; E. Berliner, *ibid.,* p. 143.

[48] Paper symposium on "Effects of Environment on the Properties of Carbon Bonds," Tetrahedron, **17**, Nos. 3/4, April, 1962.

[49] D. R. Lide, Jr., *ibid.,* p. 125.

Among the VB resonance structures for a given molecule, a specific bond may be a single bond in some and a double bond in others. On this basis, resonance theory accounts for observed bond distances being intermediate between the regular single- and double-bond values. For illustration, the contribution of the ionic VB structure to the resonance hybrid of vinyl chloride accounts for the fact that the C—Cl bond (1.726 Å) is shorter

$$CH_2\!=\!CH\!-\!Cl, \quad \overset{-}{C}H_2\!-\!CH\!=\!\overset{+}{Cl}$$

than that in ethyl chloride (1.78 Å). Furthermore, nuclear quadrupole resonance reveals a lack of symmetry of the field gradient around the axis of the C—Cl bond, which indicates that the shortening of the bond is at least partly due to conjugation and not entirely to a change in carbon hybridization.[50] Similarly, the resonance of chlorobenzene accounts for its

short C—Cl bond (1.69 Å). In cyanogen chloride, the C—Cl bond length is even shorter (1.63 Å) than that predicted from orbital hybridization,[51] which indicates that there is a large contribution from its ionic VB structure. The C—Cl bond force constant (5×10^5 dynes/cm), which is much

$$Cl\!-\!C\!\equiv\!N \quad , \quad {}^+Cl\!=\!C\!=\!N^-$$

larger than that in methyl chloride (3.4×10^5), confirms a substantial double-bond character of the bond in Cl—CN.

Although many bond lengths can be accounted for in a qualitative manner in terms of resonance, it must be recognized that bond contraction is due in part to orbital hybridization.[52] It was shown in Sec. 1.2.9(d) that bond shortening from the additivity of fixed covalent radii can be explained in terms of covalent radii of hybridized atoms. The C—C bond distance in cyclooctatetraene is 1.462 Å, and since resonance in this compound is nil owing to noncoplanarity of the C=C bonds, the bond contraction here cannot be attributed to resonance. On the other hand, the much shorter C_{sp^2}—C_{sp^2} distance in the benzene ring (1.39 Å) reveals the effect of a large resonance.

Resonance delocalization does shorten single bonds but the effect is most noticeable in molecules exhibiting isovalent resonance, such as benzene, cyanogen chloride, graphite, etc.[53] For example, the C—N bond length in nitrobenzene (1.486 Å) is essentially the same as that in nitro-

[50] D. Kivelson and E. B. Wilson, Jr., *J. Chem. Phys.,* **32,** 205 (1960).

[51] M. G. Brown, *Trans. Faraday Soc.,* **55,** 694 (1959).

[52] M. J. S. Dewar and H. N. Schmeising, *Tetrahedron,* **5,** 166 (1959).

[53] R. S. Mulliken, *Tetrahedron,* **6,** 68 (1959).

methane (1.49 Å). Thus, the ground-state resonance of nitrobenzene is not large enough to produce any bond contraction of the C—N bond. Thus, it has been estimated that only 10 per cent of the polar effect of the nitro group on the properties of the ring is due to resonance.[54] On the other hand, the isovalent resonance of aniline

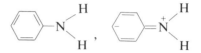

has a definite effect on its ground-state properties. As a consequence, bond shortening of the C—N bond from resonance is greater in aniline derivatives and this is verified experimentally.[55] Similarly, the C—NO_2 bond is shorter in p-nitroaniline[56] than in nitrobenzene because of considerable isovalent resonance among the forms

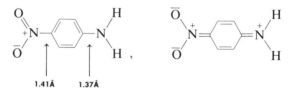

It was shown in Sec. 1.2.8 that for the maximum overlap of p orbitals on adjacent atoms to form π molecular orbitals, the p orbitals must be coplanar. Thus, for maximum conjugation between multiple bonds, the conjugated system must be coplanar. Resonance for a conjugated system will be significant only if the atoms involved are coplanar. A good example is cyclooctatetraene. It is a typical highly unsaturated compound, and it was this fact that refuted Thiele's structure for the benzene ring. Cyclooctatetraene has the puckered D_{2d} "tub" conformation[57] which allows each double bond to have a planar strain-free structure with bond distances of C—C, 1.462 Å and C=C, 1.35 Å.[58] Its infrared spectrum confirms the presence of typical C=C bonds.[59] The nonplanarity of any two double

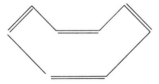

[54] B. M. Wepster, Rec. trav. chim., 75, 1473 (1956).

[55] J. Trotter, Tetrahedron, 8, 13 (1960).

[56] J. Donohue and K. N. Trueblood, Acta Cryst., 9, 960 (1956).

[57] W. B. Person, G. C. Pimentel, and K. S. Pitzer, J. Am. Chem. Soc., 74, 3437 (1952).

[58] I. L. Karle, J. Chem. Phys., 20, 65 (1952).

[59] E. R. Lippincott, R. C. Lord, and R. S. McDonald, J. Am. Chem. Soc., 73, 3370 (1951).

bonds largely prevents an extended conjugation, and this is evident from the small resonance energy (2.4–4.8 kcal/mole).
The OH group of a phenol can rotate about the C—O bond and there-

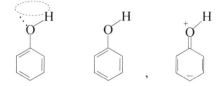

by describe a cone. However, the phenol resonance, excluding the Kekulé resonance of the ring, is significant only if the hydrogen atom is planar with the ring. This brings one of the oxygen p orbitals containing lone-pair electrons perpendicular to the plane of the ring for maximum overlap with the nuclear molecular orbital. Thus, it is said that resonance "locks" the hydrogen atom into the plane of the ring.

This is also the case for the alkyl ethers. Evidence for the coplanarity of the phenyl group and OR group was presented in Sec. 2.3.3 from dipole-moment data.

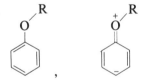

Accordingly, resonance theory explains the planarity of nitrobenzene

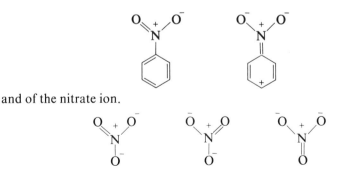

and of the nitrate ion.

Attention is called to the fact that the nitro group in nitrobenzene can be planar by a small in-plane bending of the adjacent hydrogen atoms. In m-dinitrobenzene, however, two nitro groups crowd the same hydrogen atom and as a result, each nitro group is inclined at about 11° to the plane of the benzene ring.[60] Similarly, o-dihalobenzenes are nonplanar,

[60] J. Trotter, *Acta Cryst.*, **14**, 244 (1961).

with the halogen atoms bent 12–15° out of the plane of the ring.[61] The reaction intermediate benzyne

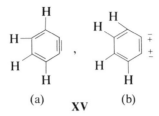

(a)   XV   (b)

has been the object of considerable interest in recent years.[62] Its structure may be regarded as a resonance hybrid (XV) in which the triple bond is a special one using trigonal sp^2 orbitals rather than linear sp orbitals.

In addition to providing an explanation for certain bond distances and the planarity of molecules, resonance theory can account for the barrier to rotation about certain bonds. For example, the resonance of butadiene gives the C_2—C_3 bond a small double-bond character which makes it harder for rotation to occur about this bond. Thus, s-cis and s-trans conformations of butadiene exist (see Sec. 3.3.1) owing to the barrier of rotation about the C_2—C_3 bond. Similarly, restricted rotation of esters about the C—OR bond and of amides[63] about the C—N bond is due to the resonance of the functional groups.

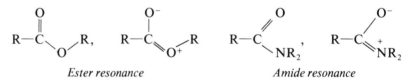

Ester resonance   Amide resonance

Very often the coplanarity of molecules is inhibited owing to steric requirements and, as a consequence, resonance is precluded. A good illustration is provided by picryl iodide. Diffraction studies[64] reveal that the p-nitro group is coplanar with the ring whereas the o-nitro groups are not.

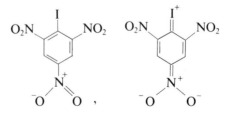

[61]O. Bastiansen and O. Hässel, *Acta Chem. Scand.,* **1,** 489 (1947).

[62]Cf. J. F. Bunnett, *J. Chem. Educ.,* **38,** 278 (1961), and references cited therein.

[63]W. D. Phillips, *J. Chem. Phys.,* **23,** 1363 (1955); H. S. Gutowsky, and C. H. Holm, *J. Chem. Phys.,* **25,** 1228 (1956).

[64]G. Huse and H. M. Powell, *J. Chem. Soc.,* 1398 (1940).

This lack of coplanarity is due to the presence of the large iodine atom. The C—N bond distance is 1.35 Å for the p-NO_2 group and 1.45 Å for the o-NO_2 group. This indicates considerable double-bond character of the *para* C—N bond (normal C—N is 1.47 Å; C=N is 1.28 Å) consistent with the resonance shown above. Such resonance does not involve the o-NO_2 groups because the iodine atom prevents their planarity with the ring. As a result, the C—N bond distance for the o-NO_2 groups is close to the aliphatic C—N length.

We see, then, that resonance theory provides a good accounting of the intermediate bond distances of a given bond type in various molecules. One way of denoting the resemblance of a given bond to a pure single, double, or triple bond is to state the *bond order*. The bond orders for pure single, double, or triple bonds are 1, 2, and 3, respectively. Unfortunately, there are in use at least three different methods of computing bond orders which give different absolute values but approximately the same relative values for a given bond. The three principal methods are the atomic and molecular orbital methods[65] and Pauling's method based on VB structures (see sec. 4.13.2). Since the present discussion is concerned with resonance theory, Pauling's method will be adopted here. It simply calculates the fraction of the major ground-state resonance structures in which a given bond is a single, double, or triple bond. For illustration, the principal resonance structures of benzene are the Kekulé structures, in which a given bond is a single bond in one structure and a double bond in the other. Thus, each bond has a bond order halfway between the values for a single bond and a double bond, or 1.5.[66] Similarly, among the resonance structures for graphite, each C—C bond is a single bond in two-thirds of the structures and a double bond in one-third, giving it a bond order of 1.33.

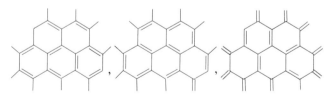

Bond orders may be determined for various bonds from a plot of carbon-carbon bond order vs. bond distance in simple compounds. The bond orders and distances for ethane, ethylene, and acetylene give three points on the curve, and the values for benzene and graphite give two more points (Fig. 4.1).

Even more useful is a relationship between bond distance and per cent

[65]C. A. Coulson, *Proc. Roy. Soc.,* **A169,** 413 (1939).

[66]For comparison, the C—C bond orders for benzene are 1.46 and 1.67 by the LCAO atomic and molecular orbital methods.

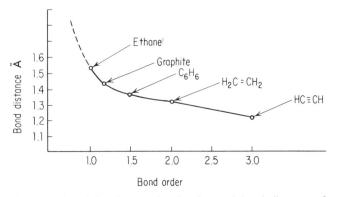

Fig. 4.1. The relation between bond orders and bond distances of carbon-carbon bonds.

double-bond character of a bond. Pauling and coworkers[67] made a graph of bond distance vs. bond character of the ethane, ethylene, benzene, and graphite carbon-carbon bonds. It was found that the curve could be approximated by the equation[68]

$$P = \frac{100(r_s - r)}{2r + r_s - 3r_d} \qquad (4-1)$$

where P = per cent double-bond character of a given bond,
  r = observed bond distance of the bond,
  r_s = normal single-bond distance (1.54 Å),
  r_d = normal double-bond distance (1.33 Å).

Table 4.5 lists the per cent double-bond character of several bonds. The bond character of other types of bonds may be computed by the same method, and some values are included in the table. The values substantiate what has been said already about the relative contributions of the VB structures to the resonance hybrids for several molecules, e.g., chlorobenzene, cyanogen chloride, picryl iodide, etc.

4.7. Resonance and ionic character of molecules

4.7.1. RESONANCE AND DIPOLE MOMENTS.[70]

As it was shown for hyperconjugation, resonance can account for the polar character of molecules in terms of the VB structures which contribute to

[67]L. Pauling, *et al., J. Am. Chem. Soc.,* **57,** 2705 (1935); **59,** 1223 (1937).

[68]W. G. Penney used a less arbitrary method of relating bond distances and bond character (*Proc. Roy. Soc.,* **A158,** 306 (1937)).

[69]G. W. Wheland, *Resonance in Organic Chemistry,* p. 185.

[70]See particularly Sec. 4.10.1.

Table 4.5. PER CENT DOUBLE-BOND CHARACTER OF SOME BONDS[69]

Bond type	Compound	Observed bond length	Per cent double-bond character
C—C	Diacetylene	1.37	65
	Cyclooctatetraene	1.50	8
	Naphthalene	1.40	44
	Thiophene	1.41	38
	Furan	1.46	18
	Acrolein	1.46	18
	Cyanogen	1.37	65
C—Cl	Cyanogen chloride	1.63	42
	Chloroacetylene	1.63	42
	Chlorobenzene	1.69	16
C—N	Picryl iodide		
	p-O_2N—C	1.35	36
	o-O_2N—C	1.45	4
	Urea	1.34	42
	Diazomethane	1.34	42

the resonance hybrid. For example, the dipole moment of ethyl chloride (2.05 D) arises from the inductive effect of the chlorine atom. Since the $C\!=\!C$ bond of vinyl chloride is more polarizable than the C—C bond, one might expect the dipole moment of vinyl chloride to be larger than that of ethyl chloride. To the contrary, it is less (1.44 D), and this is attributed to the contribution of the ionic structure among the resonance forms

$$CH_2\!=\!CH\!-\!Cl, \qquad ^-CH_2\!-\!CH\!=\!Cl^+$$

whose moment is oriented in an opposite direction to the induction moment. The contribution of the ionic form is even greater in chloroacetylene (D.M. = 0.44 D),

$$H\!-\!C\!\equiv\!C\!-\!Cl, \qquad H\!-\!\overset{-}{C}\!=\!C\!=\!Cl^+$$

and this is substantiated by the greater per cent double-bond character of the C—Cl bond (Table 4.5). Other examples of this are given in Table 4.6.

Table 4.6. DIPOLE MOMENTS OF SOME HALOGEN COMPOUNDS

X	CH_3CH_2X	$CH_2\!=\!CHX$	$HC\!\equiv\!CX$	C_6H_5X
Cl	2.05 D	1.44 D	0.44 D	1.60 D
Br	2.02	1.41	0.0	1.57
I	1.90	1.26		1.42

It is not surprising to find that the contribution of polar structures to a resonance hybrid is increased in solvents which support ionization.[71]

The moment of acrolein is larger than that of propionaldehyde and this is consistent with the resonance of the former.

$$CH_2{=}CH{-}CH{=}O, \quad {}^+CH_2{-}CH{=}CH{-}O^- \qquad \begin{array}{l} C{=}C \ = \ 1.36 \ \text{\AA} \\ C{-}C \ = \ 1.46 \ \text{\AA} \\ C{=}O \ = \ 1.21 \ \text{\AA} \end{array}$$

The implied bond characters are confirmed by bond distance data[72] which show that the $C{=}C$ bond is longer than that in ethylene and the $C{-}C$ bond is shorter than that in butadiene.

A good illustration of the parallelism between resonance contribution of ionic forms and dipole moment is found in the set of similar cyanine dyes XVI, XVII, and XVIII.[73] For these there are, respectively, one, two, and four polar structures, of the type

$$N{-}(C{=}C)_n{-}C{=}O, \qquad \overset{+}{N}{=}C{-}(C{=}C)_n{-}\overset{-}{O},$$

and this accounts for the corresponding increases in the dipole moments.

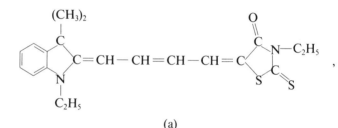

(a)

(b)

XVI

D.M. = 6.91 D

[71]R. W. Taft, Jr., R. E. Glick, I. C. Lewis, I. Fox, and S. Ehrenson, *J. Am. Chem. Soc.,* **82,** 756 (1960), and references cited therein.

[72]H. Mackle and L. E. Sutton, *Trans. Faraday Soc.,* **47,** 695 (1951).

[73]L. M. Kushner and C. P. Smyth, *J. Am. Chem. Soc.,* **71,** 1401 (1949).

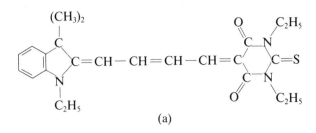

(a)

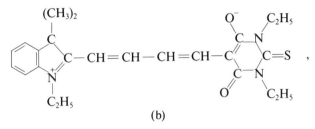

(b)

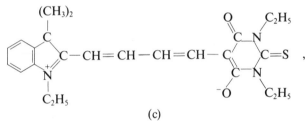

(c)

XVII

D.M. = 9.7 D

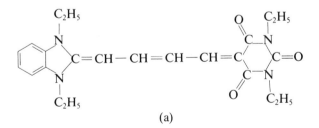

(a)

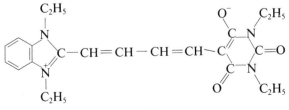

(b)

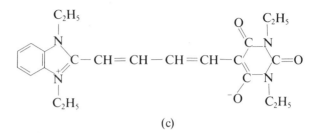

(c)

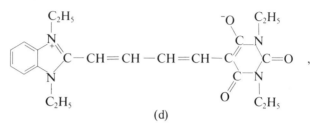

(d)

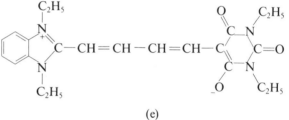

(e)

XVIII

D.M. = 17.7 D

The phosphorus ylenes provide an illustration of the intermediate position of a resonance hybrid between essentially covalent and essentially ionic substances.   Penta-phenylphosphorus is covalent with no dipole moment, is soluble in cyclohexane, and has a melting point of 124°. In contrast to this, $(C_6H_5)_4P^+I^-$ is ionic with a m.p. 334–344°. The intermediate $(C_6H_5)_3PO$ is very polar and should be written $(C_6H_5)_3P^+\!\!-\!O^-$ to indicate the coordinate covalent P—O bond. The phosphorus ylene, $\phi_3P\!=\!C\phi_2$, where ϕ is phenyl, m.p. = 170–172°, contains a π bond between phosphorus and carbon, and is a resonance hybrid (**XIX**). The nucleophilic

$$\phi_3P\!=\!C\phi_2, \qquad \phi_3\overset{+}{P}\!\!-\!\overset{-}{C}\phi_2$$

(a)   (b)

XIX

character of the carbon in these phosphorus ylenes is revealed by the fact that they readily undergo a nucleophilic substitution reaction with alkyl halides.

$$\phi_3P{=}CH_2, \overset{+}{\phi_3}P{-}\overset{-}{CH_2} + CH_3I \longrightarrow (\overset{+}{\phi_3}P{-}CH_2CH_3)I^-$$

The interest in phosphorus ylenes grew rapidly after Wittig discovered their use in preparing olefins from carbonyl compounds.[74]

$$\phi_3P{=}CH_2 + R_2C{=}O \longrightarrow \phi_3P{=}O + R_2C{=}CH_2$$

When the resonance moment and the induction moment of an aryl compound are oriented in the same direction, the D.M. of the aryl compound will be greater than that of a similar aliphatic compound. For illustration, the moments of nitroalkanes are approximately 3.29 D, and that of nitrobenzene is 3.95 D.

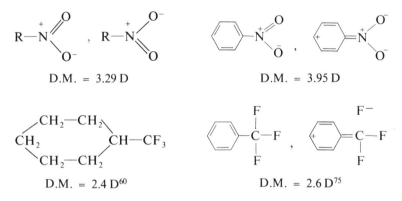

D.M. = 3.29 D   D.M. = 3.95 D

D.M. = 2.4 D[60]   D.M. = 2.6 D[75]

4.7.2. DIPOLE MOMENTS AS CRITERIA FOR RESONANCE STRUCTURES

Having established a relationship between ionic resonance structures and dipole moments, one can reverse the procedure and use dipole moments to support the contribution of a given ionic VB structure to the resonance hybrid of a molecule. For example, the moments of some nitriles are listed in Table 4.7 along with their chief ionic resonance forms. The fact that the moment of acrylonitrile is less than that of propionitrile indicates that the form $CH_2{-}CH{=}C{=}N^+$ makes a significant contribution to the resonance hybrid.

Another good example is urea, for which the ionic structures make almost a 50 per cent contribution to the resonance hybrid.

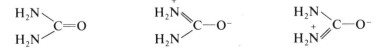

[74]G. Wittig, et al., Angew. Chem., **68**, 505 (1956), and earlier papers; F. Ramirez and S. Levy, J. Org. Chem., **21**, 488 (1956).
[75]J. D. Roberts, R. L. Webb, and E. A. McElhill, J. Am. Chem. Soc., **72**, 408 (1950).

Table 4.7. DIPOLE MOMENTS OF SOME NITRILES[76]

Compound	Dipole moment	Chief ionic resonating structures
H—C≡N	2.93 D	$\overset{+}{H}$—$\overset{-}{C}$=N :
CH_3CH_2—C≡N	4.02	CH_3—CH=C=$\overset{-}{N}$: $\overset{+}{H}$
CH_2=CH—C≡N	3.88	$\overset{+}{CH_2}$—CH=C=$\overset{-}{N}$:, $\overset{-}{CH_2}$—CH=C=$\overset{+}{N}$
CH_3—CH=CH—C≡N	4.50	H^+CH_2=CH—CH=C=$\overset{-}{N}$:

Not only does it have a very large resonance energy (41 kcal/mole) for such a small molecule but it has a large polar character (D.M. = 4.56 D).[77] It is one of the few substances which raises the dielectric constant of water upon going into solution. The large contribution of the ionic structure is further confirmed by the bond force constants[78] and bond distances.[79] For instance, the carbon-oxygen bond distance (1.26 Å) is longer than that of a normal C=O bond (1.21 Å) and the carbon-nitrogen bond (1.33 Å) is considerably shorter than a typical C—N bond (1.47 Å) and quite close to the C=N bond length (1.28 Å). Consequently, a polar structure for urea

$$H_2^{\delta+}N \diagdown$$
$$\phantom{H_2^{\delta+}N}\diagdown C—O^{\delta-}$$
$$H_2^{\delta+}N \diagup$$

is as good a representation of the molecule as is the nonpolar structure. Similarly, the bond distances in formamide[80] reveal a substantial contribution of the dipolar structure to the resonance hybrid. This view is substantiated by its large dipole moment (3.71 D) and the large barrier

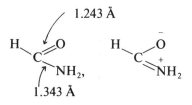

(18 kcal/mole) to rotation of the NH_2 group about the C—N bond.[81] Also, it can be deduced that N,N-dimethylformamide has a planar structure on a

[76]M. T. Rogers and J. D. Roberts, *J. Am. Chem. Soc.*, **68**, 843 (1946).

[77]W. D. Kumler and G. M. Fohlen, *J. Am. Chem. Soc.*, **64**, 1944 (1942).

[78]L. Keldner, *Proc. Roy. Soc.*, A**177**, 456 (1941).

[79]P. Vaughan and J. Donohue, *Acta Cryst.*, **5**, 530 (1952).

[80]R. J. Kurland and E. B. Wilson, *J. Chem. Phys.*, **27**, 585 (1957).

[81]B. Sunners, L. H. Piette, and W. G. Schneider, *Can. J. Chem.*, **38**, 681 (1960).

basis of its nuclear magnetic resonance spectrum.[82] The contribution of the polar structure gives the C—N bond considerable double-bond character and restricts rotation about this bond. In the planar structure, the two methyl groups are in different electrical and magnetic environments and this nonequivalence is readily detected by its n.m.r. spectrum.

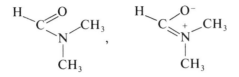

4.7.3. INDUCTION AND RESONANCE MOMENTS

Sutton made the proposal in 1931[83] that the differences in dipole moments of aromatic and aliphatic compounds are largely due to a resonance moment. He expressed the total moment of a compound as the vector sum of a group moment μ_g (the moment of the substituent), a moment μ_i induced in the carbon chain by the group moment, and a resonance moment μ_r. By comparing the moments of aromatic compounds with those of the respective t-butyl compounds, where the μ_i's would be approximately the same, he calculated μ_r for a number of groups as the difference between the moments of corresponding t-butyl and aryl derivatives. Some values are given in Table 4.8. For atoms or linear groups, μ_r is simply $\mu_{arom} - \mu_{ali}$, whereas for bent groups, corrections have been made for the angle between the resultant moment and the C_1—C_4 axis.

Table 4.8. RESONANCE MOMENTS OF SOME MONOSUBSTITUTED BENZENES[85]

Substituent	μ_{arom}	μ_{ali}	μ_r
$N(CH_3)_2$	1.61	0.86	1.66
NH_2	1.48	1.32	1.02
OCH_3	1.35	1.23	0.8
OH	−1.6	−1.7	0.6
I	−1.7	−1.92	0.22
Br	−1.73	−2.00	0.27
Cl	−1.70	−2.01	0.31
F	−1.59	−1.89	0.30
CH_3	0.35	0	0.35
CF_3	−2.60	−2.40	−0.2
CN	−4.39	−3.60	−0.79
$COCH_3$	−3.0	−1.57	−1.43
NO_2	−4.21	−3.25	−0.96

[82] W. D. Phillips, *J. Chem. Phys.*, **23**, 1363 (1955).
[83] L. E. Sutton, *Proc. Roy. Soc.*, **A133**, 668 (1931).

This procedure leads only to qualitative resonance moments. Furthermore, most of the data are taken from solution measurements. Groves and Sugden[84] worked with vapors and made a more detailed approximation of the induced moments. This led to different values of resonance moments and to the opposite order for the halogens.

Group: OH   F   Cl   Br   I OCH_3 CN $COCH_3$ NO_2
μ_r^{84}: 1.12   1.00   0.97   0.89   0.87   0.40 -0.05 -0.17 -0.29

However, it is doubtful that iodine has a larger positive μ_r than OCH_3, which raises a question about the reliability of these values too.

4.7.4. INTERACTION RESONANCE

When two groups with resonance moments of opposite sign are attached *ortho* or *para* to the benzene ring, there is an unusually large contribution from ionic resonance structures. For illustration, the dipole moments of nitrobenzene and aniline are in opposite directions with respect to the ring. It would be expected from the treatment in Sec. 2.3.3 that the dipole moment of *p*-nitroaniline would be the sum of the moments of nitrobenzene and aniline, or 5.48 D.

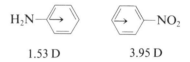

1.53 D   3.95 D

Instead, the observed moment of *p*-nitroaniline is 6.10 D, and the difference (6.10 − 5.48 = 0.62) is attributed to a large contribution to the resonance hybrid from the structure

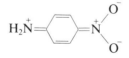

In other words, there is an extra resonance interaction between the substituents which may be called *interaction resonance*. Several examples are given in Table 4.9. The effect occurs only when the groups are oriented *ortho* or *para* to each other, because interaction between *meta* groups would require *meta*-quinoidal structures. Because of the long bond in the *meta* quinoidal structure, it is very unstable and makes no significant contribution to resonance hybrids.

[84]L. G. Groves and S. Sugden, *J. Chem. Soc.*, 1992 (1937).

[85]L. E. Sutton, *Determination of Organic Structures by Physical Methods,* ed. E. A. Braude and F. C. Nachod (New York: Academic, 1955), p. 395.

Table 4.9. SOME INTERACTION RESONANCE MOMENTS FOR p-X—C_6H_4—Y

X	Y	Observed moment	Calculated moment $(\mu_x \pm \mu_y)$	Interaction moment
CH_3	CHO	3.30	3.15	0.15
CF_3	NH_2	4.28	4.13	0.15
CN	$N(CH_3)_2$	5.90	5.55	0.35
CF_3	$N(CH_3)_2$	4.62	4.18	0.44
NO_2	NH_2	6.10	5.48	0.62
NO_2	$N(CH_3)_2$	6.87	5.53	1.34

| ortho quinoidal structure | meta quinoidal structure | para quinoidal structure |

The principles expressed in Sec. 4.3 regarding the relative importance of resonance structures provide some bases for the *interaction resonance* effect. Owing to the charge separation and/or fewer bonds in the ionic forms of nitrobenzene, for example, the latter structures make only a small contribution to the resonance hybrid of nitrobenzene. However, the ionic forms for the *o*- or *p*-disubstituted benzene, having a *m*- and an *o,p*-directing group, at least have the same number of σ and π bonds as does the nonpolar structure.

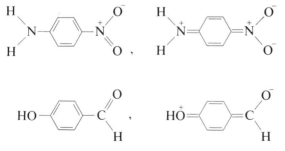

This equality in number of bonds gives the ionic structures greater significance, and the compounds thereby have a greater resonance energy.

4.7.5. STERIC INHIBITION OF RESONANCE

As stated in Sec. 4.6, atoms involved in resonance structures must be coplanar for maximum resonance energy. Often spatial requirements prevent such coplanarity and, accordingly, it is found that resonance is inhibited. When the principal resonance structures are ionic, steric inhibition of resonance is accompanied by a marked decrease in polar character, which may be manifested in several ways: dipole moments, solubilities, melting points, etc. For examples, the moments in benzene solution of N,N-dimethylaniline and trimethylamine are 1.61 D and 0.86 D, respectively. The directions of the bond moments and resultant moments (μ_R) have been assigned as follows:[86]

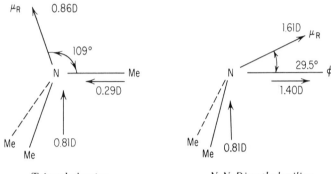

Trimethylamine   *N,N-Dimethylaniline*

Any inhibition of resonance in the aromatic compound should lower its moment, and indeed, this is observed for 2,6-dimethyl-N,N-dimethylamine, whose moment (0.94) is near that of aliphatic tertiary amines.

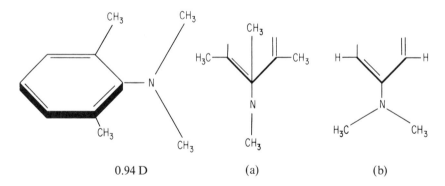

0.94 D   (a)   (b)

The *o*-methyl groups prevent the N-methyl groups from lying near the plane of the molecule (a) and this prevents the nitrogen lone-pair electrons from overlapping with the π-orbital system of the ring. The *o*-hydrogen atoms of the N,N-dimethylaniline (b) do not produce the same spatial hindrance. The ring methyl groups would have the effect of slightly raising

[86]J. W. Smith, *J. Chem. Soc.*, 81 (1961).

the moment, as shown by the moments of aniline (1.53 D) and 2,6-di-methylaniline (1.63 D).

Several other examples of this effect of inhibition of resonance on dipole moments are given in Tables 4.10 and 4.11. In the durene derivatives,

Table 4.10. DIPOLE MOMENTS OF DURENE AND MESITYLENE COMPOUNDS WITH CORRESPONDING METHYL AND PHENYL DERIVATIVES

X	CH_3X	C_6H_5X	Durene—X	Mesitylene—X
NO_2	3.29	3.95	3.62	3.65
NH_2	1.39	1.53	1.39	1.40
OH	1.67	1.61	1.68	
$COCH_3$	2.72	2.88	2.68	2.71
COCl	2.40	3.32		2.95

Table 4.11. DIPOLE MOMENTS OF DISUBSTITUTED DURENES AND CORRESPONDING METHYL AND PHENYL COMPOUNDS

X	Y	p-X—C_6H_4—Y	$XCH_3 + YCH_3$	X—Durene—Y
NO_2	NH_2	6.10	4.56	4.98
NO_2	OC_2H_5	4.74	4.47	3.68
NO_2	$N(CH_3)_2$	6.16	4.03	5.11
Br	NH_2	2.99	2.84	2.75
Br	NO_2	2.60	1.71	2.36
OH	NO_2	5.04	4.86	4.08

resonance involving the substituent and the ring is depressed because the *ortho* methyl groups prevent approximate coplanarity of the substituents with the ring. Thus, the moments approach the values for the corresponding aliphatic compounds. These data reveal information about the directions of the induction and resonance moments of aniline, phenol, and nitrobenzene. It is observed that steric inhibition of resonance decreases the moment of aniline, and that *para* groups which are electron-withdrawing by resonance have exalted dipole moments, e.g., *p*-nitroaniline. Since μ_i and μ_r for aniline are in opposite directions, the resultant moment in aniline must be towards the ring, and μ_r must be larger than μ_i. In phenol, steric inhibition of resonance *increases* the moment of phenol and since μ_i and μ_r are in opposite directions, μ_i must be larger than μ_r, and the resultant moment must be away from the ring. These comments, of course, refer to the projections of μ_i along the C—N and C—O axes in aniline and phenol, respectively, The dipole moment of *p*-nitrophenol is greater than the difference between the moments of nitrobenzene and phenol, so, apparently, the resonance moment of *p*-nitrophenol must outweigh the μ_i of phenol to give a moment for the *p*-nitrophenol greater than that even of nitrobenzene. This also shows that the moment of phenol is away from the ring, for if it were toward the ring, then the moment of *p*-nitrophenol would be larger than the sum of the moments of nitrobenzene and phenol. In nitrobenzene, μ_i and μ_r are each directed away from the ring so the observed moment is also away from the ring and steric inhibition of resonance decreases its moment.

Apparently, some π-overlap can occur between the lone-pair electrons on an N-methyl group and the ring when there is only one *o*-methyl group, for the moments[86] of several *o*-substituted N-methylanilines exceed those of the respective anilines by small amounts. However, with two *ortho*

Compound	ϕ—NH$_2$	ϕ—NHMe	ϕ—NMe$_2$
Aniline	1.53 D	1.68 D	1.61 D
o-Toluidine	1.59	1.76	0.96
2,4-Xylidine	1.40	1.54	0.71
2,4-Dibromoaniline	2.65	2.88	

substituents, the moments decrease slightly for the N-methyl compounds and substantially for the N,N-dimethylaniline.

Compound	ϕNH$_2$	ϕNHMe	ϕ—NMe$_2$
Mesidine	1.45 D	1.22 D	1.03 D
2,4,6-Tribromoaniline	1.73	1.68	1.02

When the ionic character of a compound is reduced, it is probable that its melting point will decrease. Ionic compounds have high melting points because many large ionic forces must be overcome to bring about the process of melting, whereas only weak van der Waals forces need be overcome for melting of nonpolar compounds. Of course, several factors affect melting points so that caution must be taken in trying to relate this property to ionic character. Nevertheless, a parallelism is not unusual for closely related compounds. For example, as CH$_3$ groups are attached to nitrogen in 2,4,6-trichloroaniline, there is a decrease in melting point. This can be attributed to the increased steric inhibition of resonance and therefore less contribution from the respective ionic resonance structures.

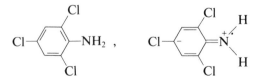

Other examples are listed in Table 4.12.

Table 4.12. MELTING POINTS OF SOME STERICALLY
HINDERED COMPOUNDS

Derivative	ϕ—NH_2	ϕ—NHMe	ϕ—NMe_2
2,4,6-Trichloro	78.5°	32°	Liquid
2,4,6-Tribromo	122	39	Liquid
2,4,6-Triiodo	185	106	70
2,6-Dinitro	138		78
2,3,5,6-Tetramethyl-4-nitro	161		90
2-Methyl	−16		−60
4-Nitronaphthalenes			
1-Amino		191°	
1-Methylamino		184	
1-Ethylamino		176	
1-Benzylamino		156	
1-Dimethylamino		65	
1-Diethylamino		Liquid	

4.8. Resonance and chemical equilibria

In the foregoing discussion, it has been shown how resonance theory can be used to interpret certain physical properties of molecules, one property being thermal stability. In this section, we will use resonance theory to interpret another energy aspect of chemical systems. From thermodynamics we have the familiar equations

$$\Delta F = -RT \ln K \quad \text{and} \quad \Delta F = \Delta E + P\,\Delta V + T\,\Delta S$$

where ΔF = standard free energy change for a reaction, K = the equilibrium constant for the reaction, R = the gas constant, T = the absolute temperature, ΔS, ΔV, and ΔE are the changes in entropy, volume, and internal energy for the reaction, respectively, and P is the pressure on the system. Essentially in all instances of considering the resonance effect on an equilibrium, we study the change in equilibrium with molecular structural changes. For example, we study the effect of substituents on the dissociation constant of benzoic acid or effects on an equilibrium by substitution into a reference compound. The comparisons are normally made under approximately the same conditions of solvent, concentration, or temperature. Therefore, changes in $P\,\Delta V$ will be negligible for the family of compounds involved. The change in $T\,\Delta S$ may not be negligible but will be sufficiently small usually not to change the sign of ΔF. Therefore, we may write

$$\Delta F = \Delta E + P\Delta V + T\Delta S = -RT \ln K$$

$$\Delta(\Delta E) \simeq \Delta(-RT \ln K)$$

That is, the change in internal energy for the equilibria of a family of compounds will be approximately equal to the changes in $\ln K$.

Now, $\Delta E = E_p - E_r$, where E_p and E_r are the sums of the internal energies of the products and reactants, respectively. We have, therefore,

$$E_p - E_r = -RT \ln K \quad \text{or} \quad E_r - E_p = RT \ln K$$

Thus, if resonance energy stabilizes the products more than the reactants, $E_r - E_p$ gets larger and so does K. That is, the equilibrium shifts towards the products. On the other hand, if resonance energy stabilizes the reactants relative to the products, $E_r - E_p$ gets smaller and the equilibrium shifts towards the reactants. Recall that stabilization of a molecule means that E gets smaller. This generalization can serve as a guide in predicting the resonance effect on equilibria.

4.8.1. DISSOCIATION OF ACIDS AND BASES[87]

Consider the dissociation of a saturated aliphatic alcohol.

$$\text{ROH} \rightleftharpoons \text{RO}^- + \text{H}^+ \quad (K_a \simeq 10^{-16})$$

Any structural modification which brings about a net stabilization of either the alcohol or its anion will be accompanied by a change in the equilibrium constant. For demonstration, when R is an aryl group, the acid and also the anion have a certain resonance stabilization.

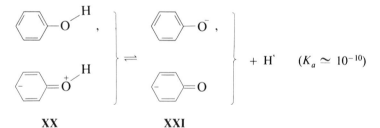

XX   XXI

The resonance of the ion is greater than that of the acid because the latter is reduced by charge-separation. Hence, there is a greater resonance stabilization of the ion, and the equilibrium lies further on the right side than for an alcohol as confirmed by the millionfold increase in K_a. Also, the ionic form of the acid (XX) decreases the electron density on the oxygen to facilitate removal of the hydrogen, and the ionic form of the ion (XXI) decreases the negative charge on the oxygen to diminish its attraction for a proton. Thus, the resonance effect here has an energy stabiliza-

[87]B. M. Wepster, *Progress in Stereochemistry,* vol. 2, ed. W. Klyne and P. B. D. de la Mare (New York: Academic, 1958), chap. 4.

tion factor and a charge-density factor both of which tend to increase K_a of the phenol.

An acid-strengthening resonance also occurs for carboxylic acids.

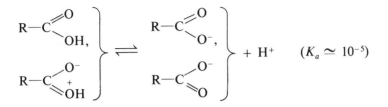

$$+ H^+ \qquad (K_a \simeq 10^{-5})$$

Again, resonance for the acid is not as great as it is for the ion because the former is diminished by charge-separation and the latter is favored by equivalency of the resonance structures. As a result, K_a is even larger than it is for phenols. Again the resonance charge-density effect tends to shift the equilibrium towards dissociation.

These same principles provide an explanation for the much smaller base strengths of aromatic amines than aliphatic amines.

$$RNH_2 + H^+ \rightleftharpoons RNH_3^+ \qquad (K_b \simeq 10^{-5})$$

$$(or\ RNH_2 + H_2O \rightleftharpoons RNH_3^+ + OH^-)$$

In the case of the aliphatic amine, neither the free base or its ion is significantly affected by resonance. However, the aromatic amine has a resonance energy above that of the benzene ring of about 10 kcal/mole, whereas its ion has none. Thus, there is a net resonance stabilization of the free base giving it a smaller K_b or larger pK_a.[88]

In the absence of steric effects, substituents affect the differential resonance energy of acid and base dissociation largely through *resonance interactions*. For example, groups which will accept the negative charge in the ionic structures of **XX** and **XXI** will further stabilize the ionic structures, e.g.,

[88]$pK_a = \log 1/K_a$, hence the larger is pK_a the smaller is K_a; that is, the greater is the base strength of the amine.

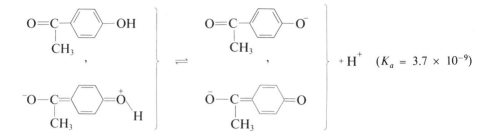

Both the acid and its ion have increased stability by the presence of the CH_3CO group; the effect is greater for the ion because the electrons in the ion are already more polarizable than in the acid and the substituent produces a greater delocalization.[89] For similar reasons, the K_a of p-nitrophenol (ca. 10^{-8}) is larger than that of phenol. With more such groups in the *ortho* or *para* positions, the acid-strengthening resonance is further magnified, and this is demonstrated by the K_a's of polynitrophenols.

Acid	K_a
Phenol	1.3×10^{-10}
p-Nitrophenol	6.9×10^{-8}
2,4-Dinitrophenol	1×10^{-4}
2,4,6-Trinitrophenol	4.2×10^{-1}

Thus, picric acid is a strong acid.

Similarly, interaction resonance in aromatic amines decreases their base strengths. For instance, K_b's for aniline and p-nitroaniline are approximately 10^{-9} and 10^{-12}, respectively.

The steric effect. The steric effect may operate in several ways to modify acid and base association constants. The steric factor may hinder resonance and thereby affect K_a or K_b, or it may be involved in F-, B-, or I-strain, or it may produce a differential solvation of the reactants and products. Some of these effects were discussed in Sec. 3.4. Since increased resonance lowers the pK_a of phenols and anilines, any steric inhibition of resonance should decrease the acid strength of a phenol and increase the base strength of an aniline. For example, 2,6-dimethyl-4-nitrophenol (XXII) is a stronger acid than is the 3,5- isomer (XXIII). In the latter compound, the methyl groups block the acid-strengthening nitrophenol resonance by preventing the nitro group from lying coplanar with the ring.

---

[89]As the Bible scripture is often reworded, "Them that has, git—and them that have not will lose that which they seemingly have."

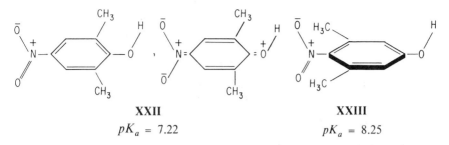

XXII

$pK_a = 7.22$

XXIII

$pK_a = 8.25$

The introduction of first one and then two *ortho* methyl groups into aniline progressively decreases the base strength of aniline, but in the case of N,N-dimethylaniline, the first *o*-Me group is base-strengthening and the second *o*-Me group is markedly base-weakening.

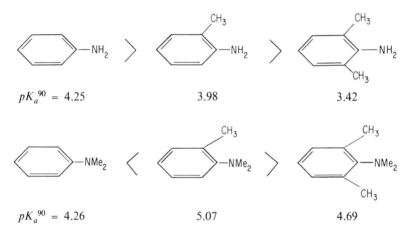

An explanation for this nonparallelism was offered by Brown.[91] In the free base of **XXIV**, for example, spatial crowding around the nitrogen atom is relieved by rotation of the almost planar NR'_2 group to a plane perpendicular to the ring. Protonation of the nitrogen atom converts it to a tetrahedral configuration and thereby increases the spatial crowding about this

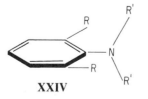

XXIV

[90] In 50 per cent ethanol at 25°. Cf. H. C. Brown, D. H. McDaniel, and O. Hafliger, *Determination of Organic Structures by Physical Methods,* ed. E. A. Braude and F. C. Nachod, chap. 14.

[91] H. C. Brown and A. Cahn, *J. Am. Chem. Soc.,* **72**, 2939 (1950).

atom. This has the effect of retarding protonation and decreases the apparent basicity of the amine. There is also a spatial hindrance to solvation of the amine salt which decreases K_b still further. This steric strain (S) accounts for the decreasing basicities of XXIV when $R' = H$ and $R = CH_3$. However, when $R' = $ alkyl groups, *steric inhibition of resonance* (R_i) becomes significant as discussed already in this section. The two effects are normally opposed since steric strain in the salt is base-weakening and steric inhibition of resonance for the free base is base-strengthening. In the case of the N,N-dimethylanilines, the first o-Me group produces a larger R_i than S effect and the overall effect is base-strengthening. The second o-Me group has the opposite order of relative magnitudes of R_i and S effects which produces a weaker base.

Of course, superimposed on these resonance and steric effects is an inductive effect (I). For example, less electronegative groups on the nitrogen atom tend to increase its basicity. This effect is hard to demonstrate because it simultaneously introduces F-strain and the steric S effect. Groups in the *meta* and *para* positions also exert an inductive effect and without introducing a steric change. For example, the $^+NMe_2$ group increases the acid strength of benzoic acid and lowers the base strength of aniline, and like a truly inductive effect, it diminishes with distance.

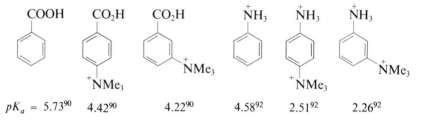

$pK_a = 5.73^{90}$ 4.42^{90} 4.22^{90} 4.58^{92} 2.51^{92} 2.26^{92}

As an aid in correlating these several structural effects, Brown[91] schematically represented the energy quantities by a chart such as in Fig. 4.2. This chart shows, for example, that the resonance energy of B is slightly smaller than that of A as a result of a small inhibition of resonance between the o-Me groups and the H's on the nitrogen. The o-Me groups exert a small $+I$ effect (base-strengthening), and a larger S effect. The net result (ΔE) for B is larger than that of A (compare pK_a's; basicity decreases with increasing ΔE for the reaction). In a similar fashion, the relative magnitudes of these resonance, steric, and inductive effects are assessed for the other anilines in the chart.

It appears that as a first approximation, alkyl groups on the nitrogen increase the base strength primarily through the R_i (and I) factor whereas the same alkyl groups in the *ortho* positions decrease the base strength mainly through the S factor. For example, for all the cases in Table

[92]J. D. Roberts, R. A. Clement, and J. J. Drysdale, *J. Am. Chem. Soc.,* **73,** 2181 (1951).

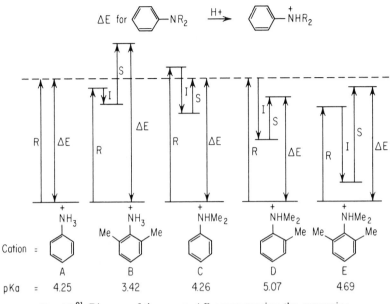

Fig. 4.2.[91] Diagram of the energy ΔE accompanying the conversion of an aniline base into its anilinium ion. The components of ΔE are: resonance energy (R), inductive (I), and steric strain in the ion (S). The larger ΔE is the weaker the amine is as a base.

4.13, a given *o*-alkyl group *decreases* the base strength of aniline and the same N-alkyl group *increases* the base strength of aniline. Furthermore, the magnitude of these effects grows with increasing size of the groups.

Table 4.13. BASE STRENGTHS OF SOME SUBSTITUTED ANILINES[87]

Substituent	pK_a	Substituent	pK_a
2-Me	4.09	N-Me	4.29
2-Et	4.04	N-Et	4.71
2-*i*Pr	4.06	N-*i*Pr	5.14
2-*t*-Bu	3.38	N-*t*-Bu	6.51
2,6-di-Me	3.49		

4.8.2. DISSOCIATIONS INTO FREE RADICALS

It is well established now that hexaarylethanes, as first reported by Gomberg,[93] dissociate in solution into free radicals according to the equation

[93] M. Gomberg, *Ber.*, **33**, 3150 (1900).

$$R_3C\!-\!CR_3 \rightleftharpoons 2\ R_3C\cdot \qquad (4\text{-}2)$$

There are several physical methods employed to study this equilibrium, particularly cryoscopic,[94] spectroscopic,[95] and magnetic susceptibility methods.[96]

(i) Experimental methods. If the molecular weight of a hexaarylethane in solution is determined by measuring the melting-point lowering or boiling-point elevation of the solvent, a value is obtained which is intermediate between that calculated for the ethane and for the free radical. Taking an m molar solution of an ethane, of molecular weight M, of which a fraction α is dissociated into two free radicals, the concentration of free radicals would be $2\alpha m$, and the concentration of undissociated ethane would be $(1 - \alpha)m$. The total concentration of particles would therefore be $(1 - \alpha)m + 2\alpha m$, or $(1 + \alpha)m$. The observed molecular weight M_o would then be the weight of solute per liter, mM, divided by the total number of moles in a liter of solution, $(1 + \alpha)m$.

$$M_o = \frac{mM}{(1 + \alpha)m} = \frac{M}{1 + \alpha}$$

The degree of dissociation can thus be calculated from the observed molecular weight and the formula weight of the ethane. Although this procedure appears simple, the results are far from accurate. Another disadvantage of the cryoscopic and ebullioscopic method is that it can be used only at two temperatures: the freezing and boiling points of the solvent.

An absorption spectroscopic method takes advantage of the fact that the hexaarylethanes are usually colorless while the free radicals are colored. According to Beer's law, absorption of light by a solute is proportional to its concentration. Failure of a solution to obey this law is an indication that the solute is undergoing some type of dissociation or association. By measuring the absorbance (a measure of the amount of light absorbed at a given wavelength) of the hexaarylethane solution at various concentrations, the degree of dissociation may be calculated from the expression $\alpha = A/A_\infty$ where A_∞ is the absorptivity at infinite dilution (it is assumed that the ethane would be completely dissociated at infinite dilution). The equilibrium constant K is then

$$K = \frac{(2\alpha m)^2}{(1 - \alpha)m} = \frac{4\alpha^2 m}{1 - \alpha}$$

[94]P. Walden, *Chemie der freien Radikale* (Leipzig: Hirzel, 1924).

[95]K. Ziegler and L. Ewald, *Ann.*, **473**, 163 (1929).

[96]P. W. Selwood, *Magnetochemistry* (New York: Interscience, 1956); *Techniques of Organic Chemistry*, vol. 1, pt. IV ed. A. Weissberger (3rd ed.; New York: Interscience, 1960), pp. 2873 ff.

where m is the initial molar concentration of the hexaarylethane. A test of the validity of the method is whether or not K is independent of concentration; indeed, this has been found to be true.[95] The experimental procedure for a magnetic method of studying the equilibrium (4-2) was discussed in Sec. 1.2.13(a). This method usually gives lower values for K than do the other two methods. All three methods are tedious to carry out, for they must be performed in the rigid absence of air. Although the spectroscopic and magnetic methods give different values of K, they do give approximately the same values of its temperature coefficient.[97] It is found that the heat of dissociation of hexaarylethanes in various solvents is in the range 10–12 kcal/mole.

More recent methods, such as electron-spin resonance spectroscopy, offer more versatility in studying free radicals and will be used in increasing amounts as the equipment becomes more readily available.

(ii) The steric factor. There are two important structural parameters which have a pronounced effect on the dissociation of hexaarylethanes into free radicals: (1) steric hindrance, which weakens the C_1—C_2 bond in the substituted ethane, and (2) resonance stabilization of the free radicals once they are formed. Evidence for the steric effect is found in several facts. First, the aliphatic C_1—C_2 bond distance of hexaphenylethane is longer than the C—C bond distance of unsubstituted ethane. Secondly, the amount of free radical in a solution of tetra-p-biphenylethane is not measurable, whereas a dilute benzene solution of tetra-p-biphenyl-di-t-butylethane is about 70 per cent dissociated at 5°.[98] Moreover, thermochemical studies give a semiquantitative measure of the steric and resonance effects.[99] Bent and his collaborators[100] have found from several studies that the C_1—C_2 bond of hexaphenylethane is weakened by about 30 kcal/mole. Thus, in the absence of a resonance effect, the heat required to convert one mole of hexaphenylethane into free radicals should be about 80 − 30 = 50 kcal/mole. It is found by several methods already mentioned that the heat of dissociation of hexaphenylethane is only about 11 kcal.[101] The difference, 39 kcal, can be attributed to resonance stabilization of the two free radicals. Therefore, steric hindrance and resonance are about equally respon-

[97]E. Müller and I. Müller-Rodloff, *Ann.*, **521**, 89 (1936); R. Preckel and P. W. Selwood, *J. Am. Chem. Soc.*, **63**, 3397 (1941). See also the calorimetric values of C. B. Wooster, *ibid.*, **58**, 2159 (1936).

[98]J. B. Conant and R. F. Schultz, *J. Am. Chem. Soc.*, **55**, 2098 (1933).

[99]N. V. Sidgwick, *The Chemical Elements and Their Compounds* (London: Oxford U. P., 1950), p. 542.

[100]H. E. Bent *et al.*, *J. Am. Chem. Soc.*, **58**, 170, 1624 (1936), and earlier papers.

[101]See also K. Ziegler, *et al.*, *Ann.*, **504**, 131, 162 (1933); R. C. Mithoff and G. E. K. Branch, *J. Am. Chem. Soc.*, **52**, 255 (1930); P. W. Selwood and R. F. Preckel, *J. Am. Chem. Soc.*, **65**, 895 (1943).

sible for the dissociation of hexaphenylethane. It must be remembered, however, that these values are worked out for hexaphenylethane, which shows only a small dissociation (1–3 per cent). For compounds discussed below, where the dissociations run as high as 100 per cent, the resonance factor is by far the more important.

(iii) The resonance factor. Qualitative evidence for the resonance effect is found in the fact that hexaalkylethanes do not dissociate. Moreover, tetraphenyl-di-cyclohexylethane, which has a greater intramolecular crowding than hexaphenylethane, does not dissociate in any measurable amount in solution, in contrast to the 1–3 per cent dissociation of hexaphenylethane. Also, it will be shown presently that structural modifications that increase resonance in the free radicals also increase the degree of dissociation of the parent hexaarylethane.

Resonance affects the dissociation of hexaarylethanes by a net resonance stabilization of the free radicals. For illustration, consider hexaphenylethane.

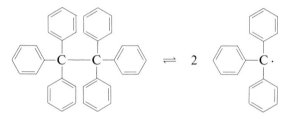

The benzene resonance can occur with the six phenyl groups of the ethane as well as with the phenyl groups of the radicals, so that there would be no relative resonance stabilization if this were the only resonance possible. However, in the free radical there are additional forms in which the odd electron is located on the *ortho* or *para* carbon atoms in any one of the three phenyl rings. Furthermore, when the odd electron is on a nuclear carbon atom, the other two phenyl rings may have either Kekulé form independently of each other, so that there are four forms in which the odd electron is at any one *ortho* or *para* carbon atom. For example, when the odd electron is located at a *para* carbon, there are the following four forms:

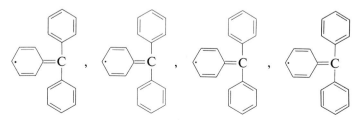

There are nine nuclear carbon atoms which may possess the odd electron, resulting in a total of 36 additional forms to contribute to the resonance hybrid of the free radicals. These additional resonance structures produce a net resonance stabilization of the free radicals over that of the undissociated ethane.

If one of the phenyl groups in the triphenylmethyl radical is replaced by a biphenyl group, there are 84 forms in which the odd electron is in the aromatic portion of the radical.

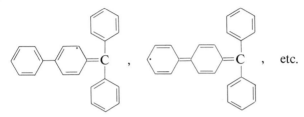

The Kekulé resonance of each benzene ring is independent of the rest of the molecule so that when the odd electron is on an *ortho* or *para* carbon atom of either phenyl group, or of the inner ring of the biphenyl group, there are eight Kekulé forms, making $9 \times 8 = 72$ forms. Each position of the odd electron in the outer biphenyl ring is associated with four Kekulé forms, adding 12 more forms. The replacement, then, of a phenyl group by a biphenyl group in triphenylmethyl, increases the number of Kekulé resonance structures from 36 to 84, and is accompanied by an increase in the degree of dissociation from 1–3 per cent for hexaphenylethane to about 5 per cent for tetraphenyl-di-*p*-biphenylethane.[102] As expected, diphenyltetra-*p*-biphenylethane and hexa-*p*-biphenylethane are dissociated to an even greater degree: 16 and 37 per cent, respectively.[103] The 12 resonance forms of diphenyl-biphenylmethyl, in which the odd electron is in the outer ring of the biphenyl group, make only a small contribution to the resonance, because they occur at the expense of the Kekulé resonance of the inner ring. Evidence for this is found in the experimental observation[102] that tetraphenyl-di-*m*-biphenyl ethane, for which the extra 12 forms are not possible, is dissociated only to a slight degree less than is tetraphenyl-di-*p*-biphenylethane. It is difficult to make a close comparison of these compounds from literature data because the values vary with temperature and concentration and few results are reported for identical experimental conditions.

It is noteworthy that separation of two phenyl groups from the ethane carbon atoms of hexaphenylethane by two vinyl groups, a step which diminishes the crowding about the ethane carbon atoms, leads to a large

[102] C. S. Marvel, M. B. Mueller, and E. Ginsburg, *J. Am. Chem. Soc.,* **61,** 2008 (1939).

[103] C. S. Marvel, J. W. Shackleton, C. M. Himel, and J. Whitson, *J. Am. Chem. Soc.,* **64,** 1824 (1942).

dissociation. For instance, tetraphenyl-divinylethane and tetraphenyl-anisylvinylethane are largely dissociated even in the solid state.[104] Even more striking is the fact that pentaphenyl-cyclopentadienyl is completely monomeric at room temperature.[105]

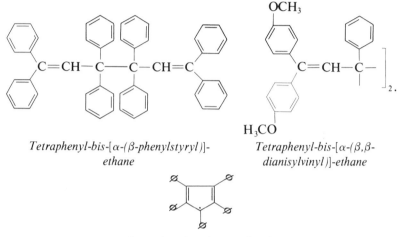

Tetraphenyl-bis-[α-(β-phenylstyryl)]-ethane

Tetraphenyl-bis-[α-(β,β-dianisylvinyl)]-ethane

Pentaphenyl-cyclopentadienyl

The naphthyl ring promotes dissociation of hexaarylethanes to a greater degree than does the biphenyl nucleus, but it has not been determined to what extent this is due to the inherent steric advantage of the naphthyl group. The larger dissociation of hexa-α-naphthyl-ethane over that of hexa-β-naphthyl-ethane is explicable on the basis that there are seven forms for the α-naphthyl isomer with the odd electron in the aromatic nucleus as compared with six for the β-naphthyl ring. For illustration, the resonance forms of the α-naphthyl group containing the odd electron are:

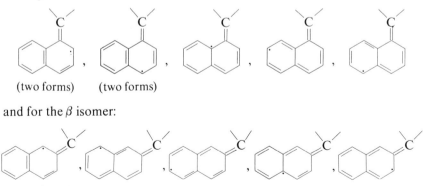

(two forms)   (two forms)

and for the β isomer:

(two forms)

[104] K. Ziegler and C. Ochs, *Ann.*, **434**, 34 (1923); *Ber.*, **55**, 2257 (1922).
[105] E. Müller and I. Müller-Rodloff, *Ber.*, **69**, 665 (1936).

Also, there is some significance in the fact that four of the seven forms
with the odd electron in the α-naphthyl ring, in contrast to two of the six
for the β-naphthyl ring, include the Kekulé resonance.

The effect of substituents in the phenyl groups of triphenylmethyl
can also be interpreted in terms of resonance theory. For example, in
the p-anisyl group, the oxygen atom offers an additional position for
the odd electron, which makes possible a number of additional resonance
forms.

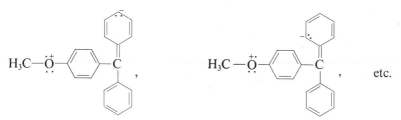

The latter form not only permits the Kekulé resonance, but also the
negative charge can be distributed among the nine *ortho* and *para* carbon
atoms of the three phenyl rings, e.g.,

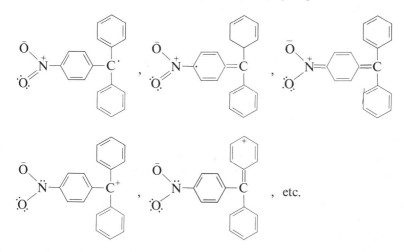

An analogous situation exists for the p-nitrophenyl group.

As a result of the contribution made by the forms with the odd electron
on the oxygen atoms, the dissociation is increased from about 3 per cent for
hexaphenylethane to close to 100 per cent for hexa-p-anisyl- and hexa-p-
nitrophenylethane, all in solution. Note that the large dissociation occurs

with *o,p*-directing groups as well as with *m*-directing groups in the phenyl rings.

It might be well to see how these structures are interconvertible. Instead of the usual electron-pair shifts, the pairs are uncoupled, with single electrons migrating in opposite directions. For demonstration, the shifts are indicated for the conversion of one structure to another for diphenyl-*p*-anisylmethyl. Only the pertinent electrons are shown.

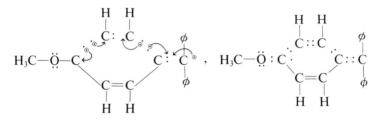

Following the foregoing treatment, it is possible to account for the observed trend of increasing effectiveness of groups to promote dissociation of hexaarylethanes. The general sequence is: phenyl $<$ *p*-alkylphenyl $<$ β-naphthyl $<$ *p*-biphenyl $<$ xanthyl, *p*-anisyl $<$ *o*-anisyl, *o*-chlorophenyl $<$ α-naphthyl $<$ *p*-nitrophenyl, 1-phenanthryl.

Other types of compounds dissociate into free radicals too, namely, metal ketyls,[106]

$$R_2C-CR_2$$

tetraarylhydrazines,[107]

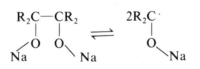

and others.

It might be explained here why a resonance stabilization of the free radicals facilitates their formation. In a reversible reaction there are three energy quantities of major importance. These are the activation energies for the forward and reverse reactions and the enthalpy change (i.e., the difference in potential energy of the reactants and the products). The activation energy is obtainable from the temperature coefficient of the rate of reaction and the heat of reaction from the temperature coefficient of the

[106] E. Müller and W. Janke, *Z. Elektrochem.*, **45**, 380 (1939).
[107] L. G. Cole and E. C. Gilbert, *J. Am. Chem. Soc.*, **73**, 5423 (1951).

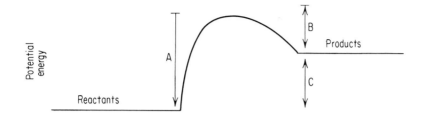

equilibrium constant. In the diagram, A and B are the activation energies for the forward and reverse reactions, respectively, and C is the heat of reaction. The reaction is endothermic in this case. For dissociations into free radicals, it is assumed that B is zero (see also p. 44), hence, the activation energy for dissociation of hexaarylethanes is set equal to the dissociation energy. Therefore, since resonance energy stabilizes the products, it also decreases the activation energy, i.e. the bond dissociation energy is lowered.

The steric effect can lead to an increase in the proportion of free radical for a molecular compound by inhibiting the recombination of the free radicals. For illustration, 2,6-di-t-butylphenols of the type **XXV** can be oxidized to form a stable free radical (**XXVI**).[108] The o-t-butyl groups prevent dimerization of the free radicals and they are also stabilized by resonance energy. The large resonance energy of **XXVI** is not surprising in

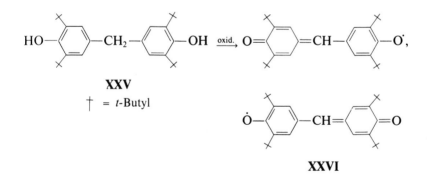

view of the two equivalent structures, and it is confirmed by the observation that the compound has only one $C=O$ infrared absorption band, at a frequency to indicate a large single-bond character.

(iv) **Biradicals.** Some substances possess an even number of electrons, yet they are paramagnetic corresponding to two unpaired electrons. Such molecules are called *biradicals* and they are usually very reactive.

[108] M. S. Kharasch, and B. S. Joshi, *J. Org. Chem.*, **22**, 1435, 1439 (1957).

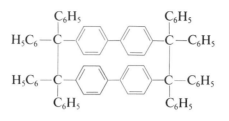

XXVII

One of the first organic molecules reported to be a biradical is the Tschitschibabin hydrocarbon XXVII.[109]   It can be formed through the series of reactions:

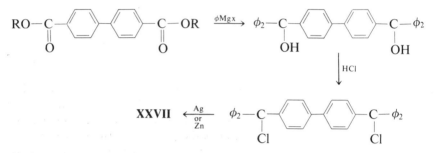

Although the hydrocarbon is diamagnetic, its solutions absorb oxygen. If the two unpaired electrons were independent, the substance would be paramagnetic. On the other hand, the hydrocarbon catalyzes the *para* to *ortho* hydrogen conversion, a property which indicates the presence of unpaired electrons. To explain these properties of XXVII, one can write a resonance for the substance among the forms (a)–(d), in which (d) represents all forms containing the odd electrons on any of the *ortho* or *para* carbon atoms of the six phenyl rings.

(a) ϕ_2—Ċ— ⟨⟩—⟨⟩ —Ċ—ϕ_2

(b) ϕ_2—C= ⟨⟩=⟨⟩ =C—ϕ_2

(c) ϕ_2—C̈— ⟨⟩—⟨⟩ —C⁺—ϕ_2

(d) ϕ_2—C= ⟨⟩·⟨⟩ =C—ϕ_2

Among the conditions for resonance, discussed in Sec. 4.3, is the one that resonance structures must be of the same multiplicity, i.e., have the same

[109]A. E. Tschitschibabin, *Ber.*, **40**, 1810 (1907).

number of unpaired electrons. To satisfy this condition, the odd electrons of forms (a) and (d) must have opposite spins; this is also necessary in order that they can pair up to form covalent bonds to give form (b).

By studying the *para-ortho* conversion of hydrogen, it was estimated that the hydrocarbon XXVII is about 10 per cent biradical in a dilute benzene solution,[111] which is in fair agreement with the value (4%) obtained by electron spin resonance spectroscopic measurements.[110] Now, if any factor were to prevent structure (a) from going into the quinoidal form (b), it would increase the biradical character of the substance. Accordingly, the *meta* isomer (XXVIII), which cannot have a quinoidal form, is found to have a small paramagnetism. The biradical readily dimerizes, but magnetic studies indicate it to be about 6–8 per cent dissociated in solution at 75°.

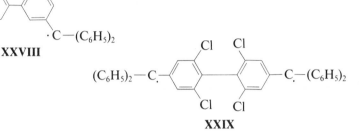

The quinoidal structure of type (b) above can also be prevented by steric hindrance. Thus, the compound XXIX is paramagnetic, and is about 28 per cent biradical in benzene at 80°.[112] Compound XXX is 67–83 per cent biradical at the same temperature.[113]

A biradical of structure (a) has the Kekulé resonance energy in its favor with respect to the quinoidal structure (b). With increasing number of phenyl groups between the two ethane carbon atoms possessing an odd electron, the Kekulé resonance gives the biradical form greater importance until finally the two odd electrons may become independent and the mole-

[110]G. L. Sloan and W. R. Vaughan, *J. Org. Chem.,* **22,** 750 (1957).

[111]G. M. Schwab and N. Agliardi, *Ber.,* **73,** 95 (1940).

[112]E. Müller and H. Neuhoff, *Ber.,* **72,** 2063 (1939).

[113]E. Müller and E. Tietz, *Ber.,* **74,** 807 (1941).

cules have a mass paramagnetism. This was also found to be true for the hydrocarbons **XXXI** and **XXXII**, which are paramagnetic both in the solid state and in solution.

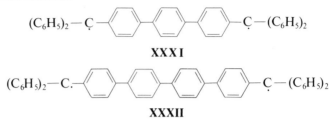

XXXI

XXXII

Steric hindrance also prevents the dimerization of the biradical **XXXIII**. It may be recrystallized from benzene in deep purple, paramagnetic prisms and melts at 280°.[115]

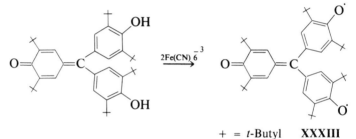

+ = *t*-Butyl   **XXXIII**

A biradical of current interest is methylene, $\cdot CH_2\cdot$. It is not commonly obtained in an equilibrium mixture but generated by the photolysis of diazomethane or by the action of zinc metal on methylene iodide, CH_2I_2. The two lone electrons are unpaired, hence methylene is a biradical and reacts as such. Of greater synthetic use have been the halocarbenes, $:CX_2$. The lone electrons in these species are paired and give the carbenes electrophilic properties. They are stabilized by resonance,

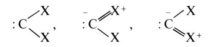

although they still have short half-lives ($< 10^{-3}$ sec).

4.8.3. ADDITIONS TO MULTIPLE BONDS

A number of types of addition reactions can be interpreted in terms of resonance theory. For example, consider the exothermic Diels-Alder reaction.

[114]E. Müller and H. Pfanz, *Ber.*, **74**, 1051 (1941).

[115]N. C. Yang and A. J. Castro, *J. Am. Chem. Soc.*, **82**, 6208 (1960).

$$\begin{array}{c} \text{C} \diagdown \\ \text{C} \end{array} \begin{array}{c} \text{C} \diagup \\ \text{C} \end{array} + \quad \begin{array}{c} \text{C} \\ | \\ \text{C} \end{array} = \begin{array}{c} \text{C} \\ | \\ \text{C} \end{array} \quad \rightleftharpoons \text{ adduct} + 12\text{–}18 \text{ kcal/mole} \quad (4\text{-}3)$$

The resonance energy of the diene is lost in this reaction and if it outweighs the ΔH for the reaction, little or no addition will take place under ordinary conditions. This is the case for benzene[116] and ferrocene. For naphthalene, the loss of resonance energy is that of naphthalene less that of benzene (since the adduct has a benzene ring) or about 25 kcal. This is small enough to give a trace (< 1 per cent) of addition product. Larger aromatics give larger amounts of adduct but still the equilibrium of Eq. (4-3) lies more to the left.

The addition of a halogen to an alkene is an exothermic reaction.

$$\begin{array}{c} \diagdown \quad \diagup \\ \text{C}{=}\text{C} \\ \diagup \quad \diagdown \end{array} + \text{ Br}_2 \quad \rightleftharpoons \quad \begin{array}{c} \diagdown \quad \diagup \\ {,}\text{C}{-}\text{C} \\ \diagup | \quad | \diagdown \\ \text{Br} \quad \text{Br}^- \end{array} + \text{ heat} \qquad (4\text{-}4)$$

It was pointed out in Sec. 3.5.2 that Cl_2 and H_2, but not Br_2, will add to tetraphenylethylene. With aryl groups attached to the olefin, the resonance interaction shifts the equilibrium to the left. Chlorine and hydrogen have a larger ΔH and smaller spatial demands, and as a consequence they will add to the tetraphenylethylene. With aryl groups, the steric factor eventually outweighs the resonance and ΔH factors until with tetraphenanthrylethylene, not even H_2 will add.

Sodium metal does not react with ethylene but it does react with tetraphenylethylene.

$$CH_2{=}CH_2 + \text{ Na} \longrightarrow \text{ no reaction} \qquad (4\text{-}5)$$

$$\phi_2 C{=}C\phi_2 + 2\,\text{Na} \rightleftharpoons \phi_2 \overset{-}{C}{-}\overset{-}{C}\phi_2 + 2\,\text{Na}^+ \qquad (4\text{-}6)$$

The resonance energy of the latter dianion shifts the equation to the right in this case.

[116]Benzene and other aromatics will react in the presence of peroxides,[117] acid catalysts,[118] or high temperatures,[119] but under these conditions, the reaction probably proceeds by a radical mechanism.

[117]H. J. F. Angus and D. Bryce-Smith, *Proc. Chem. Soc.,* (London), 326 (1959).

[118]P. Yates, *J. Am. Chem. Soc.,* **82,** 4436 (1960).

[119]C. G. Krespan, B. C. McKusick, and T. L. Cairns, *J. Am. Chem. Soc.,* **82,** 1515 (1960).

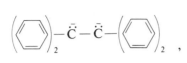   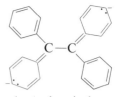

(several equivalent
structures)

4.8.4. 1,3-TAUTOMERISM

Three-atom tautomerism

$$\underset{A-B=C}{\overset{H}{\diagdown}} \rightleftharpoons \underset{A=B-C}{\overset{H}{\diagup}}$$

is very prevalent, with one tautomer usually being much more stable than
the other. For example, the summations of bond energies correctly predict
the greater stabilities of amides, oximes, and aliphatic hydrazones over the
isomeric imidols, nitroso compounds, and aliphatic azo compounds, respectively.[120]

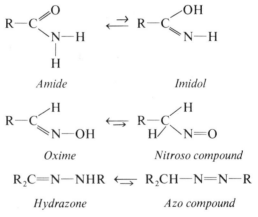

R₂C=N—NHR ⇆ R₂CH—N=N—R

Hydrazone   *Azo compound*

Another common pair of tautomers is the ketone-enol couple.

$$\underset{C-C=O}{\overset{H}{\diagdown}} \rightleftharpoons \underset{C=C-O}{\overset{H}{\diagup}}$$

From bond energies, the keto isomer is more stable by about 18 kcal/mole,
and indeed, the presence of the enol form can hardly be detected in simple

---

[120]Phenylhydrazones of aliphatic ketones and aldehydes exist in the solid state as the
hydrazone, but in solution they rapidly change to the azo tautomer. A nitro group in the
phenyl ring stabilizes the hydrazone form and a methyl group stabilizes the azo tautomer.
Cf. R. O'Connor, *J. Org. Chem.*, **26**, 4375, 5208 (1961).

aldehydes and ketones where the enol content ranges from 10^{-4} to 10^{-1} per cent.[121]

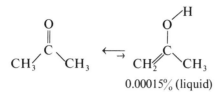

0.00015% (liquid)

Effects of Resonance and H Bonding. Resonance may shift the keto-enol equilibrium by a net stabilization of the enol. For example, phenol exists essentially 100 per cent in the enol form because the Kekulé resonance makes the enol form more stable than the keto form by about 15 kcal.

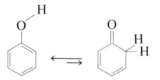

However, the bond energies of several keto groups may counterbalance the Kekulé resonance energy. 1,3,5-Trihydroxybenzene, for instance, gives a dark color with aqueous ferric chloride (typical of enols) and also gives a trioxime. This shows that the compound can react as though both tautomers were present.

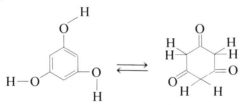

When a keto group is introduced β to a carbonyl group, the corresponding enol is somewhat stabilized by an intramolecular H bond. This reduces the difference in potential energy of the keto and enol tautomers by some 7 kcal/mole, and shifts the equilibrium toward the enol side. The entire

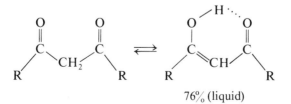

76% (liquid)

[121]Cf. A. Gero, *J. Org. Chem.*, **19**, 469, 1960 (1954); G. Schwarzenbach, *et al.*, *Helv. Chim. Acta*, **30**, 669 (1947), and earlier papers.

shift is not due to the H bond, however; part of the shift can be attributed to a net resonance stabilization of the enol form. For the keto form, the resonance is simply that of two isolated carbonyl groups.

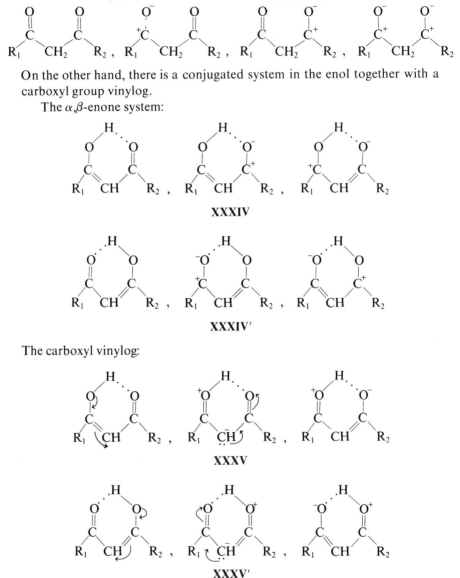

On the other hand, there is a conjugated system in the enol together with a carboxyl group vinylog.

The α,β-enone system:

XXXIV

XXXIV'

The carboxyl vinylog:

XXXV

XXXV'

The α, β-enone system has a resonance energy comparable to that of the diketone. The carbonyl group vinylog should have a resonance energy at least 60 per cent of that of a carboxylic acid or about 15 kcal. Also, the

H bond in the enol is unusually strong owing to the favorable charge distribution in the polar resonance structures. This notion is supported by the infrared absorption spectra of 1,3-diketones, as discussed in Sec. 5.4.3. The near equivalence of the resonance structures XXXIV to XXXIV' and XXXV to XXXV' increases the significance of the enol resonance. The combined net stabilization of the enol tautomer through resonance and H bonding in simple 1,3-diketones is approximately $15 + 7 - 18 = 4$ kcal/mole. This accounts for the preponderance of enol tautomer in the mixture.

When an OR group is substituted for one of the R groups in XXXIV, thereby producing an acetoacetic ester, there is a decrease in enol content. This can be attributed largely to a cross-conjugation between the ester group and the enol structure. The resonance of the ester group occurs at

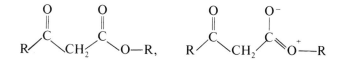

the expense of the resonance of the enol ring. This destabilizes the enol with respect to the keto tautomer and shifts the equilibrium toward the ketone. As to be expected, the diester ethyl malonate has even a smaller enol content (7.7×10^{-3} per cent[121, 122]).

	Enol content
$EtO-CO-CH_2-CO-OEt$	< 1%
$CH_3-CO-CH_2-CO-OEt$	7.7
$\phi-CO-CH_2-CO-OEt$	21
$CH_3-CO-CH_2-CO-CH_3$	76
$\phi-CO-CH_2-CO-CH_3$	89
$\phi-CO-CH_2-CO-\phi$	100

The substitution of a phenyl group increases the resonance energy of the keto as well as the enol tautomer, but much more so for the latter.

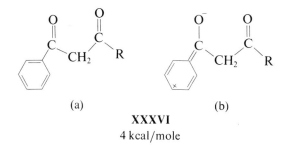

(a)   (b)

XXXVI

4 kcal/mole

[122] W. Gordy, *J. Chem. Phys.*, **8**, 516 (1940).

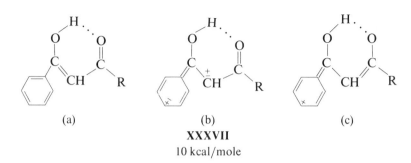

(a)   (b)   (c)

XXXVII

10 kcal/mole

The styryl resonance [XXXVII(a), (b)] of the enol tautomer has a slightly greater resonance energy (ca. 7 kcal) than the benzoyl resonance [XXXVI (a), (b)] of the diketone tautomer, so this produces a small shift toward the enol side. However, the cinnamoyl resonance [XXXVII(a), (c)] has an even greater resonance stabilization of the enol tautomer. Consequently, diaroylmethanes, $(\phi CO)_2 CH_2$, are essentially 100 per cent enolic. The strong H bond in these compounds is shown not only by infrared absorption data but by their chemical properties. For instance (cf. Sec. 1.6.3), the compounds do not undergo acetylation with acetic anhydride, do not give methane when treated with $CH_3 MgBr$, nor do they give N_2 with diazomethane. Furthermore, they do not exhibit the typical carbonyl property of forming Schiff bases. Thus, there is a strong H bond and a large electron delocalization in the enol ring.

Intermolecular H bonding can help stabilize the enol too. For example, XXXVIII cannot form an intramolecular H bond because the C=O group in the enol is too far from the OH group. However, infrared data show that

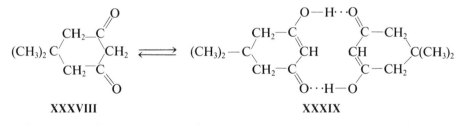

XXXVIII   **XXXIX**

the compound exists largely as the enolic tautomer XXXIX and that it has a chelated enol structure similar to that of XL.[124] Compound XL does not even give a $FeCl_3$ test, demonstrating that the H bond is very strong. Again, the ester resonance in XLI decreases the enol resonance and it is found that XLI has only a negligible enol content.[125]

[123] Cf. G. O. Dudek and R. H. Holm, *J. Am. Chem. Soc.*, **83**, 3914 (1961), and references cited therein.

[124] R A. Abramovitch, *Can. J. Chem.*, **36**, 151 (1958); D. F. Martin, M. Shamma, and W. C. Fernelius, *J. Am. Chem. Soc.*, **80**, 5851 (1958).

[125] R. A. Abramovitch, *Can. J. Chem.*, **37**, 1 (1959).

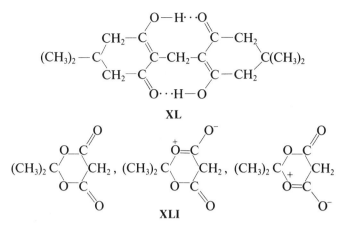

The effect of resonance in stabilizing the enols of α-diketones is also demonstrable. For illustration, the enol content in ethyl pyruvate is too small to give a reaction with diazomethane. However, ethyl *p*-nitropyruvate (XLII) is 42 per cent enolic in alcohol solution.[106] Here again the enol

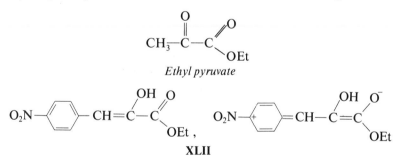

is stabilized by the "cinnamoyl" resonance energy. The compound exhibits an OH infrared absorption band and reacts with diazomethane to give the methyl ether of the enol. Other benzyl glyoxals have large enolic contents, too, and some range up to 100 per cent.

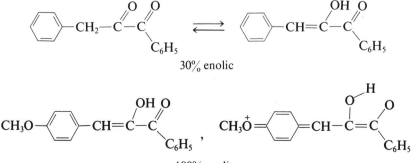

The combined effects of resonance and H bonding in ketamines make them more stable than the isomeric enol-imine or ketimine forms.[123]

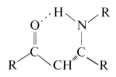

Ketamine

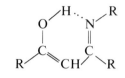

Enol-imine

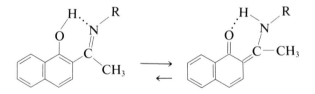

Ketimine

Infrared and n.m.r. spectral data indicate that in solution the ketamine is present in greater than 95 per cent proportion. The magnitude of the resonance and H bonding effect of the chelate ring is revealed by the fact that the Schiff bases of α-hydroxynaphthaldehydes exist predominantly in the ketamine form in spite of the fact that the latter isomer has lost part of the Kekulé resonance of the naphthalene ring.[123]

Solvent effects. So far in this section it has been shown that resonance and H bonding have a pronounced effect on the keto-enol equilibrium. Four other factors which affect the equilibrium are solvation, induction, steric requirements, and entropy. Although the ionic forms contribute to the resonance hybrid structures of the enol, it is less polar than the ketone because of the H bond in the enol. Consequently, polar solvents should stabilize the ketone form, and the enol content should be higher in non-polar solvents. Also, hydroxylic solvents would form H bonds with the solute oxygen atoms to compete with the intramolecular H bond in the enol. This would further decrease the enol content of 1,3-diketones. These considerations are substantiated by the data in Table 4.14.

Table 4.14. ENOL CONTENT OF SOME 1,3-DIKETONES IN VARIOUS SOLVENTS

Diketone	Per cent enol	Solvent
C_6H_5—CS—CO—CO_2—C_2H_5	95 [127]	Isooctane
	87	Ethanol
CH_3—CO—CH_2—$CO_2C_2H_5$	46.4	Hexane
	16.2	Benzene
	10.5	Ethanol
	10.1	Nitrobenzene
	8.2	Chloroform
	7.7	Pure liquid
	7.3	Acetone
	6.9	Methanol
	5.7	Acetic Acid
	0.4	Water
CH_3—CO—CH_2—CO—CH_3	92	Hexane
	15	Water
CH_3—CO—CHϕ—$CO_2C_2H_5$	67	Hexane
	31	Water

Inductive effects. Enolization probably takes place by ionization of an α hydrogen atom and short electron-pair shifts. Therefore, the more electronegative are the groups attached to the α carbon atom, the easier it is for an

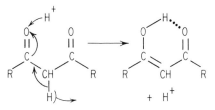

α hydrogen atom to escape as a proton. This expectation is fully substantiated in the substituted acetoacetic esters CH_3CO—CHR—CO_2Et, in which the enol content increases with increasing electronegativity of the R group.

R in $CH_3COCHCO_2Et$ | R	Per cent enol (liquid)
C_2H_5	3
CH_3	4
H	7.5
C_6H_5	30
CO_2Et	44

[126] A. M. Stock, W. E. Donahue, and E. D. Amstutz, *J. Org. Chem.*, **23**, 1840 (1958).
[127] Z. Reyes and R. M. Silverstein, *J. Am. Chem. Soc.*, **80**, 6367, 6373 (1958).

Similarly, trifluoromethyl groups attached to the carbonyl group shift the keto-enol equilibrium towards the enol side. For example, in the liquid state, $CH_3COCH_2CO_2Et$ is 80% enolic whereas $CF_3COCH_2CO_2Et$ is 89% enolic.[128] The significant enol content of the monoketone, $CF_3COCH_2CH=CH_2$,[129] is attributable to the inductive effects of the CF_3 and vinyl groups plus resonance stabilization of the enol.

$$
\underset{\mathstrut}{CF_3{-}\overset{\displaystyle \overset{OH}{|}}{C}{=}CH{-}CH{=}CH_2,} \qquad CF_3{-}\overset{\displaystyle \overset{+OH}{\|}}{C}{-}CH{=}CH{-}\bar{C}H_2
$$

The inductive effect alone, however, is only a minor factor. For example, ethyl cyanoacetate has only a 0.25 per cent enol content. Another illustration is provided by the ketosulfones (RSO_2CH_2COR) and β-disulfones ($RSO_2{-}CH_2{-}SO_2R$) which are hardly enolized at all and are weaker acids than the corresponding β-diketones.[130] The sulfones do not form chelates and the keto sulfones exhibit typical $C{=}O$ infrared absorption and no $O{-}H \cdots O$ bands. On the other hand, thiobenzoylacetates are more enolic than the corresponding benzoylacetates.[127]

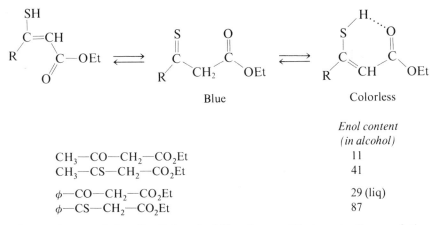

| | Blue | | Colorless |

	Enol content (in alcohol)
$CH_3{-}CO{-}CH_2{-}CO_2Et$	11
$CH_3{-}CS{-}CH_2{-}CO_2Et$	41
$\phi{-}CO{-}CH_2{-}CO_2Et$	29 (liq)
$\phi{-}CS{-}CH_2{-}CO_2Et$	87

The weakness of the $C{=}S$ bond shifts the equilibrium in favor of the thioenol. Since the $S{-}H \cdots O$ bond is not as strong as the $O{-}H \cdots O$ bond, some of the thioenol exists in a nonchelated structure.

Steric and entropy effects. Finally, it can be shown that steric requirements and entropy changes can have a profound effect upon the keto-enol equilibrium. A diketone $R_1{-}CO{-}CHR_3{-}CO{-}R_2$ may exist in several conformations.

[128] R. Filler and S. M. Naqvi, *J. Org. Chem.*, **26**, 2571 (1961).

[129] J. D. Park, R. E. Noble, and J. R. Lacher, *J. Org. Chem.*, **23**, 1396 (1958).

[130] E. H. Holst and W. C. Fernelius, *J. Org. Chem.*, **23**, 1881 (1958).

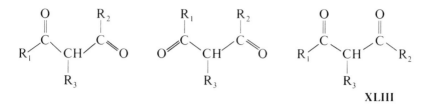

XLIII

Owing to dipole-dipole repulsion, XLIII should be the least stable. Large spatial demands of R_1 and R_2 destabilize all three conformations and accordingly, as R_1 and R_2 increase in bulkiness, the keto-enol equilibrium shifts toward the enol.

R in R—CO—CH$_2$—CO—R	K = enol/ketone (in acetonitrile)
Me	1.4
i-Pr	1.8
t-Bu	6.1

The di-t-butyl derivative, dipivaloylmethane, exhibits no detectable diketo isomer in the pure liquid.[131] On the other hand, an increase in size of R_3 increases steric hindrance in the enol (XLIV) and has the opposite effect on

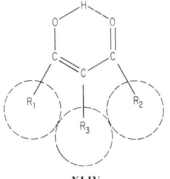

XLIV

the equilibrium.[132] As R_3 gets larger, the equilibrium shifts toward the keto form and also the enol present exists more in the *trans* rather than chelated *cis* conformation.[132]

When one compares the enol contents of aliphatic and cyclic homologous series of monoketones, there are two features which are noticed immediately: (1) the alternation in enol content, (2) the larger enol percentage of the cyclic series.[133]

[131] G. S. Hammond, W. G. Borduin, and G. A. Guter, *J. Am. Chem. Soc.*, **81**, 4682 (1959).
[132] M. I. Kabachnik, S. T. Ioffe, E. M. Popov, and K. Vatsuro, *Tetrahedron*, **12**, 76 (1961).
[133] A. Gero, *J. Org. Chem.*, **26**, 3156 (1961).

Compound	Per cent enol content[134]	Compound	Per cent enol content[134]
2-Butanone	0.12	3-Pentanone	0.07
2-Pentanone	0.01	3-Hexanone	0.05
2-Hexanone	0.11	3-Heptanone	0.17
2-Heptanone	0.10	3-Octanone	0.01
2-Octanone	0.92		

Ring size of cyclanone	Per cent enol content[134]
4	0.55
5	0.09
6	1.18
7	0.56
8	9.3
9	4.0
10	6.1

The approximate tenfold increase in enol content of the cyclanones over the alkanones has been attributed to a differential entropy loss in enolization for the two series.[135] The double bond of the open-chain enols locks part of the chain in a rigid orientation so that enolization is accompanied by partial loss of freedom of rotation of the chain. This loss in entropy favors retention of the keto structure. On the other hand, the cyclanones already have a semirigid structure and therefore there is less loss in entropy with enolization. In the absence of other factors, such as bond-angle strain and nonbonding repulsions, the cyclanones can be expected to have larger enol contents than corresponding alkanones.

A satisfactory explanation for the alternation of enol content for the homologous series above cannot be offered.[133] Such periodicity has been observed for several other properties of homologues, such as the melting points of alkanoic acids, the yields of α-bromomethyl ketones obtained from the bromination of methyl ketones,[136] and the stabilities of the charge-transfer complexes between alkylbenzenes and picric acid.[137] It is also observed for the enol content of ethyl cyclanone-2-carboxylates,[138] as well as for the infrared carbonyl frequencies of the cyclanones.[139]

[134] These values are extrapolated to the "liquid" state for comparison purposes.[133]
[135] G. Schwarzenbach and E. Felder, Helv. Chim. Acta, 27, 1701 (1944).
[136] H. M. E. Cardwell and H. E. H. Kilner, J. Chem. Soc., 2430 (1951).
[137] H. D. Anderson and D. Ll. Hammick, J. Chem. Soc., 1089 (1950).
[138] G. Schwarzenbach, M. Zimmermann, and V. Prelog, Helv. Chim. Acta, 34, 1954 (1950).
[139] V. Prelog, J. Chem. Soc., 420 (1950).

Ring size of $(CH_2)_n$ $\begin{matrix} C=O \\ / \\ CHCO_2Et \end{matrix}$	Per cent enol content (in 95% EtOH)[138]
5	5
6	57
7	12
8	40
9	15
10	50
11	9
12	5

Summary. In summary, then, it can be said that the keto-enol equilibrium provides a good system for the application of the modern structural theory of organic chemistry in which the concepts of resonance, H bonding, induction, solvation, entropy, and steric requirements must each be invoked judiciously in order to account for the effects of structure upon this equilibrium. A similar approach has been used in discussing their acid dissociation constants.[140]

4.9. Aromatic character of cyclic compounds[141, 142]

Derivatives of benzene, naphthalene, pyridine, pyrrole, azulene, etc., have molecular formulas which indicate that the atoms of the rings form multiple bonds. Their complete or partial failure to exhibit typical olefinic properties, e.g., rapid oxidation, polymerization, addition reactions, etc., is defined as their "aromatic character," and the term refers to their low chemical reactivity. On the other hand, the modern definition of an aromatic compound,[143] a cyclic compound with a large resonance energy and in which all of the annular atoms form a single conjugated system, is based on the thermochemical stability of a compound.[144]   Often, low chemical re-

Heptafulvene

[140] G. S. Hammond, *Steric Effects in Organic Chemistry,* ed. M. S. Newman (New York; Wiley, 1956), chap. 9.

[141] *Non-Benzenoid Aromatic Compounds,* ed. D. Ginsburg (New York: Interscience, 1959).

[142] W. Baker, *Perspectives in Organic Chemistry,* ed. A. Todd (New York: Interscience, 1956), pp. 28–67; W. Baker and J. F. W. McOmie, *Progress in Organic Chemistry.,* vol. 3, ed. J. W. Cook (New York: Academic, 1955), chap. 2; R. Waack, *J. Chem. Educ.,* **39,** 469 (1962).

[143] M. J. S. Dewar, *Electronic Theory of Organic Chemistry* (Fair Lawn, N.J.: Oxford U. P., 1949), p. 160.

[144] D. Peters, *J. Chem. Soc.,* 1274 (1960).

activity and high thermochemical stability (low potential energy) occur together but not necessarily so. For example, heptafulvene has a resonance energy of 36 kcal/mole, equal to that of benzene, but it is typically olefinic.[145] Whereas benzene is aromatic according to the classical as well as the modern definition, tropylium and cyclopentadienide ions have large delocalization energies but are very reactive. Therefore, all three species are aromatic but not for the same reasons. The chemical and physical properties of aromatic compounds are interpreted and accounted for qualitatively in terms of the modern structural theory. As a part of this theory, the concept of resonance energy has provided a semiquantitative measure of the thermochemical stabilities of aromatic compounds.

Over the past decade, considerable interest has developed in the aromatic character of cyclic compounds from the standpoint of the modern definition. Therefore, it is appropriate that some of the recent developments in this area be discussed.

4.9.1. SIX-π-ELECTRON RINGS

Hückel first pointed out through a molecular orbital treatment that there is a large resonance stabilization associated with a closed shell of $(4n + 2)$ π electrons, and that such closed rings would have marked aromatic character. His arguments were based on the number of π electrons necessary for filled orbitals with respect to the angular momentum quantum number for electronic motion about the center of the ring.[146] Three such rings containing six π electrons are C_6H_6, $C_5H_5^-$ and $C_7H_7^+$.

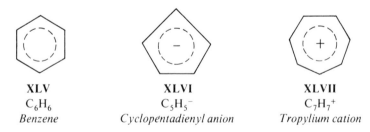

XLV	XLVI	XLVII
C_6H_6	$C_5H_5^-$	$C_7H_7^+$
Benzene	*Cyclopentadienyl anion*	*Tropylium cation*

The cyclopentadienyl anion is simply prepared by reacting an alkali metal with cyclopentadiene.[147]

[145] W. von E. Doering and D. W. Wiley, *Tetrahedron,* **11,** 183 (1960).
[146] E. Hückel, *Z. Physik,* **70,** 204 (1931).
[147] J. Theile, *Ber.,* **34,** 68 (1901).

Salts of cyclopentadienide ion with organic cations are also known.[148] The unusual stability of this organic anion was first attributed to the presence of a sextet in 1928,[149] and its aromatic character in metallocenes was discussed in Sec. 1.5.1. The anion may be regarded as a resonance hybrid of five equivalent forms [XLVIII(a)-(e)], and the resonance energy has been

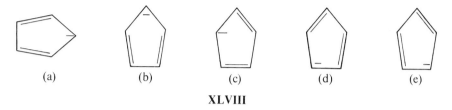

(a)   (b)   (c)   (d)   (e)

XLVIII

calculated to be about 42 kcal/mole.[150] This resonance hybrid structure is supported by the observation that when cyclopentadiene—C_1^{14} is reacted with potassium metal to yield the cyclopentadienide ion (XLVIII) and the latter is hydrolyzed to regenerate cyclopentadiene, the radioactivity is equally distributed among the carbons of the ring.[151] Thus, the charge on the cyclopentadienide ion is distributed about the ring and when water attacks it, each carbon atom has an equal chance of becoming protonated to produce cyclopentadiene.

The presence of electron-withdrawing groups give the ring added stability and make the cyclopentadiene a stronger acid. For illustration, XLIX is essentially as strong an acid as HCl_{aq}, and the anion is very stable.[152]

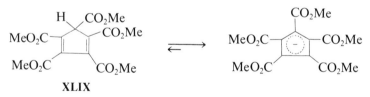

XLIX

The tropylium cation can be made by several methods,[153] and although the actual yield is not the best, the simplest way to prepare it on paper is through the reaction series:

[148] E. M. Kosower and B. G. Ramsey, *J. Am. Chem. Soc.*, **81**, 856 (1959); F. Ramirez and S. Levy, *J. Am. Chem. Soc.*, **79**, 67 (1957); D. Lloyd and N. S. Sneezum, *Tetrahedron*, **3**, 334 (1958).

[149] F. R. Goss and C. K. Ingold, J. Chem. Soc., 1268 (1928); see also chap. 3 of *Non-Benzenoid Aromatic Compounds.*

[150] J. D. Roberts, A. Streitwieser, Jr., and C. M. Regan, *J. Am. Chem. Soc.*, **74**, 4579 (1952).

[151] R. Tkachuk and C. C. Lee, *Can. J. Chem.*, **37**, 1644 (1959).

[152] R. C. Cookson, J. Hudec, and B. Whitear, *Proc. Chem. Soc.*, (London), 117 (1961).

[153] Cf. T. Nozoe, *Non-Benzenoid Aromatic Compounds,* chap. 7.

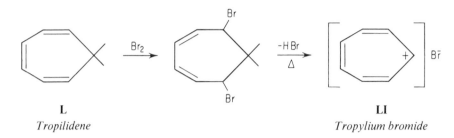

L	LI
Tropilidene	*Tropylium bromide*

Tropylium bromide melts at 203°, is miscible with water, insoluble in non-polar solvents, gives an immediate precipitate with aqueous silver nitrate, and yields cycloheptane upon catalytic hydrogenation. It can be regarded as a resonance hybrid of seven equivalent forms in which the positive charge has an equal chance of residing on any of the carbon atoms. As in benzene, each of the C—H bonds of the cyclopentadienyl and tropylium rings are equivalent, and infrared and Raman spectra reveal the symmetry of the rings.[154]

Heterocyclic rings which conform to the $(4n + 2)$ π-electron rule may also possess varying degrees of aromatic character. For example, the pyrrole ring has six π electrons available, including the lone-pair on nitrogen.

The ring exhibits a moderate degree of aromatic character, e.g., substitution reactions, resistance to oxidation, etc. On the other hand, the lone-pair electrons of nitrogen are not available in the salt, and it is observed that the ring loses its aromatic character.

It is noted that $C_5H_5^-$, not $C_5H_5^+$, and $C_7H_7^+$, not $C_7H_7^-$, are the stable aromatic species. Accordingly, tropylidene is not acidic as is cyclopentadiene, for the $C_7H_7^-$ ion lacks the stability of the $C_5H_5^-$ ion. Other examples of the stability of the $C_5H_5^-$ and $C_7H_7^+$ rings can be given. Dimethylfulvene (LII) has a larger resonance energy (12 kcal/mole)[155] than an acyclic triene, and its dipole moment (1.48 D) is much larger than that of unsaturated aliphatic hydrocarbons. This can be attributed to the unusually large contribution of the ionic structure [LII(b)].

[154] R. D. Nelson, W. G. Faleley, and E. R. Lippincott, *J. Am. Chem. Soc.,* **78,** 4870 (1956); *J. Chem. Phys.,* **26,** 1471 (1957).

[155] J. H. Day and C. Oestreich, *J. Org. Chem.,* **22,** 214 (1957).

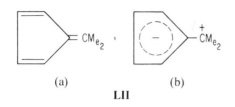

(a)   (b)

LII

Tropone (LIII) has a large polar character. It forms salts with acids, it resists formation of a 2,4-dinitrophenylhydrazone, and its dipole moment (4.3 D) is significantly larger than that of crotonaldehyde (3.67 D). On the other hand, all attempts to prepare the corresponding five-membered ring

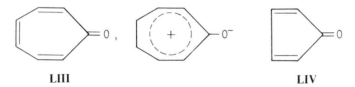

LIII   LIV

(LIV) have been successful. Not only would the ionic structure not conform to the $(4n + 2)$ π-electron rule but the ring has a large bond-angle strain. It is interesting, in this connection, that cyclopentane-1,3-dione (LV) is completely enolic while cyclopentene-3,5-dione (LVI) is completely ketonic.[156] This further supports the notion that the cyclopentadienone ring

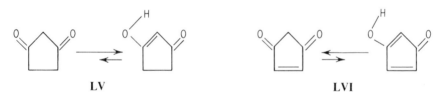

LV   LVI

is very unstable because of the bond-angle strain.

Azulene (LVII) can be regarded as a resonance hybrid of two Kekulé structures [LVII(a) and (b)] plus a number of ionic structures [LVII(c)] in which the five-membered ring has a negative charge and the seven-membered ring a positive charge. This charge distribution in azulene is revealed

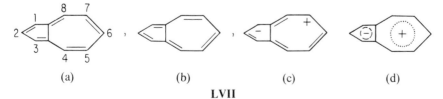

(a)   (b)   (c)   (d)

LVII

[156] C. H. DePuy, et al., J. Am. Chem. Soc., 81, 4920 (1959); 82, 2909 (1960); 1,3-diketohydrindene also has a very small enol content (G. Schwarzenbach and E. Felder, Helv. Chim. Acta, 27, 1044 (1944).

by the fact that the C_5 ring is prone to electrophilic substitution[157(a)] and the C_7 ring undergoes nucleophilic substitution.[157(b)]

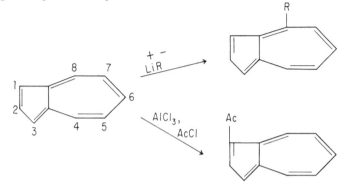

The molecule has a dipole moment of 1.08 D, which indicates the ionic structures make some, but not the major, contribution to the resonance hybrid. The direction of the dipole is confirmed by the fact that the moment is increased when electronegative groups are introduced in the 1 position, e.g., 1-chloroazulene, D.M. = 2.69 D; 1-nitroazulene, D.M. = 6.06 D.[158]

Another illustration of the stability of $C_7H_7^+$ rather than $C_7H_7^-$ is the observation that tropilidene, unlike cyclopentadiene, reacts with a metal carbonyl without the loss of hydrogen.

$$C_7H_8 + M(CO)_6 \longrightarrow C_7H_8M(CO)_3 + 3\,CO$$
$$C_5H_6 + M(CO)_6 \longrightarrow C_5H_5M(CO)_3 + 3\,CO + \tfrac{1}{2}\,H_2$$

However, $(C_6H_5)_3CBF_4$ will take a hydride ion from $C_7H_8M(CO)_3$ to form the tropylium metallocene.[159]

$$C_7H_8M(CO)_3 \xrightarrow{\ \phi_3CBF_4\ } [C_7H_7M(CO)_3]^+ BF_4^- + \phi_3CH$$

Other molecules of unusual stability for the apparent functional group present are LVIII and LIX. As mentioned in Sec. 4.7.1, there is a signifi-

LVIII[160]   LIX[161]

[157] (a) T. I. Bieber, J. Chem. Educ., 35, 235 (1958); S. S. Danyluk and W. G. Schneider, J. Am. Chem. Soc., 82, 998 (1960); A. G. Anderson, J. A. Nelson, and J. J. Tazuma, J. Am. Chem. Soc., 75, 4980 (1953); D. H. Reid, in Developments in Aromatic Chemistry, Spec. Publ. No. 12 (London: Chem. Soc., 1958), pp. 69 ff.; (b) K. Hafner, C. Bernhard, and R. Müller, Ann., 650, 35 (1961).

[158] A. G. Anderson, Jr., and B. M. Steckler, J. Am. Chem. Soc., 81, 4941 (1959).

[159] H. J. Dauben and L. R. Honnen, J. Am. Chem. Soc., 80, 5570 (1958).

[160] F. Ramirez and S. Levy, J. Org. Chem., 21, 488 (1956).

[161] W. von E. Doering and C. H. DePuy, J. Am. Chem. Soc., 75, 5955 (1953).

cant nucleophilic character of the olefinic carbon of phosphinemethylenes.

$$\phi_3P{=}CR_2, \qquad \phi_3P^+{-}\bar{C}R_2$$

The more readily the $^-CR_2$ group will accept the negative charge, the more stable is the phosphinemethylene.

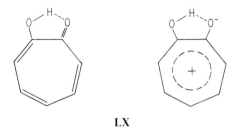

LX

Tropolone

The tropylium ring has been studied most extensively in the form of tropolone and its derivatives.[162, 163] This aromatic ring was first conceived by Dewar[164] and soon became the object of considerable interest. Tropolone melts at 49–50°, is soluble in water and most organic solvents; it is an acid with pK_a = 6.7 in equilibrium with a yellow anion, gives a green coloration with $FeCl_{3_{aq}}$ and yields a green, chloroform-soluble copper chelate. Tropolone undergoes substitution reactions such as bromination, it couples with diazonium salts to yield azo dyes, it can be nitrated in dilute nitric acid, it gives a picrate, and it yields an unstable monohydrochloride in ether. Furthermore, the aromaticity of the ring is confirmed by the facts that the C—C bonds are all equivalent with a bond distance of 1.40 Å and the ring is planar.[165] It has a resonance energy of 36 kcal/mole. It has an unusually strong H bond, which is confirmed by the observation that the compound is monomeric in solution,[166] and the C=O bond is so strongly tied up by the H bond that the compound does not form a 2,4-dinitrophenylhydrazone.[167]

The H bond makes a significant contribution to the stability of tropolone because tropone (LIII) does not have the marked stability of tropolone. Tropone, for example, is rapidly oxidized by aqueous permanganate

[162] *Non-Benzenoid Aromatic Compounds*, chap. 7.

[163] W. von E. Doering, Kekulé Symposium on *Theroetical Organic Chemistry* (London: Scientific Publ., 1959), pp. 35 ff.

[164] M. J. S. Dewar, *Nature*, **155**, 50 (1945).

[165] J. M. Robertson, *J. Chem. Soc*, 1222 (1951); E. Heilbronner and K. Hedberg, *J. Am. Chem. Soc.*, **73**, 1386 (1951).

[166] Nevertheless, tropolone is extensively intermolecularly H bonded in the solid state (K. Kuratani, M. Tsuboi, and T. Shimanouchi, *Bull. Chem. Soc. Japan*, **25**, 250 (1952)).

[167] J. W. Cook, A. R. Gibb, R. A. Raphael, and A. R. Somerbille, *J. Chem. Soc.*, 503 (1951).

and undergoes addition rather than substitution reactions.[168] The H bond of tropolone reduces the polar character of tropone (D.M. = 4.3 D), for tropolone has a dipole moment of 3.71 D.[169] The direction of the dipole is away from the ring, as to be expected, and as shown by the fact that the moment of the 5-bromo derivative is smaller (2.07 D).[170] Surprisingly, chemical properties imply a smaller aromatic character of tropone than does its magnetic susceptibility exaltation (see Table 4.15).

It is not surprising that borazole has much less aromatic character than benzene. Although the compound has six π electrons, the electrons are more localized on the much more electronegative nitrogen atoms.

Borazole

Up to this point, the discussion in this section has been devoted to rings with six π electrons. Hückel's rule also applies to rings with two, ten, fourteen, eighteen, etc. π electrons. His theory indicates, however, that this delocalization effect diminishes with increasing ring size and eventually double-single bond alternation will prevail in very large-ring annulenes. Some examples follow.

4.9.2. TWO-π-ELECTRON RINGS

The C_3 ring of LXI has two π electrons ($n = 0$ in $4n + 2$ rule), and it is found from nuclear magnetic resonance measurements that the three cyclopropyl carbon atoms are equivalent.[171] Hence, LXI(b) makes a major contribution to the resonance hybrid and it is found that the cation is unusually stable for a carbonium ion. The diphenylcyclopropenium ion has also been prepared and found to be stable.[172]

---

[168] H. J. Dauben and H. J. Ringold, *J. Am. Chem. Soc.*, **73**, 876 (1951); W. von E. Doering and F. L. Detert, *J. Am. Chem. Soc.*, **73**, 876 (1951).

[169] M. Kubo, T. Nozoe, and Y. Kurita, *Nature*, **167**, 688 (1951).

[170] Y. Kurita, T. Nozoe, and M. Kubo, *Bull. Chem. Soc. Japan*, **26**, 242 (1953).

[171] R. Breslow, *et al.*, *J. Am. Chem. Soc.*, **80**, 5991 (1958); **83**, 1763 (1961).

[172] D. G. Farnum and M. Burr, *J. Am. Chem. Soc.*, **82**, 2561 (1960).

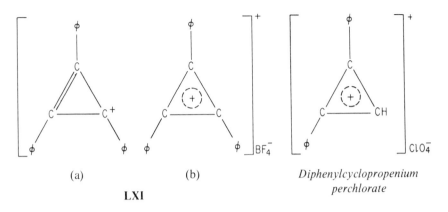

(a)   (b)   *Diphenylcyclopropenium*

LXI   *perchlorate*

4.9.3. TEN-π-ELECTRON RINGS

It was brought out in Sec. 4.6 that adjacent C=C bonds in the cyclo-octatetraene ring are not coplanar and, accordingly, there is little electron delocalization in the eight-π-electron ring. Furthermore, it exhibits only a small diamagnetic susceptibility exaltation. As was discussed in Sec. 1.2.13, the "flow" of electrons in the molecular orbital of benzene gives it a large diamagnetism, and the difference between the observed value and that calculated from Pascal's constants (not including his constitutive constants) is called the exaltation ($\Delta\chi$). The exaltations per carbon atom for several compounds are listed in Table 4.15 where it can be seen that the exaltations for aromatic rings are much greater than for the nonaromatic cyclooctate-traene. The small resonance energy of cyclooctatetraene also reveals the small degree of conjugation between the alternating double and single bonds, and this inhibition can be attributed to the lack of overlap of the π orbitals of the double bonds.

Table 4.15. SUSCEPTIBILITY EXALTATIONS IN SOME MOLECULES[173]

Compound	$-10^6 \chi$ (exptl.)	Pascal sum	$-\Delta\chi$/carbon atom
Benzene	55.6	36.9	3.1
Naphthalene	91.9	55.7	3.6
Biphenyl	102.9	68	3.5
Azulene	91	55.7	3.5
Cyclooctatetraene	51.9	49.2	0.3
Tropolone	61	45.8	2.2
Tropone	54	41.2	1.8

[173] D. P. Craig, *Non-Benzenoid Aromatic Compounds,* chap. 1.

Cyclooctatetraene has eight π electrons and to conform to the $(4n + 2)$ π-electron rule, it would have to lose or gain two electrons. Recently, the cyclooctatetraenyl dianion, $C_8H_8^=$, was prepared, and indeed, it was observed to have a planar ring with all C—H bonds equivalent.[174(a)] This is a remarkable verification of the applicability of Hückel's rule.[175] Also, pentalene has defied all attempts at its preparation, but its dianion $C_8H_6^=$, which conforms to Hückel's rule, is a fairly stable salt.[174(b)] The pentalenyl dianion is to the cyclopentadienide ion what naphthalene is to benzene.

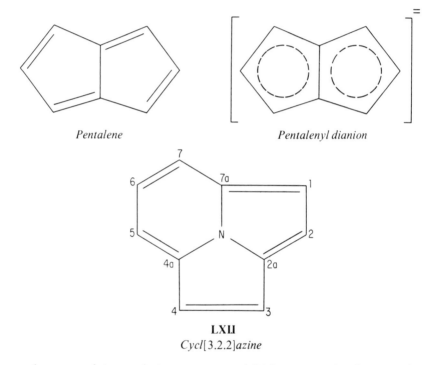

Pentalene   Pentalenyl dianion

LXII
$Cycl[3.2.2]azine$

An unusual ten-π-electron system exhibiting aromatic character has been prepared by Boekelheide and his coworkers.[176] This compound, LXII, is a crystalline, yellow, fluorescent, nonbasic material which is very stable toward light, heat, and air. Its odor resembles that of naphthalene. It undergoes substitution reactions, with the number 1 position being most reactive.

[174] (a) T. J. Katz, *J. Am. Chem. Soc.,* **82,** 3784 (1960); (b) T. J. Katz and M. Rosenberger, *J. Am. Chem. Soc.,* **84,** 865 (1962).
[175] Molecular orbital calculations support the experimental work that the cyclooctatetraene dianion has a planar structure with equal carbon-carbon bond lengths of 1.409 Å (C. A. Coulson, *Tetrahedron,* **12,** 193 (1961)).
[176] R. J. Windgassen, Jr., W. H. Saunders, Jr., and V. Boekelheide, *J. Am. Chem. Soc.,* **81,** 1459 (1959).

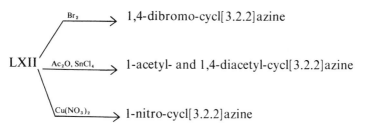

$\xrightarrow{\text{Br}_2}$ 1,4-dibromo-cycl[3.2.2]azine

LXII $\xrightarrow{\text{Ac}_2\text{O, SnCl}_4}$ 1-acetyl- and 1,4-diacetyl-cycl[3.2.2]azine

$\xrightarrow{\text{Cu(NO}_3)_2}$ 1-nitro-cycl[3.2.2]azine

Strictly, Hückel's rule does not apply to such polycyclic systems, however, molecular orbital calculations[177] indicate that it is generally applicable to such compounds. For instance, other conjugated carbocyclic rings held planar by attachment to an internal atom exhibit aromatic character.[176]

It has been proposed recently that the aromaticity of a 1-amino-7-iminotropylidene system (LXIII) is more in accord with a ten-π-electron system (LXIV) than a six-π-electron ring (LXV) analogous to that of tropolone.[178] Nuclear magnetic resonance and infrared absorption spectra confirm the equivalency of the ring protons and of the two nitrogen atoms of LXIII. In LXIV the four formal double bonds and the lone-pair electrons on the secondary nitrogen atom supply the ten π electrons. This proposed structure was based on the facts that the dipole moment of LXIV (1.24 D) is directed towards the ring (it rises to 2.52 D upon bromination in the 4 position), n.m.r. data indicate that the ring protons are less positive than those in tropolone, and the ring undergoes electrophilic substitution more readily than tropolone.

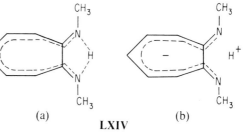

LXIII   (a)   (b)
              LXIV

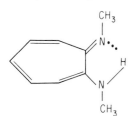

LXV

[177] J. D. Roberts, A. Streitwieser, Jr., and C. M. Regan, *J. Am. Chem. Soc.*, **74**, 4579 (1952).

[178] R. E. Benson, *et al.*, *J. Am. Chem. Soc.*, **82**, 5948 (1960); **83**, 3125 (1961).

4.9.4. EIGHTEEN-π-ELECTRON RINGS

[10]Annulene (cyclodecapentaene) and [14]annulene, the first two members following benzene which comply with Hückel's $(4n + 2)$ π-electron rule, cannot be planar because of transannular interferences of the internal hydrogen atoms in the planar molecule. This prevents the two compounds from being aromatic. Scale drawings of [18]annulene indicate that it possibly could be planar[179] in contradiction to theoretical calculations[180(a)] and contrary to the prediction[180(b)] that [30]annulene is the smallest annulene that will comply with Hückel's rule and also be coplanar.[183] [18]-Annulene has now been synthesized[179] and found to be aromatic according to the modern definition but not chemically aromatic. That is, X-ray diffraction confirms the planar structure, and its ultraviolet spectrum indicates that all nine double bonds are conjugated. However, it undergoes addition reactions rather than substitution.

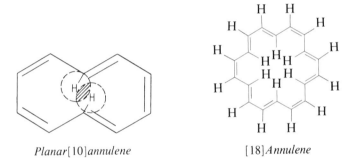

Planar[10]*annulene*   [18]*Annulene*

In addition to resonance energy and magnetic susceptibility exaltation, proton magnetic resonance chemical shifts provide a measure of aromaticity of cyclic compounds. One essential feature of an aromatic system is the complete delocalization of π electrons by which it sustains an induced ring current. The relative magnitude of this ring current can be determined from the degree of shielding of protons attached directly to the aromatic nucleus (see Sec. 5.3.4). Protons attached to the ring have resonance signals at low fields ($\tau \cong 1$–3 p.p.m.) whereas protons lying near the center of the ring have signals at much higher fields ($\tau > 10$ p.p.m.). Accordingly, [18]annulene has

[179] F. Sondheimer, R. Wolovsky, and Y. Amiel, *J. Am. Chem. Soc.*, **84**, 274 (1962).

[180] (a) Recent calculations suggest that [18]annulene cannot possibly be planar (C. A. Coulson and A. Golebiewski, *Tetrahedron,* **11**, 125 (1960); (b) K. Mislow, *J. Chem. Phys.,* **20**, 1489 (1952).

[181] L. M. Jackman, F. Sondheimer, Y. Amiel, D. A. Ben-Efraim, Y. Gaoni, R. Wolovsky, and A. A. Bothner-By, *J. Am. Chem. Soc.*, **84**, 4307 (1962).

[182] F. Bohlmann, *Chem. Ber.,* **85**, 386 (1952).

[183] [30]Annulene appears not to be very stable. Cf. F. Sondheimer, R. Wolovsky, and D. A. Ben-Efraim, *J. Am. Chem. Soc.*, **83**, 1686 (1961).

two broad bands, one at τ = 11.8 p.p.m. for the six intra-annular protons and a second band at τ = 1.1 p.p.m. of twice the former intensity for the 12 peripheral protons.[181] In contrast to this, the nonplanar hydrocarbon, [14]annulene, lacking a shielding ring current, exhibits a single band at τ = 4.42, which is close to that observed for cyclooctatetraene (τ = 4.31).[181]

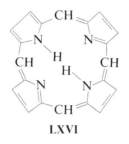

LXVI

The porphyrin ring (LXVI) also has nine conjugated double bonds, and is found to be a very stable, planar ring. The intra-annular imino protons in coproporphyrin-1 are subject to intense shielding and have a high τ value of 13.98 p.p.m., which is 13 p.p.m. higher than that for the imino proton of pyrrole.[181]

4.9.5. THE CYCLOBUTADIENE RING

It is noteworthy that despite many, many attempts, cyclobutadiene, which has only four π electrons, has not been isolated.[184] A number of similar cyclic C_4 compounds have been prepared, such as biphenylene (LXVII) and phenylcyclobutadienoquinone (LXVIII).[185] However, cyclobutadiene has been isolated as the silver nitrate[186(a)] and nickel bromide[186(b)] charge-transfer complexes. The strain energy of the cyclobutadiene ring has been calculated to be in the range 45–74 kcal/mole.[185]

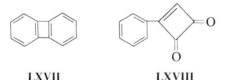

LXVII   LXVIII

[184] *Non-Benzenoid Aromatic Compounds,* chaps. 1 and 2.

[185] E. J. Smutny, M. C. Caserio, and J. D. Roberts, *J. Am. Chem. Soc.,* **82,** 1793 (1960).

[186] (a) M. Avram, E. Marica, and C. D. Nenitzescu, *Chem. Ber.,* **92,** 1088 (1959); (b) H. H. Freedman, *J. Am. Chem. Soc.,* **83,** 2194 (1961). See H. P. Fritz, *Z. Naturforschung,* **16b,** 415 (1961), for the infrared spectra of these complexes.

4.9.6. ALTERNANT AND NONALTERNANT MOLECULES

Ring systems are distinguishable by a rather subtle but fundamental difference, and are designated as *alternant* or *nonalternant* molecules.[187] First referred to in terms of a "starring process,"[188] the alternant molecule is one in which the ring atoms may be divided into two groups, the starred and the unstarred, such that no member of one group is next to a member of the same group, and the π electrons are fairly uniformly distributed over the unsaturated atoms. For illustration, one particular starring for naphthalene is shown in LXIX in which a starred atom is always surrounded by unstarred ones, and vice versa. Such a division is not possible in a nonalterant molecule. Obviously, all molecules with an odd-numbered ring must be nonalterant molecules. Thus, azulene, fulvene, and similar ones are nonalternant molecules. The distinction between alternant and nonalternant molecules is not just a question of whether equivalent Kekulé

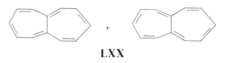

LXIX

structures can be written. In the hydrocarbon heptalene (LXX), for example, two Kekulé structures can be written, but the molecule is a nonalternant hydrocarbon. It can be seen that it does not conform to the

LXX
Heptalene

$(4n + 2)$ π-electron rule. Although the nonalternant hydrocarbon pentalene has eluded all attempts at its preparation, heptalene has recently been prepared. As expected from the present discussion, heptalene has little aromatic character.[190]

The major difference between alternant and nonalternant hydrocarbons is that owing to the unequal distribution of charge, the latter have dipole moments. For instance, the nonalternant hydrocarbons azulene and fulvene have dipole moments whereas the isomeric hydrocarbons naphthalene and benzene do not have moments.

---

[187] These two terms are not to be confused with *aromatic* and *pseudo-aromatic*. These latter terms introduced by Craig[189] stem from quantum mechanical calculations which find aromatic molecules to have totally symmetric ground-state wave functions whereas the pseudo-aromatics do not.

[188] C. A. Coulson and R. S. Rushbrooke, *Proc. Cambr. Phil. Soc.,* **36,** 193 (1940).

[189] D. P. Craig and A. Maccoll, *J. Chem. Soc.,* 964 (1949).

[190] H. J. Dauben, Jr., and D. J. Bertelli, *J. Am. Chem. Soc.,* **83,** 4659 (1961).

4.10. Bonding in halobenzenes and alkylbenzenes

4.10.1. HALOBENZENES[191]

The net electrical effects of halogen atoms when attached to a conjugated system have been an enigma in the theory of chemical bonding. The halogens are generally electron-releasing through resonance (mesomeric electron release) and electron-withdrawing through the inductive effect. There is no question about the order of the latter effect being $F > Cl > Br > I$, but there have been two schools of thought regarding the former. Interpretation of various physical properties and chemical reactivities of halobenzenes gives an order for the mesomeric electron release as being either $F > Cl > Br > I$ or just the opposite. Let us now examine some of the properties of the halobenzenes and develop some view on the bonding therein. Always, we must be mindful of whether or not a given property is concerned primarily with the ground state or with excited states of molecules.

The problem of assessing the mesomeric electron release of halogens is complicated by the simultaneous, oppositely oriented inductive effect. As a result, the net electrical effect will not necessarily be F, Cl, Br, I, or I, Br, Cl, F, but may be a jumbled order with respect to their positions in the periodic table.

(i) Chemical reactivity. The strongest evidence that the mesomeric electron release is in the order $F > Cl > Br > I$ comes from the chemical reactivities of halobenzenes.[192] For illustration, the large inductive effect of the halogens lowers the overall electron density of the ring to make them react slower than benzene towards electrophilic reagents. The direction of their dipole moments and the positive sign of the Hammett sigma constants for the halogens provides additional evidence that the overall electron shift is away from the ring. However, the ionic resonance of the aryl halides among forms LXXI, involving p electron-donor action by the halogen atom, increases the electron density at the *ortho* and *para* positions relative to that at the *meta* positions. The result is that the halogen atoms are *o,p*-directing. Furthermore, the trend of the partial rate factors of the *para*

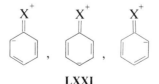

LXXI

[191] G. Baddeley, G. M. Bennett, S. Glasstone, and B. Jones, *J. Chem. Soc.,* 1827 (1953).

[192] G. Baddeley and G. M. Bennett, *J. Chem. Soc.,* 261, 1112 (1933); B. Bettman, G. E. K. Branch, and D. L. Yabroff, *J. Am. Chem. Soc.,* **56**, 1865 (1934).

carbon in the aryl halides, as listed in Table 4.16, indicates that the p-π resonance of LXXI decreases in significance from F to Br, with I being irregular.

Table 4.16. PARTIAL RATE FACTORS IN AROMATIC SUBSTITUTION
OF THE ARYL HALIDES, ϕ—X

Reaction	H	p-F[193]	p-Cl	p-Br	p-I
Chlorination[194]	1.0	6.3	0.4	0.25	
Bromination[195]	1.0	2.14	1.07	0.52	
Bromination[196]	1.0	4.6	0.14	0.06	0.08
Nitration[197]	1.0	0.85	0.15	0.10	0.46

Taft modified the Hammett treatment for the determination of sigma constants and was able to evaluate the inductive (σ_I) and resonance (σ_R) contributions to the substituent constants of various groups.[198] He found the resonance sigma constant (σ_R) for the halogens to decrease in the order suggested above, namely, F > Cl > Br > I (a negative sign indicates electron shift towards the ring.)

	F	Cl	Br	I
σ_R	-0.44	-0.24	-0.22	-0.10
σ_I	0.50	0.47	0.45	0.38

(ii) **Nuclear magnetic resonance shielding parameters.** Another measure of the electrical interaction of halogens with the ring is found in nuclear magnetic resonance shielding parameters in substituted benzenes,[199] chlorobenzenes,[165] and fluorobenzenes.[200] The change in shielding parameters upon introduction of a substituent is taken as an index of the change in electron density at the reference atom produced by the substituent. In all studies (see Table 4.26) the chemical shifts for p-halosubstituents are in the direc-

[193] Fluorine activates the *para* position in detritiation and molecular halogenation,[195] the p-π mesomeric electron release outweighing the electron-withdrawing inductive effect, but fluorine deactivates the *para* position in nitration, proto-, mercuri-, and bromo-desilylation, in protodegermylation, and in protodestannylation (C. Eaborn and R. Taylor, *J. Chem. Soc.*, 2388 (1961)); L. M. Stock and H. C. Brown, *J. Am. Chem. Soc.*, **84**, 1668 (1962).
[194] P. B. de la Mare, *J. Chem. Soc.*, 4450 (1954).
[195] L. N. Ferguson, A. Y. Garner, and J. L. Mack, *J. Am. Chem. Soc.*, **76**, 1250 (1954).
[196] G. Illuminati and G. Marino, *J. Am. Chem. Soc.*, **78**, 4975 (1956).
[197] J. D. Roberts, J. K. Sanford, F. J. L. Sixma, H. Cerfontain, and R. Zagt, *J. Am. Chem. Soc.*, **76**, 4525 (1954).
[198] R. W. Taft, Jr., *J. Am. Chem. Soc.*, **79**, 1045 (1957).
[199] H. Spiesecke and W. G. Schneider, *J. Chem. Phys.*, **35**, 731 (1961).
[200] H. S. Gutowsky, *et al.*, *J. Am. Chem. Soc.*, **74**, 4809 (1952); R. W. Taft, Jr., *et al.*, *J. Am. Chem. Soc.*, **81**, 5352 (1959); P. J. Bray and R. G. Barnes, *J. Chem. Phys.*, **27**, 551 (1957).

tion corresponding to p-π electron-releasing resonance of the halogens and in the decreasing order F > Cl > Br > I.

(iii) **Polarographic reductions.**   In general, a group G in p-X—C_6H_4—G becomes easier to reduce as the *para* X group withdraws electrons from G. This is logical because reduction is the addition of electrons, and the process is facilitated by electrons being withdrawn from the reduced group as reduction takes place. In the case of *para* halogen substituents, the trend in half-wave potentials of several reducible groups indicates that the net electron-donating effect of the halogens decreases in the order Cl > Br > I.[201]

$$-E_{1/2} \text{ for X in } p\text{-X}—C_6H_4—G$$

G	X:	H	Cl	Br	I
NO$_2$		0.935	0.930	0.854	0.780
CHO		1.506	1.422	1.410	1.400

(iv) **Dipole moments.**   A good procedure for ascertaining resonance moments of groups has not yet been developed. The simplest approach is that of Sutton[202] in which he equates the resonance moment to the vector difference between the moments of an aryl compound ϕ—X and a corresponding aliphatic compound R—X (cf. Sec. 4.7). However, even when vapor-phase data are used, some type of approximation should be made for the moments induced in the hydrocarbon portions of the molecules. Such corrections, as made by Groves and Sugden,[203] give an opposite order of resonance moments for the halogens.[204]   For illustration, the resonance moments for the halogens as determined by the two treatments are as follows:

	F	Cl	Br	I
Sutton	−0.41	−0.41	−0.43	−0.50
Groves and Sugden	−1.00	−0.97	−0.89	−0.87
Audsley and Goss[205]	−1.04	−0.95	−0.74	−0.51

The negative sign denotes an electron shift towards the ring.   Since the aromatic moments are less than the aliphatic moments (see Table 4.17), it is tempting to say that resonance between the halogen and benzene ring shifts electrons towards the ring as represented by LXXI.[206]   It is apparent from

[201] E. Gergely and T. Iredale, *J. Chem. Soc.,* 3226 (1953).

[202] L. E. Sutton in *Determination of Organic Structures by Physical Methods,* ed. E. A. Braude and F. C. Nachod (New York: Academic, 1955), chap. 9.

[203] L. G. Groves and S. Sugden, *J. Chem. Soc.,* 1992 (1937).

[204] Compare N. J. Leonard and L. E. Sutton, *J. Am. Chem. Soc.,* **70,** 1571 (1948).

[205] A. Audsley and F. R. Goss, *J. Chem. Soc.,* 358, 497 (1942).

[206] An alternative explanation is to attribute the smaller moments of the aryl halides to the greater electronegativity of the sp^2 hybridized aromatic carbon atom.

the literature[207] that there still is no clear interpretation of dipole-moment data of organic halides.

Table 4.17. Dipole Moments of Alkyl and Phenyl Halides

	$CH_3X_{gas}^{208}$	$t\text{-}BuX_{benzene}^{207}$	Cyclo- $C_5H_9X_{benzene}^{210}$	$C_6H_5X_{gas}^{209}$	$C_6H_5X_{benzene}^{202}$
F	1.81	2.05	1.86	1.59	1.48
Cl	1.87	2.15	2.08	1.73	1.60
Br	1.78	2.21	2.20	1.71	1.57
I	1.62	2.13	2.06	1.7	1.42

These methods of evaluating the mesomeric electron shift of the halogens have an additional inadequacy, because they neglect at least two effects: (1) The contribution to the dipole moment from the lone-pair electrons which may not be the same in the alkyl and aryl series owing to resonance in the aryl series. Unfortunately, an evaluation of this effect has not been made. (2) The possibility for d-orbital acceptance resonance in the case of Cl, Br, and I.

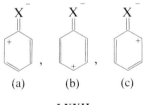

(a)   (b)   (c)

LXXII

X = Cl, Br, I

Several authors, notably Mulliken[211] and Baliah,[212] have pointed out that the halogens Cl, Br, and I may use their d orbitals for electron-acceptor action. Thus, in the case of these aryl halides, there is a possibility for $d\text{-}\pi$ acceptor resonance among forms LXXII. Mulliken attributed the greater strength of the Cl—Cl bond in Cl_2, compared to the F—F bond in F_2, to the $3d$-bonding in Cl_2. He estimated that only 5 per cent of $d\text{-}\pi$ character leads to 20 per cent double-bond character in the Cl—Cl bond. Presumably, a similar situation exists in Br_2 and I_2, whereas the F atom lacks d orbitals for such valency-shell expansion. Consequently, with opposite orders of decreasing contributions from forms LXXI and LXXII

[207] R. H. Knipe, *J. Chem. Phys.*, **23**, 2089 (1955); R. P. Smith and E. M. Mortensen, *J. Am. Chem. Soc.*, **78**, 3932 (1956).

[208] "Table of Dielectric Constants and Electric Dipole Moments," N.B.S. Circular 537, National Bureau of Standards, 1953.

[209] C. G. LeFevre and R. J. W. LeFevre, *Aust. J. Chem.*, **7**, 33 (1954).

[210] M. T. Rogers and J. D. Roberts, *J. Am. Chem. Soc.*, **68**, 843 (1946).

[211] R. S. Mulliken, *J. Am. Chem. Soc.*, **77**, 884 (1955).

[212] V. Baliah and M. Uma, *Naturwissenschaften*, **21**, 512 (1958).

for the halogens, the combined p-π donor and d-π acceptor resonance of the aryl halides could give regular or jumbled trends in the net and resonance dipole moments.

(v) Acid and base strengths. Apparently, the importance of the d-π acceptor resonance of LXXII can become significant when strong electron-donating groups are *ortho* or *para* to the halogen atom. This view is substantiated by the observation that the spectroscopic moments of Br and I are reversed in the respective halogenated anisoles. The spectroscopic moment is a measure of the change of the transition moment of benzene and has been calculated from absorption intensities of the secondary band of benzene.[213] It is positive for electron-donating groups and negative for electron-withdrawing groups; thus it is positive for OCH_3, CH_3, and the halogens. With disubstituted benzenes, the spectroscopic moments are greater than those of the respective mono-derivatives if the moments of the latter are parallel, and less if the directions are antiparallel. It is found that the spectroscopic moments of the haloanisoles are 11.9, 0, -1.4, and -4.2 for F, Cl, Br, I, with the signs of the Br and I moments reversed from their normal direction.[214] Thus, the strong electron-donating methoxy group has reversed the mesomeric character of these two halogens from electron-donating to electron-accepting. It has been shown that this d-π acceptor resonance of Cl, Br, and I also provides an explanation for the trend in acidities of p-halophenols and basicities of p-haloanilines.[212] For illustration, p-fluorophenol has approximately the same acidity as phenol but the other halophenols are significantly *more* acidic than phenol, with the acidity increasing in the order Cl $<$ Br $<$ I.

	H	F	Cl	Br	I
$10^{11} K_a$ of p-X—C_6H_4OH[217]	3.2	2.6	13.2	15.5	21.9
pK_a of p-X—C_6H_4OH[216]	10.0	9.91	9.42	9.42	9.31

In the case of p-haloanilines and p-halo-N,N-dimethylanilines, the basicities of the fluoro derivatives are not very different from those of the parent compounds but the other halogen derivatives are markedly less basic.

	H	F	Cl	Br	I
$10^{12} K_b$ of p-X—$C_6H_4NH_2$[217]	126	120	28.8	21.9	15.1
pK_a of p-X—$C_6H_4NH_2$[216]	4.60	4.65	3.98	3.86	3.78
pK_a of p-X—C_6H_4—NMe_2[218]	4.21	4.01	3.33	2.82	2.73

[213] J. R. Platt, *J. Chem. Phys.*, **19**, 263 (1951).
[214] L. Goodman and L. G. Frolen, *J. Chem. Phys.*, **30**, 1361 (1959).
[215] J. R. Hogland and L. Goodman, *J. Phys. Chem.*, **64**, 1816 (1960).
[216] Spectrophotometric data: A. I. Biggs and R. A. Robinson, *J. Chem. Soc.*, 388 (1961).
[217] Potentiometric titration data: G. M. Bennett, G. L. Brooks, and S. Glasstone, *J. Chem. Soc.*, 1821 (1935).
[218] W. C. Davis and H. W. Addes, *J. Chem. Soc.*, 1622 (1937).

These observed orders can be explained by saying that in the case of fluorine, its opposed inductive and p-π donor resonance effects are both large and of comparable magnitude to nullify each other. However, the increasing magnitude of the d-π acceptor resonance of types LXXIII and LXXIV is acid-strengthening and base-weakening for the phenols and anilines, respectively. Additional support for this view is found in the infrared spectra of p- and m-halophenols (cf. Sec. 5.4).

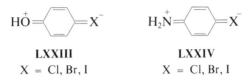

LXXIII   **LXXIV**

X = Cl, Br, I   X = Cl, Br, I

It appears that the p-π donor resonance of the halogens is the dominant type in the absence of strong electron-donating groups. For example, in the boron trihalides, BX_3, the decreasing double-bond character of the B—X bonds as calculated from bond distances[219] indicates that the p-π donor resonance (LXXV) decreases in the order F > Cl > Br > I.[220] Also,

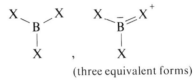

(three equivalent forms)

LXXV

	F	Cl	Br	I
Per cent double-bond character in B—X[219]	33	22	15	6

the force constants,[221] k, of the X—C and C≡N bonds in the cyanogen halides X—C≡N show that the contribution from the ionic resonance form LXXVI(b) decreases in the order F > Cl > Br > I.[222]

$$X—C{\equiv}N, \qquad \overset{+}{X}{=}C{=}\overset{-}{N}$$

(a)   (b)

LXXVI

[219] L. Pauling, *Nature of the Chemical Bond* (3rd ed.; Ithaca, N.Y.: Cornell U. P., 1960), p. 318.

[220] To the contrary, quadrupole data and a different procedure of calculating the double-bond character from bond distances give the opposite order. (Cf. W. G. Laurita and W. S. Koski, *J. Am. Chem. Soc.,* **81**, 3179 (1959).)

[221] E. E. Aynsley and R. Little, *Spectrochim. Acta,* **18**, 667 (1962).

[222] Strangely, the CN infrared absorption frequencies are reported in the reverse order: M. F. A. El-Sayed and R. K. Sheline, *J. Inorg. Nucl. Chem.,* **6**, 187 (1958).

	F	Cl	Br	I
$10^{-5}k_{X-C}$	8.70	5.01	4.10	2.92
$\% \Delta k_{X-C}$	55	47	41	27
$10^{-5}k_{C \equiv N}$	17.44	17.61	17.80	17.94

$$\% \Delta k_{X-C} = 100 \left(\frac{k_{X-CN} - k_{X-CH_3}}{k_{X-CH_3}} \right)$$

That is, the greater importance of LXXVI(b) in the case of F gives the F—C bond the largest double-bond character and the C≡N bond the least triple-bond character. If the per cent change in k_{X-C} is assumed to parallel the change in double-bond character of the X—C bond, the data show that the double-bond character in X—CN decreases from F to I. In fact, the C≡N bond in the halocyanides is longer than in hydrogen cyanide and longest in FCN.[223] Thus, LXXVI(b) makes the largest contribution in the case of FCN, and this contention is further substantiated by the nuclear quadrupole coupling constants for the halocyanides.[224]

(vi) **Ultraviolet spectra.** It is difficult to give a consistent interpretation to the ultraviolet spectra of aromatic compounds containing halogen substituents.[215] The picture is clouded by the fact that the principal absorption bands of X—C_6H_4—R compounds are shifted to longer wavelengths in the order X = I > Br > Cl > F for both types of groups, R = electron-withdrawing and R = electron-donating.[225] Some data are given in Table 4.18. The order of wavelengths λ_m for the halogens cannot be explained completely in terms of p-π donating resonance[226] or d-π acceptor resonance of the halogens.[227]

Table 4.18. Ultraviolet Absorption Wavelengths of Some Halogenated Compounds p-X—C_6H_4—R

R	X = H	F	Cl	Br	I
H(H_2O or EtOH)[228]	203 mμ	204 mμ	210 mμ	210 mμ	207 mμ
CH_3O (gas)[225]	215	214.1	222.8	223.7	229.6
HO (gas)	206	205	220	220	227
NH_2 (gas)	229	228	237	237	240
CH_3S (EtOH)[212]	254	252	260	262	264
NO_2 (gas)[225]	239.1	245.1	251.3	254.6	264.1
$COCH_3$ (gas)	230.1	233.3	241.3	244.8	253.7

[223] J. Sheridan, et al., Nature, **185**, 96 (1960).

[224] P. A. Casabella and P. J. Bray, J. Chem. Phys., **28**, 1182 (1958).

[225] W. M. Schubert, et al., J. Am. Chem. Soc., **82**, 1353, 1357 (1960); **81**, 2695 (1959).

[226] W. F. Forbes, et al., Can. J. Chem., **34**, 1447 (1956); **35**, 488 (1957).

[227] The proposal of Baliah[212] in terms of d-π resonance accounts for the data when R is electron-donating but not when R is electron-accepting.

[228] F. M. Beringer and I. Lillien, J. Am. Chem. Soc., **82**, 5137 (1960); E. Bowden and E. A. Brande, J. Chem. Soc., 1068 (1952).

A plausible explanation[229] of the data can be given in terms of the polarizability of X, plus secondary effects of p-π resonance. For illustration, the primary absorption band of these compounds can be attributed to excitation to excited states approximately described by LXVII and LXVIII for R = electron-donating and R = electron-withdrawing groups, respectively.

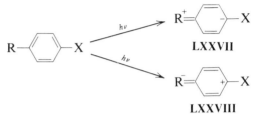

LXXVII

LXXVIII

The excited state is stabilized with respect to the ground state by an amount depending upon the polarizability of X. It is observed that the shift in λ_m for the substituted halobenzenes (Table 4.18) parallels the polarizability of

	X = H	F	Cl	Br	I
Polarizability of X[230]	0.42	0.38	2.28	3.34	5.11

X, except for F when R is electron-withdrawing. In this case, it is probable that the large p-π resonance of F

further stabilizes the excited state with respect to the ground state and produces a small increase of λ_m over that of H.

(vii) C—X bond distances.[231] The per cent decreases in bond distances of the C—X bond in aryl halides are:

	F	Cl	Br	I
C—X$_{ali}$	1.381	1.767	1.937	2.135
C—X$_{arom}$	1.30	1.70	1.85	2.05
Decrease	5.9%	3.8%	4%	3.5%

These data are consistent with the idea that the C—F bond has the largest double-bond character, and since it cannot undergo d-π acceptor resonance (LXXII), it must have the largest p-π donor resonance.

[229] Others have interpreted ultraviolet spectra in terms of polarizability effects. Cf. Refs. 225 and 230.

[230] A. Burawoy and A. R. Thompson, *J. Chem. Soc.*, 4313 (1956).

[231] "Tables of Interatomic Distances," Publication No. 11 (London: The Chemical Society, 1958).

(viii) **Miscellaneous properties.** Some properties of aryl halides appear to be related more to the polarizabilities of the molecules than to their permanent polarizations. For example, the decreasing ionization potentials and the increasing charge-transfer complex stabilities of the aryl halides are in the order F, Cl, Br, I, which coincides with the increasing polarizabilities of the halogen atoms.

	H	F	Cl	Br	I
Ionization potentials[232] (volts)	9.52	9.19	9.07	8.98	8.73
Relative CT complex stability					
towards Ag^{+} [233]	1.0	0.19	0.29	0.40	2.07
TNB[234]	1.0	0.57	0.84	1.15	
Relative CT complex stability of					
1-halonaphthalene towards picric					
acid[235]	1.0	0.56	0.74	0.82	0.86

Summary. It has been observed that the halogens display some interesting regularities with respect to their effects upon the properties of aryl groups. We may conclude from the foregoing discussion that (1) there is a net withdrawal of electrons from the benzene ring by halogens in aryl halides arising from the inductive and polarization effects, (2) the decreasing order of electron release through p-π donor resonance is F > Cl > Br > I, (3) when there are strong electron-donating groups *ortho* or *para* to the halogen atoms, d-π acceptor resonance may become significant and decrease in the order I > Br > Cl, with F unable to exhibit such resonance, and (4) some properties of halobenzenes, such as chemical reactivities, n.m.r. shielding parameters, and polarographic reductions, are best explained in terms of p-π donor resonance and induction of the halogens, while other properties, notably ionization potentials and ultraviolet spectra, can be correlated better with the polarizabilities of the halogens.

4.10.2. ALKYLBENZENES

The mechanism of the electronic effects of alkyl groups in alkylbenzenes is another very controversial issue. The groups are electron-releasing through at least four processes:

α C—H hyperconjugation   Me > Et > *i*-Pr > *t*-Bu
α C—C hyperconjugation[44]   *t*-Bu > *i*-Pr > Et > Me
Induction   *t*-Bu > *i*-Pr > Et > Me
Polarization   *t*-Bu > *i*-Pr > Et > Me

[232] K. Watanabe, *J. Chem. Phys.,* **26,** 542 (1957). Compare other values of W. C. Price, *Chem. Revs.,* **41,** 257 (1947), and J. D. Morrison, *J. Chem. Phys.,* **20,** 1021 (1952).

[233] L. J. Andrews and R. M. Keefer, *J. Am. Chem. Soc.,* **74,** 4500 (1952).

[234] G. Briegleb, *Z. Elektrochem.,* **59,** 184 (1955).

[235] P. D. Gardner and W. E. Stump, *J. Am. Chem. Soc.,* **79,** 2761 (1957).

The *t*-Bu group is the most electron-releasing by all but the first process. In an attempt to explain the unexpected relative rates of reaction of *p*-substituted benzyl bromides towards pyridine, Me > Et > *i*-Pr > *t*-Bu, Baker and Nathan proposed that the trend of the *net* electron-releasing ability of these groups when attached to a benzene ring is opposite to that of the inductive order (cf. Sec. 4.5). Subsequently, this order was proposed to occur by α C—H hyperconjugation and the mechanism is now referred to as the Baker-Nathan (B-N) effect.

According to the B-N order, in those reactions favored by electron accession, a *p*-Me compound will react faster than a *p-t*-Bu compound

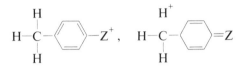

and in a reaction involving a nucleophilic attack in the rate-determining step, a *p-t*-Bu compound will react faster than the *p*-Me compound. This is found to be the case in general, and some typical examples are listed in Tables 4.19 and 4.20. It can be seen there that a wide variety of reactions can be correlated in terms of the B-N effect.[249] It is especially significant that the orders for the electrophilic substituent constants σ^+ and nucleophilic substituent constants σ^- substantiate the B-N order, because these constants correlate a substantial number of chemical reactivities.

Table 4.19. SOME REACTIONS SHOWING THE BAKER-NATHAN ORDER OF ELECTRON RELEASE

| | | Rel. Reaction Rate | |
Reaction	H	*p*-Me	*p-t*-Bu
Bromination of benzenes (Br$_2$, HOAc)[236]	1	2420	770
Bromination of benzenes (HOBr, H$^+$)[248]	1	59	38.5
Chlorination of benzenes (Cl$_2$, HOAc)[237]	1	280	92.5
Benzoylation of benzenes[239]	1	589	430
Benzoylation of benzenes[238]	1	830	615
Brominolysis of ArSiMe$_3$ by Br$_2$[240]	1	49	29
Protonolysis of ArSiMe$_3$[241]	1	21.1	15.6
Solvolysis of ArCMe$_2$Cl[242]	1	26.0	14.4
Beckmann rearrangement of ArCOCH$_3$ oximes[243]	1	1.91	1.83
Ionization of anilinium ions, pK_a water[244]	1	1.11	1.08

[236] H. C. Brown and L. M. Stock, *J. Am. Chem. Soc.,* **79**, 1421 (1957); P. W. Robertson, P. B. D. de la Mare, and B. E. Swedlund, *J. Chem. Soc.,* 782 (1953).

[237] L. M. Stock and A. Himoe, *J. Am. Chem. Soc.,* **83**, 1937, 4605 (1961).

[238] H. C. Brown, B. A. Bolto, and F. R. Jensen, *J. Org. Chem.,* **23**, 414 (1958).

[239] H. C. Brown and F. R. Jensen, *J. Am. Chem. Soc.,* **80**, 2296 (1958).

[240] C. Eaborn and D. E. Webster, *J. Chem. Soc.,* 4449 (1957).

Table 4.20. SOME NUCLEOPHILIC REACTIONS SHOWING THE
Me > *t*-Bu ORDER OF ELECTRON RELEASE

Alkaline hydrolysis of ethyl benzoates (85 wt % EtOH)[245]	1	0.44	0.56
Ethanolysis of benzoyl chlorides[246]	1	0.57	0.67
Reaction of 2-nitrobromobenzenes with piperidine[247]	1	0.146	0.170

	H	Me	*t*-Bu	
σ^+	0	−0.29	−0.25	i.e., Me more activating for electrophilic reactions
σ^-	0	−0.17	−0.20	i.e., t-Bu more activating for nucleophilic reactions

Bartlett[250] made an interesting analysis of the electron-releasing effects of the Me and *t*-Bu groups on the ionization of triphenylmethyl chlorides in liquid sulfur dioxide.

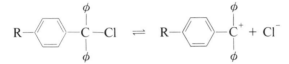

Free energy changes ΔF^0 can be calculated from the equilibrium constants, and the change in ΔF^0 in going from H to R can be denoted as $\Delta\Delta F^0$.

R	$10^5 K$	ΔF^0	$\Delta\Delta F^0$	$\Delta\Delta F^0_I$	$\Delta\Delta F^0_R$
H	4.03	+5.49			
m-Me	9.2	5.04	−0.45	−0.45	0
m-t-Bu	16.0	4.74	−0.75	−0.75	0
p-Me	71.0	3.93	−1.56	−0.38	−1.18
p-t-Bu	76.0	3.90	−1.59	−0.63	−0.96

The $\Delta\Delta F^0$ values for *m*-Me and *m-t*-Bu support the expectation that the *t*-Bu group, through induction, has the greater electron-releasing ability. If it is assumed that resonance makes no measurable contribution to the electron-releasing effect of these groups in the *meta* position and that the

[241] C. Eaborn, *J. Chem. Soc.,* 4858 (1956).

[242] H. C. Brown, J. D. Brady, M. Grayson, and W. H. Bonner, *J. Am. Chem. Soc.,* **79,** 1897 (1957).

[243] P. J. McNulty and D. E. Pearson, *J. Am. Chem. Soc.,* **81,** 612 (1959).

[244] B. M. Wepster, *Rec. trav. chim.,* **76,** 357 (1957).

[245] E. Berliner, *Tetrahedron,* **5,** 202 (1959).

[246] C. W. L. Bevan, E. D. Hughes, and C. K. Ingold, *Nature,* **171,** 301 (1953).

[247] E. Berliner and L. C. Monack, *J. Am. Chem. Soc.,* **74,** 1574 (1952).

[248] P. B. D. de la Mare and J. T. Harvey, *J. Chem. Soc.,* 131 (1957); 36 (1956).

[249] However, nitration, the most exhaustively studied aromatic reaction, is an exception. (Cf. L. M. Stock, *J. Org. Chem.,* **26,** 4120 (1961).)

inductive effect from the *para* position is five-sixths that from the *meta* position,[251] then the contributions to $\Delta \Delta F^0$ from resonance $(\Delta \Delta F^0_R)$ and induction $(\Delta \Delta F^0_I)$ can be computed as given in the table. These calculations give semiquantitative support to what is already believed in a qualitative fashion: (1) that the inductive effect of the *t*-Bu group is larger than for Me from the *meta* as well as the *para* position, (2) that the resonance effect of the *p*-Me group (C—H hyperconjugation) is greater than that of the *p*-*t*-Bu group (C—C hyperconjugation), and (3) that the resonance of the *p*-*t*-Bu group is not nil. The figures also indicate that the combined C—C hyperconjugation and inductive effects of the *p*-*t*-Bu group may outweigh the effect of C—H hyperconjugation and inductive effects of the *p*-Me group. Other workers have also proposed that C—H and C—C hyperconjugation in alkyl groups must be considered to account for their electron-releasing character, and that the contribution of C—C hyperconjugation is about 80 per cent of that from C—H hyperconjugation.[252]

Taft[253] used a slightly modified Hammett approach and attributed the effects of substituents to induction plus resonance, e.g.

$$\log (k^p/k_0) = I + R$$

where k^p/k_0 is the relative reaction rate or equilibrium constant for the *para* and unsubstituted reference compound, I is the inductive effect and R is the effect of resonance. From suitable data, he was able to calculate R for alkyl groups from the relationship

$$R = n_H h_H + n_C h_C$$

where n_H and n_C are the number of C—H and C—C bonds, respectively, and h_H and h_C are constants designating the relative degree of C—H and C—C hyperconjugation. From a study of about thirty reactions, it was found that the ratio h_H/h_C hovers close to the value 1.3 and the R value for *p*-Me is 20–30 per cent greater than for *p*-*t*-Bu. Taft[198] also calculated the inductive and resonance contributions to the Hammett *para* substituent constants in terms of σ_I and σ_R, respectively.

	σ_I	σ_R
Me	− 0.046	− 0.102
Et	− 0.055	− 0.094
i-Pr	− 0.064	− 0.086
t-Bu	− 0.074	− 0.078

[250] P. D. Bartlett, *J. Chem. Educ.*, **30**, 22 (1953).

[251] J. D. Roberts, R. A. Clement, and J. J. Drysdale, *J. Am. Chem. Soc.*, **73**, 2182 (1951).

[252] S. E. Ehrenson, *J. Am. Chem. Soc.*, **83**, 4493 (1961); H. C. Brown, J. D. Brady, M. Grayson, and W. H. Bonner, *J. Am. Chem. Soc.*, **79**, 1897 (1957).

[253] R. W. Taft, Jr., and I. C. Lewis, *Tetrahedron*, **5**, 210 (1959).

Thus, we see that the inductive electron-releasing effect of the t-Bu group is greater than that of the Me group and the reverse order occurs for resonance activation; however, the combined inductive and resonance electron-releasing abilities of the four groups are very close to the same value.

Owing to its good success in correlating most of the chemical reactivities of alkylbenzenes, the Baker-Nathan hypothesis has enjoyed widespread acceptance and has stimulated much research. However, evidence has accumulated in the recent literature to call attention to the fact that the B-N order can also be explained in terms of other effects[254-258] and, in particular, it does not account for most physical properties. The alternate hypothesis with strongest experimental support is that the principal mode of electron release parallels the inductive order and that steric hindrance to solvation of the polar transition complex by the larger alkyl groups inverts the inductive order to give the observed B-N order.[255]

Several persons have shown that solvent effects can have a pronounced influence on the *relative* reactivities of the alkylbenzenes. For illustration:

Process	Relative rates	Solvent
Alkaline hydrolysis of ethyl benzoates[245]	$k_{p\text{-Me}} > k_{p\text{-}t\text{-Bu}}$	56% aq. acetone
	$k_{p\text{-Me}} < k_{p\text{-}t\text{-Bu}}$	85% ethanol
Solvolysis of 3-alkylbenzhydryl chlorides[255]	$k_{m\text{-Me}} > k_{m\text{-}t\text{-Bu}}$	80% acetone
	$k_{m\text{-Me}} < k_{m\text{-}t\text{-Bu}}$	90% ethanol
Detritiation of p-alkyl-tritiobenzenes $R—C_6H_4T$[259]	$k_{p\text{-Me}} > k_{p\text{-}t\text{-Bu}}$	71 wt.% H_2SO_4
	$k_{p\text{-Me}} < k_{p\text{-}t\text{-Bu}}$	$CF_3CO_2H—H_2SO_4$

Thus, the activating effects of the Me and t-Bu groups, in *para* as well as *meta* positions, can be reversed upon a change in solvent. The difficulty in evaluating the relative merits of the two hypotheses, the B-N effect and the inhibition-to-solvation effect, is that experimental factors which favor one also favor the other. For instance, the greater the electron deficiency created in the transition state, the more pronounced should be the B-N effect and also the greater would be the solvation energy by a polar solvent. In support of the latter point, it has been observed[257] that protodesilylation

$$R—C_6H_4Si(CH_3)_3 + H^+ \longrightarrow R—C_6H_4H$$

[254] V J. Shiner, Jr., *Tetrahedron,* **5**, 243 (1959).

[255] W. A. Sweeney and W. M. Schubert, *J. Am. Chem. Soc.,* **82**, 6188 (1960) and earlier papers in this series.

[256] A. Burawoy and E. Spinner, *J. Chem. Soc.,* 3752 (1954).

[257] R. A. Benkeser and T. V. Liston, *Science,* **130**, 1412 (1959).

[258] R. A. Clement and J. N. Naghizadeh, *J. Am. Chem. Soc.,* **81**, 3154 (1959).

[259] C. Eaborn and R. Taylor, *J. Chem. Soc.,* 247 (1961).

follows the B-N order for R, while mercuridesilylation

$$R—C_6H_4—Si(CH_3)_3 + Hg(OAc)_2 \longrightarrow R—C_6H_4—HgOAc$$

does not. Both reactions have been shown to be electrophilic, but the former takes place in a very polar medium (mineral acid or aq. HOAc) whereas mercuridesilylation is carried out in a mildly polar solvent (glac. HOAc).

Schubert[255] has offered kinetic evidence in support of the solvent effect, which he finds inconsistent with the B-N effect. He has shown, for example, that his hypothesis correctly predicts that in solvents in which the rate constants for mono *m*-alkyl compounds are in the order $k_{Me} > k_{t\text{-}Bu}$, the B-N order should become more pronounced for the corresponding dialkyl compounds, and in solvents in which the rate constants for the mono compounds are in the inductive order, $k_{t\text{-}Bu} > k_{Me}$, then the difference should become smaller in the dialkyl compounds.

One observation in support of the B-N mode of stabilization is the fact that charge-transfer complexes of hexamethylbenzene are only 100-fold more stable than the corresponding benzene charge-transfer complexes, whereas the difference in stability of the σ complexes is a factor of 10^6 (cf. Table 1.21). In the CT complexes, polarization and induction play a major role in the ground state, and the stabilization factor of 100 is not unreasonable. However, it was shown in Sec. 1.5.2 that hyperconjugation (but not polarization or induction) nicely accounts for the increased stability of the protonated methylbenzenes.

The major weakness in interpreting the effects of alkyl groups in terms of the B-N effect is that it is not well correlated with physical properties of the alkylbenzenes.[260] The order usually observed for electron-releasing ability of the alkyl groups parallels the inductive order, which also coincides with the order of polarizabilities of the alkyl groups. For illustrations, consider the following physical properties.

Dipole Moments.

	H	Me	Et	*i*-Pr	*t*-Bu
$\mu_{(gas)}^{261}$ (debyes)	O	0.37	0.58	0.65	0.70
σ^* .	0.49	0	−0.10	−0.19	−0.30
$\alpha (\times 10^{-25} cm^3)$		27	46	65	84

σ^* = polar substituent constant.[262] α = calculated polarizability.[263]

[260] Of course, the B-N effect was proposed to account for chemical reactivities. Nevertheless, if it correctly describes the electron-releasing abilities of the alkyl groups it should also apply to their physical properties.

[261] J. W. Baker and L. G. Groves, *J. Chem. Soc.,* 1144 (1939).

[262] R. J. Taft, Jr., *Steric Effects in Organic Chemistry,* ed. M. S. Newman, (New York: Wiley, 1956), chap. 13.

[263] T. L. Brown, *J. Am. Chem. Soc.,* **81,** 3229 (1959).

It can be seen that the dipole moments of the alkylbenzenes, although not greatly different, are in the order of the inductive effect.[264] This order coincides with the decreasing relative electronegativity of the groups (identified with the polar substituent constant $\sigma*$) and the increasing estimated group polarizabilities α. The fact that all of the respective substituted cyclohexanes have zero dipole moments suggests that the moments of these alkylbenzenes stem either from resonance or from polarization of the alkyl groups by the phenyl group. If it were an inductive effect, there would be a difference in the moments of the alkylcyclohexanes too.

It has been shown that even with electron-withdrawing groups *para* to the alkyl groups that there is little indication from dipole moments that there is significant ground-state C—H hyperconjugation in the groups.[265, 266] For demonstration, the moments in debyes of some substituted alkylbenzenes are as follows.

R in C_6H_5R

System	H	Me	Et	*i*-Pr	*t*-Bu
C_6H_5—R [261]	0	0.37	0.58	0.65	0.70
p-O_2N—C_6H_4—R	3.96	4.43			4.61
p-NC—C_6H_4—R	4.08	4.42	4.53	4.60	4.64

Any appreciable C—H hyperconjugation should give the Me compound a larger moment than that of the *t*-Bu derivative, or at least bring the two values closer together. Even when the observed moments are corrected for moments induced in the alkyl groups by the electronegative substituents, there is no evidence that hyperconjugation makes an important contribution to the dipole moments.[265]

Apparently polarization is an important factor not to be neglected when considering electronic effects of an alkyl group. For example, this view offers an explanation[263] for the decrease in heat of hydrogenation of benzene, toluene, and ethylbenzene to the respective cyclohexanes.

benzene	49.25 kcal/mole
toluene	48.94
ethylbenzene	48.17

[264] The suggestion[267] was made that the inductive order prevails here because there is no strong demand for electrons. Upon electron demand, the C—H hyperconjugation release increases more rapidly than inductive electron release until finally C—H hyperconjugation becomes the predominant mode of electron release, thereby resulting in the B-N order observed in chemical reactivities.

[265] T. L. Brown, *J. Am. Chem. Soc.,* **81**, 3232 (1959).

[266] This view is also held by R. C. Ferreira, *Nature,* **188**, 848 (1960), and by A. N. Sharpe and S. Walker, *J. Chem. Soc.,* 4522 (1961).

[267] J. W. Baker, *Hyperconjugation* (Fair Lawn, N. J.: Oxford U. P., 1952).

Cyclohexane is less polarizable than benzene, so that hydrogenation produces a loss in dispersion energy which is greatest for the most polarizable group.

Ionization potentials. The first ionization potentials of the alkylbenzenes also follow the inductive and polarizability order.

	H	Me	Et	i-Pr	t-Bu
I.P. (ev)[268]	9.24	8.92	8.75	8.6	8.5

It might be expected that if C—H hyperconjugation were the principal mode of electron release by the R groups, that the ionization potentials would follow the B-N order, particularly since C—H hyperconjugation stabilizes excited states more than ground states. Yet this is not the case for the alkylbenzenes. It is noteworthy that a different situation exists in the methylethylenes. It was shown in Table 4.3 that the order of decreasing ionization potentials follows the order of increasing number of conjugated methyl groups and therefore the order of increasing α C—H hyperconjugation. This implies that there is some fundamental difference in mode of electron release in the alkylbenzene system which does not occur in the simple alkylolefin system.

Ultraviolet spectra. The "primary" or principal absorption band of a benzene derivative ϕ—Y can be attributed to an electronic oscillation along the long axis of the molecule, and the ground and excited states can be approximately described by the VB structures LXXIX and LXXX, respectively.[269]

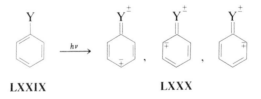

LXXIX   LXXX

The sign of the charge on Y will depend on whether it is a mesomeric electron-acceptor or electron-donator. The more readily Y accepts the charge, the more it stabilizes the excited state and the longer is the wavelength of absorption. One would expect therefore that if C—H hyperconjugation is the major electron-releasing mechanism of the alkyl groups, then the order of wavelengths of the primary band of the alkylbenzenes would parallel the B-N order. To the contrary, there is no regular difference in the positions of this band for the Me, Et, i-Pr, and t-Bu benzenes.

[268] W. C. Price, *Chem. Revs.*, **41**, 257 (1947).

[269] W. T. Simpson and A. G. Albrecht, *J. Am. Chem. Soc.*, **77**, 4455 (1957).

$$\lambda_m \text{ of primary band (m}\mu) = \begin{array}{ccccc} H & Me^{270} & Et^{270} & i\text{-Pr}^{272} & t\text{-Bu}^{271} \\ 203.5 & 216 & 217 & \sim 215 & 207.5 \end{array}$$

Similarly, the wavelength of the charge-transfer band (largest λ_m) of alkyl-

pyridinium iodides $R—\langle \bigcirc N^+ —CH_3 \rangle I^-$ is not altered significantly as R is

changed from Me to t-Bu.[273] These spectral observations can be attributed to a stabilization by the alkyl groups operating through more than one mechanism, i.e., C—H and C—C hyperconjugation, induction, and polarization, and the net effect is in a mixed order with respect to Me, Et, i-Pr, and t-Bu.

When o,p-directing and m-directing groups are $para$ to each other in the benzene ring, the interaction resonance produces an unusually large bathochromic shift of the primary band of benzene.[274] This spectral effect has sometimes been used as a guide in ascertaining whether a group is primarily a mesomeric electron-donor or electron-acceptor. When $para$ substituents are introduced into the alkylbenzene ring, there is no spectral evidence for significant C—H hyperconjugation in the alkyl groups. For illustration, the wavelengths of the primary band of some substituted alkylphenyl compounds are listed in Table 4.21. It is observed there that in the gas $phase$ as well as in polar solvents, the order of λ_m values is opposite to the B-N order, but coincides with the inductive and polarizability order of the alkyl groups. Again it was found that the solvent can produce an inversion of the order to that of the B-N order.[276]

Table 4.21.[275, 276] λ_m VALUES FOR THE PRIMARY BAND
OF SOME ALKYLPHENYL COMPOUNDS (mμ)

System	R = H	Me	Et	i-Pr	t-Bu
p-R—$R_6H_4NO_2$, gas	239.1	250.2	251.0	251.3	251.5
p-R—$C_6H_4COCH_3$, gas	231.3	238.9	239.5	239.7	239.8
p-R—CH_2—$C_6H_4NO_2$, gas	250.2	251.0	251.6	252.5	253.2
p-R—C_6H_4COOH	228.0	236.5			237.5
p-R—$C_6H_4C(CH_3)$=OH	295.5	312.5		315.0	315.5
$(p$-R—$C_6H_4)_3C^+$	431	452		456	458
$(p$-R—$C_6H_4)_2 CH^+$	442	472			480

[270] J. R. Platt and H. B. Klevens, *Chem. Revs.*, **41**, 301 (1947).

[271] E. Bowden and E. A. Braude, *J. Chem. Soc.*, 1068 (1952).

[272] V. J. Hammond, W. C. Price, J. P. Teegan, and A. D. Walsh, *Disc. Faraday Soc.*, **9**, 53 (1950).

[273] E. M. Kosower and J. A. Skorcz, *J. Am. Chem. Soc.*, **82**, 2195 (1960).

[274] L. Doub and J. M. Vandenbelt, *J. Am. Chem. Soc.*, **69**, 2714 (1947); 2414 (1949).

[275] W. M. Schubert and W. A. Sweeney, *J. Org. Chem.*, **21**, 119 (1956).

[276] W. M. Schubert, J. Robind, and J. L. Hairn, *J. Am. Chem. Soc.*, **79**, 910 (1957).

It is noteworthy that even when an electron-donating group is introduced *para* to an alkyl group, λ_m is shifted to longer wavelengths. Values of λ_m for the primary band of some alkyl phenols, anisoles, anilines, and N,N-dimethylanilines in the *gas phase* are given in Table 4.22. Although there is no significant difference between the values for Me and *t*-Bu, there is a distinct increase in λ_m over the corresponding H values. This indicates

Table 4.22.[277] VALUES OF λ_m (mμ) FOR THE PRIMARY BAND
OF SOME SUBSTITUTED ALKYLBENZENES

Z	p-Z—C$_6$H$_4$—R		
	R = H	Me	*t*-Bu
OH	206.3	216.1	216.0
OMe	215.0	219.8	219.9
NH$_2$	229.4	233.7	232.7
NMe$_2$	241.8	243.5	244.5

that the excited state (LXXXII) is more stabilized with respect to the ground state by an alkyl group than by H, and suggests that the net stabilization is determined by the polarizability of R (for polariation *away*

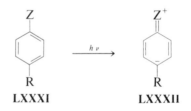

LXXXI   LXXXII

from as well as *toward* the ring). This explanation does not apply to the net chemical reactivities, for it was shown (Tables 4.19 and 4.20) that the B-N order (irrespective of whether it is due to decreasing C—H hyperconjugation or increasing inhibition of solvent stabilization of electron-deficient sites) is followed for electrophilic reactions and reversed for nucleophilic reactions. It can be concluded that, for electronic transitions of the type responsible for the primary band, λ_m can best be correlated with the polarizabilities of substituents. This was observed also for the halobenzenes.

It should be pointed out here that the low-intensity 0,0 band of benzene is shifted to slightly longer wavelengths by alkyl groups in the B-N order.[278]

[277] W. M. Schubert, J. M. Craven, R. G. Minton, and R. B. Murphy, *Tetrahedron*, 5, 194 (1959).

[278] F. A. Matsen, W. W. Robertson, and R. L. Choake, *Chem. Revs.*, 41, 273 (1947).

	R in ϕ—R				
	H	Me	Et	*i*-Pr	*t*-Bu
λ_m of 0,0 band	262.5	266.3	265.9	265.3	265.0

The trend is quite definite. However, there is a strong difference of opinion on the nature of this electronic transition. Some authors attribute the trend to the decreasing electron-releasing resonance (total C—H and C—C hyperconjugation of the alkyl groups,[253, 267, 278] while others do not agree that the transition should be associated with resonance.[270, 271, 272, 276, 277, 279]

N.M.R. shielding parameters. Nuclear magnetic resonance chemical shifts for aromatic protons of the alkylbenzenes follow the B-N order in nonpolar and in polar solvents.[280]

Proton chemical shift	Me	Et	*i*-Pr	*t*-Bu
in cyclohexane	5.9	4.4	3.8	~1.1
in nitromethane	6.8	5.3	4.7	~1.2

Similar measurements on *p*-bromotoluene and *p*-bromo-*t*-butylbenzene indicate that the protons *ortho* to the Me group are shielded more than those *ortho* to the *t*-Bu group. Thus in contrast to the evidence from dipole moments, ionization potentials, and ultraviolet spectra, n.m.r. measurements support the B-N order of electron release by alkyl groups.

Conclusions. From the foregoing discussion, it can be concluded: (1) that alkyl groups have significant electron-releasing ability compared with a hydrogen atom through C—H and C—C hyperconjugation, induction, and polarization, but the differences are rather small when compared to one another; (2) that the Baker-Nathan hypothesis of electron release will account for most chemical reactivities but for few physical properties of the alkylbenzenes; (3) that the B-N order can also be explained in terms of steric inhibition to solvent stabilization, and (4) that polarization of the alkyl groups provides most often a fair correlation of the physical properties of the alkylbenzenes.

4.11. Electrical effects in substituted benzenes

The effects of substituents in the benzene ring upon the physical and chemical properties of the nuclear carbon atoms or upon other substituents in the

[279] A. G. Albrecht and W. T. Simpson, *J. Chem. Phys.*, **21**, 940 (1953).
[280] R. B. Moodie, T. M. Coonor and R. Stewart, *Can. J. Chem.*, **38**, 626 (1960).

ring is one of the most exhaustively investigated areas in organic chemistry. It was early recognized that the various substituents produce preferential orientation in aromatic substitution, and considerable effort was made to analyze the mode of operation of this directed aromatic substitution and to correlate it with the molecular properties of the substituents.[281] Several physical properties of substituted benzenes have been measured in an attempt to evaluate the separate contributions of resonance, induction, polarization, solvation, and other factors to the electrical effects of substituents, and the results have been expressed in various forms. The numerical values do not always form parallel series, because the several factors of resonance, induction, polarization, etc., may make different relative contributions to the properties being measured. Even constants to represent the chemical effects of substituents have been developed in the form of Hammett-type substituent constants. As might be expected, there is a strong correlation between the physical and chemical effects of a series of substituents, which implies that both types of properties reflect the operation of the same factors. It should be of interest and highly worth while to compare some of these different ways of denoting the relative influences of substituents on nuclear carbon atoms and other substituents attached to the benzene ring.

It is well known that groups are commonly divided into *meta-* or *ortho, para-*directing groups depending on whether they give more or less than the statistical amount of 40 per cent *meta* isomer in electrophilic substitution. Even though there is a continuous gradation of *meta* orientation by groups, this way of classifying groups is convenient and will be used here.

4.11.1. THE HAMMETT EQUATION

As stated previously, chemists are always seeking empirical relationships by which to predict chemical, physical, or even biochemical properties of a molecule on a basis of its structure, or by which to design the structure of a molecule that would have a certain desired property. The two most widely used generalizations of this type are the periodic table and electronegativity. Another extensively used relationship is that developed by L. P. Hammett.[282] Hammett reasoned that if a series of *meta* substituents or a series of *para* substituents have the same relative effects on two different reactions, then, when the effects on one reaction are plotted against the effects on the second reaction, the result should be a straight line. For illustration, if one plots the log of the dissociation constants of substituted

[281] L. N. Ferguson, *Chem. Reviews,* **50,** 47 (1952).
[282] L. P. Hammett, *Physical Organic Chemistry,* (New York: McGraw-Hill, 1940), pp. 184 ff.
[283] G. E. K. Branch, D. L. Yabroff, and B. Bettman, *J. Am. Chem. Soc.,* **56,** 937, 1850, 1865 (1934).
[284] J. F. J. Dippy, *Chem. Revs.,* **25,** 151 (1939).

benzoic acids against the log of the dissociation constants of the similarly substituted phenylboric acids, one gets a reasonably straight line (Fig. 4.3). The line can be reproduced by an equation of the form

$$\log K = \rho \log K' + C \qquad (4\text{-}7)$$

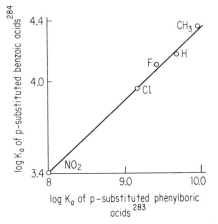

Fig. 4.3. Plot of log of the dissociation constants of similarly substituted benzoic and phenylboric acids.

where K and K' are the two dissociation constants for a given substituent, ρ is the slope of the line, and C is the intercept. Since the linear relationship involves the logarithms of equilibrium constants, it implies that the substituents exert their influence through changes of potential energy and that steric and entropy changes remain constant throughout the series. Hence, Eq. (4-7) is referred to as a *linear free energy* relationship. If similar plots are made for other equilibria involving the same substituents, such as the ionization constants of the correspondingly substituted phenylacetic acids or of substituted benzyl chlorides in liquid sulfur dioxide, then other straight lines are obtained, each with its own slope. If the equilibrium constants for the unsubstituted compounds are denoted by K_0 and K_0' in Eq. (4-7), then

$$\log K_0 = \rho \log K_0' + C \qquad (4\text{-}8)$$

and by subtracting Eq. (4-8) from Eq. (4-7) for the same pair of equilibria, one gets

$$\log K/K_0 = \rho \log K'/K_0' \qquad (4\text{-}9)$$

This equation would be applicable to any two pairs of equilibria, and one may be selected as a reference for comparing all the rest. Since the dissociation constants of substituted benzoic acids were known very accurately for a large number of substituents, Hammett chose this reaction as a standard. Accordingly, a new constant may be chosen equal to $\log K'/K'_0$ which would be characteristic of each substituent. This reduces Eq. (4-9) to

$$\log K / K_0 = \rho \sigma \qquad (4\text{-}10)$$

in which σ, called the *substituent constant*, is regarded as a measure of the effect which the substituent has upon the electron density at the reaction center and ρ, the so-called *reaction constant*, is a measure of the sensitivity of the equilibrium in question to a change in electron density at the reaction center. Not only does Eq. (4-10) apply to equilibria but to rates of reactions, in which case rate constants are used in place of equilibrium constants.

Hammett carried out this procedure for a large number of equilibria and rates of reactions, with the ionization constants of substituted benzoic acids as the reference equilibrium. Each series of reactions yields a specific σ value for a given substituent. Such values for σ vary over a small range for a given substituent and a mean value must be chosen. In this fashion, Hammett determined a set of "best value" *meta* and *para* substituent constants for a fairly large number of substituents. Having established a set of σ constants, ρ for a given reaction is obtained from the slope of the line which best fits the data when values of $\log K/K_0$ or $\log k/k_0$ are plotted against σ's. On the other hand, if σ is unknown for any substituent from ionization constants, the value may be obtained from Eq. (4-10) and the known values for $\log K$ (or $\log k$) and ρ. When σ is obtained in this manner, it is called a secondary substituent constant and is generally not as accurate as those computed from dissociation constants of the respective benzoic acids.[285]

From new and better data, revised values for the Hammett σ constants have been compiled;[285] some representative values are given in Table 4.23. Since *para* and *meta* groups are too far from the reaction center to have a noticeable steric effect on the reactions, σ constants reflect only electronic effects. In fact, only the *meta* and *para* positions have been considered in order to eliminate steric effects. In recent years *ortho* substituent constants have been proposed, but little use has been made of them.[286,287,288]

Several persons, including Hammett, have noted that with reactions involving strong mesomeric electron-donating groups such as the OH and NH_2 groups, different σ constants should be used for strong mesomeric

[285] D. H. McDaniel and H. C. Brown, *J. Org. Chem.*, **23**, 420 (1958); compared with R. W. Taft, Jr., N. C. Deno, and P. S. Skell, *Ann. Rev. Phys. Chem.*, **9**, 292 (1958).

[286] A. C. Farthing and B. Nam, Steric Effects in Conjugated Systems, ed. G. W. Gray (London: Butterworths, 1958), pp. 131 ff; P. Mamalis and H. N. Rydon, *Nature*, **166**, 404 (1950).

[287] P. J. Bray and R. G. Barnes, *J. Chem. Phys.*, **27**, 551 (1957).

[288] H. W. Thompson and G. Steel, *Trans. Faraday Soc.*, **52**, 1451 (1956).

Substituent	Per cent *meta* isomer in electrophilic nitration	Hammett σ [285]		Electrophilic σ^+ [289]	
		para	*meta*	*para*	*meta*
$N(CH_3)_2$	. .	-0.83	-0.211		
NH_2	. .	-0.66	-0.16		
OH	. .	-0.37	$+0.121$		
OCH_3	2.0	-0.268	$+0.115$	-0.764	$+0.0465$
CH_3	4.4	-0.170	-0.069	-0.306	-0.0652
Et	6.5	-0.151	-0.07	-0.291	-0.0625
i-Pr	7.7	-0.151		-0.276	-0.0589
t-Bu	11.5	-0.197	-0.10	-0.250	-0.0581
H	(40)	0	0	0	0
F	0.5	$+0.062$	$+0.337$	-0.0714	$+0.346$
Cl	0.9	$+0.227$	$+0.373$	$+0.112$	$+0.391$
Br	1.2	$+0.232$	$+0.391$	$+0.148$	$+0.399$
I	2.1	$+0.18$	$+0.352$	$+0.132$	$+0.353$
COOH	80.2	ca $+0.45$	$+0.37$		
COOEt	72.0	$+0.45$	$+0.37$		
$COCH_3$	55	$+0.502$	$+0.376$		
CF_3	99	$+0.54$	$+0.43$		
CN	81	$+0.660$	$+0.56$		
NO_2	93.3	$+0.778$	$+0.710$	$+0.777$	$+0.662$
$^+N(CH_3)_3$	100	$+0.82$	$+0.88$		

Substituent	Nucleophilic σ^- [252]	σ_R [296]	σ_I [296]	σ^* [295]
$N(CH_3)_2$				
NH_2		-0.76	$+0.10$	
OH		-0.60	$+0.25$	$+1.55$
OCH_3		-0.51	$+0.25$	$+1.46$
CH_3		-0.11	-0.05	0.000
Et				-0.100
i-Pr				-0.190
t-Bu		-0.09	-0.07	-0.30
H		0	0	$+0.49$
F		-0.44	$+0.52$	$+3.08$
Cl	$+0.265$	-0.24	$+0.47$	$+2.94$
Br	$+0.289$	-0.22	$+0.45$	$+2.80$
I	ca. $+0.318$	-0.11	$+0.38$	$+2.38$
COOH	$+0.728$			$+2.94$
COOEt	$+0.678$	$+0.11$	$+0.32$	$+1.99$
$COCH_3$	$+0.874$	$+0.15$	$+0.28$	$+1.65$
CF_3	$+0.74$	$+0.09$	$+0.41$	$+2.58$
CN	$+1.00$	$+0.10$	$+0.58$	$+3.64$
NO_2	$+1.27$	$+0.16$	$+0.63$	$+3.92$
$^+N(CH_3)_3$		0	$+0.86$	$+5.32$

electron-withdrawing groups. For instance, the nitro group has a σ_p value of 0.778, but for p-nitrophenol or p-nitroaniline a value of 1.27 should be used. This situation arises from the fact that in substituted anilines, for example, there is a strong interaction resonance involving a mesomeric electron-withdrawing substituent as in p-nitroaniline.

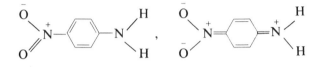

Since this type of resonance interaction is insignificant in similarly substituted benzoic acids, the respective substituent constants do not reflect this factor. These dual sets of σ constants for the mesomeric electron-withdrawing groups immediately drew attention to the sensitivity of σ constants to resonance, temperature, solvation, and other factors. As a result, it has been convenient to recognize three major electrical effects as contributors to inherent σ values: (i) induction, I; (ii) a polar effect of the resonance between the substituent and the ring, designated R; and (iii) the effect of resonance between the substituent and the reaction center. This view has led to the development of induction substituent constants σ_I, resonance substituent constants σ_R^0, and special substituent constants for electrophilic or nucleophilic reactions, σ^+ and σ^-, respectively.

4.11.2. ELECTROPHILIC AND NUCLEOPHILIC SUBSTITUENT CONSTANTS

In electrophilic aromatic substitution reactions or reactions involving an electron-deficient side-chain, groups which are electron-donating by resonance (designated $-R$ groups) are better suppliers of electrons than would be indicated by the Hammett σ constant, and this can be attributed to resonance stabilization of the transition states:

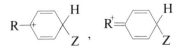

Resonance stabilization of
transition state in
electrophilic substitution

[289] H. C. Brown and Y. Okamoto, *J. Am. Chem. Soc.*, **79**, 1913 (1957); *J. Org. Chem.*, **22**, 485 (1957).

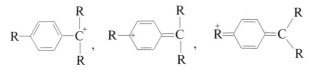

Resonance stabilization of
electron-deficient side-chain
transition state

It was observed by several authors that the Hammett equation holds well for these electrophilic reactions for *meta* derivatives, where such resonance effects are negligible, but not for *para* derivatives. Therefore, Brown[289] used the Hammett equation for the solvolysis of aryldimethylcarbinyl chlorides for *meta* derivatives to obtain the reaction constant ρ. Then, using this constant in a modified Hammett equation,

$$\log k/k_0 = \rho \sigma^+ \tag{4-11}$$

where σ^+ represents substituent constants for electrophilic reactions, he calculated σ^+ for *para* substituents using the observed rate data and ρ obtained with the *meta* derivatives. These constants have been listed in Table 4.23. It will be noted that there is a large difference between σ and σ^+ for $-R$ groups, such as the OCH_3 group, which exhibit large resonance interaction with an electron-deficient *para* position. On the other hand, the difference is essentially zero for the NO_2 group because there is no such resonance involving a $+R$ group (one whose resonance is electron-withdrawing).

It is easy to see that the difference $\Delta\sigma_R^+ = (\sigma^+ - \sigma)$ should vary with the electron demand at the reaction center. In order to correct for this variability, Eq. (4-11) has been modified to (4-12),[291]

$$\log k/k_0 = \rho(\sigma + r\,\Delta\sigma_R^+) \tag{4-12}$$

where σ and σ^+ are the Hammett and Brown substituent constants, respectively, $\Delta\sigma_R^+ = \sigma^+ - \sigma$, r is a constant which adjusts for the resonance interaction of the substituent with the reaction center, and ρ is the reaction constant identified with ρ_m. Equations (4-10) and (4-11) are in satisfactory accord for reactions having r values within the range 0.7 to 1.3. However, Eq. (4-12) gives a better fit for reactions with small (ca. 0.4) or large (ca. 2.0) r values.[291]

With essentially an analogous approach, nucleophilic substituent constants have been developed[290,292] and some values are listed in Table 4.23.

[290] J. Miller, *Australian J. Chem.*, **9**, 61 (1956).
[291] Y. Yukawa and Y. Tsuno, *Bull. Chem. Soc. Japan*, **32**, 971 (1959).
[292] H. H. Jaffe, *Chem. Revs.*, **53**, 191 (1953).

4.11.3. INDUCTIVE AND RESONANCE SUBSTITUENT CONSTANTS

The application of the Hammett equation, including the use of appropriate electrophilic or nucleophilic substituent constants, allows the semiquantitative correlation of thousands of rate and equilibrium data as well as many physical properties (to be discussed presently). However, the precision considering all applications, is estimated to be only about ± 15 per cent.[292]   The precision has been markedly improved by various innovations,[293] among which the most common technique is to make some type of adjustment for additive polar and resonance contributions.[295]

A study was made of the reactivities of substituted bicyclo [2.2.2]octane-1-carboxylic acids and esters (LXXXIII) in which it was found that the substituent group X clearly has a profound influence on the reactivity of the COOH or COOR group.[294]   This influence can only be exerted through induction and can provide a measure of the contribution of induction to the Hammett σ constant. The relative orders of the effects of various substituents X on three types of reactions of COOR were fairly closely the same, which means that a Hammett-type treatment may be used. An equation similar to (4-10) can be written

$$\log k/k_0 = \sigma'\rho' \tag{4-13}$$

in which the primed constants refer to the bicyclooctane system. It was observed that in the same reaction medium, ρ' is the same as ρ for ionization of benzoic acids. Hence, from the $\log k/k_0$ data and ρ' already set, σ' values can be computed. Some values can be compared with the respective *para* σ constants (σ_p).

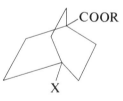

LXXXIII

Group	σ'	σ_p
H	0	0
OH	0.283	-0.37
COOEt	0.297	0.45
Br	0.454	0.232
CN	0.579	0.660

[293] J. Hine, *J. Am. Chem. Soc.*, **82**, 4877 (1960).
[294] J. D. Roberts and W. T. Moreland, Jr., *J. Am. Chem. Soc.*, **75**, 2167 (1953).

Thus, the σ_p values for the *meta* directing groups (COOEt and CN) are larger than the σ' values because the former reflect resonance and inductive effects, both of which pull electrons from the ring. In contrast to this, the OH and Br substituents are electron-withdrawing by induction and electron-donating by resonance and therefore σ_p is smaller than σ'.

The σ' values, then, may be taken as a measure of the contribution of induction to the Hammett σ constant. Later, Taft noted that there is a constant ratio of σ' for a group X to his *polar* substituent constant σ^* for a group XCH_2 (to be discussed presently) which is obtained from the relative rates of hydrolysis of aliphatic esters.[295] Since σ^* had been determined for many groups, this provided a means of computing σ' values for a much larger number of groups than the four above. This gave what might be called the inductive substituent constant σ_I as determined from the aliphatic series.

σ_I may also be determined from a series of aromatic compounds. The chemical shifts of F^{19} in *m*-substituted fluorobenzenes produced by the shielding effects of the *meta* substituents is precisely correlated with σ_I values by the relationship

$$\sigma_I = \frac{\delta_m^F + 0.05}{0.61}$$

in which δ_m^F are the respective chemical shifts.[296] A comparison of the two sets of σ_I values is made in Table 4.24. The average deviation of the two series is ± 0.03 units and roughly random. This close agreement between the σ_I values obtained by two different methods lends support to the reliability of σ_I values for assessing the inductive effects of substituents. At the same time, it reveals the limitation of precision of this treatment, for it implies that the inductive effects at the *meta* and *para* positions are equal. Data from different sources suggest that this is approximately the case,[297] although there are opposing views.[298]

The Hammett equation can be expressed as (4-14), in which the regular Hammett σ constant is equal to $\sigma_I + \sigma_R$, induction and resonance substitu-

$$\log k/k_0 = (\sigma_I + \sigma_R)\rho \qquad (4\text{-}14)$$

ent constants, respectively. σ_R can be obtained separately for the *para* and *meta* positions,

[295] R. W. Taft, Jr., *Steric Effects in Organic Chemistry*, ed. M. S. Newman (New York: Wiley, 1956), chap. 13.

[296] R. W. Taft, Jr., and I. C. Lewis, *J. Am. Chem. Soc.*, **81**, 5343 (1959).

[297] *Ibid.*, fn. 9.

[298] C. K. Ingold, *Structure and Mechanism in Organic Chemistry* (Ithaca, N.Y.: Cornell U.P., 1953), chap. 6.

Table 4.24. COMPARISON OF INDUCTIVE SUBSTITUENT CONSTANTS [296]

Substituent	σ_I Aliphatic series	σ_I F^{19} n.m.r. spectra
CH_3	−0.05	−0.09
NH_2	+0.10	+0.11
OH	+0.25	+0.23
OCH_3	+0.25	+0.26
CH_3CO	+0.28	+0.26
CF_3	+0.41	+0.43
Br	+0.45	+0.44
Cl	+0.47	+0.43
F	+0.52	+0.58
CN	+0.58	+0.58
NO_2	+0.63	+0.63

$$\sigma_R^p = \sigma_p - \sigma_I \qquad\qquad \sigma_R^m = \sigma_m - \sigma_I$$

para   *meta*

for which it is assumed that σ_I is the same for the two positions. A comparison of such values is made for a number of groups in Table 4.25. It is readily noticed that substituents even in the *meta* position exert a small resonance effect on the reaction site Z by a relayed electrostatic force from

para   *meta*

the charges imposed at the *ortho* position through resonance of the substituent and the ring. This polar effect of resonance σ_R is greater from the *para* position, of course, because the *para* group produces a change in charge density at the carbon to which Z is attached whereas this carbon is one carbon away from Z in the case of a *meta* substituent. There is almost a constant ratio of 3:1. Nevertheless, it is significant that σ_R for *meta* groups is not zero.

The σ_R and σ_I constants provide support for several deductions made from other data and expressed elsewhere in this book. For example, the resonance and inductive effects are in opposite directions (σ_R and σ_I are of opposite signs) for the halogens, OH, OR, and NH_2 groups, in the same

[299] R. W. Taft, Jr., S. Ehrenson, I. C. Lewis, and R. E. Glick, *J. Am. Chem. Soc.,* **81,** 5352 (1959).

Table 4.25.[300]

Group	$\sigma_R^p = \sigma_p - \sigma_I$	$\sigma_R^m = \sigma_m - \sigma_I$
NH_2	-0.76	-0.25
OH	-0.60	-0.17
OCH_3	-0.51	-0.17
F	-0.44	-0.17
Cl	-0.24	-0.10
Br	-0.22	-0.06
I	-0.11	-0.04
CH_3	-0.11	-0.02
t-Bu	-0.09	-0.04
H	0	0
COOEt	$+0.11$	$+0.04$
$COCH_3$	$+0.15$	$+0.07$
CN	$+0.10$	$+0.04$
CF_3	$+0.09$	$+0.01$
NO_2	$+0.16$	$+0.08$

direction towards the ring for alkyl groups, and in the same direction but away from the ring for the NO_2, COOEt, $COCH_3$, CF_3, and CN groups (compare Sec. 4.7). Also, the σ_R values for the halogens indicate that in the absence of strong electron-donating groups situated *para* to the halogen, the electron-donating resonance of the halogens decreases in the order F > Cl > Br > I (see Sec. 4.10).

Accordingly, one may separate the electrical influence of substituents as expressed by the Hammett equation into an induction and a resonance parameter, I and R, respectively; e.g., $\log k/k_0 = I + R$. The I parameter correlates precisely with observed data and can be expressed as

$$I = \sigma_I \rho \qquad (4\text{-}15)$$

but R is greatly influenced by the nature of the reaction and the substituent. This limits the generality of the relationship $\log k/k_0 = R + I$. However, there is a select group of rate and equilibrium reactions for which it is very precise.[296] These are reactions in which (i) there is essentially no resonance between the substituent and the reaction center, and (ii) the first atom of the side chain of the reaction site does not bear a formal charge and thereby does not produce any significant polarization of the substituent.[299] For these specific reactions, one may write Eq. (4-16), in which

$$\log k/k_0 = (\sigma_I + \sigma_R^0)\rho \qquad (4\text{-}16)$$

σ_R^0 is a substituent constant reflecting the resonance interaction of the substituent with the ring. σ_R^0 values are given in Table 4.26 for some $-R$

[300] R. W. Taft, Jr., N. C. Deno, and P. S. Skell, *Ann. Rev. Phys. Chem.*, **9**, 287 (1958).

groups. This same sequence of resonance parameters is observed for the quantity $(\delta_p^F - \delta_m^F)$ for these groups, where δ_p^F and δ_m^F are the chemical shifts of the n.m.r. F^{19} signals in the respective fluorobenzenes. These $(\delta_p^F - \delta_m^F)$ differences may be taken as a measure of the R effects of the substituents because even if the I effects at the *para* and *meta* positions are not equal, δ_p^F values are so much larger than δ_m^F values that the deviations from equality of I effects at the two positions will not alter the order of $(\delta_p^F - \delta_m^F)$ values.

Table 4.26. σ_R^0 VALUES FOR SOME $-R$ GROUPS[299]

Substituent	σ_R^0	$(\delta_p^F - \delta_m^F)$
$N(CH_3)_2$	-0.54	-1.69
NH_2	-0.48	-1.43
OCH_3	-0.41	-1.26
OH	-0.40	-1.17
F	-0.35	-0.97
Cl	-0.20	-0.51
Br	-0.19	-0.47
I	-0.12	-0.38
CH_3	-0.10	-0.42
H	0	0

Consequently, the data in Table 4.26 provide two parallel measures of the magnitude of the resonance interaction of $-R$ groups. They show, for example, that qualitatively one may say that ground-state resonance for these groups is appreciable only for the $N(CH_3)_2$, NH_2, OH, and OR groups and possibly the F atom. This substantiates, for instance, the conclusion reached from bond-distance data that ground-state resonance is appreciable in aniline but negligible in nitrobenzene (Sec. 1.2.9). There, it was shown that C—N bond contraction from resonance is significant in aniline but very slight in nitrobenzene.

The availability of σ_I and σ_R values allows a correlation of properties with much better precision than is possible with σ, σ^+, or σ^- values. For example, the proton shielding parameters for substituted benzenes do not correlate well with the latter constants[301,302] but are precisely given by relationships of the form:[299,302]

$$\delta^H = \alpha\sigma_I + \beta\sigma_R + C$$

where α, β, and C are constants.

[301] H. Spiesecke and W. G. Schneider, *J. Chem. Phys.*, **35**, 731 (1961).
[302] R. R. Fraser, *Can. J. Chem.*, **38**, 2226 (1960).

4.11.4. POLAR SUBSTITUENT CONSTANTS

Before discussing some of the applications of Hammett-type substituent constants, another type of group constant should be taken up. The transition states for acid- and base-catalyzed hydrolyses of ethyl esters are thought to resemble the following structures: [303]

in acid   in base

The principal difference in spatial relations in these two structures is that from two protons, and since the reacting carbon is saturated, there is no resonance interaction between this carbon and the substituent R. Therefore, the only property of two different R groups by which they will have different stabilizing effects on the transition states will be their electronegativities. Accordingly, the relative rates of hydrolysis of substituted ethyl esters, R—COOEt, can be used to provide a measure of the inductive effects of the respective R groups. For this purpose, Taft[295] developed the equation

$$\log (k/k_0)_B - \log (k/k_0)_A = 2.48\,\sigma^* \qquad (4\text{-}17)$$

in which k and k_0 are the rate constants for hydrolysis of the esters RCOOEt and CH_3COOEt, respectively, the subscripts B and A refer to basic and acidic conditions, and σ^* is the *polar substituent constant* for the group R. Thus, σ^* for the CH_3 group is arbitrarily set $= 0$. Values of σ^* for some groups of interest are given in Table 4.23.

The polar substituent constants reflect only inductive effects and are compared with other measures of electronegativity in Table 2.7. It is of interest, for instance, that σ^* values reveal that the inductive effect falls off by about one-third across each C—C bond. E.g.,

	CF_3	CF_3CH_2	$CF_3CH_2CH_2$	$CF_3CH_2CH_2CH_2$
$\sigma^* =$	2.7	0.92	0.32	0.12

	ϕ	ϕCH_2	ϕCH_2CH_2	$\phi CH_2CH_2CH_2$
$\sigma^* =$	0.60	0.215	0.080	0.02

[303] Cf. F. Becker, Z. *Naturforschung,* **16b,** 236 (1961), for pertinent references.

4.11.5 APPLICATIONS OF HAMMETT-TYPE RELATIONSHIPS

Now, in Table 4.23 there is a set of substituent constants to provide fairly precise measures of the electrical effects of substituents on the reactivity of nuclear carbon atoms or on side chains in the *meta* and *para* positions of the benzene ring. From a casual inspection of Table 4.23 it can be seen that the substituent constants are positive for electron-withdrawing groups and negative for electron-donating groups. Also, σ_m is more positive (i.e., less negative) than σ_p for *o,p*-directing groups while the reverse is true for *m*-directing groups. This is in accord with the observations that the halogens and the $CH{=}CH{-}NO_2$ group are ring-deactivating for electrophilic substitution (that is, they lower the electron density of the ring) but are *o,p*-directing. Of course, values are known for many more substituents, and only the more common ones are included in Table 4.23.

It is recognized that the Hammett equation (4-10) is very general and not very exact.[304] The σ and ρ terms are not true constants, and are affected by structural parameters as well as experimental conditions.[292] However, the precision can be improved by the modifications discussed above.

It should be pointed out here that several modified and special extensions of the Hammett approach have been used.[305] For examples, σ constants have been developed for other aromatic nuclei[306] as well as for aliphatic compounds,[307] and constants have been established to reflect steric effects.[308,309] For illustration, the rates of hydrolysis of *m*- and *p*-substituted alkyl benzoates can be expressed quantitatively by the equation

$$\log k = 0.174 + 2.22\sigma + 1.53\sigma^* + 0.668E_s$$

where σ is the Hammett substituent constant and σ^* and E_s are the polar and steric substituent constants for the alkyl groups.[310] The additive effects of more than one group in a single ring are generally expressible by a summation of the appropriate substituent constants,[311] except where there are

[304] H. V. Bekkum, P. E. Verkade, and B. M. Wepster, *Rec. trav. chim.,* **78**, 815 (1959); J. Hine, *J. Am. Chem. Soc.,* **81**, 1126 (1959).

[305] S. Winstein, E. Grunwald, and H. W. Jones, *J. Am. Chem. Soc.,* **73**, 2700 (1951); **70**, 846 (1948); S. I. Miller, *J. Am. Chem. Soc.,* **81**, 101 (1959); L. Wilputte-Steinert, P. J. C. Fierens, and H. Hannaert, *Bull. soc. chim. Belges,* **64**, 628 (1955).

[306] C. C. Price and R. H. Michel, *J. Am. Chem. Soc.,* **74**, 3652 (1952); H. H. Jaffe and G. O. Doak, *J. Am. Chem. Soc.,* **77**, 4441 (1955); M. S. Melzer, *J. Org. Chem.,* **27**, 496 (1962).

[307] Cf. references cited by M. Charton, *J. Org. Chem.,* **26**, 735 (1961).

[308] W. A. Pavelich and R. W. Taft, Jr., *J. Am. Chem. Soc.,* **79**, 4935 (1957).

[309] C. K. Hancock, E. A. Meyers, and B. J. Yager, *J. Am. Chem. Soc.,* **83**, 4211 (1961).

[310] C. K. Hancock and C. P. Falls, *J. Am. Chem. Soc.,* **83**, 4214 (1961).

[311] H. H. Jaffe, *Chem. Revs.,* **53**, 250 (1953); C. K. Hancock, R. F. Gilby, Jr., and J. S. Westmoreland, *J. Am. Chem. Soc.,* **79**, 1917 (1957); J. Weinstein and E. McIninch, *J. Am. Chem. Soc.,* **82**, 6064 (1960); H. Kwart and M. M. Baevsky, *J. Am. Chem. Soc.,* **80**, 580 (1958); P. J. Bray and R. G. Barnes, *J. Chem. Phys.,* **27**, 551 (1957).

strong interactions between adjacent groups such as strong dipole-dipole repulsion between two adjacent chlorine atoms.[312]

Not only does the Hammett approach allow the storage of a vast amount of data and the empirical prediction of other data, but it can be used in a qualitative fashion for the study of reaction mechanisms. Some of these applications of the Hammett-type equations can now be considered briefly.

Information about reaction mechanisms can be obtained from the Hammett reaction constant and also from the knowledge of which set of substituent constants σ, σ^+, or σ^-, best fits the data. For illustration, in the decomposition of alkyl chlorocarbonates to alkyl chlorides and CO_2,

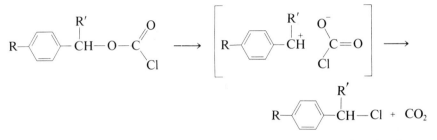

the asymmetric carbon retains its configuration, and a carbonium ion intermediate might not be ascribed for this reaction. However, the reaction rates for various substituted phenyl derivatives follow σ^+ rather than σ, which fact lends support to a carbonium ion (ion-pair) intermediate.[313,321]

It has been proposed that the Hammett reaction constant ρ is a measure of the difference in charge at the reaction site between that in the transition state and the reactant.[314] The greater is the increase in positive charge at the reaction site in the transition state, the more will electron-donating substituents aid the reaction, or the greater is the decrease in positive charge the more will electron-withdrawing groups aid the reaction.[322] Or, as stated previously, positive ρ constants imply an increase in negative charge at the reaction site in the transition state. There is a continuous spectrum of Hammett reaction constants from highly negative values for Friedel-Crafts reactions of t-halides with benzene to highly positive constants for reactions of aryl halides with hydroxide ion, and there is no apparent grouping of ρ values into categories that correspond to different kinds of reaction mechanisms.[314] Nevertheless, ρ constants can provide information about reaction mechanisms. For example, 9-decalyl hydroperoxide benzoates (LXXXIV) rearrange to the corresponding 1-benzoyloxy-1,6-epoxycyclo-decane (LXXXV) upon standing in ionizing solvents. The relative rates of

[312] J. G. Mather and J. Shorter, *J. Chem. Soc.*, 4744 (1961).
[313] Y. Okamoto and H. C. Brown, *J. Org. Chem.*, **22**, 485 (1957).
[314] C. G. Swain and W. P. Langsdorf, Jr., *J. Am. Chem. Soc.*, **73**, 2813 (1951).

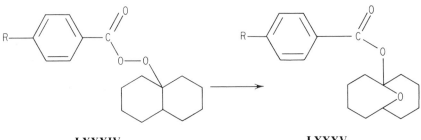

LXXXIV   **LXXXV**

reaction follow the Hammett equation with a reaction constant ρ = 1.34. The sign and size of ρ in this case supports an ionic rather than free radical mechanism for the reaction.[315]

In another case, on the basis that the *ortho*-Claisen rearrangement of cinnamyl-aryl ethers and allyl phenyl ethers is best correlated with σ^+ and a negative ρ, it was concluded that the transition state must involve a depletion of electrons in the aryl and allyl portions of the molecules.[316]

The magnitude of ρ has been used as a measure of the conjugative transmission of side chains. For example, under approximately identical conditions, the ρ constant for dissociation of substituted *trans*-cinnamic acids, β-phenylpropionic acids, and *trans*-2-phenylcyclopropane carboxylic acids are +0.466, +0.212, and +0.182, respectively. Since ρ for the cyclopropane acids is closer to that of the phenylpropionic acids, it was concluded that the cyclopropane ring does not exhibit any conjugative ability in the ground state.[317]

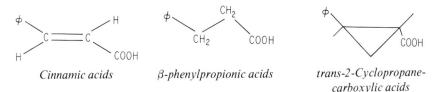

   Cinnamic acids   *β-phenylpropionic acids*   *trans-2-Cyclopropane-*
                                                                carboxylic acids

The polar substituent constant has been used, too, for inference about the mechanism of a reaction. For instance, it has been proposed that steric effects play a prominent role in the hydrolysis of phosphate esters of the type $(RO)_2$—$PO \cdot O \cdot PO$—$(OR)_2$, because rates of hydrolysis of unsymmetrical esters could not be predicted from the rates of symmetrical esters. However, it was later shown that the rates of all of the esters are well correlated with $\Sigma\sigma^*$ of the respective R groups.[318] This indicates that, indeed,

---

[315] P. D. Bartlett and J. L. Kice, *J. Am. Chem. Soc.,* **75,** 5591 (1953).

[316] W. N. White and W. K. Fife, *J. Am. Chem. Soc.,* **83,** 3846 (1961).

[317] E. N. Trachtenberg and G. Odian, *J. Am. Chem. Soc.,* **80,** 4018 (1958).

[318] F. H. Brock, *J. Org. Chem.,* **22,** 1114 (1957).

the reaction is influenced chiefly by inductive and not steric effects, and the correlation with σ^* provides the basis for a more probable mechanism.

Not only can Hammett-type substituent and reaction constants be used as diagnostic tools for the study of reaction mechanisms but they can provide a wide variety of information about the electronic properties of organic groups. For example, substituent constants are used to detect conjugative ability of a given group. That is, if σ_p for a group is larger in the phenol than benzoic acid series, then the group undergoes an electron-withdrawing resonance interaction with the OH group ($+R$), or if σ_p is larger for electrophilic substitution than for the ionization of benzoic acid, then it is capable of electron-donating resonance ($-R$).[319] In this way, for instance, it was shown that CH_3S exhibits a small $-R$ effect.[320] Similarly, it was shown that the Me_3Si group exhibits a weak electron-releasing inductive effect to the phenyl ring, but with a strong $+R$ group in the *para* position, Me_3Si becomes a $-R$ group by making use of the d orbitals of silicon.[321]

In addition to serving as an index of the resonance interaction of groups attached to a benzene ring, the use of σ_R and σ_I constants can reveal the relative importance of induction and resonance effects on certain properties. For illustration, the rates of ionization of substituted methanes

$$R-CH_3 + H_2O \rightleftharpoons RCH_2^- + H_3O^+$$

can be expressed fairly precisely by the equation[322]

$$\log k_r = 26\sigma_R^- + 4\Sigma\sigma_I - 24.8 + \log n_H \qquad (4\text{-}18)$$

where k_r is the rate constant for the respective substituted methane, $\sigma_R^- = \sigma^- - \sigma_I$ with the latter two constants having the usual connotation, and n_H is a statistical correction for the number of ionizable hydrogen atoms in a polysubstituted methane. The larger coefficient for the resonance parameter indicates that resonance stabilization of the ion must be the major factor in facilitating ionization. In contrast to this, the ΔpK_a's of m-substituted anilines are precisely expressed by the equation

$$\Delta pK_a = (1.05\sigma_I + 0.33\sigma_R)\rho$$

where ΔpK_a is the difference in pK_a of the substituted and unsubstituted aniline in aqueous solution and ρ is the slope when pK_a is plotted against the quantity in parenthesis.[323] In this case, the inductive effect of the substituent has the major influence on ΔpK_a.

[319] The relationship is not quantitative. Cf. L. D. Freedman and G. O. Doak, *J. Org. Chem.*, **21**, 811 (1956).

[320] F. G. Bordwell and P. J. Boutan, *J. Am. Chem. Soc.*, **78**, 87 (1956).

[321] R. A. Benkeser and H. R. Krysiak, *J. Am. Chem. Soc.*, **75**, 2421 (1953).

[322] R. W. Taft, Jr., *J. Am. Chem. Soc.*, **79**, 5075 (1957).

[323] A. Bryson, *J. Am. Chem. Soc.*, **82**, 4867 (1960).

As another illustration of the use of substituent constants, aside from the correlation of most physical properties to be discussed in the next section, it was shown that the effects of substituents in one ring of ferrocene on the dissociation of a COOH group in the other ring

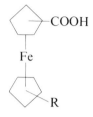

are primarily inductive with little or no interannular resonance effect.[324] That is, it was found that a poor correlation exists between the ionization constants of the ferrocene carboxylic acids and Hammett σ constants, but there is an excellent agreement with polar substituent constants σ^*. In another case, it was observed that the λ_m of 2,4-dinitrophenylhydrazones of substituted acetophenones undergoes a bathochromic shift when measured in chloroform and basic chloroform solution and the difference, expressed as

$$\Delta\nu = \frac{1}{\lambda_m} - \frac{1}{\lambda'_m}$$

where λ_m and λ'_m refer to $CHCl_3$ and basic $CHCl_3$ solutions, respectively, is precisely correlated by the equation

$$\Delta\nu = 4620 + 2330\sigma + 520\sigma^*$$

This relationship holds only for the *syn* isomers, and deviations may be used as evidence for an *anti* structure.[325]

4.11.6. CORRELATIONS OF PHYSICAL PROPERTIES WITH SUBSTITUENT CONSTANTS

The success of the Hammett approach for generalizing chemical reactivities and equilibria soon led to its application to physical properties. It is not surprising to find parallel correlations since chemical and physical properties can be interpreted in terms of the same parameters (resonance, induction, polarization, etc.). The use of Hammett-type relationships has become as prevalent for correlating physical properties as chemical rates and equilibria. This treatment has been applied to almost every measured physical property of benzene derivatives, including infrared, ultraviolet and n.m.r. spectra, quadrupole resonance,[326] dipole moments, electronegativi-

[324] R. A. Benkeser and L. W. Hall, Jr., Air Force OSR report, Purdue University, 1959.
[325] L. E. Scoggins and C. K. Hancock, *J. Org. Chem.*, **26**, 3490 (1961).
[326] P. J. Bray and R. G. Barnes, *J. Chem. Phys.*, **27**, 551 (1957).

ties, polarographic redox potentials, dissociations in various media, intramolecular H bonding,[327] ionization potentials,[328] and others. A few examples can be given here for illustration.

Infrared spectra. The infrared absorption frequency for a bond A—B in R—A—B is directly related to the force constant of the bond, and the band intensity is proportional to the change in ionic character of the bond during excitation. Both spectral characteristics, then, are affected by the electronegativity of R. With increasing electronegativity of R, the A—B bond force constant and the polar character of A increase, and there is an accompanying increase in infrared frequency and intensity. Since Hammett constants reflect largely the polar effect (inductive and polar effect of resonance) of substituents, it follows that there should be a fairly good correlation as expressed by the equation

$$\log A/A_0 = k\sigma \qquad (4\text{-}19)$$

where A and A_0 are the integrated intensities of the infrared absorption bands for a given bond A—B in p- or m-R—C_6H_4—A—B, σ are the Hammett substituent constants, and k is the slope of the line when $\log A/A_0$ is plotted against σ. This type of study has been made on several classes of aromatics, such as the phenols, anilines, acetophenones, aldehydes, benzonitriles, methyl benzoates, and others.[329] Qualitative agreement is observed in all cases. That is, increased polar character of the compounds as a result of induction, resonance, and polarization is attended by greater absorption intensity. However, there is considerable scatter in some cases, which is probably due to variable resonance contributions involving the substituents and the infrared absorbing group. Measurements on the benzonitriles included *ortho* substituted isomers, and it was found that the data for *ortho* substituents fell on the same line as that for the *meta* and *para* derivatives.[330] This implied that there is no steric effect involved, and provided a means of determining *ortho* substituent constants.

Since the polar effect of groups on the OH infrared band in alcohols involves only induction and no resonance, σ^* is to be used in Eq. (4-19) in place of σ.[331]

Infrared *frequencies* also conform fairly well to a Hammett-type equa-

[327] A. W. Baker and A. T. Shulgin, *J. Am. Chem. Soc.*, **81**, 1523 (1959); G. M. Badger and A. G. Moritz, *J. Chem. Soc.*, 3437 (1958).

[328] J. J. Kaufman and W. S. Koski, *J. Am. Chem. Soc.*, **82**, 3262 (1960).

[329] Cf. J. L. Mateos, R. Cetina, E. Olivera, and S. Meza, *J. Org. Chem.*, **26**, 2494 (1961) for earlier references; M. Oki and M. Hirota, *Spectrochim. Acta*, **17**, 583 (1961); A. Cabana, *et al., J. Phys. Chem.*, **64**, 1941 (1960); C. N. R. Rao and R. Venkalaraghavan, *Can. J. Chem.*, **39**, 1757 (1961).

[330] H. W. Thompson and G. Steel, *Trans. Faraday Soc.*, **52**, 1451 (1956).

[331] T. L. Brown and M. T. Rogers, *J. Am. Chem. Soc.*, **79**, 577 (1957).

tion such as

$$\log \nu/\nu_0 = k\sigma \tag{4-20}$$

where ν and ν_0 are the band frequencies for the substituted and parent compound, σ is the Hammett substituent constant, and k is the slope of the line when $\log \nu/\nu_0$ is plotted against σ. This has been observed for the *para* C—H in monosubstituted benzenes,[342] (Table 4.27), for the C≡N bond in substituted benzonitriles,[330] the C=O bond in substituted acetophenones,[332] the N—H bond of substituted anilines,[336] and for the asymmetric stretching vibration of the NO_2 group in substituted nitrobenzenes.[335] Again, σ^* constants are to be used for aliphatic series.[333] Thus, infrared frequencies for two such series can be calculated quite precisely by the equations:[334]

$$\nu_{CO} = 1690 + 52.56\sigma^* \quad \text{for R—CO—CH}_3$$

$$\nu_{NO} = 1500 + 110.1\sigma^* \quad \text{for R—N=O}$$

Numerous other examples of such correlations are reported in the literature.[292]

N.M.R. spectra. Another physical property which provides a good index of the ground-state electrical effects of substituents transmitted to the *meta* or *para* positions of a substituted benzene is the n.m.r. spectrum. (See also Sec. 4.13.) Owing to "field" effects and magnetic anisotropy, such investigations are best made with *meta* or *para* substituents, and several such studies have been made.[299,301,337-340] In order to verify that the effects transmitted at the *para* position (H or substituent) correspond to changes in electron density at the *para* carbon atom, the n.m.r. proton chemical shifts and also the C^{13} chemical shifts at the *para* position of the same molecules were measured for a series of monosubstituted benzenes.[301] These data are tabulated in Table 4.27. It can be seen that the correspondence between proton and C^{13} chemical shifts do not correlate well with Hammett constants[260] but they can be calculated precisely by expressions of the type, $\delta = \alpha\sigma_I + \beta\sigma_R$.[299,338]

[332] R. N. Jones, W. F. Forbes, and W. A. Mueller, *Can. J. Chem.*, **35**, 504 (1957).

[333] T. L. Brown, *J. Am. Chem. Soc.*, **80**, 3513 (1958).

[334] D. G. O'Sullivan and P. W. Sadler, *J. Chem. Soc.*, 4144 (1957).

[335] R. D. Kross and V. A. Fassel, *J. Am. Chem. Soc.*, **78**, 4225 (1956).

[336] E. V. Titov, *et al.*, *Chem. Abs.*, **55**, 20624d (1961).

[337] P. L. Corio and B. P. Dailey, *J. Am. Chem. Soc.*, **78**, 3043 (1956); P. Diehl, *Helv. Chim. Acta*, **44**, 829 (1961).

[338] P. C. Lauterbur, *J. Am. Chem. Soc.*, **83**, 1846 (1961); P. Diehl, *Helv. Chim. Acta*, **45**, 568 (1962).

[339] A. A. Bothner-By and R. E. Glick, *J. Chem. Phys.*, **26**, 1651 (1957).

[340] H. S. Gutowsky, D. W. McCall, B. R. McGarvey, and L. H. Meyer, *J. Am. Chem. Soc.*, **74**, 4809 (1952).

[341] L. Doub and J. M. Vandenbelt, *J. Am. Chem. Soc.*, **69**, 2714 (1947).

[342] E. D. Schmid and J. Bellanato, *Z. Elektrochem.*, **65**, 362 (1961).

Table 4.27. Physical Indexes of Electrical Effects of Substituents at *para* Positions in Substituted Benzenes

Substituent	Per cent *meta* in electrophilic nitration	Dipole moment of monosubstituted benzene[a]	N.M.R. C^{13} chemical shifts[b]	N.M.R. proton chemical shifts[c]	N.M.R. F^{19} chemical shifts[d]	Δλ first primary band[e]	Spectroscopic moment[f]	*para* ν_{C-H} stretch[342]
$N(CH_3)_2$	··	+1.6D	+11.8	+36.9	(−1.68)		34	3048
OH	··	−1.6	+9.5	+37.5	−1.08	7.0	··	3037
NH_2	··	+1.48	+8.1	+22.0	−1.41	26.5	31	
OCH_3	2.0	+1.35	+2.8		−1.15	13.5	7	3028
CH_3	4.4	+0.36	+4.4	+13.0	−0.54	3.0	21	3051
F	0.5	−1.59	+2.0	+7.0	−0.68		6	3068
Cl	0.9	−1.70	+1.0	+1.8	−0.32	6.0	4	3069
Br	1.2	−1.73	+0.4	+2.0	−0.25	6.5	21	3068
I	2.1	−1.7			(−0.12)		0	
H	(40)	0	0	0	0	0	−28	
COOH	80.2	(−1.64)			+0.61	26.5		
COOEt	72	(−1.8)			+0.94	46.0		
CHO	79	−3.1	−6.0	−16.5	+0.66	42.0		
$COCH_3$	55	−3.0	−4.2		+0.99	20.5	−19	
CN	81	−4.39		−20.0	+0.97	65.0		3068
NO_2	93.3	−4.21	−6.0		+0.51		−15	3077
CF_3	99	(−2.6)						3076

[a] − indicates negative pole away from the ring. Values in parentheses for solution data.

[b] In cps at 60 Mc/sec relative to benzene at 5 mole per cent in cyclohexane.[301]

[c] In p.p.m. relative to benzene at 5 mole per cent in cyclohexane.[301]

[d] In dilute CCl_4 solution relative to fluorobenzene.[299] Values in parentheses from Ref. 340.

[e] Shift in mμ of 203-mμ band of benzene.[341]

[f] J. R. Platt, *J. Chem. Phys.*, **19**, 263 (1951).

Ultraviolet spectra. Since the positions of ultraviolet absorption bands are related to transitions to excited states, it is not surprising to find that λ_m values are not precisely correlated by Hammett σ constants. Neither are $\Delta\lambda$ values of monosubstituted benzenes closely related to σ_R constants, where $\Delta\lambda$ is the shift in the primary absorption band of a compound relative to the 203-mμ band of benzene, because σ_R constants reflect essentially only ground-state resonance. However, there is a fair correlation for p-disubstituted benzenes having substituents of opposite orienting character, i.e., o,p vs. m-directing. Thus, the relationship

$$\Delta\lambda = \rho\sigma + C \qquad (4\text{-}21)$$

where ρ is the slope of the line and C the intercept when $\Delta\lambda$ is plotted against the Hammett σ constants, was found to hold quite well for p-substituted nitrobenzenes, aryl azides and benzoic acids containing o,p-directing substituents, and for p-substituted phenols and anilines containing m-orienting substituents.[343] The halogens were exceptional, and it was found that better precision was observed when σ_R was substituted for σ in Eq. (4-21). This is not surprising, because in the case of such p-disubstituted benzenes, $\Delta\lambda$ is more related to the resonance interaction of the substituents than to their inductive effects.

Dipole moments and electronegativity. One of the strong arguments in support of the use of σ^* constants as measures of inductive effects of groups is the fact that dipole moments may be computed from σ^* constants in high precision. For example, the dipole moments of several aliphatic series can be calculated from the relationships:[254]

$$RCl: \quad \mu = -1.416\sigma^* + 1.823 \quad \text{debyes}$$

$$RCN: \quad \mu = -0.444\sigma^* + 3.51 \quad \text{debyes}$$

$$R_3N: \quad \mu = 0.53\Sigma\sigma^* + 0.92 \quad \text{debyes}$$

Consequently, σ^* serves as a good method of determining relative electronegativities of groups, and as such, was included in the section on group electronegativities (Sec. 2.2).

Correlations of dipole moments of mono- and disubstituted benzenes with substituent constants have lacked precision.[335,344,345] Plots of σ against μ or against log μ/μ_0 show considerable scatter, where μ and μ_0 are the dipole moments of the substituted and parent compounds.

[343] C. N. R. Rao, *Chem. and Ind.*, (London), 666 (1956); 1239 (1957).
[344] C. N. R. Rao, W. H. Wahl, and E. J. Williams, *Can. J. Chem.*, **35**, 1576 (1957).
[345] L. K. H. Van Beek, *Rec. trav. chim.*, **76**, 729 (1957).

Electroredox potentials.[346] It might be expected that the change in ease of oxidation or reduction of an atom attached to the benzene ring would be directly related to the change in electron density at the C_1 carbon atom brought about by a *meta* or *para* substituent, for redox potentials are merely measures of the energy required to add or remove an electron from the atom in point. Thus, it is no surprise to find good correlations of reduction potentials ($E_{1/2}$ values) with σ constants for substituted aryl ketones or their Schiff bases,[347] benzaldehydes,[347,351,353] nitrobenzenes,[348,349] iodobenzenes,[348] and ferrocenes,[350] and of the oxidation potentials with σ for substituted anilines.[352] The precision has been quite good considering the fact that the potentials are very sensitive to experimental conditions.[353]

Whereas ultraviolet light absorption amounts to shifting an electron from the highest occupied bonding orbital to the lowest unoccupied nonbonding orbital in the excited state, polarographic reduction has been visualized as the placement of an electron from an external system into this same unoccupied orbital in the excited state. Therefore, there should be a correlation between reduction potentials and the frequency of the longest-waved ultraviolet band.[354] Such a correlation has been observed between ν_{max} (corresponding to λ_{max}) and $E_{1/2}$ for substituted nitrosobenzenes.[355]

For aliphatic compounds, good correlations are observed between $E_{1/2}$ and σ^* constants. A variety of series have been examined and the applicability of the Taft constants appears to be quite general.

4.11.7. CONCLUSION

In Sec. 4.11 it has been shown that a wide variety of generalizations and predictions of chemical reactivity and physical properties of molecules can be made based on Hammett-type reaction and substituent constants. Furthermore, under suitable conditions, when biological activity in a given system is controlled by a single process, it is sometimes possible to correlate biological activity with substituent constants. For example, isatin catalyzes the dehydrogenation of amino acids, and not only is this activity well cor-

[346] S. Wawzonek, *Anal. Chem.*, **30**, 661 (1958).
[347] R. W. Brockman and D. E. Pearson, *J. Am. Chem. Soc.*, **74**, 4128 (1952).
[348] E. Gergely and T. Iredale, *J. Chem. Soc.*, 3226 (1953).
[349] A. R. Lawrence and L. N. Ferguson, *Nature*, **183**, 1469 (1959).
[350] O. E. Bublitz, G. Hoh, and T. Kuwana, *Chem. and Ind.* (London), 635 (1959).
[351] L. Holleck and H. Marsen, *Z. Elektrochem.*, **57**, 944 (1953).
[352] I. Fox, R. W. Taft, Jr., and J. M. Schempf, Technical Rept. No. 22 to ONR, Project No. NR055-328, Pennsylvania State University, 1959.
[353] R. M. Powers and R. A. Day, Jr., *J. Am. Chem. Soc.*, **80**, 808 (1958).
[354] D. Brück and G. Scheibe, *Z. Elektrochem.*, **61**, 901 (1957).
[355] L. Holleck and R. Schindler, *Z. Elektrochem.*, **60**, 1142 (1956).

related with Hammett σ constants but the infrared carbonyl stretching frequency also shows a parallel change with σ.[356]

4.12. Homoconjugation and nonclassical resonance

Throughout the text, resonance has involved π-π or σ-π conjugated systems, but in the past decade this conventional type of resonance has been supplemented in order to account for more recently observed phenomena. The concept of *neighboring group participation* or *anchimeric assistance*[357] is a familiar one in reaction mechanisms study,[358] whereby a nearby group, most often in the β position, facilitates a reaction by formation of a more or less stable intermediate identified with LXXXVI.

LXXXVI

When the intermediate is a carbonium ion, LXXXVII is then referred to as a nonclassical carbonium ion (LXXXVIII).

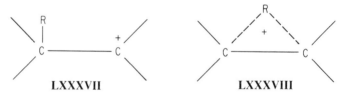

LXXXVII   LXXXVIII

The first of the nonclassical cations involving a neighboring olefinic group was that of the cholesteryl cation formed by ionization of the tosylate.[359]

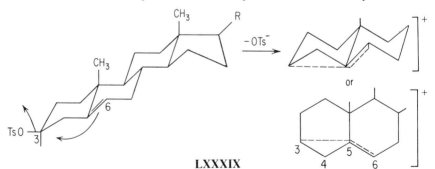

LXXXIX

[356]Cf. D. G. O'Sullivan and P. W. Sadler, *Archives Biochem. & Biophysics,* **66,** 243 (1957).
[357]S. Winstein, *et al., J. Am. Chem. Soc.,* **75,** 147 (1953).
[358]Cf. the excellent reviews by A. Streitwieser, Jr., *Chem. Revs.,* **56,** 571 (1956), and W. Lwowski, *Angew. Chem.,* **70,** 483 (1958).
[359]M. Simonetta and S. Winstein, *J. Am. Chem. Soc.,* **76,** 18 (1954).

In LXXXIX there is partial 3,5 bonding and weakened 5,6 bonding. This structure is based, among other considerations, on the enhanced rates of ionization of these derivatives, which is attributable to a delocalization of the positive charge in the transition state. The nonclassical ion also accounts for the observed reaction of the intermediate with nucleophilic reagents at C_6 or C_3 to yield products with overall retention of configuration from XC to XCI and XCII.[359] The allyl system XCIII (ion or free

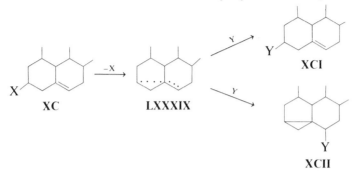

radical) is a classical one in resonance theory, and LXXXIX can be regarded as the next homolog with a methylene group inserted between the

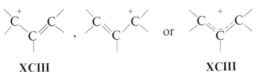

XCIII   XCIII

cationic center and the π bond. This analogy led to the designation of the latter system (XCIV) *homoallylic*.[359] The 1,3 interaction in the homoal-

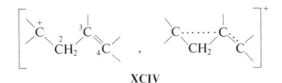

XCIV

lylic system can be considered as a delocalization of the 3,4-π-electron cloud into an available orbital on C_1 as pictured in XCV. Thus, with a

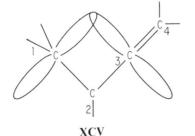

XCV

suitable geometry (more sigma than π overlap), there can be charge de-localization or resonance across a saturated group. This has been also observed in a number of bicyclic systems.[360,361] For example, with a norbornenyl bromobenzenesulfonate, the *exo* isomer (XCVI) reacts about 10^4 times as fast as the *endo* isomer (with the OBs group down instead of up).

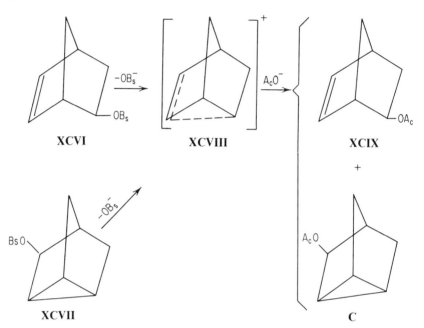

Also, XCVI gives a mixture of the *exo*-5-acetate (XCIX) *without* any *endo* and the nortricyclyl acetate (C). This same mixture can be obtained from the nortricyclyl bromobenzenesulfonate (XCVII). The enhanced reactivity of XCVI over that of the *endo* isomer is the result of anchimeric as-

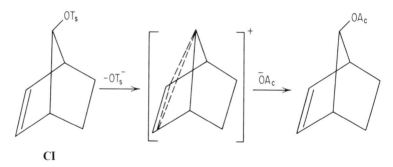

[360]S. Winstein, H. M. Walborsky, and K. Schreiber, *J. Am. Chem. Soc.,* **72**, 5795 (1950).
[361]S. Winstein, *et al., J. Am. Chem. Soc.,* **78**, 592 (1956), and earlier papers.

sistance from the *beta* π electrons facilitating the release of the OBs⁻ anion. In the *endo* isomer, the OBs group blocks this neighboring group effect. This anchimetric assistance via a nonclassical resonance hybrid is even greater in the *anti*-7-norbornenyl derivative (CI) as shown by acetolysis of the tosylate. The relative rates of acetolysis of these compounds are:

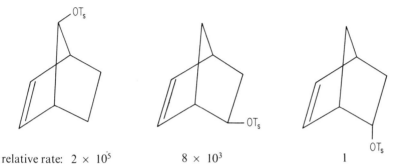

relative rate: 2×10^5 8×10^3 1

The anchimetric effect of the β π-electrons is further emphasized when the reactivities of the unsaturated and saturated compounds are compared, e.g.,

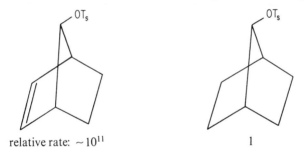

relative rate: $\sim 10^{11}$ 1

The restrictive geometry required for the homoallylic system is revealed by the fact that ions CII and CIII are individual ions. Solvolysis of CIV and CV yields different products, in which anchimetric assistance and stereospecific replacement are shown in each case but through the dis-

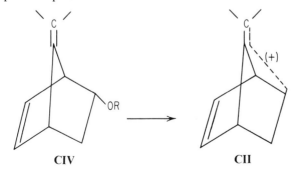

CIV   **CII**

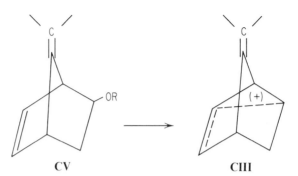

CV   CIII

tinctly different nonclassical ions CII and CIII, respectively.[362]   Thus, the
two homoallylic systems are cross conjugated and independent of each
other.

In order to have a molecule in which a symmetrical nonclassical carbonium ion might arise, the bicyclohexane derivative CVI was designed
and its synthesis worked out.[363]

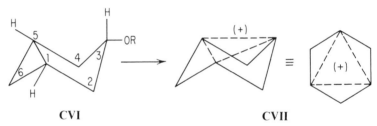

CVI   CVII

These 3-bicyclo[3.1.0]hexanol derivatives have a *chair* conformation which
gives the cyclopentane ring an *envelope* shape.   Thus, the group in the 3-
position can be *axial* or *equatorial.*

Three types of data support the idea that *cis*-3-bicyclo[3.1.0]hexyl
toluenesulfonate (CVIII) reacts via a nonclassical carbonium ion of type
CVII, whereas the *trans* isomer (CIX) does not.[363]   For illustration, it
was found that CVIII undergoes acetolysis about 30 times as fast as CIX,
and whereas CVIII gives a quantitative yield of almost pure *cis* product
(i.e., retention of configuration), CIX gives a *cis* product plus 33 per
cent olefin.   Secondly, the acetolysis of CIX showed no special salt effect
whereas CVIII exhibited a marked rate increase with the addition of salts.
This indicates that the transition state for CIX is not greatly more polar
than the reactant but the transition state for CVIII possesses considerably
more charge than the reactant.   Finally, when the 3-deuterated compounds
were prepared and acetolysis carried out, it was found that very little
scrambling of deuterium occurred with the *trans* isomer but with the *cis*

[362]C. H. DePuy, I. A. Ogawa, and J. C. McDaniel, *J. Am. Chem. Soc.,* **83,** 1668 (1961).
[363]S. Winstein and J. Sonnenberg, *J. Am. Chem. Soc.,* **83,** 3235 (1961).

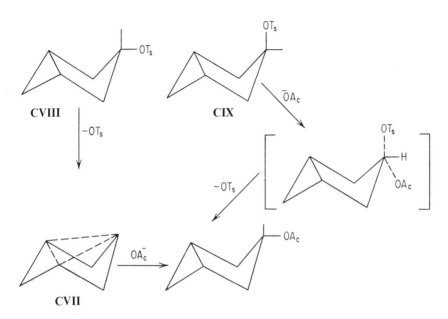

CVIII   **CIX**

CVII

compound, deuterium was equally distributed over carbon atoms 1, 3, and 5 in the product. These three types of experimental observations are in good accord with the reaction scheme shown above for CVIII and CIX. Because of the resemblance of CVII to the cyclopropenyl cation CX, the former ion has been called the trishomocyclopropenyl cation.[364] This, in

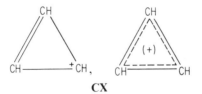

CX

turn, led to the notion that the trishomocyclopropenyl ion may be one of several aromatic homologs or "homoaromatic" systems in which methylene groups are added between each aromatic carbon atom (p. 440).[364] The syn-synthesis and the aromatic character of these higher homoaromatic systems remain to be shown. In the meantime, the number of other nonclassical carbonium ion intermediates produced continues to grow.[365] In at least one case, the carbonium ion is sufficiently stable to survive isolation. In the nonclassical ion (CXI), an orbital of C_2 can overlap with the π electron cloud of the C_6 : C_7 double bond when the ring function is *cis* but not in the *trans* isomer. Accordingly, it was observed that the *cis* phenyl carbinol

[364] S. Winstein and J. Sonnenberg, *J. Am. Chem. Soc.,* **83,** 3244 (1961).
[365] Cf. L. De Vries, *J. Am. Chem. Soc.,* **82,** 5242 (1960).

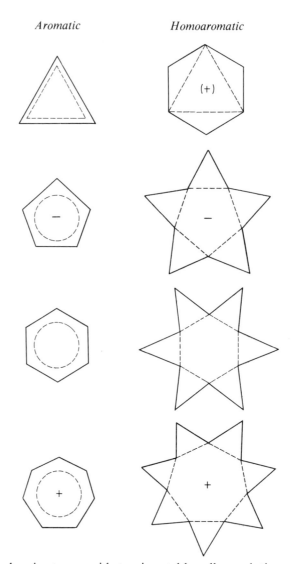

Aromatic   *Homoaromatic*

(CXII) dissolves in strong acids to give stable yellow solutions whereas the *trans* isomer does not.[366]   Presumably, the nonclassical ion (CXI), R = C_6H_5, is produced from the *cis* carbinol.   It has absorption bands in sulfuric acid at 386 and 427 mμ.   The chloride in benzene immediately precipitates AgCl and a yellow solid containing the perchlorate ion.   This solid is stable below $-40°$, and in 60 per cent sulfuric acid gives the same spectrum as CXII.   The *cis* hydrocarbon (CXIII) also dissolves in 60 per cent sulfuric acid to give the stable nonclassical ion (CXI).

[366]G. Leal and R. Pettit, *J. Am. Chem. Soc.*, **81**, 3160 (1959).

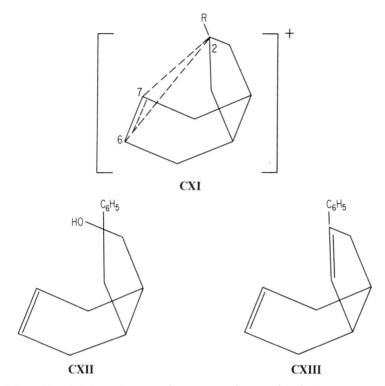

CXI

CXII   CXIII

Also, ultraviolet spectra reveal resonance interaction between separated but suitably oriented π-electron systems (cf Sec. 5.4.2(b)). For illustration, compounds of type CXIV–CXVII exhibit absorption bands in the 214–228 mμ region, typical of $\pi \rightarrow \pi$ transitions, and the carbonyl $n \rightarrow \pi^*$ band has a marked increase in intensity as a result of some mixing of the $\pi \rightarrow \pi$ and $n \rightarrow \pi^*$ transitions.[367] Furthermore, by increasing the electron-donor

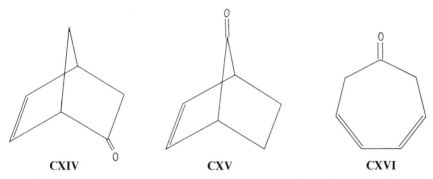

CXIV   CXV   CXVI

[367]Cf. R. C. Cookson, R. R. Hill, and J. Hudec, *Chem. and Ind.,* (London), 589 (1961); H. Labhart and G. Wagniere, *Helv. Chim. Acta,* **42,** 2219 (1959); J. Meinwald, *et al., J. Am. Chem. Soc.,* **77,** 4401 (1955).

ability of the donor group, as in CXVII, the $n \rightarrow \pi^*$ band undergoes an additional hyperchromic change. Thus, with $X=H$, CH_3, or OCH_3, the intensities of the $n \rightarrow \pi^*$ band ($\lambda \sim 330$ mμ) are 5150, 6250, and 7750, respectively.[368] Also, the $\pi \rightarrow \pi$ band undergoes the usual bathochromic shift with change of solvent from hydrocrabon to ethanol. These spectral characteristics are typical of the classically conjugated α,β-enone system. The respective saturated ketones do not have the $\pi \rightarrow \pi$ band nor an $n \rightarrow \pi^*$ band of enhanced intensity.

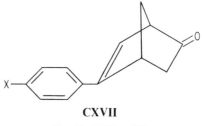

CXVII

$X=H, OCH_3, CH_3$

As noted elsewhere in this chapter, π-electron delocalization in the ground state is small for all except isovalence. This is also true for the nonconjugated chromophores. For example, the heat of hydrogenation of bicycloheptadiene (CXVIII) gives no indication of homoconjugation in the ground state.[369] Hence, any stabilizing delocalization of charge in the excited state should produce bathochromic shifts, which is in accord with general observations. Theoretical calculations are also consistent with this view and indicate partial bonding between carbon atoms 2 and 6 (and 3 and 5) and weakened bonding between $C_5:C_6$ (and $C_2:C_3$).[370]

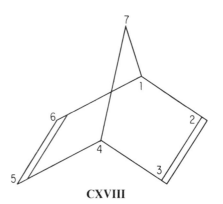

CXVIII

[368] R. C. Cookson and S. MacKenzie, *Proc. Chem. Soc. (London)*, 423 (1961).
[369] R. B. Turner, W. R. Meador, and R. E. Winkler, *J. Am. Chem. Soc.*, **79**, 4116 (1957).
[370] C. F. Wilcox, Jr., S. Winstein, and W. G. McMillan, *J. Am. Chem. Soc.*, **82**, 5450 (1960).

4.13. Charge densities by theoretical methods[371]

This chapter has dealt with an interpretation of chemical and physical properties of molecules in terms of the modern structural theory. This approach makes extensive use of resonance structures to indicate sites of high and low electron densities and to give some indication of the various bond orders within a molecule. This section will now present a superficial description of semitheoretical methods to derive this same information. Although applicable to saturated molecules, these methods are of greatest importance for treating conjugated systems. The lone-pair and σ electrons of a molecule are relatively "localized," and their location presents no particular problem. The π electrons, to the contrary, are "delocalized," and their mobility makes it difficult to assign their distribution within a conjugated system. Resonance theory and the theories of this section, then, are attempts to represent the distribution of π or mobile electrons over a molecular framework. Also, the π-electron distribution is particularly important for an understanding of the physical properties of unsaturated molecules, such as their spectra, ionization potentials, and dipole moments.

A widespread notion, and a valuable one, is that the chemical reactivity of a molecule could be reasonably predicted from a knowledge of the weak bonds present and of the charge distribution over the molecule. In several places in this book we have seen that bond order, bond length, and bond strength are intimately related. Thus, the molecular parameters that are sought for an adequate description of the reactive sites in a molecule are bond order, electron charge density, and, as a measure of unused chemical bonding capacity, the free valence. A convenient way to summarize these parameters is by means of a molecular diagram. In such a diagram, the bond order is written along the bond, the π-electron density (in units of one electron) is written at each atom, and the free valence is written at the tip of an arrow from each atom.

There are two principal approaches used in the theoretical study of the electronic structures of molecules: the valence bond method and the method of molecular orbitals. Both methods are useful, although the molecular orbital (M.O.) approximation seems to be more convenient mathematically.

4.13.1. BOND ORDER AND FREE VALENCE BY THE VALENCE BOND METHOD

The valence bond method starts with a group of bonded formulas and employs rules[372] to indicate which formulas are to be used in the succeeding

---

[371]The author is indebted to Dr. Aetius R. Lawrence, Ph.D., Howard University, for providing the original draft of this section.

[372]L. Pauling, L. O. Brockway, and J. Y. Beach, *J. Am. Chem. Soc.*, **57**, 2705 (1935).

calculations. This proper set of formulas is called a *canonical* set. Next, each formula of the canonical set is represented by a wave function ψ. The complete wave function describing the molecule is then considered to be a combination of the wave functions of the canonical set. These formulas of the canonical set, however, are of unequal importance in the description of the molecule, and each wave function corresponding to a particular formula must be labeled to denote its relative importance. These labels are represented by coefficients placed before each wave function. For example, consider the canonical set of formulas for benzene to be the two Kekulé and the three Dewar structures:

The complete wave function for benzene would then be a combination of the individual wave functions corresponding to these different structures:

$$\Psi_{C_6H_6} = a_1(\psi_1 + \psi_2) + a_2(\psi_3 + \psi_4 + \psi_5)$$

Here, the coefficients a_1 and a_2 are labels which denote the respective importance or contribution of each structure. By performing the proper calculations, these coefficients can be evaluated and numerical values assigned.[373]

In valence bond theory, the double-bond character of a bond is given by the *mobile bond order*. This is defined as the sum of the weights of all the formulas for a molecule in which a given bond is represented as a double bond.[372] For benzene, for illustration, the weight of the Kekulé formulas is 39 per cent and that of the Dewar formulas is 7.3 per cent.[374] Hence, the mobile bond order of a carbon-carbon bond in benzene is $0.39 + 0.073 = 0.46$.

In contrast to the definition of mobile bond order, *free valence* is described in terms of bonds between distant atoms. It arises from the idea that "long bonds" which appear in Dewar-type structures are so weak that the electrons of the bond are free to engage in other bonding. Consequently, free valence can be regarded as the total weight of such structures in which a long bond terminates at a given atom.[375]   It is the modern version of Thiele's concept of *residual valence*. In benzene, for example, each carbon atom is connected by a bond to a distant carbon atom in only one Dewar structure, and the free valence of a carbon atom in benzene

[373]L. Pauling and G. Wheland, *J. Chem. Phys.*, **1**, 362 (1933).
[374]C. A. Coulson, *Valence* (Fair Lawn, N.J.: Oxford U. P., 1952).
[375]R. Daudel and A. Pullman, *C. R. Acad. Sci., Paris*, **220**, 888 (1945); *J. de Phys.*, **7**, 59, 74, 105 (1946).

will be 0.073. It is much more complicated to determine the free valence of larger molecules.

Using the valence bond method, then, the free valence and bond orders in various molecules can be calculated. These quantities for naphthalene and anthracene are as follows:

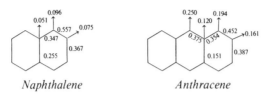

Naphthalene   Anthracene

4.13.2. BOND ORDER AND FREE VALENCE BY THE M.O. METHOD[376]

The second of the two methods used in the determination of electron density is the method of molecular orbitals. In this method, each π electron is considered separately and is described by a molecular orbital. This M.O. is a wave function which extends over the entire molecular frame and is considered to be constructed of the π-electron atomic orbitals. For example, in benzene each π-electron is described by a molecular orbital of the form:

$$\phi_j = c_{1j}\psi_1 + c_{2j}\psi_2 + c_{3j}\psi_3 + c_{4j}\psi_4 + c_{5j}\psi_5 + c_{6j}\psi_6$$

where ϕ_j is the jth M.O., ψ_i indicates an atomic orbital associated with the ith carbon atom, and the c_{ij}'s are coefficients which measure the respective contribution of each atomic orbital to the M.O. under consideration. The square of one of these coefficients gives the probability that an electron in the respective M.O. will be found near the corresponding atom. From a set of n atomic orbitals it is always possible to construct n different M.O.'s; hence, there are as many M.O.'s as there are π electrons. Whether or not a particular M.O. is occupied in the ground state will depend on its energy and the total number of π electrons. If there are $2x$ π electrons, these will occupy in pairs the x M.O.'s of lowest energy.[377] To find the energy of the jth M.O. and the associated coefficients $c_{ij}, \ldots, c_{nj}$, one has to solve a set of simultaneous equations, which for benzene are

$$yc_{1j} = c_{6j} + c_{2j} \qquad yc_{4j} = c_{3j} + c_{5j}$$
$$yc_{2j} = c_{1j} + c_{3j} \qquad yc_{5j} = c_{4j} + c_{6j}$$
$$yc_{3j} = c_{2j} + c_{4j} \qquad yc_{6j} = c_{5j} + c_{1j}$$

[376](a) R. Daudel, R. Lefebvre, and C. Moser, *Quantum Chemistry* (New York: Interscience, 1959); p. 31; (b) A. Streitwieser, Jr., *Molecular Orbital Theory for Chemists* (New York: Wiley, 1961); (c) J. D. Roberts, *Notes on Molecular Orbital Calculations* (New York: W. A. Benjamin, Inc., 1961).

[377]H. C. Longuet-Higgins, *Proc. Chem. Soc. (London)*, 157 (1957).

where y is the binding energy of the orbital in units of a quantity β, called the $C{=}C$ resonance integral. The six solutions to these six equations lead to a determination of π-electron charge densities, bond orders, and free valences for a given molecule. However, these quantities are calculated in a different fashion than in the valence bond method. For illustration, the mobile bond, p_{rs}, in a conjugated system is defined as[378]

$$p_{rs} = 2 \sum_{i=1}^{m} c_{ri} c_{si}$$

or, in words, the mobile bond order between atoms r and s is the sum of all products $c_{ri} c_{si}$ taken over all orbitals from $i = 1$ to $i = m$ (in benzene, $m = 3$), and the sum is counted twice for doubly occupied orbitals. Here, as before, c_{ri} and c_{si} are the coefficients of the atomic orbitals of atoms r and s in the ith M.O. For benzene, the mobile bond order between atoms 1 and 2 is

$$p_{12} = 2 \left[\left(\frac{1}{\sqrt{6}} \cdot \frac{1}{\sqrt{6}} \right) + \left(\frac{1}{2\sqrt{3}} \cdot \frac{2}{2\sqrt{3}} \right) + \left(\frac{1}{2} \cdot 0 \right) \right]$$

$$= 2 \left[\left(\frac{1}{6} \right) + \left(\frac{1}{6} \right) \right] = \frac{2}{3} = 0.667$$

In order to define free valence, an additional concept is required. We define a quantity called *bond number*, N_r,

$$N_r = \sum p_{rs}$$

where s stands for all carbon atoms adjacent to carbon atom r.[379] Bond number represents the bonding power of atom r; it is the part of the maximum bonding power of atom r which has been used to form bonds with adjacent atoms. Further, we have described by implication another quantity, the maximum bonding capacity of an atom, and will represent it by the symbol, N_{max}. Finally, free valence is described as[379]

$$F_r = N_{max} - N_r.$$

The free valence of atom r is the difference between the maximum bonding capacity of that atom and the bonding power of that atom as found in some reference molecule. The bond orders and free valences in naphthalene, anthracene, and butadiene calculated by the M.O. method are shown in the accompanying diagrams.

[378]C. A. Coulson and H. C. Longuet-Higgins, *Proc. Roy. Soc.*, **191A**, 39 (1947).

[379]C. A. Coulson, *Disc. Faraday Soc.*, **2**, 9 (1947).

[380]B. Pullman and A. Pullman, "Free Valence in Conjugated Organic Molecules," in *Progress in Organic Chemistry*, vol. 4, ed. J. W. Cook (New York, Academic, 1958), p. 31.

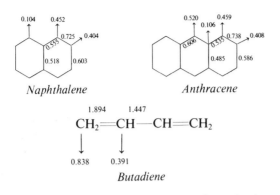

Naphthalene   Anthracene

$$CH_2\!\!=\!\!CH\!-\!CH\!\!=\!\!CH_2$$

1.894   1.447

0.838   0.391

Butadiene

The numbers obtained by the valence bond method and the M.O. method will, in general, differ; the relative values, however, give good agreement with each other.[381]

4.13.3. MOLECULAR DIAGRAMS AND CHEMICAL REACTIVITY

One of the principal aims of theoretical chemists has been to be able to assign some type of reactivity index to the atoms of a molecule. One of the more successful methods has followed the pioneering work of Wheland and Pauling[382] and the modification of Coulson and Longuet-Higgins[383] for calculating bond orders and charge densities. In the absence of overriding steric and solvation effects, the inherent reactivity of the atoms of a molecule towards electrophilic reagents will increase with increasing elec-

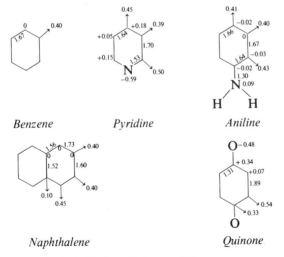

Benzene   Pyridine   Aniline

Naphthalene   Quinone

[381] Section 4.6. See also C. A. Coulson, *Valence*, p. 257.
[382] G. W. Wheland and L. Pauling, *J. Am. Chem. Soc.*, **57**, 2086 (1935).
[383] H. C. Longuet-Higgins and C. A. Coulson, *Trans. Faraday Soc.*, **43**, 87 (1947).

tron density and decrease in reactivity towards nucleophilic reagents. Alternately, free valences serve as an index of reactivity for radical reactions. Molecular diagrams for a number of compounds are given on p. 447.[383] In these diagrams, relative net-charges rather than π-electron densities are given and values are not duplicated for equivalent atoms or bonds. Also, total bond orders are given, which equal the mobile bond orders plus one.

These molecular diagrams provide a semiquantitative basis for some of the observed properties of these compounds. For instance, pyridine is much less reactive towards electrophilic reagents than is benzene owing to the low electron density at the pyridine carbon atoms, and when reaction does occur, it takes place at the β position.

Charge densities have been reported for other molecules which are in good agreement with their reactivities. Some examples are given below.

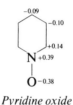

Pyridine oxide

Pyridine oxide. Reacts at the β and γ positions with electrophilic reagents and in the α position with nucleophilic reagents. Charge density consistent with resonance among forms

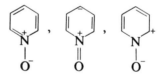

Pyrrole. Undergoes monosubstitution by electrophilic reagents primarily in α position.

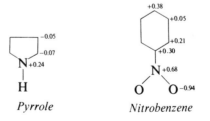

Pyrrole   *Nitrobenzene*

Nitrobenzene. Electrophilic substitution more difficult than with benzene but occurs at meta position. Charge density consistent with resonance

among forms

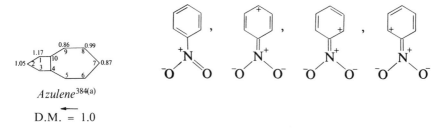

Azulene[384(a)]

D.M. $\overleftarrow{= 1.0}$

Azulene. These π-electron densities are consistent with the direction of dipole moment and the fact that electrophilic substitution occurs in the five-membered ring at position 1.

Cycl[3.2.2]azine[384(b)]

Atom	Charge density	Free valence
1(4)	1.168	0.482
2(3)	1.062	0.336
2a	1.188	0.061
4a	1.058	0.124
5(7)	0.997	0.462
6	1.043	0.450
8	1.196	0.367

Cycl[3.2.2]azine. These π-electron charge densities are in accord with the observation that cycl[3.2.2]azine undergoes nitration at C_1, dibromination at C_1 and C_4, Friedel-Crafts reaction at C_1, and diacylation at C_1 and C_4. Carbon 2a has a higher electron density than C_1 but C_{2a} has no replaceable hydrogen atom. Free valences predict that the compound should react at C_1 in radical substitution.

Another experimental check on the reliability of calculated π-electron densities of aromatic molecules has been provided by n.m.r. measurements. It was shown in Sec. 4.11 that C^{13} and proton chemical shifts are related to π-electron densities at nuclear carbon atoms. In order to determine the proportionality factor between chemical shift and π-electron density, C^{13} and H^1 resonance signals have been measured for $C_5H_5^-$, C_6H_6, $C_7H_7^+$, and $C_8H_8^=$ for which the π-electron densities per carbon atom are known to be 6/5, 1, 6/7, and 10/8, respectively.[385(a),(b)] Accordingly, it was found that

[384](a) C. A. Coulson, *J. Chem. Soc.,* 2069 (1955); (b) R. J. Windgassen, Jr., W. A. Saunders, Jr., and V. Boekelheide, *J. Am. Chem. Soc.,* **81,** 1459 (1959).

[385](a) H. Spiesecke and W. G. Schneider, *Tetrahedron Letters,* no. 14, 468 (1961); (b) W. Seiffert, H. Zimmermann, and G. Scheibe, *Angew. Chem.,* **74,** 249 (1962); (c) R. D. Brown and M. L. Heffernan, *Aust. J. Chem.,* **13,** 38 (1960).

the C^{13} and H^1 chemical shifts are linearly related to π-electron densities ρ by the equations

$$\delta_{C^{13}} = 160\,\rho, \qquad \delta_{H^1} = 10.6\,\rho$$

On this basis, π-electron densities of azulene were determined from measured chemical shifts, and the results compare well with π-electron densities calculated by theoretical methods.[385(c)]

Position in azulene	Electron density	
	From $\delta_{C^{13}}$[385(a)]	Theoretical[385(c)]
2	0.977	0.988
3 & 1	1.061	1.059
4 & 8	0.967	0.954
5 & 7	1.045	1.011
6	0.962	0.969

A second general approach to the theoretical determination of chemical reactivities is to study activation energies.[386] One of the early works using this approach is the localization theory of chemical reactivities.[387] In this theory, the structure of a molecule in the transition state is modified with respect to the initial state according to the influence of the attacking reagent. In the transition state or activated complex, the carbon atom undergoing reaction is assumed to have four single bonds each containing a pair of electrons. These single-bond electrons do not form part of the delocalized or π-electron system. The transition state for benzene, for example, would be:

The delocalized bond extends over the entire carbon frame except at the carbon atom undergoing attack. The electrons needed to form the $C-X$ bond come from: (1) X, if it is a negative ion, (2) the π-electron system if X is a positive ion, and (3) one electron from X and one from the π-electron system if X is a radical. Thus, the π-electron system must supply no electrons, a pair of electrons, or one electron, depending on the nature of the attacking reagent. The ease with which the π-electron system can fill these requirements determines the point of attack.

A quantity called the *localization energy* is then defined as the amount of energy needed to localize or fix the appropriate number of electrons at the carbon atom being attacked. The localization energy may be thought

[386]K. Fukui, T. Yonezawa, C. Nagato, and H. Shingu, *J. Chem. Phys.,* **31,** 550 (1959), and earlier papers; M. J. S. Dewar, *J. Am. Chem. Soc.,* **74,** 3357 (1952).

of as the difference between the energy of the π-electron system in the activated complex and the energy of the π-electron system in the initial state. Consequently, the smaller the localization energy, the greater the ability of a given atom to undergo substitution. This means that the most reactive position in a molecule will be the one for which the π-electron energy of the activated complex is lowest or the resonance energy the highest.

Moreover, development of the localization theory[380] has shown that (1) there is a good correspondence between free valence and localization energy and (2) the same amount of energy is required to fix one, two, or zero electrons at a given carbon atom. It follows then that free valence is a good index of reactivity in substitution reactions, and that the atom with the highest free valence will undergo substitution irrespective of the nature of the attacking reagent. For example, naphthalene is substituted at the α position by the NO_2^+ ion, and by free radicals.

An interesting comparison of the application of the modern structural theory and molecular orbital theory to the structure of a molecule has been made for biphenylene.[388,389] Five homopolar structures (CXIX) can be drawn for the molecule, one [(a)] is pictured as a derivative of cyclobutane, two [(b) and (c)] as a cyclobutene, and two [(d) and (e)] as a cyclo-

(a)   (b)   (c)   (d)   (e)

CXIX

butadiene. In simple resonance theory the five canonical forms contribute equally, but the modern structural theory recognizes the extreme strain of the cyclobutadiene ring, the smaller strain in the cyclobutene ring, and the loss of Kekulé delocalization energy for form CXIX(e). Consequently, forms CXIX(a)–(e) make unequal contributions to the hybrid structure of biphenylene in the order (a) $\gg$ (b) = (c) > (d) > (e). The relative contributions of these forms will affect the bond orders of the various bonds, of course. With equal contributions, for example, bonds A, B, and C would have 2/5, 3/5, and 2/5 double-bond character, respectively, whereas if only forms (a)–(c) made a contribution, the double-bond character of bonds A, B, and C would be 2/3, 1/3, and 2/3. Notice that this reverses the relative bond orders from A < B > C to A > B < C. It might be expected, then, that a knowledge of the actual bond distances would reveal important information about the bonding in biphenylene.

[387]G. W. Wheland, J. Am. Chem. Soc., 64, 900 (1942).
[388]T. C. W. Mak and J. Trotter, J. Chem. Soc., 1 (1962).
[389]J. Waser and V. Schomaker, J. Am. Chem. Soc., 65, 1451 (1943).

It was shown in Sec. 4.6 that bond orders may be determined from experimental bond lengths. The one controversial issue is the proper length to use for the sp^2 hybridized C—C single bond [Sec. 1.2.9(d)]. From a curve based on the total bond order-bond length values of (1.0, 1.527), (1.33, 1.421), (1.50, 1.392), and (2.00, 1.339), the bond lengths of the bonds in biphenylene were calculated for various weightings of forms CXIX(a)–(e) and compared with the most recent experimental values.[388] (See Table 4.28.) Also listed in the table are the bond distances as calculated by two different M.O. calculations.

Table 4.28. MEASURED AND CALCULATED BOND LENGTHS (Å) IN BIPHENYLENE[388]

					Bond:	A	B	C	D	E
		Measured lengths:				1.35	1.42	1.38	1.38	1.52
Modern Structural Theory										
Weights of forms CXIX(a)–(e)										
	(a)	(b)	(c)	(d)	(e)					
(i)	1	1	1	1	1	1.41	1.38	1.41	1.41	1.45
(ii)	4	2	2	1	1	1.38	1.41	1.38	1.43	1.48
(iii)	4	2	2	1	0	1.37	1.42	1.37	1.42	1.53
(iv)	2	1	1	0	0	1.36	1.44	1.36	1.44	1.53
(v)	1	0	0	0	0	1.34	1.53	1.34	1.53	1.53
Molecular Orbital Theory										
Calculation (i)[389]						1.38	1.40	1.38	1.41	1.47
Calculation (ii)[390]						1.39	1.41	1.39	1.41	1.47

It can be seen from Table 4.28 that equal weightings of forms CXIX (a) to (e) [model (i)] gives very poor agreement between calculated and observed bond distances, that form CXIX (a) alone [model (v)] is equally poor, and that model (iii) gives about the best agreement among those chosen. This is consistent with the relative order of contributions previously predicted by the modern structural theory, i.e., (a) >> (b) = (c) > (d) > (e). Furthermore, the agreement between calculated and observed data for model (iii) is better than that for the M.O. models. However, the modern structural theory has the disadvantage of not being able to produce these numerical data directly as is done by M.O. theory.[391]

---

[390]M. A. Ali and C. A. Coulson, *Tetrahedron,* **10**, 41 (1960).

[391]In contradiction to statements in the literature[388,392] that resonance theory predicts a 2-substituted biphenylene with an *ortho,para*-directing substituent to react with electrophilic reagents at position 1 whereas M.O. theory predicts reaction at position 3,[377] the

STUDY QUESTIONS

1. Predict the order of heats of hydrogenation to the respective cyclohexanes of benzene, ethylbenzene, and mesitylene.

2. Since cyclopentene has greater ring strain than cyclohexene, offer an explanation for the smaller heat of hydrogenation of the former.

3. Offer an explanation for the short C—C bond in CF_3CN (1.46 Å).

4. Which group would exhibit the greater hyperconjugation, $-CH_2Br$ or $-CH_2NO_2$?[393]

5. How would you explain the fact that the C—C bond distance in benzene is closer to the aliphatic double-bond distance than to the single-bond distance? Then, explain why the C—N bond distance in pyridine (1.37 Å) is midway between the normal C=N (1.28 Å) and the C—N (1.47 Å) bond distances.

6. Write resonance structures to account for the observed distances in (a) through (d). Some normal bond distances are

$$C—O, 1.43 \text{ Å} \qquad C—C, 1.54 \text{ Å} \qquad C—N, 1.47 \text{ Å}$$
$$C=O, 1.21 \qquad\quad C=C, 1.33 \qquad\quad C=N, 1.28$$

(a) Carbon-oxygen bond in $CO_3^=$ ion is 1.3 Å.

(b) $C_1—C_1'$ in biphenyl $= 1.48$ Å.

(c) Carbon-nitrogen bond in diazomethane $= 1.34$ Å.

---

modern structural theory not only agrees with M.O. theory in predicting substitution at position 3 but predicts substitution in unsubstituted biphenylene at position 2. This is based on the relative stability of the resonance forms which can be drawn for the "transition state" for reaction in position 2 of biphenylene in comparison to that for reaction in position 1, and for the relative resonance stabilization of the "transition state" for reaction at position 1 or 3 of a 2-substituted biphenylene. For example,

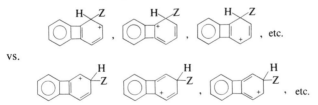

vs.

When bond D is a double bond, it restricts the Kekulé delocalization of the other six-membered ring in order to avoid a butadiene center ring. Reaction at position 2 yields a "transition state" for which fewer such restricted forms need to be written and, hence, a more stable "transition state." Similarly, the "transition state" for reaction in position 3 of a 2-substituted biphenylene is more stable than that from reaction at position 1. Thus, theory satisfactorily accounts for the observations that electrophilic substitution reactions occur solely in position 2 of biphenylene and that 2-acetamidobiphenylene monobrominates at position 3.[392]

[392]W. Baker, J. F. W. McOmie, D. R. Preston, and V. Rogers, *J. Chem. Soc.*, 414 (1960).

[393]Cf. J. W. Baker, *Conference on Hyperconjugation*, Indiana Univ., June, 1958 (New York: Pergamon, 1959), p. 135.

(d)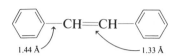

7. Do you predict the C—N bond distance in nitromesitylene to be closer to that of nitrobenzene or to that of nitromethane?[394]

8. The bond distances in crotonaldehyde are C_1—C_2, 1.46 Å; C_2—C_3, 1.36 Å; C_3—C_4, 1.52 Å. Offer an explanation for these bond distances in terms of hybridization of bond orbitals and in terms of resonance theory.

9. Offer an explanation for the observation that the *ortho* isomers of copper chloro- and iodobenzoate are readily soluble in benzene containing 10 per cent ethanol but the *p*-isomers are insoluble. It is found that copper hydrocinnamate is also soluble in this solvent whereas copper cinnamate is not.

10. Offer an explanation for K_a of *p*-phenylphenol (7.9×10^{-10}) being larger than that of phenol (1.3×10^{-10}).

11. Why should guanidine [$(H_2N)_2C{=}NH$] be a strong base?

12. Predict the relative acid strengths of

13. Predict the relative base strengths of 4-nitro-α-(N,N-dimethylamino-)-naphthalene and 4-nitro-α-naphthylamine.[394]

14. Which should be the stronger base, the *ortho* or *para* isomer of trifluoromethylaniline?[397]

15. Predict the relative base strengths of the N,N-dimethylanilines: 2-Me, 2-*i*-Pr, 2-*t*-Bu, and 2-Me-6-*t*-Bu.[398]

16. Why should a *p*-CH$_3$O or *p*-HO group in a benzal-N-alkylamine, ϕCH{=}N— R, be base-strengthening whereas an *o*-HO group is base-weakening?[399]

17. Predict the relative C—C bond dissociation energies for ethane and biphenyl.

18. How can you account for the relative enolic contents in the following compounds (ϕ = phenyl; Mes = mesityl):

[394]For data, cf. J. Trotter, *Tetrahedron,* **8,** 13 (1960).

[395]For data, cf. G. W. Wheland and A. A. Danish, *J. Am. Chem. Soc.,* **62,** 1125 (1940).

[396]For data, cf. R. T. Arnold, G. Peirce, and R. A. Barnes, *J. Am. Chem. Soc.,* **62,** 1627 (1940).

[397]Cf. J. D. Roberts, R. L. Webb, and E. Am. McElhill, *J. Am. Chem. Soc.,* **72,** 408 (1950).

[398]Cf. B. M. Wepster, *Progress in Stereochemistry*, vol. 2, ed. W. Klyne and P. B. de la Mare (New York: Academic, 1958), chap. 4.

[399]Cf. C. D. Wagner and E. D. Peters, *J. Am. Chem. Soc.,* **69,** 2914 (1947).

ϕ—CH$_2$—CO—CO—Mes,   100%   Mes—CH$_2$—CO—CO—ϕ,   0%
ϕ—CH$_2$—CO—CO—ϕ,   31% ϕ_2CH—CO—CO—ϕ,   0%

19. Vinyl alcohols are normally unstable with respect to the corresponding carbonyl compounds. However, the enol Mes—C(CH$_3$)=C(OH)—Mes and its isomeric ketone Mes—CH(CH$_3$)—CO—Mes are each isolable and interconvertible only with vigorous catalysis.[400] How would you explain the sluggishness of this reversible reaction?

20. Offer an explanation for the observations that α,α-disubstituted tetronic acids have no acidic properties and are easily hydrolyzed, whereas the tetronic acids which are unsubstituted in the α position are unusually resistant to alkali for a lactone and are stronger acids than acetic acid.[401]

Tetronic acid

21. Predict the enolic character of compound CXX.[392]

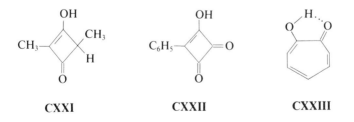

CXX

22. The dipole moment of 1,1-diphenylfulvene is 1.34 D. Would you expect the moment of 1,1-*bis*-(*p*-chlorophenyl-)-fulvene to be larger or smaller than this value?

23. Predict the relative acid strengths of CXXI, CXXII, and CXXIII, and give the basis of your predictions.[402]

CXXI   **CXXII**   **CXXIII**

24. Triphenylamine has a small dipole moment. What can be said about its structure from the standpoint of resonance and steric requirements?

[400] R. C. Fuson and T-L. Tan, *J. Am. Chem. Soc.*, **70**, 602 (1948).
[401] L. J. Haynes and J. R. Plimmer, *Quart. Revs.*, **14**, 292 (1960).
[402] Cf. J. W. Cook, *et al.*, *J. Chem. Soc.*, 503 (1951).

25. How can you account for the observation that the ratio K_1/K_2 is much larger for tetramethylsuccinic acid (6135) than for succinic acid (19.2)?[403]

26. Explain, in terms of either the B-N hypothesis or solvation energies, the following relative activating effects of the Me and t-Bu groups:

	H	m-Me	m-t-Bu
Nitration of alkylbenzenes (HOAc)	1	2.5	4.0
Bromination of alkylbenzenes (HOBr, H^+)	1	2.5	2.6
Solvolysis of $Ar(C_6H_5)CHCl$	1	1.93	2.29
Ionization of pyridinium ions	1	1.01	1.03

27. Predict the relative order of dipole moments of Me, Et, i-Pr, and t-Bu chlorides.

28. Predict the relative K_a's of the alcohols, MeOH, EtOH, i-PrOH, and t-BuOH, and the bond orders of the C—O bond in the respective alkoxide ions, if anionic hyperconjugation occurs in the alkoxide ions, e.g.,[404]

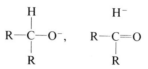

29. Why should the ionization potential of cyclopropene (9.95 v) be higher than that of cyclopentene (9.27 v)?[405]

30. Although the relative stabilities of trinitrobenzene and silver ion charge-transfer complexes of aryl halides increase in the order F < Cl < Br < I, p-F—C_6H_4CN forms a more stable coordination compound with Sn(IV)Cl than does p-Cl—C_6H_4CN.[406] How can one account for this observation?

31. Offer an explanation for the fact that most o-substituted benzoic acids are stronger acids than the *para* isomers regardless of the polar nature of the substituent, although the di-o-substituted acids may be weaker.[407]

32. Predict the approximate dipole moment of cyclobutyl bromide from the moments of the C_3, C_5, and C_6 cycloalkyl bromides.[408]

33. How would you account for the greater acid strength of acrylic acid over that of propionic acid?[409]

34. Why should the halogen in p-nitrohalobenzenes be more susceptible to nucleophilic replacement when it is thought that the major ionic resonance of the compounds is of the type $\bar{O}_2N\!\!=\!\!C_6H_4\!\!=\!\!\overset{+}{X}$, giving the C—X bond a double-bond character?

[403] Cf. P. D. Bartlett, *J. Chem. Educ.*, **30**, (1953).
[404] F. H. Seubold, Jr., *J. Org. Chem.*, **21**, 156 (1956).
[405] J. Collin and F. P. Lossing, *J. Am. Chem. Soc.*, **81**, 2064 (1959).
[406] T. L. Brown and M. Jubota, *J. Am. Chem. Soc.*, **83**, 331 (1961).
[407] M. S. Newman and H. Boden, *J. Am. Chem. Soc.*, **83**, 115 (1961).
[408] J. D. Roberts and V. C. Chambers, *J. Am. Chem. Soc.*, **73**, 5030 (1951).
[409] O. H. Wheeler and I. Learner, *J. Am. Chem. Soc.*, **78**, 63 (1956).

35. Would you expect the polarographic reduction of iodobenzene to be easier or more difficult when a methyl group is introduced *para* to the iodine atom?

36. Which would you predict to be reduced more readily, nitrobenzene or 2,6-di-methylnitrobenzene, and why?[410]

37. Why should F be more susceptible to alkaline hydrolysis in p-CF_3—C_6H_4—SH than in m-CF_3—C_6H_4—SH?[411]

38. It has been proposed[412] that there is no significant resonance between the CO and OR groups of the ester functional group, COOR, and that the abnormally short C—O_{ali} bond length (1.37 Å) is due to the short sp^2 hybridized covalent radius of the carbonyl carbon atom. If this is so, could you account for the lack of rotation of the OR group about the C—O_{ali} bond?

39. Offer an explanation for the observation[413] that ϕ_3C—Siϕ_3 and ϕ_3C—Geϕ_3 do not dissociate into free radicals as does ϕ_3C—Cϕ_3.

40. Predict which system has the greater resonance energy, a diene or enone system. How does your prediction compare with the conclusion reached from the C—C bond distance in butadiene (1.483 Å) and acrolein (1.46 Å)?[414]

41. How can you account for the fact that tetramethylphosphonium salts ($Me_4P^+X^-$) exchange protons readily whereas the tetramethylammonium salts do not?[415]

42. How should the following groups affect the stability of the cyclopentadienide ion: NH_3^+, NO_2, OR?

43. Why should the hydrocarbon CXXIV be reversibly soluble in 0.1 N aqueous alkali?[416]

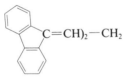

CXXIV

44. In an equation of the type (4–19), how will the slopes k compare when the equation is applied to substituted phenols and benzonitriles?

45. Would you expect the ionization potentials of substituted benzyl bromides to correlate better with σ or with σ^+?[417]

[410]F. L. Lambert and K. Kobayashi, *J. Am. Chem. Soc.*, **82**, 5325 (1960).

[411]J. D. Roberts, *et al.*, *J. Am. Chem. Soc.*, **72**, 408 (1950); R. G. Jones, *J. Am. Chem. Soc.*, **69**, 2346 (1947).

[412]D. Cook, *J. Am. Chem. Soc.*, **80**, 54 (1958).

[413]A. G. Brook and H. Gilman, *J. Am. Chem. Soc.*, **76**, 77 (1954).

[414]R. B. Turner, *et al.*, *J. Am. Chem. Soc.*, **79**, 4133 (1957).

[415]H. D. Kaesz and F. G. A. Stone, *J. Am. Chem. Soc.*, **82**, 6214 (1960).

[416]R. Kuhn and H. Fischer, *Angew. Chem.*, **73**, 435 (1961).

[417]A. G. Harrison, P. Kebarle, and F. P. Lossing, *J. Am. Chem. Soc.*, **83**, 777 (1961).

46. Which set of substituent constants would you expect to be best for correlating the degree of protonation of aromatic aldehydes and acetophenones?[418]

47. Predict the relative magnitude of σ^* for the CF_3 and CHF_2—CF_2 groups.[419]

48. In the solvolysis of p-substituted benzyl tosylates, what sign should the Hammett reaction constant have? On this basis, should a p-F atom enhance or deter the rate of reaction?[420]

49. The para C—H infrared stretching frequency for the monosubstituted benzenes R—C_6H_5, R = $(CH_2)_3Cl$, $(CH_2)_2Cl$, CH_2Cl, $CHCl_2$, and CCl_3 were found to be 3068, 3034, 3034, 3031, and 3029 cm^{-1}. However, the samples were unlabeled. Which frequencies would you assign each compound and on what basis do you make your assignments?

50. On what basis might one predict a difficulty in the resolution of geometric isomers of diazo compounds of the type C_6H_5—N=N—$COCH_3$?[421]

51. The π-electron densities for the various atoms in benzaldehyde are 1.92, 1.00, 0.98, 0.85, 0.85, and 0.56. Assign these values to the six numbered atoms in the accompanying structure.

52. In terms of resonance and induction, offer an explanation for the following relative rates of bromine addition and for the direction of addition of ICl to crotonic acid.

Compound	Relative rate of bromination	Compound	Relative rate of bromination
$(CH_3)_2C$=$C(CH_3)_2$	14	CH_3—CH=CH—COOH	0.26
$(CH_3)_2C$=CH_2	5.5	CH_2=CH—COOH	< 0.03
CH_3—CH=CH_2	2	CH_2=CH—Br	< 0.03
CH_2=CH_2	1		

$$CH_3\text{—CH=CH—COOH} \xrightarrow{ICl} CH_3\text{—}\overset{Cl}{\underset{I}{C}H}\text{—CH—COOH}$$

53. A hydrocarbon having the benzene Dewar-type structure has been isolated.[422] Does this have any effect on the modern structural theory of organic chemistry? Does it make a difference whether or not the compound is planar?

[418] R. Stewart, et al., J. Am. Chem. Soc., 82, 4059 (1960); Can. J. Chem., 37, 664 (1959).
[419] Cf. P. Ballinger and F. A. Long, J. Am. Chem. Soc., 82, 795 (1960).
[420] Cf. G. S. Hammond, et al., J. Am. Chem. Soc., 80, 563 (1958).
[421] Cf. C. D. Ritchie, J. D. Saltrit, and E. S. Lewis, J. Am. Chem. Soc., 83, 4601 (1961).
[422] E. E. van Tamelen and S. P. Pappas, J. Am. Chem. Soc., 84, 3789 (1962).

5.1. Spectroscopy as a tool

The use of spectroscopy in chemistry mushroomed during the years immediately following World War II when commercial instruments became readily available, and now it is the most widely used tool in chemistry. Almost every theoretical or practical problem in chemistry can use some form of spectroscopy to an advantage. The great British physicist and mathematician Lord Kelvin (1824–1907) is quoted as saying, "If it cannot be expressed with numbers, we do not know much about it." In the same spirit, it can be said, "If it has not been studied spectrophotometrically there is more to be learned about it."

Spectroscopy has provided quick, accurate analyses for guidance in research and process control; it has contributed to fundamental knowledge about chemical bonding; and it has facilitated the unraveling of complex molecular structures so that more useful substances could be synthesized, such as the synthetic plastics, textiles, rubbers, drugs, detergents, dyes, lubricants, and a host of other commodities. It is standard procedure now, when reporting the preparation of a new compound, not only to give its melting or boiling point, but to give some of its spectral characteristics

ABSORPTION SPECTRA

as a means of its future identification. Thousands of reference spectra are on file for making comparisons in the identification of compounds or for chemical analysis.

The literature abounds with material on spectroscopy, and there are entire books devoted to each type of spectroscopy.[1] A single chapter cannot hope to be exhaustive for such a large topic. Rather than present a review of the literature, we will attempt to illustrate the principles and uses of spectroscopy; for this purpose most of the chapter will discuss the applications of some of the types of spectroscopy.

---

[1] For general references, see: (a) *The Encyclopedia of Spectroscopy*, ed. G. L. Clark (New York; Reinhold, 1960); (b) *Techniques of Organic Chemistry,* vol. 9, pts. 3 and 4, ed. A. Weissberger (3rd ed.; New York: Interscience, 190); (c) *Determination of Organic Structures by Physical Methods,* ed. E. A. Braude and F. C. Nachod (New York: Academic, 1955), chaps. 3–6, 12; (d) infrared: L. J. Bellamy, *The Infrared Spectra of Complex Molecules* (2nd ed.; New York: Wiley, 1958); C. R. Brown, M. Y. Ayton, T. C. Goodwin, and T. J. Derby, *Infrared, A Bibliography* (Washington, D. C.: Library of Congress, 1954); (e) ultraviolet-visible: (S. F. Mason, *Quart. Revs.* (London), **15,** 287 (1961); A. E. Gillam and E. S. Stern, *Electronic Absorption Spectroscopy* (2nd ed.; London: Arnold, (1957); M. Pestemer and D. Brück in *Methoden der Organischen Chemie*, ed. E. Muller (4th ed.; Houben-Weyl), pp. 597–763; (f) microwave: C. H. Townes and A. L. Schawlow, *Microwave Spectroscopy* (New York: McGraw-Hill, 1955); (g) nuclear magnetic resonance: see Refs. 48 and 49.

5.2. The electromagnetic spectrum and spectrophotometry

We know from experience that X-rays penetrate flesh but not bones, and darken a photographic plate to reveal the shapes of bones; that long exposure to sunlight produces painful skin burns; that heat lamps (infrared radiation) can warm you inside without heating up the air around you, and can bring about relief from certain body aches and pains. These various forms of radiation—heat, visible light, X-rays—are all parts of the total electromagnetic spectrum and differ merely in wavelength. The electromagnetic spectrum is an ordered arrangement of radiation according to wavelength. Our present-day knowledge extends from the short-waved cosmic rays to the long-waved radio waves (see Table 5.1). The range of most use to a chemist is from the ultraviolet up to the microwave region. In Sec. 1.2.12, the molecular absorption of energy was discussed together with the molecular changes accompanying absorption of energy from each of the several ranges [see Table 1.12].

Table 5.1. REGIONS OF THE ELECTROMAGNETIC SPECTRUM

Approximate wavelength	Region	Some special uses
10^{-4} Å	Cosmic rays	
0.1 Å	Gamma rays	Nuclear chemistry
100 Å	X-rays	Medicine
4000 Å	Ultraviolet light*	Luminescent lamps
8000 Å	Visible light	Colorimetry, human sight
1 μ	Near infrared*	Physical therapy
100 μ	Far infrared	Jet engine thermometry, missiles, serial reconnaisance
3 cm	Microwave	Airborne radar
30 m	Radar	FM radio, ground radar, Tacan, military communications
300 m	Radio waves	AM radio, long-range communications

* The term *ultraviolet* once meant extreme *violet* end of the visible range and the term *infrared* meant beyond the *red* end of the visible range.

A spectroscope is an instrument that separates the regions of light into a spectrum. A very simple spectroscope uses a prism to separate the visible ranges into its colors. An eyepiece may then catch each color separately. When a scale for reading the wavelength of light is attached to the spectroscope, the instrument is called a *spectrometer*. Bunsen and Kirchoff constructed the first practical spectrometer, with which they carried out spectroscopic analyses for elements in substances. This led to the discovery of other elements (Cs, Te, Ga, In, Th, rare earths, etc.) and to the identification of elements in the gaseous envelope about the sun.[2] A *spectrograph* makes a photographic record of the spectrum, and a *spectrophotometer* uses a photoelectric cell to provide a quantitative measure of light intensity at each wavelength.

Simply, one can expect that when a light beam is passed through a sample of a given compound, the ratio of the intensities of incident light and transmitted light, I_0/I, will depend on how many molecules the light

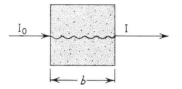

beam encounters. Thus, such factors as concentration, temperature, and the length of light path, b, have a marked effect on this ratio. Bouguer and Lambert independently demonstrated that at a given wavelength, I_0/I is related to b by the equation

$$\ln (I_0/I) = ab$$

where a is a constant, called the *absorptivity*. Beer showed that the light absorption is proportional to the concentration. Hence, these two relationships can be combined to give

$$\log I_0/I = acb \qquad (5\text{-}1)$$

in which c is the molar concentration. Equation (5-1) is frequently called the Beer-Lambert law, but Bouguer deserves equal recognition. The quantity $\log (I_0/I)$, called the *absorbance A*,[3] and the *transmittance, T* = $\log (I/I_0)$, are usually read directly from the spectrophotometer. It is to be noted that e, the *molar absorptivity* ($\epsilon = a \cdot$ mol. wt.) is a characteristic constant for a given compound at each wavelength. Just as two different compounds may have the same melting point, or two other compounds may have the same boiling point, rarely do two compounds have the same m.p. and b.p. It is much less likely that two compounds would have the same set of e values at the hundreds of wavelengths at which they can be

[2] M. Harmelin, *chim. anal.*, **42**, 277 (1960).

[3]Unfortunately, workers in different parts of the world have used different terms to express spectral data. It appears at last that there may be wide acceptance of a uniform system of terminology (cf. *Anal. Chem.*, **33**, 1968 (1961)) which will be adopted in this text. The former terms *optical density* and *molar extinction coefficient* are replaced by *absorbance* and *molar absorptivity*.

It is common practice to use wavelength (in Å or mμ units) to express the regions of the spectrum in the ultraviolet and visible ranges, to use wavelength (in μ) for the near infrared (0.5–2.0 μ), and to use wavelength (in μ) or wave numbers (in cm^{-1}; the trend is toward the latter) for the regular infrared (500–4000 cm^{-1}).

measured. Consequently, the set of *e* values (the absorption spectrum) for a given compound is unique for that compound and serves as a much stronger characterizing property than any single-point physical constant, such as b.p., m.p., index of refraction, viscosity, etc.

5.3. The origin of spectra

As stated in Sec. 1.2.12, absorption of energy from the far infrared region of the spectrum produces molecular rotations, absorption of near infrared radiation produces the rotations plus atomic vibrations, and absorption of ultraviolet and visible light produces not only molecular rotations and atomic vibrations but also electronic oscillations, or *electronic* excitations. This light absorption produces changes in the internal energy of molecules from which much can be learned about molecular structure and intramolecular forces. In this section we will examine in greater detail the origin of some of the forms of spectroscopy. We will limit the discussion to infrared, Raman, ultraviolet-visible, and n.m.r. spectroscopy. A more comprehensive treatment would also include emission spectra, flame spectra, electron-spin resonance spectra,[4] optical rotation,[5] and others.

5.3.1. INFRARED SPECTRA

It was the Danish physical chemist Niels Bjerrum who in 1915 first showed that the infrared spectra of molecules can best be understood if we think of atoms as small charged balls and of covalent bonds as metal springs holding the balls together. Each springlike bond has its "elasticity" or own natural vibration frequency and when a ray of light of this same frequency passes the molecule, the molecule absorbs some of the incident light energy, which is recorded by the spectrophotometer.[6] Over a period of time, following the pioneering work of W. W. Coblentz and J. Lecomte, it has

---

[4] D. H. Whiffen, *Quart. Revs.*, **12**, 250 (1958).

[5] C. Djerassi, *Optical Rotatory Dispersion: Applications to Organic Chemistry* (New York: McGraw-Hill, 1960).

[6] Vibrating mechanical molecular models were first used by C. F. Kettering, L. W. Shults, and D. H. Andrews (*Phys. Rev.*, **36**, 531 (1930)) to demonstrate modes of vibration in various molecules. The atoms were represented by weights and the bonds by helical springs. When the model is freely supported and connected through a loose coupling to an eccentric on a variable-speed motor, the model performs all of the normal modes of vibration. When the altered frequency produced by the eccentric oscillation matches one of the natural vibrational frequencies of the model, resonance occurs and the model vibrates. At other frequencies, the model remains quiet.

been observed that certain frequency ranges can be associated with certain bond-types, some of which are given in Table 5.2.[7]

Table **5.2.** FUNDAMENTAL INFRARED ABSORPTION REGIONS
(CM^{-1}) OF SOME BOND-TYPES

Bond	Frequency range	Bond	Frequency range
C—O	1060–1270	C—H (paraffins)	2850–2960
C—F	1000–1400	C—H (olefins)	3010–3040
C—Cl	600–800	C—H (alkynes)	3250–3300
C—Br	500–600	C=C	1620–1680
O—H	3590–3650	C=O	1650–1825
S—H	2500–2600	C≡C	2100–2260
N—H	3300–3500	C≡N	2215–2260

The actual situation is more complex than Table 5.2 implies. Again let us refer to the ball-and-spring analogy. If a ball hanging from the ceiling by a spring is pulled down and released, it is set into oscillation. Each time the ball is pulled down to the same mark and released, it will vibrate with the same amplitude and frequency. If a second ball is hung from the first by a second spring and the top ball is pulled down to the same former mark and released, its vibrations will be different from the original amplitude and frequency. Thus, the vibratory motion between two balls A and B joined by a spring is somewhat altered by the types of other balls and springs attached to A and B.

In a similar fashion, a molecule may be regarded as a mechanical system of atoms all interconnected by springs of different tensile strengths. When one bond is set into vibration, the entire system is affected and the specific resonant frequency of a given bond-type will depend upon the entire molecule.[8] Thus, the C—H bond does not absorb at an exactly identical frequency in all molecules. Fortunately, the range of frequencies for each bond-type is sufficiently narrow that usually an observed absorption band can be attributed to the presence of a certain bond-type.

Furthermore, a given bond may undergo several different types of vibratory motions. For example, the C—H bonds of a CH_2 group may stretch or bend, sometimes in unison and sometimes out of phase, to give rise to several different modes of molecular distortions. Some of the different modes of vibration are shown in Fig. 5.1. Each mode of vibration requires a different amount of energy and, accordingly, absorbs radiation at different wavelengths. Hence, each bond-type gives rise to several absorption bands, and the absorption spectrum of a molecule is quite com-

---

[7]See the concise charts of N. B. Colthup (*J. Opt. Soc. Amer.,* **40,** 397 (1950)), or R. N. Jones (NRC Bulletin No. 6, Ottawa, 1959).

[8]Cf. N. B. Colthup, "Vibrating Molecular Models," *J. Chem. Educ.,* **38,** 394 (1961).

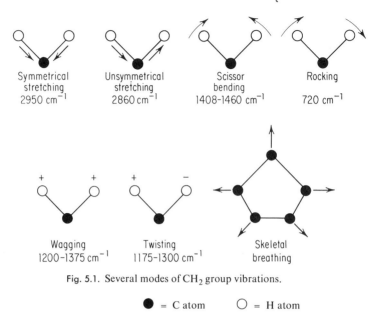

| Symmetrical stretching 2950 cm^{-1} | Unsymmetrical stretching 2860 cm^{-1} | Scissor bending $1408\text{-}1460 \text{ cm}^{-1}$ | Rocking 720 cm^{-1} |

| Wagging $1200\text{-}1375 \text{ cm}^{-1}$ | Twisting $1175\text{-}1300 \text{ cm}^{-1}$ | Skeletal breathing |

Fig. 5.1. Several modes of CH_2 group vibrations.

● = C atom   ○ = H atom

+ and − refer to vibrations perpendicular to the page.

plex. Nevertheless, most of the bands in a spectrum can be assigned to certain chemical bonds. An example is shown in Fig. 5.2 for the spectrum of acrylonitrile, $CH_2{=}CH{-}C{\equiv}N$.

In quantum mechanical concepts, the infrared spectra of substances arise from transitions to higher vibrational energy levels of the molecules involved. For a molecule consisting of n atoms, there will be $3n - 6$ fundamental or normal modes of vibration,[9] although they may not all be different. For illustration, for the linear CO_2 molecule, $n = 3$, hence there are $9 - 5 = 4$ modes of vibration.

$$\overleftarrow{O}{-}C{-}\overrightarrow{O} \qquad \overrightarrow{O}{-}\overleftarrow{C}{-}\overrightarrow{O} \qquad \overset{\downarrow}{O}{-}\overset{\uparrow}{C}{-}\overset{\downarrow}{O} \ \text{or} \ \overset{+}{O}{-}\overset{-}{C}{-}\overset{+}{O}$$

Symmetrical stretch, v_1 *Unsymmetrical stretch*, v_3 *Bending*, v_2

[9] The expression $3n - 6$ is based on the number of coordinates required to establish the position of n atoms relative to some fixed origin. For n atoms, it takes $3n$ Cartesian coordinates for each atom. Since each of the $3n$ coordinates may change with time, the molecule has $3n$ degrees of freedom. However, some of the $3n$ degrees of freedom correspond to certain motions of the molecule as a whole, which are the three coordinates which fix the center of mass of the molecule and the three which specity its orientation with respect to the origin. Hence, the number of possible modes of vibration for an n-atom molecule will be $3n - 6$. A linear molecule needs only two coordinates to establish its orientation, and it will therefore have one more mode of vibration.

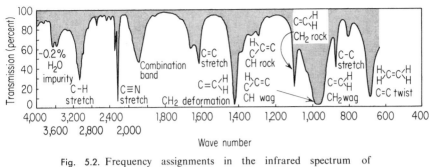

Fig. 5.2. Frequency assignments in the infrared spectrum of acrylonitrile.

Because of the symmetry of the molecule, the two bending modes are equivalent, i.e., doubly degenerate. As a second example, the molecule CH_3Cl should have $3 \times 5 - 6 = 9$ vibrational frequencies.

If we regard the molecule as a set of diatomic vibrators, then we expect one C—Cl stretching vibration and three C—H stretching vibrations of which two are degenerate. This leaves three discrete frequencies which must be of the bending type. The observed frequencies are given in Table 5.3.

Table **5.3.** INFRARED FREQUENCIES FOR CH_3Cl[10]

Non-degenerate	C—H	stretch	2966 cm^{-1}
	C—H	bend	1355
	C—Cl	stretch	732
Doubly degenerate	C—H	stretch	3042
	CH_3	bend	1455
	CH_3	rock	1015

The intensity of an infrared absorption band is approximately proportional to the square of the change in dipole moment per unit distance at the instant of absorption, and accordingly, infrared bands are observed usually only for unsymmetrical vibrations. Fortunately, the symmetrical vibrations produce strong Raman lines (Sec. 5.3.2) and their frequencies may thus be determined.

The physical motions of a simple pendulum, of a mass suspended by a

[10] W. T. King, J. M. Mills, and B. L. Crawford, *J. Chem. Phys.*, **27**, 455 (1957).

spring, and of a diatomic molecule are similar in that each involves a mass whose motion is resisted by a force proportional to the distance from an equilibrium position. That is, each approximates a harmonic oscillator, for which Hooke's law applies, $F = -kR$, where F is the force, R the displacement from the equilibrium position, and k is a constant. The potential energy for a diatomic molecule can be represented by the solid curve in Fig. 5.3. For small displacements, the actual energy of the molecule follows Hooke's law closely but as R (r_{AB} in Fig. 5.3) gets away from the

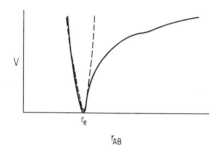

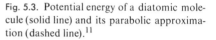

Fig. 5.3. Potential energy of a diatomic molecule (solid line) and its parabolic approximation (dashed line).[11]

equilibrium position r_e, the motion deviates from harmonic motion. The problem has been for chemists to develop a potential function $v = f(R^2)$ which best fits the actual curve.[12]

For the system of two masses m_A and m_B moving in the potential field $V = \frac{1}{2} kr_{AB}^2$, where r_{AB} is the interatomic distance and k is the bond force constant, the resulting vibration will have a frequency ν_0

$$\nu_0 = \frac{1}{2\pi c} \sqrt{k/M} \tag{5-2}$$

where c is the velocity of light and M is the effective mass for the combined vibration. Usually M can be replaced by the reduced mass μ

$$\mu = \frac{m_A m_B}{m_A + m_B}$$

and hence, this leads to the equation

$$\nu = 1307 \sqrt{k/\mu} \text{ cm}^{-1} \tag{5-3}$$

With Eq. (5-3), one could estimate the absorption frequency of a given bond. For illustration, for the C—H bond in methane, k and μ have values close to 5×10^5 dynes/cm and 1, respectively. Hence, $\nu_{C-H} = 1307 \sqrt{5/1} = 2920 \text{ cm}^{-1}$. For the C=O bond in acetone, $k = 12 \times 10^5$ dynes/cm and

[11] D. A. Dows, J. Chem. Educ., 35, 629 (1958).
[12] Cf. E. R. Lippincott and R. Schroeder, J. Am. Chem. Soc., 78, 5171 (1956).

μ = 6.8, so that $\nu_{C=O}$ = 1307 $\sqrt{12/6.8}$ = 1730 cm^{-1}. In the infrared spectra of these two compounds, there are strong bands at 2915 and 1744 cm^{-1}, respectively.

Equation (5-3) indicates that ν varies inversely with the reduced mass, and this is commonly observed. For example, the infrared frequencies for some bands involving isotopes are as follows:

Compound	$\nu_{C=O}$	$\nu_{C=O^{18}}$
Benzophenone[13]	1664 cm^{-1}	1635 cm^{-1}
Benzamide[14] (in CCl_4)	1690	1666
Methyl benzoate[14]	1727	1696
	ν_{C-H}	ν_{C-D}
Methane	3020	2258
	ν_{O-H}	ν_{O-D}
Methyl alcohol	3620	2680

There are indirect mass effects too. For example, the $\nu_{C=O}$ bands in form-aldehyde and formaldehyde-d_2 are at 1743 and 1700 cm^{-1}, respectively. Thus, the masses attached to a given bond affect its fundamental vibration frequency.

Since the vibrational energy is quantized, as it is with all forms of molecular internal energy, the energy of the infrared light absorbed, ΔE, is related to the frequency of the absorption band by the equation

$$E = h\nu_0(v + \tfrac{1}{2}) \qquad (v = 0, 1, 2, \ldots) \qquad (5\text{-}4)$$

in which v is the vibrational quantum number. For a transition of $\Delta v = 0 \rightarrow v = 1$:

$$\Delta E = h\nu_0(1 + \tfrac{1}{2}) - h\nu_0(\tfrac{1}{2})$$
$$= h\nu_0 \qquad (5\text{-}5)$$

However, the vibrations of chemical bonds are not pure harmonic vibra-tions, and transitions will take place in which Δv is more than ± 1. The corresponding absorption bands are referred to as *harmonic overtones*—or frequently as just overtones. The frequencies of the first and higher over-tones are given by

$$\nu = [1 - (v + 1)x]v\nu_0 \qquad (5\text{-}6)$$

where x is the anharmonicity constant. Thus, ν for the first, second, etc. harmonics will be

$$\nu_1 = (1 - 2x)\nu_0$$
$$\nu_2 = (1 - 3x)2\nu_0$$
$$\nu_3 = (1 - 4x)3\nu_0$$

[13] M. Halmann and S. Pinchas, *J. Chem. Soc.,* 1703 (1958).

[14] S. Pinchas, D. Samuel, and M. Weiss-Broday, *J. Chem. Soc.,* 1688, 2382, 3063 (1961).

The value of the anharmonicity constant is usually very small; hence, the first and second overtones occur at approximately twice and three times the frequency of the fundamental band. For example, for the C—H bond, x is generally 0.01 to 0.05.

Stretching vibrations give rise to absorption between 2.5 and 20 μ and bending vibrations between 10 and 25 μ. The overtones of the bending vibrations occur as very weak bands in the 2–10 μ region and hence are usually hidden by the much stronger fundamental stretching bands. However, most overtones of fundamental stretching frequencies fall below 2 μ in a region which is otherwise free from absorption bands. The expected wavelengths of overtones of some common bonds are listed in Table 5.4.

Table 5.4.[15] Approximate Wavelengths of Certain Overtones
of Some Common Bond-Types

Bond	Overtone	Wavelength
C—H	First	1.7 μ
	Second	1.1
O—H	First	1.4
	Second	0.95
N—H	First	1.4
S—H	First	1.95
C—C	Third	1.75
C—O	Third	1.85
C—Cl	Sixth	1.9
Si—H	Second	1.5
	Third	1.15

Only the moderately strong bands below 2 μ are included. Spectroscopy in this near infrared region of the spectrum is used in the same general fashion as in the regular infrared region. Hydrogen bonding, for example, has been studied extensively in the first overtone and second overtone regions of the O—H group.[16] Similar studies have been made of H bonding involving N—H groups.[17] The near infrared offers the opportunity to distinguish groups whose fundamental frequencies might overlap with other groups, and has been shown to be quite good for identifying cyclopropyl groups.

As stated earlier, the specific absorption frequency for a given bond-type will depend upon the molecular environment. It can be written that

$$k = f\left(\frac{nD}{r}\right)$$

[15] An excellent review on spectroscopy in the near infrared region has appeared: O. H. Wheeler, *Chem. Revs.*, **59**, 629 (1959).

[16] O. R. Wulf and V. Liddell, *J. Am. Chem. Soc.*, **57**, 1464 (1935); W. Lüttke and R. Mecke, *Z. Elektrochem.*, **53**, 241 (1949); *J. Chem. Phys.*, **21**, 1606 (1953).

[17] I. C. Kogon, *J. Am. Chem. Soc.*, **79**, 2253 (1957).

where k is the bond force constant, n is a function of the electronegativities of the bonded atoms, D is the bond dissociation energy, and r is the bond distance. Accordingly, various structural changes that affect any of these three factors, n, D, or r, will alter k and hence affect ν. Thus, resonance, H bonding, additional bonding, molecular crowding, ring strain, electronegativity, and orbital hybridization have been shown to affect k. For illustration, when a ketone forms a charge-transfer complex with a molecular halogen, $R_2C\overset{+}{=}\overset{-}{O}\cdots X—X$, stretching of the $C=O$ bond is facilitated while bending of this bond is made more difficult. In other words, the stretching force constant is decreased, which should lower the infrared carbonyl stretching frequency. This is indeed the case.[18]

	Infrared Bands	
		Cyclohexanone-I_2
	Cyclohexanone	charge-transfer complex
C=O stretching overtone	$3412\ \text{cm}^{-1}$	$3389\ \text{cm}^{-1}$
C=O stretch	1715	1698
C—C=O bend	487	493
	Acetone	Acetone-I_2 complex
C=O stretch	1716	1700
C—C=O bend	529	534

Similarly, association of the carbonyl bond with an OH group through H bonding lowers the H—O stretching frequency and raises the bending frequency (cf. Sec. 5.4.3). The effects of other structural parameters on bond force constants will be discussed in Sec. 5.4.

As a first approximation, a polyatomic molecule can be regarded as $3n - 6$ simple vibrators. However, sometimes there is considerable coupling between the vibrators. For illustration, it is known from classical physics that if two balls are hanging by strings from a single bar which itself is free to swing, and if one ball is set to swinging, the swinging ball transmits some of its motion to the second ball at a sacrifice of its amplitude of oscillation. Similarly, when two vibrating bonds in a molecule are sufficiently close, there is a certain amount of mechanical interaction or coupling between them. In general, the larger frequency gets higher and the smaller frequency gets lower. In an analogous manner, two identical bonds, which would have the same frequency in the absence of any interaction, give rise to two closely lying absorption peaks (a doublet) whose average is approximately at the position for a single group of the same type.

[18] H. Yamada and K. Kozima, *J. Am. Chem. Soc.*, **82**, 1543 (1960).

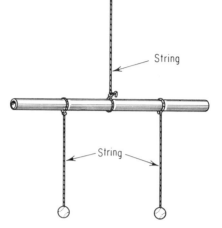

For illustrations, the equivalent carbonyl groups in simple anhydrides or imides produce doublets,[19, 20] e.g.,

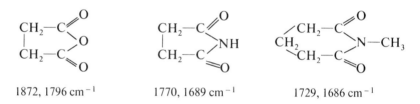

| 1872, 1796 cm^{-1} | 1770, 1689 cm^{-1} | 1729, 1686 cm^{-1} |

As another example, it was shown that in cyclic α, β-unsaturated ketones, the α-H atom has a bending vibration at 856–862 cm^{-1} whose first overtone should be close to 1700 cm^{-1}. This is the frequency range for the C=O stretching frequency. It was observed that the compounds having α-H atoms exhibited a band near 860 cm^{-1} and the CO band occurred as a doublet, while the compounds lacking an α-H atom did not exhibit a carbonyl doublet.[21] Apparently, the C=O vibration couples with the α-H bending vibration to give a doublet. In some molecular systems, coupling between certain vibrational modes is serious and the concept of "group frequency" may not be applicable. Such a situation appears to exist with strong chelates,[22] and cyclanones.[23] It could very well account for the alternation in certain bond frequencies with position of functional groups

[19] H. K. Hall, Jr., and R. Zbinden, *J. Am. Chem. Soc.*, **80**, 6428 (1958).

[20] C. M. Lee and W. D. Kumler, *J. Am. Chem. Soc.*, **83**, 4586 (1961).

[21] P. Yates and L. L. Williams, *J. Am. Chem. Soc.*, **80**, 5896 (1958).

[22] K. Nakamoto, P. J. McCarthy, A. Ruby, and A. E. Martell, *J. Am. Chem. Soc.*, **83**, 1272, 1066 (1961).

[23] C. F. Wilcox, Jr., and R. R. Craig, *J. Am. Chem. Soc.*, **83**, 3866 (1961).

in the chain of an alkane system. For illustration, the O—H, C=O, and C=N bond infrared frequencies show a surprising alternation with position in the octadecane carbon chain.[24]

Position of OH	ν_{OH}	Position of C=O	ν_{CO} (liq.)	Position of C=NOH group	$\nu_{C=N}$ (liq.)
1	3290 cm^{-1}				
2	3360	2	1712 cm^{-1}	2	1655 cm^{-1}
3	3325	3	1710	3	1656
4	3400	4	1717	4	1658
5	3320	5	1702	5	1655
6	3330	6	1718	6	1657
7	3320	7	1705	7	1654
8	3330	8	1725	8	1657
9	3325	9	1723	9	1656

Absorption of energy from the far infrared and microwave regions of the spectrum produces only molecular rotations. The rotational energy of a rigid symmetrical molecule is given by the expression

$$\frac{E_r}{hc} = BJ(J + 1) + (A - B)K^2$$

where E_r = rotational energy in ergs,

c = velocity of light,

h = Planck's constant,

$\dfrac{Jh}{2\pi}$ = total angular momentum,

$\dfrac{Kh}{2\pi}$ = the component of the angular momentum parallel to the axis of symmetry of the molecule,

$A = \dfrac{h}{8\pi^2 c I_a}$

$B = \dfrac{h}{8\pi^2 c I_b}$

I_a = moment of inertia of the molecule about an axis through its center of gravity and perpendicular to the molecular symmetry axis.

I_b = moment of inertia of the molecule about its axis of symmetry.

The quantum-mechanical selection rules for transitions between the rotational energy levels are $\Delta J = +1$, $\Delta K = 0$, so that the frequencies, in

[24] G. Geiseler, P. Richter, and K. Schmiedel, Z. *Elektrochem.*, **65**, 750 (1961).

megacycles, of the rotational transitions are

$$\nu = 2B (J + 1) = \frac{1,677,400 (J + 1)}{I_b}$$

where J is the angular momentum quantum number for the lower rotational state, and I_b is in g-cm^2 × 10^{-40}. Thus, from the infrared or microwave spectrum, the moment of inertia of a substance may be determined.

The moment of inertia of a body about an axis passing through its center of gravity, I_{cg}, for example, is given by the expression

$$I_{cg} = I - \frac{\left(\sum_i m_i r_i \right)^2}{M}$$

$$= \sum_i m_i r_i^2 - \frac{\left(\sum_i m_i r_i \right)^2}{M} = I_b$$

where M = molecular weight of the molecule,

m_i = masses of individual atoms,

I = moment about any reference axis perpendicular to the axis of symmetry of the molecule,

r_i = the perpendicular distances of the atoms from the reference axis,

Hence, for a given molecule, this can be expressed in terms of atomic weights of the atoms in the molecule and the respective bond distances. For example, in the molecules HCN,

$$I_b = m_C r_{CN}^2 + m_H (r_{CN} + r_{HC})^2 - \frac{[m_C r_{CN} + m_H (r_{CN} + r_{HC})]^2}{27}$$

where r_{HC} and r_{CN} are the H—C and C≡N bond distances, m_C and m_H are the atomic weights of carbon and hydrogen, and 27 is the molecular weight of HCN.

By this general procedure, bond distances have been calculated for simple molecules with higher accuracy than by diffraction techniques. The method offers the advantage that bond distances involving hydrogen atoms may be determined precisely.

5.3.2. RAMAN SPECTRA [25]

Closely related to infrared absorption spectra are Raman spectra discovered by Sir C. V. Raman in 1928. When a beam of light passes through a transparent medium and the scattered light is viewed at right angles to

[25] L. A. Woodward, *Quart. Revs. (London)*, **10**, 185 (1956).

the incident beam, in the spectrum of the scattered light there will be super-imposed upon the original spectrum additional lines which are displaced by regular frequencies from the incident lines. Raman found that a similar pattern of lines is always found for a given substance irrespective of the wavelength of the incident beam. He also showed that these frequency shifts are of the same magnitude as energy differences between vibrational states corresponding to bond vibrations within the molecules. The frequency shifts are called Raman frequencies and the set of Raman frequencies comprises the Raman spectrum. Raman excitation is active for a change in *polarizability* whereas infrared is active for a change in *dipole moment.* Since polarization is a "volume" property, Raman frequencies are active for vibrations which bring about a change in volume, which is usually the case for symmetrical vibrations. Thus, Raman and infrared spectroscopy complement each other by producing the strongest infrared bands for asymmetrical vibrations and Raman frequencies for symmetrical vibrations.

Since the Raman frequency, $\Delta\nu$, can be related to a bond vibration, we have

$$\Delta\nu = \frac{1}{2\pi c}\sqrt{\frac{k}{\mu}}$$

or
$$k = 0.05877\,\Delta\nu^2\mu \quad (10^5\text{ dynes/cm})$$

with $\Delta\nu$ in cm^{-1}. Thus, Raman spectra provide a good method of determining bond force constants; some values are listed in Table 5.5. It is noteworthy that the ranges for single, double, and triple bonds are different:

Single bonds: $< 7 \times 10^5$ dynes/cm
Double bonds: 7–15×10^5 dynes/cm
Triple bonds: $> 15 \times 10^5$ dynes/cm

This generalization often provides support for the bond character of a given bond. For example, the bond force constants of the carbon-carbon bonds in benzene are all identical, 7.6×10^5 dynes/cm, which is midway between the values for the ethane C—C bond, 5×10^5, and the ethylene C=C bond, 9×10^5 dynes/cm.

The force constant itself is used to calculate the force necessary to distort a given bond. For small displacements where Hooke's law would hold, we have $F = -kd$ and $E = \frac{1}{2}kd^2$, where E is the energy required and d is the displacement. For illustration, to stretch the C—H bond of methane 0.1 Å would take a force of

$$0.1(\times\ 10^{-8}) \times 5(\times\ 10^5) = 5 \times 10^{-4}\text{ dynes.}$$

Table 5.5. SOME BOND FORCE CONSTANTS[26]

Bond	Substance	$10^{-5}k$ (dynes/cm)	Bond	Substance	$10^{-5}k$ (dynes/cm)
H—H	H_2	.5.76	C—C	C_2H_6	4.5
F—H	HF	9.7	C—N	CH_3NH_2	4.9
Cl—H	HCl	5.2	C—O	$(CH_3)_2O$	4.5
Br—H	HBr	4.1	C—F	CH_3F	5.6
I—H	HI	3.1	C—Cl	CH_3Cl	3.4
B—H	B_2H_6	3.6	C—Br	CH_3Br	2.9
C—H	CH_4	5.0	C—I	CH_3I	2.3
N—H	NH_3	6.5	C_{ar}—C_{ar}	C_6H_6	7.6
O—H	H_2O	7.6	C=C	C_2H_4	9.8
S—H	H_2S	4.0	C=O	H_2CO	12.3
P—H	PH_3	3.1	C≡C	C_2H_2	15.6
Si—H	SiH_4	2.7	C≡N	CH_3CN	17.5
N—N	N_2H_4	3.6	C≡O	CO	18.9
Cl—Cl	Cl_2	3.3	N≡N	N_2	22.8
Br—Br	Br_2	2.5			
I—I	I_2	1.7			

The energy required to do this would be

$$0.5kd^2 = 0.5(5 \times 10^5) \times (0.1 \times 10^{-8})^2$$
$$= 2.5 \times 10^{-13} \times 6.06 \times 10^{23} \times 2.39 \times 10^{-8}$$
$$= 3.62 \text{ kcal/mole.}$$

In a similar fashion, the force required to bend an H—C—H bond one degree (1/57.3 radians) from its normal bond angle can be estimated from the bending force constant (0.5×10^{-11} dynes-cm/radian).

$$F = k\omega = 0.5 \times 10^{-11} \times 1/57.3$$
$$= 8.33 \times 10^{-14} \text{ dyne-cm.}$$

$$E = 0.5k\omega^2 = 0.5 \times \frac{(0.5 \times 10^{-11})^2}{57.3}$$
$$= 7.6 \times 10^{-15} \text{ erg/molecule}$$
$$= 0.11 \text{ kcal/mole.}$$

It is to be noticed that it is much more difficult to stretch a bond a short distance than to bend the bond through a small angle.

One useful relationship involving force constants and bond distances is Badger's rule:[27]

$$k = 1.86(r_e - d_{ij})^{-3}$$

[26] J. W. Linnett, *Quart. Revs. (London)*, **1**, 73 (1947).
[27] R. M. Badger, *J. Chem. Phys.*, **2**, 128 (1934); **3**, 710 (1935).

where r_e is the equilibrium bond distance and d_{ij} is a constant characteristic of a diatomic molecule made up of one element in the ith row and one in the jth row of the periodic table. Values of the constant d_{ij} are provided by Badger. Between Badger's rule and the relationship $\nu = 1307\sqrt{k/\mu}$, there are three physical properties involved for a given bond, ν, k, and r_e. If any two are measured, the third may be closely approximated. Sometimes, for example, certain vibrational frequencies are needed for statistical thermodynamic calculations and the frequencies have not or cannot be measured. If the force constant and the bond distance are known, then the vibrational frequency can be computed.

5.3.3. ULTRAVIOLET-VISIBLE SPECTRA

The absorption of light from the ultraviolet-visible region of the spectrum sets valence electrons into oscillation and produces an excitation of the molecule from the ground electronic state to the excited electronic state. The energies of the successive electronic energy states are given by the expression

$$E = (e + \tfrac{1}{2})hc\nu_0 \qquad (e = 0, 1, 2, \ldots)$$

where e is the electronic quantum number and ν_0 is a fundamental vibration frequency for the system. Hence, for an excitation from the ground to the first excited state

$$E_1 - E_0 = (3/2 - 1/2)h\nu_0 = h\nu_0$$

Since the wavelength $\lambda = c/\nu_0$, where c is the velocity of light, we have

$$E_1 - E_0 = \frac{hc}{\lambda} = \frac{286 \times 10^3}{\lambda}\,\text{kcal/mole}$$

with λ expressed in angstrom units. Thus, the energy of a ray of light of wavelength 3000 Å = 95.3 kcal/mole, which is enough to break most single bonds. Rearrangement of this equation gives

$$\lambda = \frac{hc}{E_1 - E_0} \qquad (5\text{-}6)$$

This is the basic relationship, which we will refer to frequently. It shows that the wavelength of ultraviolet absorption depends upon the *difference* between the energies of the ground and excited states, not just the energy of either one. The smaller the energy difference between the ground and first excited states is, the longer is the wavelength of light absorption. When more than one absorption band is observed in the spectrum of a substance, the bands are designated λ_m, λ'_m, λ''_m, starting with the band of longest wavelength, i.e., $\lambda_m > \lambda'_m$.

Now, what electronic motions arise upon the absorption of ultraviolet radiation? Several types of electronic transitions may occur depending, among other factors, on the type of valence electrons involved, σ, π, p, etc. One type of transition, called by one school an $N \longrightarrow V$ transition, is identified with the process $C{=}C \xrightarrow{h\nu} \overset{+}{C}{-}\overset{-}{C}$, in which the excited state closely resembles the polar structure. The less energy required for this transition, i.e., the more polarizable are the electrons involved, the longer is the wavelength of the $N \longrightarrow V$ band. Thus, the position of this band for multiple bonds, near 180 mμ, is at longer wavelengths than for single bonds (< 150 mμ.) A second type of electronic transition, $N \longrightarrow R$, can be identified with the process $C{=}C \xrightarrow{h\nu} (C{\overset{\cdot}{-}}C)^+$. That is, an electron is removed, and there is produced a progression of bands similar to the Rydberg series in atomic spectra followed by a continuum. These bands appear in the far ultraviolet, and organic chemists have made little use of such spectra.[29]

A third type of transition, $n \longrightarrow \pi^*$, involves a transition of a non-bonding lone-pair electron on a hetero atom (e.g., O or N) to an empty antibonding molecular orbital.[28] The absorption bands associated with such transitions are of much longer wavelength than for $N \longrightarrow V$ transitions and of very low intensity. For example, the $N \longrightarrow V$ and $n \longrightarrow \pi^*$ bands for the $C{=}C$ and $C{=}O$ groups have the following spectral characteristics:[30]

	$N \longrightarrow V$ band		$n \longrightarrow \pi^*$ band	
	λ_m	ϵ	λ_m	ϵ
$C{=}O$	188	900	279	15
$C{=}C$	185	8000	230	2

The general characteristics of $n \longrightarrow \pi^*$ bands are (1) low intensity, normally less than 1500, (2) shifted to shorter wavelengths by more polar solvents, and (3) shifted to shorter wavelengths by electron-donating groups. Thus, the 330-mμ band of nitrobenzene which was formerly

[28]Cf. J. W. Sidman, Chem. Revs., 58, 689 (1958), for a review and earlier literature references; R. S. Becker, J. Mol. Spectroscopy, 3, 1 (1959); M. Ito, K. Inuzuka, and S. Imanishi, J. Am. Chem. Soc., 82, 1317 (1960).

[29]This region is sometimes called the vacuum ultraviolet because work must be done in the absence of air, since oxygen absorbs in this region. A good recent survey on molecular spectra in this range has appeared: P. G. Wilkinson, J. Mol. Spectroscopy, 6, 1–57 (1961).

[30]E. A. Braude in Determination of Organic Structures by Physical Methods, ed. E. A. Braude and F. C. Nachod (New York: Academic, 1955), chap. 4.

regarded as an $n \longrightarrow \pi^*$ band was shown to be a $\pi \longrightarrow \pi^*$ band on the basis of the solvent and substituent effects.[31]

The relative magnitudes of these transitions are readily understood in terms of the accompanying diagram. Normally, nonbonding lone-pair

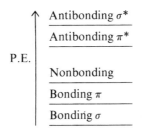

electrons are the most easily removed in a molecule, and in the bonding levels of potential energy, the π electrons have higher energies than corresponding σ electrons. In the antibonding levels this order is reversed (see diagram). Hence, in the spectra of simple molecules, $n \longrightarrow \pi^*$ transitions require the least energy and the corresponding bands are of longest wavelength. The $\pi \longrightarrow \pi^*$ ($N \longrightarrow V$) bands are of shorter wavelength and $\sigma \longrightarrow \sigma^*$ ($N \longrightarrow R$) bands lie in the far ultraviolet.

Conjugated systems. Similar transitions may occur in a conjugated system. Thus, an $N \longrightarrow V$ transition can take place with less energy,

$$C=C-C=O \xrightarrow{h\nu} {}^+C-C=C-O^-$$

and the corresponding band, called a K band from the German "Konjugation," will appear at longer wavelengths. Similarly, the R band for an $N \longrightarrow R$ transition will appear at still longer wavelengths but be of low intensity.

System	Compound	K band		R band	
		λ_m	ϵ	λ_m	ϵ
C=C—C=C	Butadiene	217 mμ	21,000		
C≡C—C=O	Butanoylacetylene	214	5,000	308 mμ	20
C=C—C=O	Crotonaldehyde	217	16,000	321	20
C=C—C=N	N-Butylcrotonaldimine	220	23,000		

Aromatic compounds. Aromatic compounds exhibit $N \longrightarrow V$ transition bands called K and E bands in the British school and *primary* bands by many in the American school. These bands are identified with transitions

[31] M. Godfrey and J. N. Murrell, *Proc. Chem. Soc. (London)*, 171 (1961).

to polar excited states, e.g.,

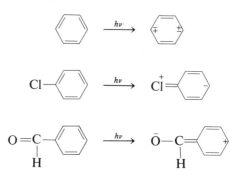

Aromatic compounds also have an absorption band accompanying a transition to a homopolar excited state. Since there is no significant increase in polarization of the molecule, the transition is forbidden. It arises by an excitation occurring during a vibration which destroys the symmetry of the aromatic ring. This band is called a *B* band in the British school and a *secondary* band in the American school. Secondary bands occur at longer wavelengths and much lower intensities than primary bands.

Compound	Second primary λ_m	ϵ	First primary λ_m	ϵ	Secondary λ_m	ϵ
Benzene			203.5 mµ	7,400	254 mµ	204
p-NH$_2$—C$_6$H$_4$—COOH	216.5 mµ	18,500	248	3,900	327	1,940
p-HO—C$_6$H$_4$—CHO	212	18,900	256	12,600	324	3,400
p-HO—C$_6$H$_4$—NO$_2$	230	3,900	278.5	6,600	351	3,200
p-NH$_2$—C$_6$H$_4$—NO$_2$	245	7,000	282.5	5,400	412	4,500

Criteria that help[32] to identify these bands of substituted benzenes are: (1)[33] the ratio of wavelengths of the secondary to primary bands remains fairly close to 1.22, and (2)[34] the ratio of wavelengths of the first (λ) to second (λ') primary bands remains less than 2 and increases as λ increases, and the ratio of the respective absorptivities, ϵ/ϵ', decreases as λ increases.

A very systematic collation[25] of the spectra of mono- and disubstituted benzenes has revealed that when the substituent groups are divided into ortho-para directing (usually electron-donating) and *meta*-orienting (usually electron-withdrawing) groups, and arranged in order of increasing dis-

[32]R. L. Hinman, *J. Org. Chem.*, **25**, 1775 (1960): W. D. Kumler, *J. Am. Chem. Soc.*, **68**, 1184 (1946); W. B. Tuemmler and B. S. Wildi, *J. Am. Chem. Soc.*, **80**, 3772 (1958).
[33]L. Doub and J. M. Vandenbelt, *J. Am. Chem. Soc.*, **69**, 2714 (1947); **71**, 2414 (1949).
[34]L. N. Ferguson, *Chem. Revs.*, **43**, 439 (1948).

placement ($\Delta\lambda$) of the first primary band of benzene (203-mμ), the following series are obtained:

o,p-directing: $CH_3 < Cl < Br < OH < OCH_3 < NH_2 < O^-$

m-orienting: $\overset{+}{N}H_3 < SO_2NH_2 < CO_2^-, CN < COOH < COCH_3 <$

$$CHO < NO_2$$

These two series appear to parallel the increasing electron migration which occurs between the substituent and the ring, irrespective of the direction of electron shift. That is, the transition

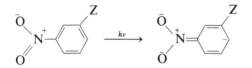

gives a primary absorption band at longer wavelengths the more readily R accepts the positive or negative charge on C_1 to stabilize the excited state. Also, the more polarizable the aromatic ring is, the lower is the transition energy and the larger is λ_m. This was demonstrated for the halobenzenes and the alkylbenzenes in Secs. 4.10.1 and 4.10.2, respectively. It is also revealed by the spectra of *meta*-substituted compounds, in which resonance interaction between substituents is absent.

The more the substituent Z donates electrons to the ring, the easier it is for the nitro group to withdraw electrons and the smaller is the transition energy. Accordingly, λ_m of m-substituted nitrobenzenes increases with increasing donor character of Z and decreases with increasing electron-withdrawing power of Z:[41]

Z	λ (mμ)
NO_2	234
$^+NH_3$	253
CO_2H	256.5
Cl	257
Br	259
H	259.5
CH_3	265
OH	269
O^-	288

Similar effects are observed in the spectra of *m*-substituted benzaldehydes, acetophenones, etc.

When two groups are of the same directing power in electrophilic substitution, then the displacement of the *p*-disubstituted benzene, $\Delta\lambda_{12}$, is close to that of the larger of the two monosubstituent displacements, $\Delta\lambda_1$ or $\Delta\lambda_2$, but when the two groups are of different directional ability, the displacement $\Delta\lambda_{12}$ is markedly larger than the sum of the displacements of the single groups, i.e., $\Delta\lambda_{12} \gg \Delta\lambda_1 + \Delta\lambda_2$. Although this empirical generalization is sometimes used for the determination of the orienting character of a group, it is not without several exceptions, particularly when $CH=CHNO_2$ and $CH=CHCOOH$ groups are involved.[35]

Chromophores. It was early recognized[36] that colored molecules possess multiple bonds and the unsaturated groups were given the name *chromophore*[37] (Gr. *chroma* color + *phoros* bearer). Multiple bonds have different chromophoric powers in the order[38]

$$C=C < C=N < C=O < N=N < C=S < N=O.$$

Groups which do not themselves confer color to an otherwise colorless substance but do increase the coloring power of a chromophore were called *auxochromes* (Gr. *auxo* increase). Examples are the NH_2, NR_2, OH, OR, and CH_3 groups. Thus, benzene, polyhydroxybenzenes, and polyaminobenzenes are colorless, but one NH_2 in the nitrobenzene ring changes the nitro compound from colorless to yellow. In recent times, however, it has been convenient to designate the chromophores and auxochromes as merely groups which exhibit π-electron and *p*- or σ-electron resonance, respectively.[39]

Summary of Ultraviolet Bands. The several types of electronic transitions discussed in this section are summarized in Table 5.6.

Whereas the wavelength of ultraviolet light absorbed is determined by the energy of the transition from ground to excited state, the intensity of the absorption band, recorded as the absorptivity, is a function of the *probability* of the transition and of the size of the molecule. For example, the λ_m of nitrobenzene, *m*-dinitrobenzene, and 1,3,5-trinitrobenzene decreases and the absorptivity increases in the order named.[41]

	λ_m	ϵ
$C_6H_5NO_2$	259.5 mμ	8.1×10^3
m-O_2N-$C_6H_4NO_2$	234	17.0
1,3,5-$(O_2N)_3C_6H_3$	224	26.9

As more nitro groups are introduced into the ring to lower the polarizability of the ring, there is an increase in the transition energy of the ϕ-NO_2

Table 5.6. CLASSIFICATION OF ELECTRONIC ABSORPTION BANDS

Electron transition	Band term	Description
$N \longrightarrow V$	Chromophore	$C{=}O \xrightarrow{h\nu} \overset{+}{C}{-}O^-$
$N \longrightarrow V$	Primary band,[40] K band	$\pi \longrightarrow \pi$ conjugation:

$$C{=}C{-}C{=}O \xrightarrow{h\nu} \overset{+}{C}{-}C{=}C{-}O^-$$

π, p conjugation:

$$R_2N{-}CH{=}CH_2 \xrightarrow{h\nu} R_2\overset{+}{N}{=}CH{-}CH_2^-$$

π,σ conjugation:

$$CH_3{-}CH{=}CH_2 \xrightarrow{h\nu} H^+CH_2{=}CH{-}CH_2^-$$

In general, electron donor *and* electron-accepting groups as well as increased dielectric constant of solvent produce bathochromic shifts.

$N \longrightarrow V$	Secondary band, B band	Forbidden, low-intensity transition.
$N \longrightarrow \pi^*$	$n \longrightarrow \pi^*$ band, R band	Excitation of lone-pair nonbonding electrons on one atom to antibonding molecular orbital. Electron donor groups and increased solvent polarity produce blue-shifts.
$N \longrightarrow R$	Rydberg series	Transitions to higher electronic levels in the direction of ionization of the molecule.

[35]B. G. Gowenlock and K. J. Morgan, *Spectrochim. Acta,* **17**, 310 (1961).

[36]C. Graebe and C. Liebermann, *Ber.,* **1**, 106 (1868).

[37]O. N. Witt, *Ber.,* **9**, 522 (1876).

[38]For an extension of this series see A. Wenzel, *J. Chem. Phys.,* **27**, 331 (1957).

[39]E. A. Braude, *Ann. Repts. Chem. Soc.,* **42**, 117 (1945).

[40]The *primary* band corresponds to the "*K* band" of the British school, to the "*B* band" of W. F. Forbes, *et al.,* and to the "*C* band" of Klevens and Platt (cf. W. F. Forbes and R. Shilton, *Symposium on Spectroscopy,* Special Technical Publication no. 269, 1959).

[41]M. J. Kamlet, J. C. Hoffsommer, and H. G. Adolph, *J. Am. Chem. Soc.,* **84**, 3925 (1962).

chromophore, but with a greater number of ϕ-NO_2 chromophores for excitation in the polynitro compounds, the transition probability is increased which is reflected by an increase in ϵ. According to electromagnetic theory, absorption can take place only if the transition is accompanied by a polarization of the molecule. The transition probability is related to the magnitude of the transition moment, which in turn is related to the length of the chromophoric system. This polarization is sometimes expressed in terms of *oscillator strength* (f) given by the equation

$$f = 4.32 \times 10^{-9} \int edv \simeq 0.5 \Delta v \, \epsilon \qquad (5\text{-}7)$$

where ϵ is the molar absorptivity and Δv is the range of wave numbers over which the absorption band extends. The oscillator strength is an approximate indication of the number of electrons per molecule involved in the light absorption process. The transition moment refers only to the moment accompanying the electronic excitation. It follows that molecules in their excited states must have significantly different dipole moments from those recorded for their ground states.

An ultraviolet absorption band is much broader than an infrared band because the former consists of an envelope of peaks. The electronic excitation energy produces vibrational and rotational changes as well as an electronic excitation. This gives a distribution of electronic transitions of slightly different energies. For instance, groups of molecules may undergo the transitions

$$E_0 v_0 r_0 \longrightarrow E_1 v_1 r_1$$

$$E_0 v_1 r_1 \longrightarrow E_1 v_2 r_2$$

$$E_0 v_1 r_2 \longrightarrow E_1 v_0 r_1 \qquad \text{etc.}$$

and each transition of different energy will produce a line or narrow peak of slightly different wavelength. However, the lines are too close to be resolved, and merely the envelope of lines is observed. As the temperature is lowered, the molecules become grouped more and more into the lower vibrational states and give a smaller distribution of excited states upon absorption of light. This produces more fine structure in the absorption band,[42] as illustrated in Fig. 5.4.

This temperature effect on fine structure is an experimental condition parameter. A molecular structure parameter which also affects fine struc-

[42]For other examples, see S. E. Sheppard and H. R. Brigham, *J. Am. Chem. Soc.*, **66**, 381 (1944).

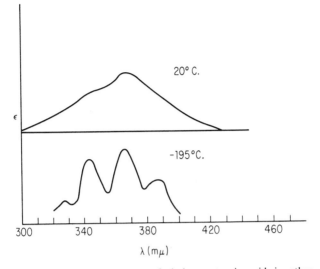

Fig. 5.4. Absorption spectrum of dodecapentaenic acid in ether-alcohol at 20° C and −195° C.[43]

ture has been termed a "loose bolt" effect.[44]   If immediately after electronic excitation occurs, some electronic energy passes into low-energy vibrational or rotational energy, it spreads out the observed distribution of excited molecules. This decreases the fine structure. This energy transformation takes place when groups which may easily rotate or vibrate are attached to the optical system.   For example, the fine structure in the

[43]K. W. Hauser, R. Kuhn, A. Smakula, *Z. physik. Chem.,* **B29,** 407 (1935).

[44]G. N. Lewis and M. Calvin, *Chem. Revs.,* **25,** 273 (1939).

[45]R. N. Jones, *J. Am. Chem. Soc.,* **65,** 1818 (1943); **67,** 2127 (1945).

[46]Two of the most unusual examples are found in compounds I and II (cf. A. Albert, *Heterocyclic Chemistry* (London: Athlone Press, 1959), p. 297). The two compounds exhibit changes in λ_m in opposite directions upon increasing the dielectric constant of the solvent. Such spectacular solvent effects are rare.

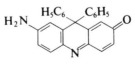

I

Blue in EtOH
Green in MeOH
Yellow in H$_2$O

II

Yellow in alkanes
Scarlet in arenes
Purple in ether
Violet in pyridine
Blue in EtOH

spectrum of ethylene is lost when phenyl groups are attached to the ethylene molecule. On the other hand, condensed-ring structures are very rigid and prevent this transformation of electronic energy into group vibrations and rotations. Consequently, the spectra of such compounds exhibit considerable fine structure, which is frequently diminished in the spectra of their derivatives.[45]

Finally, it must be added that the nature of the solvent has a profound effect upon ultraviolet spectra.[46] Many studies of solvent effects have been made, some of which are mentioned throughout the text. At least one study has a practical aspect in that it shows how the solvent effect upon the CT-band of pyridinium iodides may be used as a measure of solvent polarity.[47]

5.3.4. NUCLEAR MAGNETIC RESONANCE SPECTRA[48,49]

In a very short span of years, nuclear magnetic resonance spectroscopy (n.m.r.) has taken its place as one of the most useful and versatile physical tools for the investigation of chemical problems. Several books are available which describe the theoretical bases, experimental aspects, and most of the applications of n.m.r.[49] It was stated in Sec. 2.2 that nuclei spin in magnetic fields as tops do in the gravitational field (see Fig. 5.5). A stationary magnetic field H causes all of the atomic nuclei to precess at characteristic rates, and if an alternating magnetic field ν is superimposed, there will be an absorption of energy when the frequency of the alternating field matches the frequency of precession of any of the atoms.[50] One may hold the d-c stationary field constant and vary the frequency of the alternating

[47]Known as the Z value for a solvent (cf. E. M. Kosower, et al., J. Am. Chem. Soc., **82**, 2195 (1960) and earlier papers). Other empirical measures of solvent polarity are:

Y-value, from the rates of solvolysis of t-butyl chlorides in hydroxylic solvents (E. Grunwald and S. Winstein, et al., J. Am. Chem. Soc., **79**, 4146 (1957) and earlier papers).

log k_{ion}, from the rates of ionization of p-methoxyneophyl-p-toluenesulfonate in aprotic media (S. G. Smith, A. H. Fainberg, and S. Winstein, J. Am. Chem. Soc., **83**, 618 (1961).

Ω-values, from the product distributions (endo/exo) in the cyclopentadiene-methyl acrylate Diels-Alder adduct (J. A. Berson, Z. Hamlet, and W. A. Mueller, J. Am. Chem. Soc., **84**, 297 (1962).

All four measures are approximately linear to one another.

[48]J. C. Martin, J. Chem. Educ., **38**, 286 (1961), and references cited therein; J. E. Wertz, Chem. Revs., **55**, 829 (1955).

[49](a) J. D. Roberts, NMR in Organic Chemistry (New York: McGraw-Hill, 1959); (b) J. D. Roberts, An Introduction to Spin-Spin Splitting in High Resolution NMR Spectra (New York: W. A. Benjamin, 1961); (c) L. M. Jackman, Applications of NMR in Organic Chemistry, (New York: Pergamon, 1959); (d) J. A. Pople, W. G. Schneider, and H. J. Bernstein, High Resolution NMR (New York: McGraw-Hill, 1959); (e) E. R. Andrew, Nuclear Magnetic Resonance (New York: Cambridge U. P., 1955).

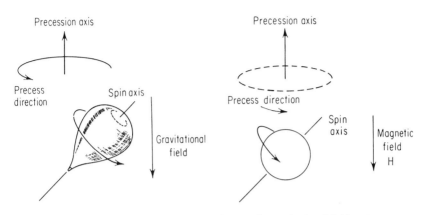

Fig. 5.5. Gyroscopic action of spinning top in gravitational field and of nucleus in magnetic field tend to tip over precessing body.

field until resonance absorption occurs or, vice versa, one may vary the intensity of the d-c stationary field with a fixed frequency of the oscillating field. It is believed that the latter technique is the more common.

The principle of n.m.r. was discovered independently but almost simultaneously by E. M. Purcell of Harvard University and F. Bloch of Stanford University in 1946.[52] Procedures analogous to ultraviolet or infrared spectroscopy are used.[55] For example, in place of a beam of light, one uses a

[50]This is the classical view of n.m.r. According to the quantum mechanical approach, a nucleus placed in a magnetic field may take only certain positions relative to the field, and in n.m.r. spectroscopy, one observes transitions between the energy levels of the nuclei. The quantized resonance absorption frequencies v can be expressed as

$$v = \frac{\gamma H_0}{2\pi} \sec^{-1} = \frac{\mu H_0}{Ih}$$

where γ = magnetogyric ratio of the nucleus,

h = Planck's constant,

H_0 = external homogeneous magnetic field strength,

I = magnetic moment of the nucleus,

μ = 5.0493×10^{-24} erg gauss.

[51]G. V. D. Tiers, *J. Phys. Chem.*, **62**, 1151 (1958).

[52]Closely related to n.m.r. is e.s.r., electron spin resonance spectroscopy, sometimes called paramagnetic resonance spectroscopy.[53] E.s.r. is concerned with magnetic resonance experiments in which electron spin rather than nuclear spin is involved. The method is useful only for molecules possessing one or more unpaired electrons; hence, it is of particular value in the study of free radicals.[54]

[53]G. K. Fraenkel, *Techniques of Organic Chemistry*, ed. A. Weissberger, vol. I, pt. IV (3rd ed.; New York: Interscience, 1960), chap. 42; *Determination of Organic Structures by Physical Methods*, vol. 2, ed. F. C. Nachod and W. D. Phillips (New York: Academic, 1962), chaps. 9 and 10.

[54]J. A. McMillan, *J. Chem. Educ.*, **38**, 438 (1961).

[55]*NMR and EPR Spectroscopy*, ed. Varian Associates (New York: Pergamon, 1960).

magnetic field; instead of working in the wavelength range of say 10^{-5} cm, one works in the region of 500 cm (FM radio); in place of a prism or grating to produce an incident spectrum, one uses a sweep generator to alter the current which energizes the magnet; rather than a photoelectric cell for a detector, one uses a radio-frequency receiver. There is one fundamental difference, however. The absorption bands exhibited by a molecule depend upon the number of nonequivalent atoms of a given element present. For example, the three types of protons of ethyl alcohol—the methyl protons, the methylene protons, and the hydroxyl proton—produce three different absorption bands. Since the range of resonance conditions for the different protons is extremely small compared to the absolute values of H and ν, it is customary to express the conditions for resonance in terms of per cent differences in H (the *chemical shift* δ). This difference is reported for the type of proton in question (in the case of proton n.m.r. spectra) and the resonance field for a type of proton in an arbitrarily chosen compound. That is,

$$\delta = \frac{H_{ref} - H_{obs}}{H_{ref}} \text{ (ppm)}$$

where H_{ref} and H_{obs} are the resonance fields for the reference compound and the proton being studied, respectively. Tiers[51] has proposed a widely used system for expressing chemical shifts based on the use of tetramethylsilane as the reference compound or internal standard. In this system, the chemical shift, τ, is expressed as the difference in parts per million (ppm) from the resonance position for tetramethyl silane on a scale which assigns a value of $\tau = 10$ to the resonance for $(CH_3)_4Si$.

$$\tau \text{ (in ppm)} = 10.00 - 10^6 \left(\frac{H_{Me_4Si} - H_{obs}}{H_{Me_4Si}} \right)$$

Under this convention, the larger is τ the greater is the shielding.

   N.m.r. spectra are exhibited only by atoms with nuclear magnetic moments, i.e., nuclei not possessing an even atomic number and an even mass number. Thus, the atoms of H^1, F^{19}, Cl^{35}, N^{14}, O^{17}, P^{31}, and C^{13} yield n.m.r. spectra but C^{12} and O^{16} do not.[56] The vast majority of work has been done with proton n.m.r. spectra, and the only commercial console model available for some years was for proton spectra.

   Inasmuch as the diamagnetic chemical shift depends on electron density around a given atom, it is not surprising to find a correlation between the chemical shift for a given atom and the electronegativities of the atoms attached to the observed atom. Such a correlation was used in Sec. 2.2 to

---

[56]For a compilation of the n.m.r. spectra of 115 organic compounds containing O^{17}, see H. A. Christ, P. Diehl, H. R. Schneider, and H. Dahn, *Helv. Chim. Acta,* **44**, 865 (1961).

establish a sequence of relative group electronegativities. However, there is one inaccuracy in the use of chemical shifts for ascertaining relative electronegativities: it is that chemical shifts are affected by magnetic anistropy of neighboring bonds. The τ values for protons, when attached to CH_3-, $HC{\equiv}C-$, $H_2C{=}CH-$, and C_6H_5- groups, decrease in that order. This order does not parallel the electronegativity of the carbon atom to which the proton is attached. Although the protons of the methyl group are more shielded than a vinyl proton, as predicted from the greater s character of the sp^2 carbon bonding orbitals, the τ value for the acetylenic proton (sp hybridization of carbon) falls between the values for the other two groups.

The anomalously high shielding of the acetylenic proton arises from the large induced field H_i parallel to the cylindrical π electron cloud about the $C{\equiv}C$ bond.[57] This is greatest when the $C-C$ axis is parallel to the

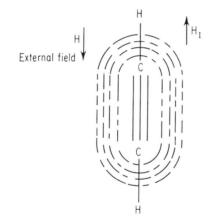

applied field. The induced current in the π electron cloud can follow the cylindrical contours of the cloud, and the induced field H_i opposes the external field in the vicinity of the proton. Molecules with other orientations would have smaller induced fields and proton shielding, but random orientation does not average out this enhanced shielding; hence, a net effect is observed.

On the other hand, the magnetic anisotropy of an aromatic ring produces an unshielding of the ring protons. The magnetic field induces the π electrons to flow around the ring in a closed circuit which sets up a magnetic field at the center opposed to the applied field. The magnetic flux will reinforce the applied field at the edges of the ring and thereby produce an unshielding effect there (Fig. 5.6), which leads to a low τ value

[57] J. A. Pople, *J. Chem. Phys.*, **24**, 1111 (1956).

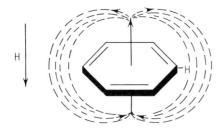

H

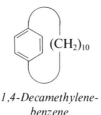

Fig. 5.6. Magnetic anisotropy of the benzene ring.

for aromatic protons.[57] Additional support for this free-electron model is found in the observation that the aromatic protons of alkylbenzenes exhibit chemical shifts much more positive (less shielding) than the side-chain protons, and the resonance signals appear at increasingly higher fields as the protons get away from the ring.[58] In 1,4-decamethylenebenzene, for example, the central CH_2 groups are confined to a region near the center of the benzene ring and experience an "induction field" of

$(CH_2)_{10}$

*1,4-Decamethylene-
benzene*

opposite sign to that exerted on the aromatic protons. Thus, δ for the ring protons is at $+2.21$ ppm, at -2.2 ppm for the α protons, about -3.5 ppm for the β protons, and -4.0 ppm for the ϵ protons (all relative to water).

With high resolution, it is observed that n.m.r. bands may consist of several smaller peaks. This fine structure is due to an effect of neighboring protons on a given proton, called *spin-spin interaction.* One explanation of this interaction attributes it to a transmitted magnetic coupling of the spins of protons on adjacent atoms. For illustration, the spin of proton H_a (heavy arrow) in Fig. 5.7 will couple with the electron in the $C-H_a$ bond whose spin is opposite to that of H_a. The other $C-H_a$ bonding electron will then be statistically nearer the carbon atom. In a similar fashion, the latter electron will couple with one of the $C-C$ bonding electrons, and this effect is transmitted to the electrons in the $C-H_b$ bond. Thereby, H_a produces a magnetic transition at H_b depending on the magnetic orientation of H_a with respect to H_b. Since H_a can have two orientations, $+1/2$ and $-1/2$, the spectrum for H_b will consist of two lines. The

[58] J. S. Waugh and R. W. Fessenden, *J. Am. Chem. Soc.,* **79,** 846 (1957).

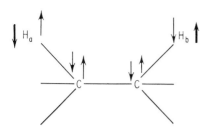

Fig. 5.7. Spin-spin coupling of H_a and H_b.

spectrum for H_a will consist of a doublet too, because its peak is "split" by spin-spin coupling with H_b.

The amount of splitting depends on the number of protons on adjacent atoms. A given band is split into $n + 1$ peaks where n is the number of protons on the adjacent atoms. Take the classical example of ethanol, in which there are three sets of nonequivalent protons. Under moderate resolution there are three resonance signals with an intensity ratio of 1:2:3. The assignment of these bands to the one hydroxyl proton, the two methylene protons, and the three methyl group protons is therefore easily made. With higher resolution, it is observed (Fig. 5.8) that the CH_3 proton band (C) consists of three peaks and the CH_2 proton band (B) has four peaks.[59]

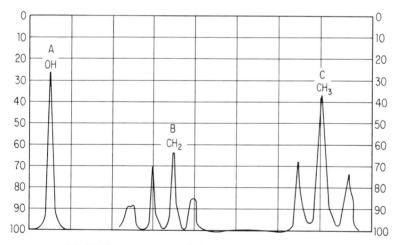

Fig. 5.8. NMR spectrum of ethyl alcohol. This spectrum shows three groups of peaks corresponding to the three chemical groups of the molecules: A, the hydroxyl group; B, the methylene group; and C, the methyl group.

[59]Work at still higher resolution has revealed a splitting of the hydroxyl band into three peaks from spin-spin coupling with the methylene protons and a further splitting of the four methylene peaks into doublets from spin-spin coupling with the hydroxyl proton (cf. I. Weinberg and J. R. Zimmerman, *J. Chem. Phys.,* 748 (1955)).

The three separate signals arise because the magnetic environments (due to bonding electrons) around the protons at the three different sites in the molecule are different.

As another example, the spectrum of 2,3,5-trimethylphenol (Fig. 5.9) shows three groups corresponding to three types of protons. Group A contains two peaks from the two chemically different ring hydrogens. The equal area under the peaks indicates the presence of an equal number of such protons—in this case, one each. The unequal doublet in group C, the methyl protons, is in accord with the presence of two types of CH_3 groups relative to the position of the hydroxyl group (i.e., activation by the OH group) and also shows that one type is twofold the other in number. Since the analysis of n.m.r. spectra consists primarily in determining the values of the coupling constant J and chemical shifts δ for each group of equivalent magnetic nuclei in a molecule, it has been convenient to classify compounds according to spin systems.[49(d)]   Thus, CH_3CH_2OH and $CH_3CH_2C{\equiv}CH$ belong to the A_3B_2C spin system and CH_3CH_2I to the A_3B_2 spin system.

Two features of the spin-spin coupling phenomenon are the amount of separation of the split peaks and their relative intensities. The relative intensities are based on the statistical weightings of angular spin energy levels and will not be discussed here.[60] The separations between peaks are expressed in terms of a spin-spin coupling constant J, which has the di-

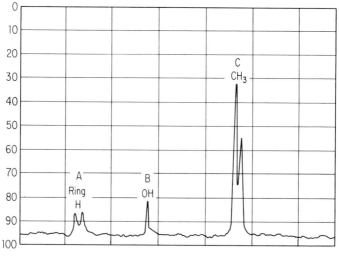

Fig. 5.9. NMR spectrum of 2,3,5-trimethylphenol.

[60]Cf. E. R. Andrew, *Nuclear Magnetic Resonance* (New York: Cambridge U. P., 1955); L. M. Jackman, *Applications of NMR Spectroscopy in Organic Chemistry* (New York: Pergamon, 1959), pp. 20 ff.

mensions of energy and is usually expressed in cycles per second (cps). For example, *cis* protons on a double bond are less strongly coupled (J = 5–11 cps) than *trans* protons (J = 13–18 cps). See Sec. 5.5.2 for an application of this generalization.

Just as two protons may couple, a C^{13} nucleus may couple with an attached proton via magnetic interactions with the intervening bonding electrons. The magnitude of this coupling interaction J_{CH} apparently depends on the probability of finding the bonding electrons at the two nuclei. Since an electron in a pure p orbital of carbon has zero probability of being found at the nucleus of the carbon atom, while this probability is finite for an electron in an s orbital, then it follows that J_{CH} should vary with the s character of hybrid s-p C^{13}—H bonds. This supposition is substantiated by the relative magnitude of C^{13}—H coupling constants found for methane, benzene, and methylacetylene.[61]

	$J_{CH}(\text{sec}^{-1})$
CH_4	125
C_6H_6	159
$CH_3C{\equiv}C^{13}$—H	248

5.4. Spectra-structure relationships

Organic chemists use spectroscopy largely in an empirical fashion. That is, spectra of compounds of known structure are studied in detail and certain relationships between structure and spectra are derived therefrom. Then, structures of new compounds are deduced on the basis of these empirically drawn generalizations. Sometimes a chemist may examine the generalization to try and ascertain some theoretical basis for the relationship, but by and large the empirical approach is used. This section, then, is the heart of this chapter, in which we will discuss some of the obvious as well as some subtle relationships between spectra and molecular structure. We will give particular attention to the influence of resonance, H bonding, electronegativity, polarization, and steric effects on spectra. Numerous examples will be given, with the hope that these will enable the reader to extend the concepts and principles to newly encountered problems.

5.4.1. RESONANCE AND SPECTRA (Also see Sect. 5.4.2)

The relationship between resonance and molecular structure is reflected in infrared spectra as typical group frequencies deviate from the normal

[61]N. Muller and D. E. Pritchard, *J. Chem. Phys.*, **31**, 768 (1959); J. N. Shoolery, *J. Chem. Phys.*, **31**, 1427 (1959).

values. If a particular valence bond resonates between a single and double bond, for example, its infrared frequency will be lower than that of the corresponding pure double bond. That is, the force constant of a single bond is smaller than that of a double bond, and the greater the single-bond character of a given bond type, the lower is its infrared frequency. For illustration, the $\nu_{C=O}$ frequency in acetophenone is 1686 cm^{-1}. When there are *para* substituents which readily accept the positive resonance charge,

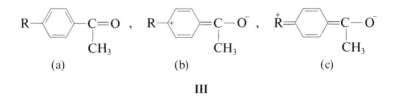

(a)   (b)   (c)

III

the resonance from III (c) increases the single-bond character of the carbonyl group and its infrared frequency is lowered.[62] A similar trend is observed for *p*-substituted benzoic acids[63] and *p*-nitrobenzenes[64] (see Table 5.7). The lack of a consistent trend for the halogens is not surprising in view of the discussion in Sec. 4.10.1. The increase in the carbonyl frequency for mesomeric electron-withdrawing groups (e.g., NO_2) is in accord with the resonance effect of these groups, which opposes that of the carbonyl group.

Table 5.7. INFRARED FREQUENCIES IN *p*-SUBSTITUTED ACETOPHENONES, BENZOIC ACIDS, AND NITROBENZENES

para Substituent	$\nu_{C=O}$ (cm^{-1}) Acetophenones[62,65]	$\nu_{C=O}$ (cm^{-1}) Benzoic acids[63]	ν_{NO_2} (cm^{-1}) Nitrobenzenes[64]
NH_2	1677	1690	1504
OCH_3	(1683)	1695	1517
CH_3	1687 (1688)	1700	1517
H	1691 (1692)	1705	1520
F	1692		
Cl	1692 (1693)	1713	1526
Br	1693 (1693)	1710	1532
I	1693 (1689)		1513
NO_2	1700 (1700)	1720	1560

[62] R. N. Jones, W. F. Forbes, and W. A. Mueller, *Can. J. Chem.,* **35,** 504 (1957); A. H. Soloway and S. L. Friess, *J. Am. Chem. Soc.,* **73,** 5000 (1951).

[63] M. St. C. Flett, *Trans. Faraday Soc.,* **44,** 767 (1948).

[64] R. D. Kross and V. A. Fassel, *J. Am. Chem. Soc.,* **78,** 4225 (1956).

The carbonyl frequency of amides is lower than that of the corresponding acids and esters as a result of the large contribution of the ionic form to the resonance of the amide.

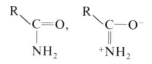

Thus, the ν_{CO} stretching band for a simple ester, acid, and amide are approximately 1730, 1700, and 1660 cm^{-1}, respectively.[66]

Most α-substituted ketones exhibit two closely spaced bands which may be attributed to the presence of *cis* and *gauche* conformations.[67]

cis   gauche

Generally, the band at higher frequency also has the larger intensity and is assigned to the *cis* conformation. The frequencies of these bands can be shown to be affected by the electronegativities, masses, and sizes of the substituents X. The fact that the compound with X = OH has only one band provides evidence that the *cis* conformation is stabilized by an intramolecular H bond to the exclusion of the *gauche* conformation

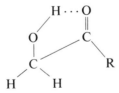

In the N—C=C—C=O system, ν_{CO} is lowered by 20–80 cm^{-1}.[68] Generally, an isolated C=O bond will absorb near 1725 ± 25 cm^{-1}, whereas an enone system, C=C—C=O, absorbs at 20–50 cm^{-1} lower, with increased intensity. Examples will be given in the section on assignment of structure (Sec. 5.5.2).

---

[65]Values in parentheses from J. Tanaka and S. Nagakura, *J. Chem. Phys.*, **24**, 311 (1956).

[66]H. H. Freedman, *J. Am. Chem. Soc.*, **77**, 6003 (1955).

[67]Cf. R. N. Jones and E. Spinner, *Can. J. Chem.*, **36**, 1020 (1958); J. L. Adelfang, P. H. Hess, and N. H. Cromwell, *J. Org. Chem.*, **26**, 1402 (1961).

[68]R. L. Frank and D. J. Wallace, *J. Am. Chem. Soc.*, **71**, 3337 (1949).

The infrared spectra of α-silyl ketones provides strong evidence for a large single-bond character of the carbonyl bond:

Compound	ν_{CO} (cm^{-1})
$\phi_3SiCO\phi$	1620
$Me_3SiCO\phi$	1620
$\phi_3SiCOMe$	1650
$\phi_3C{-}CO\phi$	1690
$\phi CO\phi$	1662
$\phi COMe$	1690
$MeCOMe$	1720

The carbonyl frequency is significantly lower than that of aryl or alkyl ketones and implies a large contribution from resonance structures [IV(b)]. The ultraviolet spectra of the silylketones are in accord with this structure,

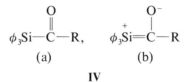

(a)   (b)

IV

and all of the compounds are visibly yellow.[69]

In Sec. 4.10.1, it was pointed out that possibly when Cl, Br, or I is *para* to a strong electron-donating group, the halogen atom may exhibit electron-acceptor resonance, i.e.,

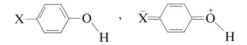

This view accounts for the effects of the halogens on the dissociation constants of *p*-halophenols and *p*-haloanilines. There is a similar trend in the O—H infrared stretching frequencies of the *p*-halophenols.[70]

X in p-X—C$_6$H$_4$OH	ν_{OH} (cm^{-1})	$10^{10}K_a$
F	3613.5	0.26
H	3610.5	0.32
Cl	3608.8	1.32
Br	3607.2	1.55
I	3605.8	2.19
NO$_2$	3593.3	121

[69]A. G. Brook, M. A. Quigley, G. J. D. Peddle, N. V. Schwartz, and C. M. Warner, *J. Am. Chem. Soc.*, **82**, 5102 (1960).

[70]A. Cabana, J. L. Patenaude, C. Sandorfy, and P. M. Bavin, *J. Phys. Chem.*, **64**, 1941 (1960).

The electrical effects of the substituents, particularly through resonance, weaken the O—H bond and produce a parallel effect on the dissociation constants and the infrared frequencies. When the substituents are in the *meta* position, the principal electrical perturbation is a polar effect of the substituent and the range in frequency is smaller, with fluorine occupying its expected position below hydrogen.

X in m-X—C$_6$H$_4$OH	ν_{OH} (cm^{-1})
H	3610.5
F	3607.5
Cl	3606.2
Br	3604.3
I	3604.0
NO$_2$	3600.5

When the bond order of a bond is increased by resonance, the corresponding absorption frequency will increase. For example, the C—O frequency in aryl ethers is greater than in alkyl ethers. Resonance among ionic forms increases the C—O bond order and force constant; the result is absorption at higher frequencies.[71]

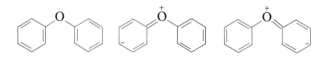

It can be seen, then, that certain substituent effects on infrared group frequencies can be accounted for in terms of resonance. Of course, other properties also affected by resonance would be expected to show similar relationships, and in turn should be correlative with infrared frequencies. Such relationships have been demonstrated for substituted quinones, for example, between ν_{CO} and resonance energies, redox potentials, and free valence indexes.[72]

Since the wavelength of ultraviolet absorption depends upon the $E_1 - E_0$ value, the effect of resonance on ultraviolet spectra depends on whether resonance stabilizes primarily the ground or the excited state. For illustration, the principal resonance of benzene is among Kekulé structures which stabilize the ground state more than the ionic forms stabilize the excited states. The observed λ_{max} corresponds to ΔE_B in Fig. 5.10. In fulvene, the principal resonance is among ionic forms.

[71]H. Tschamler and R. Leutner, *Monatsh. Chem.*, **83**, 1502 (1952).
[72]M. L. Josien, N. Fuson, J. M. Lebas, and T. M. Gregory, *J. Chem. Phys.*, **21**, 331 (1953).

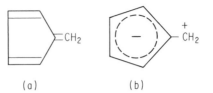

(a)   (b)

This stabilizes the excited state more than the ground state, resulting in a smaller ΔE, i.e., $\Delta E_F < \Delta E_B$. Accordingly, benzene is colorless while fulvene is yellow. A larger difference in color is observed between that of azulene (deep blue) and its colorless isomer, naphthalene. Thus, it is not the magnitude of the resonance energy that determines the effect of resonance on spectra but whether resonance stabilizes the excited state relative to the ground state or vice versa. Since hyperconjugation is a form of resonance, the effects of hyperconjugation on λ_m are the same as from resonance. Thus, substitution of alkyl groups for H's on a chromophoric system produces a bathochromic shift.[75] Most often, the increase in λ_m is 5–10 mμ per alkyl group.[76]

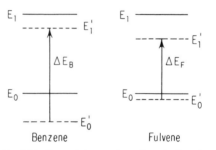

Fig. 5.10. Potential energies of excited and ground states of benzene and fulvene in absence of resonance (E_1, E_0) and with resonance stabilization (E'_1, E'_0).

Ultraviolet spectra reflect changes in energy of excited as well as ground states whereas certain other properties just reveal changes in ground-state energies. Hence, studies of ultraviolet spectra together with other properties can provide some information about the relative energy changes in the two states. For example, heats of combustion and dissociation constants of

[73]Cf. V. P. Kreiter, W. A. Bonner, and R. H. Eastman, *J. Am. Chem. Soc.*, **76**, 5770 (1954).

[74]A. R. Katritzky, A. J. Boulton, and D. J. Short, *J. Chem. Soc.*, 2954 (1960).

[75]*Bathochromic* or *red-shift* is a change of λ_m towards longer wavelengths; *hypsochromic* or *blue-shift* is a change of λ_m to shorter wavelengths; *hyperchromic* and *hypochronic* changes are increases and decreases, respectively, in the absorptivity.

[76]Cf. L. N. Ferguson, *Chem. Revs.*, **43**, 404 (1948).

biphenyl derivatives, properties concerned only with ground states, indicate that resonance interaction between the phenyl rings of biphenyl is rather small in the ground state.[73] However, the resonance interaction in 4-nitro-4'-hydroxybiphenyl in the excited state produces a λ_m much larger than the additive effect of the individual nitro and hydroxy groups. Thus, the resonance between rings is small in the ground state and has negligible

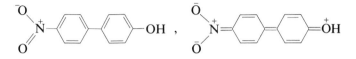

effects on properties concerned only with ground states, but the resonance in the excited state is appreciable and produces a significant bathochromic effect in its spectrum. Similarly, group interactions as determined by relative basicities on the one hand and by ultraviolet spectra on the other indicate that there is only a small resonance delocalization in the ground state of substituted stilbenes and stilbazoles but much greater resonance among polar structures in the excited states.[74]

The conjugation of chromophores normally increases the resonance stabilization of the excited states and increases λ_m. That is, more charge-separation resonance structures can be written, which brings about a net stabilization of the excited state. For illustration, $C_6H_5—CH{=}CH—CH_3$ (λ_m = 293 mμ) absorbs at a longer wavelength than $C_6H_5—CH_2—CH{=}CH_2$ (λ_m = 259 mμ).[77] Several examples of the increase in λ_m with increasing conjugation are given in Tables 5.8 to 5.10.

Table 5.8. COLOR AND λ_m OF DIPHENYLPOLYENES, $\phi—(CH{=}CH)_n—\phi$[78]

n	Visible color of compound	λ_m (mμ) (in benzene)
1	Colorless	319
2	Colorless	352
3	Pale yellow	377
4	Greenish yellow	404
5	Orange	424
6	Brownish orange	445
7	Reddish orange	465
11	Violet black	530
15	Greenish black	570

[77]R. W. Campbell, S. Linden, S. Godshalk, and W. G. Young, *J. Am. Chem. Soc.*, **69**, 880 (1947).

[78]R. Kuhn, *J. Chem. Soc.*, 605 (1938), and references cited therein.

Table 5.9. λ_{max} FOR SOME POLYENES[79]

n in $CH_3-(CH=CH)_n-CH_3$	λ_m (mμ)
2	227
3	263
4	299
5	326
6	352
8	395.5
9	412.5
10 (*cis*)	419

Table 5.10. λ_m OF SOME LINEARLY CONJUGATED
POLYNUCLEAR HYDROCARBONS

n	λ_m (mμ)		Compound	Visible color	λ_m (mμ)
0	251.5		Benzene	Colorless	203
1	280				
2	300				
3	310		Naphthalene	White	314
4	317.5				
			Anthracene	Buff	370
			Naphthacene	Yellow	460
			Pentacene	Blue	580
			Hexacene	Green	600

[79]F. Bohlmann and H. J. Mannhardt, *Chem. Ber.*, **89**, 1307 (1956).
[80]E. M. Kosower and D. C. Remy, *Tetrahedron*, **5**, 281 (1959).
[81]Most often, the dipole moments of molecules in excited states are severalfold the moments in the ground state. Cf. J. Czekalla and G. Wick, *Z. Elektrochem.*, **65**, 727 (1961).

Enone, C=C—C=O, and single carbonyl groups are readily distinguishable from their ultraviolet as well as their infrared spectra. The single C=O bond gives a low-intensity $n \longrightarrow \pi^*$ band ($\epsilon < 100$) near 275 mμ and a single C=C bond gives a high-intensity band ($\epsilon > 10^4$) near 195 mμ. When the two groups are conjugated, the two bands occur in the region 310–330 mμ and 220–260 mμ, respectively. Also, the thio-semi-carbazones of saturated and unsaturated carbonyl compounds have different absorption bands. The 230-mμ and 271-mμ bands of the saturated compounds move up to 245 and 302 mμ, respectively. These spectral differences are summarized in Table 5.11. See also Sect. 5.4.2ii.

Table 5.11. SPECTRAL CHARACTERISTICS OF CARBONYL COMPOUNDS

Basic structure	Infrared frequencies	Ultraviolet bands (λ_m in mμ)	
—CH$_2$—CO—CH$_2$ (open chain)	1725 ± 25 cm^{-1}	275	($\epsilon < 100$)
—CH=CH—C=O	1665–1685 cm^{-1}	220–260	($\epsilon > 10^4$)
		310–330	
$=$C—$\overset{\overset{\text{O}}{\|}}{\text{C}}$—C$=$	1650–1670		
R$_2$C=N—NHCSNH$_2$		230, 271	
C=C—C=N—NHCSNH$_2$		245, 302	

The conjugation of a three-membered ring and a C=O group are easily recognized spectroscopically.[82] From the data below, for example, it can be seen that the conjugation of a three-membered ring is between that of a C=C bond and a saturated bond.

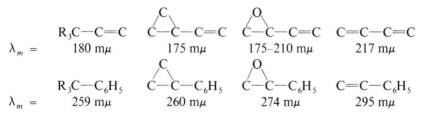

$$\lambda_m = \quad R_3C—C=C \quad\quad C\overset{\overset{\text{C}}{\triangle}}{-}C—C=C \quad\quad C\overset{\overset{\text{O}}{\triangle}}{-}C—C=C \quad\quad C=C—C=C$$
$$\lambda_m = \quad\quad 180 \text{ m}\mu \quad\quad\quad 175 \text{ m}\mu \quad\quad\quad 175\text{–}210 \text{ m}\mu \quad\quad 217 \text{ m}\mu$$

$$\quad\quad R_3C—C_6H_5 \quad\quad C\overset{\overset{\text{C}}{\triangle}}{-}C—C_6H_5 \quad\quad C\overset{\overset{\text{O}}{\triangle}}{-}C—C_6H_5 \quad\quad C=C—C_6H_5$$
$$\lambda_m = \quad\quad 259 \text{ m}\mu \quad\quad\quad 260 \text{ m}\mu \quad\quad\quad 274 \text{ m}\mu \quad\quad\quad 295 \text{ m}\mu$$

When two chromophoric systems are insulated, that is, separated by one or more saturated carbon atoms, *meta* oriented about a benzene ring, or far from being planar because of steric hindrance, the molecule will have absorption bands characteristic of each chromophoric system. If the two chromophores are identical, one band will be observed with an inten-

[82] See also N. H. Cromwell, F. A. Schumacher, and J. L. Adelfang, *J. Am. Chem. Soc.*, **83**, 974 (1961); M. F. Hawthorne, *J. Org. Chem.*, **21**, 1523 (1956).

sity approximately twice that for the single chromophore.[83] For instance, λ_m for the compound C_6H_5—CH=N—CH_3 is identical to that of C_6H_5—CH=N—CH_2—N=CH—C_6H_5, whereas the molar absorptivity of the latter compound is almost twice that of the former. Other examples[84] of this effect of insulated chromophoric systems are given in Table 5.12. When the two insulated chromophoric systems are dissimilar, the com-

Table 5.12. SPECTRAL CHARACTERISTICS OF SOME SINGLE AND INSULATED CHROMOPHORIC SYSTEMS

Compound	λ_m	ϵ
C_6H_5—CH=N—⬡	263 mμ	16,800
C_6H_5—CH=N—⬡—N=CH—C_6H_5	267	33,800
C_6H_5—CH=CH—⬡	295	26,300
C_6H_5—CH=CH—⬡—CH=CH—C_6H_5	298	52,700
CH_3—$(CH$=$CH)_2$—$CHOH$—C≡CH	230	28,500
CH_3—$(CH$=$CH)_2$—$CHOH$—C≡C—$CHOH$—$(CH$=$CH)_2$—CH_3	229	74,000

pound may exhibit two absorption bands corresponding to different excitation energies for the two chromophoric systems. For example, in an unsymmetrical benzophenone (VI), there is a cross conjugation between the C_6H_5CO and COC_6H_4X aroyl groups, and such compounds frequently exhibit two bands, one similar to that for $(C_6H_5)_2CO$ and one resembling that for $(p\text{-}XC_6H_4)_2CO$. For instance, benzophenone and 4,4'-dimethoxy-

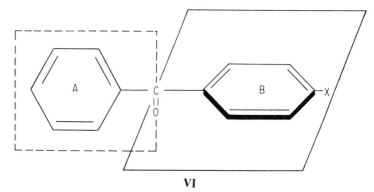

VI

[83] However, this generalization does not always apply to the relative intensities of the absorption band (cf. E. Marcus, W. M. Lauer, and R. T. Arnold, *J. Am. Chem. Soc.*, **80**, 3742 (1958).

[84] Cf. L. N. Ferguson, *Chem. Revs.*, **43**, 397–400 (1948), for other examples.

benzophenone each exhibit one band in the 230–280 mμ region while 4-methoxybenzophenone has two bands. Similarly, 4-Cl-4'-methoxybenzophenone would be expected to exhibit two bands, one corresponding to that for the p-Cl—C_6H_4CO group and one for the p-CH_3O—C_6H_4CO group. These expectations are substantiated by the data given in Table 5.13. The bands attributed to the two separate chromophoric systems are called *partials*.

Table 5.13. SPECTRAL CHARACTERISTICS OF SOME SUBSTITUTED BENZOPHENONES[89a]

Substituents in benzophenone	λ_m (mμ, in cyclohexane)	λ'_m	ϵ	ϵ'
H, H		248		20,000	
4-OCH_3, H		247	274	10,500	17,000
4-OCH_3, 4'-OCH_3			278		27,000
4-Cl, 4'-Cl		261		27,500	
4-Cl, 4'-OCH_3		257	280	15,000	17,500
H, 3-NO_2	229	246		24,000	19,500
3-NO_2, 4'-OCH_3	225		286	30,000	16,000

Some molecules have extensive conjugation in a single direction and it is convenient to classify such systems by one of two categories:[89b] in Class I are compounds of types (VIII) to (X) in which the principal resonance is among dipolar structures. These polar structures stabilize the excited states more than the ground states; hence the compounds closely resemble the nonpolar structures in which there is double-single bond alternation. It has been shown that for this class of conjugated compound, the square of λ_m varies approximately linearly with n, where n is the number of conjugated ethylenic bonds in the principal chromophoric system.[44,90a]

$$R—(CH=CH)_n—CH=CH—R, \qquad R—\overset{\mp}{C}H—(CH=CH)_n—\overset{\pm}{C}H—R$$

Polyenes

VIII

[85] J. H. Pinckard, B. Wille, and L. Zechmeister, *J. Am. Chem. Soc.,* **70**, 1938 (1948).

[86] H. Labhart and G. Wagniere, *Helv. Chim. Acta,* **42**, 2219 (1959).

[87] R. C. Cookson and N. S. Wariyar, *J. Chem. Soc.,* 2302 (1956).

[88] F. F. Caserio and J. D. Roberts, *J. Am. Chem. Soc.,* **80**, 5837 (1958).

[89] (a) E. J. Moriconi, W. F. O'Connor, and W. F. Forbes, *J. Am. Chem. Soc.,* **82**, 5454 (1960); (b) For a review of quantum mechanical treatments of linearly conjugated molecules, see S. F. Mason, *Quart. Revs.* (London), **15**, 344 (1961).

[90] (a) L. N. Ferguson, *Chem. Revs.,* **43**, 408 (1948); K. Hirayama, *J. Am. Chem. Soc.,* **77**, 373 (1955); J. J. Panouse, *Bull. soc. chim. France,* 1568 (1956); (b) L. G. S. Brooker and coworkers, *J. Am. Chem. Soc.,* **73**, 5345 (1951), and earlier papers; N. I. Fisher and F. M. Hamer, *Proc. Roy. Soc.,* **A163**, 138 (1937).

$$R-(CH=CH)_n-CHO, \qquad R-\overset{+}{C}H-(CH=CH)_n-O^-$$

Polyenals

IX

$$R-(CH=CH)_n-CH=N-N=CH-(CH=CH)_m-R,$$

$$R-\overset{+}{C}H-(CH=CH)_n-\overset{-}{N}-N=CH-(CH=CH)_m-R,$$

$$R-\overset{-}{C}H-(CH=CH)_n-N=\overset{+}{N}=CH-(CH=CH)_m-R,$$

$$R-\overset{\mp}{C}H-(CH=CH)_n-N=N-(CH=CH)_m-\overset{\mp}{C}H-R$$

Polyenazines

X

Linearly conjugated compounds in Class II are of types XI, for which

$$R_2N-(CH=CH)_n-CH=\overset{+}{N}R_2, \qquad R_2\overset{+}{N}=CH-(CH=CH)_n-NR_2$$

(a)   (b)

XI

the principal resonance is among forms that stabilize the ground states more than the excited states of the substances. That is, XI is the structure of a stable salt and represents the normal state of the substance. Owing to the equivalence of the two forms, the carbon-carbon bonds theoretically lose their single-double bond alternation. It is found experimentally that for compounds of Class II, λ_m varies linearly with the first power of n.[90b] The transition energies of these two classes of compounds have been schematically represented in Fig. 5.11.[91] The upper dashes represent the po-

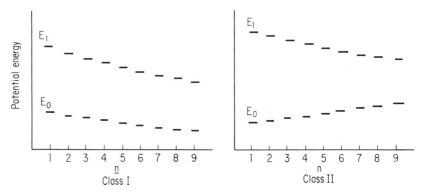

Fig. 5.11. Schematic representation of electronic transition energies of linearly conjugated compounds.[91]

[91]A. Maccoll, Quart. Revs., 1, 11 (1947).

tential energies of the excited states and the lower dashes represent the potential energies of the ground states of the compounds for a given value of n. As n increases in Class I, the excited and ground states are increasingly stabilized but since the resonance is among dipolar structures, there is an increasing net stabilization of excited states. The slope of the upper dashes in Fig. 5.11 is greater than that of the ground-state dashes, which leads to a relationship $\lambda_m^2 \alpha n$. As n increases for Class II, there is less and less resonance between forms XI(a) and XI(b), because greater electron rearrangement must occur for the positive charge to travel from one nitrogen atom to the other. This produces a small increase in potential energy of the ground states as n increases. On the other hand, polar forms of the type

$$R_2N-CH=CH-CH=CH-\overset{+}{CH}-NR_2$$

$$R_2N-CH=CH-\overset{+}{CH}-CH=CH-NR_2$$

$$R_2N-\overset{+}{CH}-CH=CH-CH=CH-NR_2$$

contribute primarily to the excited states. The longer the conjugated chain, the greater is the number of such structures possible and the greater is the resonance stabilization of the excited states. Thus, the slopes of the dashes for the excited and ground states approach each other and $E_1 - E_0$ gets smaller with increasing n at a faster rate than for Class I compounds. In this case, we have the relationship $\lambda_m \alpha n$.

It is noteworthy that compounds of either class may be converted into the other. For example, when a polyene is placed in a strong Lewis acid medium to give a carbonium ion,

$$R-CH=CH-CH=CH-R \xrightarrow{A} R-\overset{\overset{\displaystyle A^-}{\displaystyle |}}{CH}-\overset{+}{CH}-CH=CH-R,$$

$$R-\overset{\overset{\displaystyle A^-}{\displaystyle |}}{CH}-CH=CH-\overset{+}{CH}-R$$

where A is an acid, the compound changes from Class I to Class II and usually a visible color develops. For the same value of n, compounds of Class II will normally have larger λ_m's than compounds of Class I.

If a molecule has an extended conjugation in two dimensions, it can have two optical axes. Upon electronic excitation, electronic oscillations can occur along either axis to give rise to excited states of different potential energies and, hence, absorption bands of different wavelengths. It is common to associate the band of longest wavelength with the direction of greater polarizability and call it the x-band. The band corresponding to the axis at right angles to this major axis is called the y-band.[92]   Two types of molecules having substantial projections along x and y axes are triphenylcarbonium ion

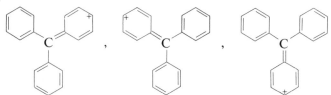

and tetracyclones.[93]

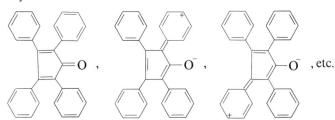

An excellent illustration of the assignment of x- and y-bands is provided by the spectra of some triphenylmethane dyes. Owing to the symmetry of crystal violet (XII), its x- and y-bands are at the same wavelength and consequently the compound exhibits only one band in the long-wavelength region. Malachite green (XIII) should have an x-band of approximately the same wavelength as crystal violet but a y-band of shorter wavelength, since the unsubstituted ring would not accept the positive charge as readily as the NMe_2 group. This gives the molecule a smaller polarizability in the y-direction. Methoxy-malachite green (XIV) should also have two bands, an x-band close to that of malachite green and a y-band of longer wavelength than the y-band of malachite green. Finally, Michler's hydrol (XV) would be expected to have an x-band near that of (XIII) and (XIV) but no y-band. These expectations are confirmed by the actual spectra of the compounds.[94]   The λ_m values are listed in Table 5.14.

Table 5.14. λ_m Values for x- and y-Bands of Some Triphenylmethane Dyes[94]

	x-Band	y-Band
Crystal violet (XII)	590* mμ	
Malachite green (XIII)	621	428
Methoxymalachite green (XIV)	608	465
Michler's hydrol (XV)	595	

*In ethanol. All other values in acetic acid.

[92] G. N. Lewis and M. Calvin, *Chem. Revs.*, **25**, 273 (1939).
[93] S. B. Coan, D. E. Trucker, and E. I. Becker, *J. Am. Chem. Soc.*, **75**, 900 (1953).
[94] G. N. Lewis and J. Bigeleisen, *J. Am. Chem. Soc.*, **65**, 2102 (1943).

XII

XIII

XIV

XV

It is noteworthy that effects which reduce the electronic oscillation in one direction tend to increase it in the other direction. For example, if there is a group in the 4 position of malachite green which repels the oscillating positive charge, then the x-band exhibits a small bathochromic shift.

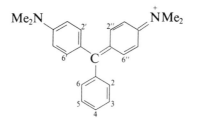

Thus, the λ_x for 4-nitromalachite green is of longer wavelength than that of malachite green. This explains why the λ_x of the dyes listed in Table 5.14 are not at identical wavelengths. A similar shunting of the charge from the x to the y direction or vice versa can be brought about by steric hindrance. For instance, substituents in the 2 or 6 position of malachite green produce small bathochromic shifts of the x-band and hyposochromic shifts of the y-band.[95] Apparently, the *ortho* substituents force the phenyl group to rotate out of the plane of the molecule, thereby partially insulating

[95]C. C. Barker, *et al., J. Chem. Soc.,* 1285 (1961).

the group from the main optical axis and increasing the electronic motion in the x-direction. It has been observed that replacement of the N-methyl groups of malachite green by other substituents produces shifts in λ_x and λ_y which at first glance seem to be correlative with the sizes of the groups.[96]

R_2N in $R_2N-\langle\bigcirc\rangle-\overset{\overset{C_6H_5}{\mid}}{C}=\langle\bigcirc\rangle=\overset{+}{N}R_2$			λ_x	λ_y
Dobner's violet	H_2N	NH_2	568 mμ	399 mμ
Malachite green	Me_2N	NMe_2	621	428
	$(C_6H_5)_2N$	$N(C_6H_5)_2$	670	470

Nevertheless, there is need for much work in this area because the effects of nuclear and nitrogen substituents and of solvents on the positions of λ_x and λ_y of malachite green have still not been clearly explained.[97]

We see, then, that resonance among polar structures can produce a marked stabilization of the excited state relative to the ground state of a molecule and lead to ultraviolet absorption at longer wavelengths. As another example, the three types of compounds XVI, XVII, and XVIII each exhibit bathochromic shifts when placed in an acidic *or* basic medium. In each case, acid or base produces an ion for which two completely equivalent structures can be written. This means that acid or base produces ions which are stabilized by resonance, more so than the neutral compound, and this leads to absorption at longer wavelengths.

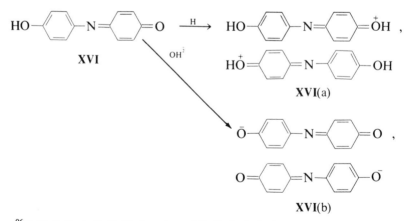

[96]B. M. Tolbert, G. E. K. Branch, and B. E. Berlenback, *J. Am. Chem. Soc.*, **67**, 887 (1945).
[97]C. C. Barker and G. Hallas, *J. Chem. Soc.*, 1529 (1961).

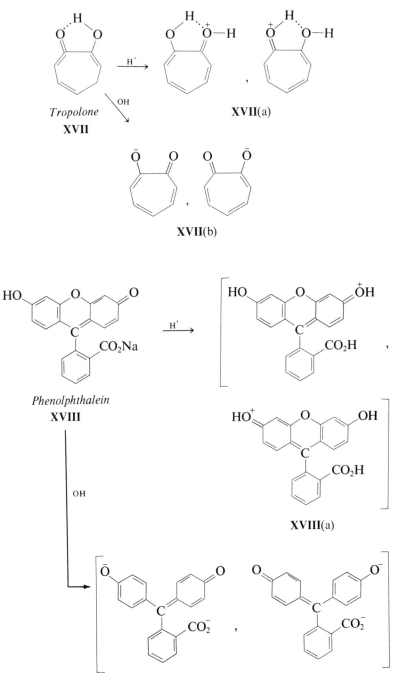

Tropolone
XVII

XVII(a)

XVII(b)

Phenolphthalein
XVIII

XVIII(a)

XVIII(b)

Resonance has a significant effect on n.m.r. proton shifts too. Electron-withdrawing groups, which generally increase the acidity of the ring protons in the order $o > p > m$, also produce proton chemical shifts to lower fields in the same order. Electron-donating groups produce shifts in the same order but to higher fields (see Table 4.24).

It must be emphasized that the major weakness in the interpretation of spectra in terms of resonance theory is that it is entirely qualitative. On the other hand, quantum mechanical theories have had considerable success in the quantitative prediction and interpretation of spectra.[98]

5.4.2 INTRAMOLECULAR ENVIRONMENT AND SPECTRA

Absorption spectral measurements are especially effective in revealing various types of intramolecular interactions. For instance, bond angle strain and transannular dipole-dipole, van der Waals, or magnetic effects in cyclic compounds, steric inhibition of resonance or H bonding, and buttressing effects (Sect. 3.3.3) are readily detected by one or more of the several types of absorption spectroscopy. Although there is considerable overlapping, we shall divide this general topic of intramolecular environment and spectra into three segments and discuss the first two in this Section and the third as part of the next Section: steric inhibition of conjugation, transannular effects in alicyclic compounds, and steric inhibition of hydrogen bonding.

5.4.2 (a) Steric Inhibition of Conjugation

When steric requirements prevent the coplanarity of two parts A and B of a conjugated system A-B, there are three types of spectral changes observed in the ultraviolet for the longest-waved band:

$$\text{Type I: hypsochromic shift} \qquad \Delta\lambda < 0$$
$$\text{Type II: negligible wavelength shift} \qquad \Delta\lambda \sim 0$$
$$\text{Type III: bathochromic shift} \qquad \Delta\lambda > 0$$

where $\Delta\lambda$ is the difference in λ_m for the corresponding hindered and unhindered systems. Essentially in all three cases there will be a decrease in intensity of absorption. This classification is merely one for convenience because examples fall in a continuous spectrum from Type I through Type III.[99a,100] The classification of a particular system into one of these three

[98]See leading references in S. F. Mason, *Quart. Revs. (London)*, **15**, 287 (1961).

[99](a) E. Heilbronner and R. Gerdie, *Helv. Chim. Acta*, **39**, 1996 (1956); (b) An alternative approach in explaining these Type I-III steric effects on ultraviolet spectra has been to use molecular orbital models. Cf. reference 99a, and M. J. S. Dewar, "Steric Effects in Conjugated Systems," edited by G. W. Gray, Butterworths, London, 1958, p. 46.

[100]W. F. Forbes, "Steric Effects in Conjugated Systems," edited by G. W. Gray, Butterworths, London, 1958, p. 62.

types depends primarily on whether steric hindrance brings about a net stabilization of the ground or of the excited states, mostly through its interference with resonance.[99b] Examples of the three types can be given here.

Type I: trans-Stilbene has a coplanar structure which permits a complete conjugation across the molecule.

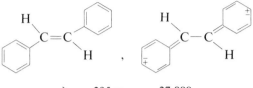

$$\lambda_m = 295 \text{ m}\mu, \epsilon = 27,000$$

Not only is the planarity confirmed by diffraction data, but the C_{ar}-C_{ali} bond distance (1.44 Å) verifies a considerable double bond character for this bond. This accounts for the absorption band at 295 mμ. The *cis* isomer, on the other hand, is not coplanar because the ortho hydrogen atoms would overlap:

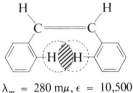

$$\lambda_m = 280 \text{ m}\mu, \epsilon = 10,500$$

This forces one phenyl ring of *cis*-stilbene to be rotated out of the plane of the rest of the molecule and produces hypsochromic shifts of the absorption maxima of *cis* isomers with respect to the corresponding *trans* isomers.[101]

The decreasing order of λ_m for 4-halonitrobenzenes is I > Br > Cl > F, and this same order would be expected for the 2-halonitrobenzenes in the absence of a steric effect. However, the observed order is F > Cl > Br > I. This reverse order can be attributed to the increasing steric inhibition of the nitrobenzene resonance by the ortho halogen atoms.[102] In support of this view, is the fact that λ_m for 2-halopyridines, where there is no steric inhibition of resonance, has the anticipated order I > Br > Cl > F.[103]

Steric hindrance in the biphenyl system has been studied extensively by ultraviolet spectroscopy as well as by other methods (Sec. 3.3.3). Biphenyl

[101]G. Riezebos and E. Havinga, *Rec. trav. Chim.,* **80,** 446 (1961); The spectral relationships of other *cis-trans* systems have been noted: e.g., F. Ramirez and A. F. Kirby, *J. Am. Chem. Soc.,* **76,** 1037 (1954).

[102]H. E. Ungnade, *J. Am. Chem. Soc.,* **76,** 6101 (1954).

[103]H. C. Brown and D. H. McDaniel, *J. Am. Chem. Soc.,* **77,** 3752 (1953).

exhibits a band near 250 mμ which is the result of a transition represented by:

Introduction of groups into ortho positions shifts λ_m to shorter wavelengths as the sizes of the groups increase:

Substituent	λ_m	$\epsilon^{104,105}$
None	249 mμ	14,500
2-Me	237	10,500
2-Et	233	9,000
2,2'-di-Me	220	—

This has been attributed to a steric hindrance to planarity of the biphenyl system.[106a] Similarly in bridged biphenyls, as φ, the angle between phenyl rings, is increased, the "biphenyl" band gradually disappears:[106b]

n	λ_m	Estimated φ	
0	264 mμ	15°	
1	247–8	49°	
2	235–9		
3	231sh	68°	

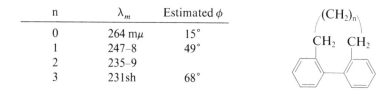

Nevertheless, it has been shown that complete coplanarity of the biphenyl system is not required for partial conjugation.[107] For instance, compound XIX has been resolved into d and l optical isomers, and optical activity here can only arise if the two phenyl rings are non-coplanar. Still, the compound has an absorption band (λ_m = 249 mμ, ϵ = 16,980) which is

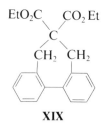

XIX

[104]W. F. Forbes and W. A. Mueller, *Can. J. Chem.*, **33**, 1145 (1955).

[105]M. T. O'Shaughnessy and W. H. Rodebush, *J. Am. Chem. Soc.*, **62**, 2906 (1940).

[106](a) E. A. Braude and E. S. Waight, "Progress in Stereochemistry," vol. I, edited by W. Klyne, Academic Press, New York, 1954, p. 142. (b) K. Mislow, *et al.*, *J. Am. Chem. Soc.*, **84**, 1449 (1962).

[107]D. C. Iffland and H. Siegel, *J. Am. Chem. Soc.*, **80**, 1947 (1958).

typical of the conjugated biphenyl system. The bridge apparently prevents the angle between phenyl rings from becoming too large to cut off all biphenyl-type resonance.

The *buttressing* effect often gives the Type I steric effect too. For illustration, the introduction of methyl groups meta to the keto group of acetophenones, which would otherwise produce a small bathochromic shift, produces a marked *decrease* in absorption.[104]

	λ_m	ϵ
R = H	251 mμ	5,600
R = CH_3	212	11,500
R = H	242 mμ	3,600
R = CH_3	216	12,000

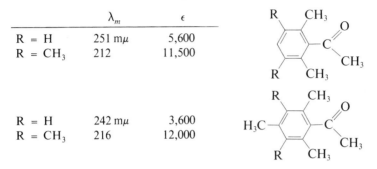

The meta groups prevent the ortho substituents from bending back away from the $COCH_3$ group and thereby produce greater strain in the excited state for the polar resonance structure:

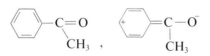

This strain increases the transition energy to produce the observed hypsochromic shift. This can be attributed to a steric effect because the expected bathochromic shift (from a *m*-methyl group) is observed when there are no ortho substituents.

The all *trans*-diphenylbutadiene has a λ_m at 328 mμ, and as the two olefinic bonds are isomerized to *cis* structures, steric hindrance reduces resonance stabilization of the excited state and light absorption occurs at shorter wavelengths and with lower intensity:[85]

Diphenylbutadiene	λ_m	ϵ
trans, trans	328 mμ	56,200
cis,trans	313	30,600
cis,cis	299	29,500

Type II: Frequently, ortho substitution does not appreciably affect λ_m but markedly decreases the band intensity. Several examples of this Type II steric effect are given in Table 5.15. The absorptivity decreases in each series as the sizes of the ortho substituents increase.

Table 5.15 MOLAR ABSORPTIVITIES OF SOME
STERICALLY HINDERED COMPOUNDS

a. Hindrance to the *nitro* group			
R in $R\text{-}C_6H_4NO_2$[108]	ϵ ($\lambda_m \approx 250$ mμ)	R in $4\text{-}Me_2N\text{-}R\text{-}C_6H_3NO_2$[109]	ϵ ($\lambda_m \approx 385$ mμ)
H	8,900	H	18,400
2-Me	6,070	2-Me	16,500
2-Et	5,300	2,6-di-Me	6,500
2-i-Pr	4,150		
2-t-Bu	1,540		
2,4,6-tri-t-Bu	830		

b. Hindrance to the NMe_2 Group			
R in $R\text{-}C_6H_4NMe_2$[108]	ϵ ($\lambda_m \approx 250$ mμ)	R in $R\text{-}C_6H_4NMe_2$[110]	ϵ ($\lambda_m \approx 250$ mμ)
H	15,500	H	14,000
2-Me	6,360	2-F	12,000
2-Et	4,950	2-Cl	7,500
2-i-Pr	4,300	2-Br	6,000
2,6-Di-Me	2,240		
2-t-Bu	630		

c. Side-chain hindrance	
R in $C_6H_5CO\text{-}R$	ϵ ($\lambda_m \approx 238$ mμ)
Me	13,000
Et	11,450
t-Bu	8,100

It has been proposed[111] that a conjugated system A-B may undergo transitions either to locally excited (L.E.) states, in which the π or n electrons originally associated with A and B in the ground state remain associated with these groups, or to electron-transfer states (E.T.) in which a π or n electron is transferred from one part of the molecule to another. Further, for E.T. transitions, steric inhibition of resonance between A and B will result in a decrease in absorption intensity without a bathochromic shift.[112]

Based on Type II steric effects on spectra, the relative resonance inhibiting powers of alkyl groups when ortho to a nitro group have been given as:[113]

[108]B. M. Wepster, "Progress in Stereochemistry," Vol. 2, edited by W. Klyne and P. B. D. de la Mare, Butterworths, London, 1958, p. 99.

[109]W. G. Brown and H. Reagen, *J. Am. Chem. Soc.*, **69**, 1032 (1947).

[110]W. R. Remington, *J. Am. Chem. Soc.*, **67**, 1838 (1945).

[111]H. C. Longuet-Higgins and J. N. Murrell, *Proc. phys. Soc. London*, **A601**, 68 (1955).

[112]J. N. Murrell, *J. Chem. Soc.*, 3779 (1956).

[113]B. M. Wepster, *Rec. trav. Chim.*, **76**, 335, 357 (1957).

H $\ll$ 2-Me $<$ 2-Et $<$ 2,3-di-Me, $\diagdown$ 2-i-Pr $\ll$ 2-t-Bu, 2,6-di-Me $<$

2,6-di-i-Pr $<$ 2,3,5,6-tetra-Me.

Note that one 2-t-Bu group is about as effective as two ortho methyl groups.

On the assumption that complete inhibition of the phenylnitro group resonance would reduce the intensity of λ_m to zero, the fraction of steric inhibition (total inhibition = 1.0) has been calculated from the ratio $(\epsilon^0 - \epsilon)/\epsilon^0$, where ϵ^0 is the absorptivity at λ_m for the parent nitrobenzene and ϵ is the absorptivity at λ_m for the ortho-substituted nitrobenzene.[113] The fraction of steric inhibition produced by ortho substituents has also been calculated from Taft resonance and induction substituent constants.[114] If it is assumed that complete inhibition of resonance would reduce the Hammett substituent constant σ to the induction constant σ_1, the fraction of inhibition of resonance can be expressed by the quantity

$$\sigma_R^0 - \sigma_R / \sigma_R^0$$

where $\sigma_R = \sigma - \sigma_I$ for the resonance inhibited group and $\sigma_R^0 = \sigma^0 - \sigma_I$ for the resonance uninhibited group. It is very gratifying to find that both methods lead to fairly close estimates of resonance inhibition by ortho substituents (Table 5.16). There are theoretical bases for the relationship

$$\text{R.E.}_\phi = \text{R.E.}_0 \cos^2\phi$$

where R.E._0 is the resonance energy for a planar conjugated system A-B and R.E._ϕ is the resonance energy for an angle ϕ between the planes of A

Table 5.16 RESONANCE INHIBITING FRACTIONS AND ANGLES OF TWIST IN SOME ORTHO-SUBSTITUTED COMPOUNDS[114]

| | | Resonance inhibition based on | | |
Compound	Hindered group	Substituent constants	Absorption intensities	Angle of twist
4-Nitroaniline:				
3-Me	NO_2	0.19	0.15	24°
2,3-Di-Me	NO_2	.42	.37	39°
3,5-Di-Me	NO_2	.67	.69	55°
2,3,5,6-Tetra-Me	NO_2	.89	.90	72°
$4\text{-}CO_2Et\text{-}C_6H_4NMe_2$:				
2-Me	NMe_2	.55	.55	47°
2,6-Di-Me	NMe_2	.75	.80	62°
$4\text{-}CO_2Et\text{-}C_6H_4OCH_3$:				
2,6-Di-I	OCH_3	.30	.38	35°
2,6-Di-Me	OCH_3	.59	.62	51°

[113] B. M. Wepster, *Rec. trav. Chim.*, **76**, 335, 357 (1957).
[114] R. W. Taft, Jr. and H. D. Evans, *J. Chem. Phys.*, **27**, 1427 (1957).

and B.[115] The angle ϕ for the hindered groups in Table 5.16 were calculated from the ratios $\dfrac{\epsilon^0 - \epsilon}{\epsilon^0} \simeq \sigma_R/\sigma_R^0 \simeq \text{Cos}^2\phi$,[114] and the values are listed in the Table. By a similar treatment, using the relationship $\dfrac{\epsilon^0 - \epsilon}{\epsilon^0} = \text{Cos}^2\phi$, values of ϕ were calculated for a number of substituted benzaldehydes and acetophenones and found to be in good agreement with values deduced from dipole moment measurements.[116]

Type III: In some systems it is clear that steric hindrance primarily affects ground state resonance and the loss in resonance energy increases E_0 to make $E_1 - E_0$ smaller. This then will produce a bathochromic shift of λ_m. For example, there is a bathochromic shift when the H's on the nitrogen atoms of **XX** are replaced by methyl groups.[117]

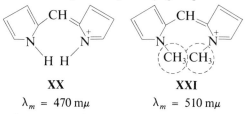

XX	**XXI**
$\lambda_m = 470 \text{ m}\mu$	$\lambda_m = 510 \text{ m}\mu$

The two pyrrole rings can no longer be coplanar because the CH_3 groups would overlap. Since the resonance of these cyanine dyes produces a net stabilization of the ground state (Sec. 5.4.1), any inhibition of this resonance increases E_0 relative to E_1 and $\Delta\lambda$ is > 0. It was shown that this shift is attributable to steric hindrance because when the rings are farther separated by another double bond as in **XXII**, the introduction of the N-methyl group produces a hypsochromic shift,[118] e.g.,

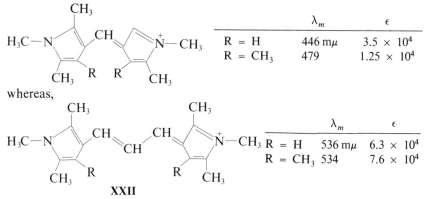

	λ_m	ϵ
R = H	446 mμ	3.5×10^4
R = CH$_3$	479	1.25×10^4

whereas,

	λ_m	ϵ
R = H	536 mμ	6.3×10^4
R = CH$_3$	534	7.6×10^4

XXII

[115]Cf. references cited by B. M. Wepster in ref. 108.
[116]E. A. Braude and F. J. Sondheimer, *J. Chem. Soc.*, 3754 (1955).
[117]K. J. Brunnings and A. H. Corwin, *J. Am. Chem. Soc.*, **64**, 593 (1942).
[118]L. G. S. Brooker, *et al.*, *Chem. Revs.*, **41**, 325 (1947).

Similarly, steric hindrance in **XXIII** produces a bathochromic shift:

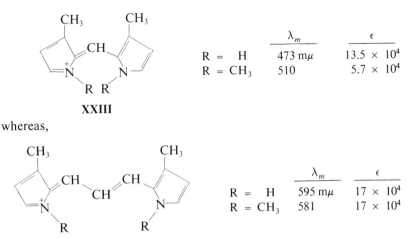

	λ_m	ϵ
R = H	473 mμ	13.5 × 10⁴
R = CH₃	510	5.7 × 10⁴

XXIII

whereas,

	λ_m	ϵ
R = H	595 mμ	17 × 10⁴
R = CH₃	581	17 × 10⁴

Type III steric hindrance is also found in cyclic systems. The 1,3-cyclodienes provide a good example:

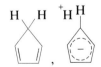

n	λ_m	ϵ
5	238.5 mμ	3,400
6	256	8,000
7	248	7,400
8	228	5,600

An open-chain 1,4-dialkyl-*trans*-1,3-diene has a λ_m at 227 mμ, however, the strain in a *cisoid* diene decreases the stability of the ground state and produces a larger λ_m. Hyperconjugation in the C_5 cyclodiene gives the

ring some aromatic stabilization of the ground state and results in λ_m being smaller than those of the cyclic C_6 and C_7 compounds. Apparently, the double bonds in the *cis,cis* C_{10} cyclodiene are almost completely non-planar for it exhibits no λ_m above 215 mμ.[119a]   Also the cyclophanes, with $n < 4$, have Type III sterically hindered systems. As n gets smaller in these compounds, the benzene ring becomes increasingly strained (and eventually lose their planarity when $n = 2$) and λ_m moves to longer wavelengths with some loss in fine structure.[119b] This indicates that the strained

[119](a) A. T. Blomquist, *et al., J. Am. Chem. Soc.,* **77**, 998 (1955); (b) D. J. Cram, N. L. Allinger, and H. Steinberg, *ibid.,* **76**, 6132 (1954).

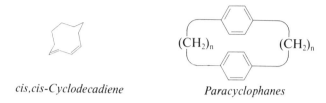

cis,cis-Cyclodecadiene   Paracyclophanes

rings lose a part of their ground state Kekulé resonance stabilization energy and thereby $E_1 - E_0$ is decreased to give larger λ_m values.

Finally, it should be pointed out that when steric hindrance completely eliminates resonance interaction between A and B of the conjugated system A-B, that the spectrum will appear as the approximate sum of the spectra of the two components A and B. For example, the spectrum of bimesityl approximates that of mesitylene,[120a] 2,2-dicarboxybiphenyl has a spectrum similar to that of benzoic acid,[120b] and the spectra of substituted benzils are close to those of the respectively substituted benzaldehydes.[120c] Such steric effects are equivalent to an insulation between the two components A and B by an intervening single bond, and the spectral effects are similar to the previously mentioned *partials*.

Infrared spectra, too, can reveal steric inhibition of conjugation. For example, the 2,7-polymethylene-4,5-benzotropones can be regarded as resonance hybrids of forms such as (a) to (c):

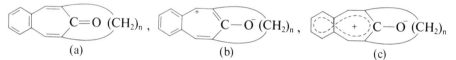

   (a)   (b)   (c)

Form (c) requires a coplanarity of the carbonyl group with the rest of the molecule, but models show that the C=O group is forced up out of the plane for $n < 7$.[121] This is reflected in the carbonyl infrared frequencies:

		$\nu_{C=O}$
2,7-Dimethyl-4,5-benzotropone		1596 cm^{-1}
Polymethylene-4,5-benzotropone	$n = 4$	1724
	5	1675
	6	1651
	7	1609
	8	1604
	9	1611
	12	1590
	13	1602

[120](a) L. W. Pickett, G. F. Walter, and H. France, *J. Am. Chem. Soc.,* **58,** 2296 (1936); (b) B. Williamson and W. H. Rodebush, *ibid.,* **63,** 3018 (1941); (c) N. J. Leonard, R. T. Rapala, H. L. Herzog, and E. R. Blout, *ibid.,* **71,** 2997 (1949).
[121] A. Eschenmoser, E. Heilbronner, *et al., Helv. Chim. Acta,* **39,** 786 (1956).

With $n < 7$, forms (b) and (c) make less and less contribution until at $n = 4$ they are insignificant and the C=O bond is a simple nonconjugated carbonyl bond.

5.4.2(b) Transannular Effects in Alicyclic Compounds

Various transannular interactions have been detected by ultraviolet, infrared, and also n.m.r. spectroscopy, and some of the spectral observations are extremely valuable in facilitating an understanding of intramolecular forces (Cf. Sec. 3.3).

$$\lambda_m = 195, 275\,m\mu$$
$$e = 900, 22$$

$$\lambda_m = 295\,m\mu$$
$$\epsilon = 27$$

Ultraviolet spectra. Simple ketones have an intense band at $\sim 185\,m\mu$ ($\epsilon \sim 10^4$) and a low-intensity $n \longrightarrow \pi^*$ band at $\sim 280\,m\mu$ ($\epsilon \sim 20$–50). For a conjugated α,β-enone system the $\pi \longrightarrow \pi^*$ band of the C=C bond moves to 220–260 mμ ($\epsilon \sim 10^4$) and the $n \longrightarrow \pi^*$ band shifts to 300–350 mμ ($\epsilon \sim$

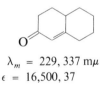

$$\lambda_m = 229, 337\,m\mu$$
$$\epsilon = 16,500, 37$$

50). With suitably oriented C=C (or phenyl) and C=O groups, the π orbitals of the two groups may overlap in either (1) π fashion in which all four atoms are coplanar (either end-to-end as in XXIV.A or side-by-side as in XXIV.B–XXIV.D or (2) by sigma-type overlap of the carbonyl carbon and olefin carbon p orbitals (homoconjugation) as in XXIV.F–XXIV.I. This makes the p_n nonbonding carbonyl oxygen orbital and the C=C π orbital become almost parallel.

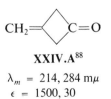

XXIV.A[88]

$$\lambda_m = 214, 284\,m\mu$$
$$\epsilon = 1500, 30$$

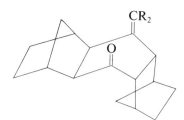

XXIV.B   R = H
XXIV.C   R = H, CH$_3$
XXIV.D   R = CH$_3$

Compound[122a]	Solvent*	λ_m	ϵ	λ'_m	ϵ'
XXIV.B	H	209.5	3110	298.4mμ	32
	A	214sh	1810	297	43
XXIV.C	H	219	2720	301.6	27
	A	224.5	1455	297	33
XXIV.D	H	239	3940	306	31
	A	244	2530	302sh	50

*H = hexane
 A = alcohol

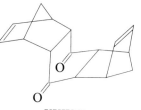

XXIV.E

	λ_m	ϵ	λ'_m	ϵ'
H	220sh	1100	306 mμ	33
A	228sh	1000	300	43

The first type of transannular interaction (π overlap) has the characteristics of an α,β-enone system in that it produces a band in the 200–230 mμ range and the band undergoes a red-shift when the polarity of the solvent is increased or when terminal alkyl groups are added. Solvents have the opposite effect on the $n \longrightarrow \pi^*$ band. It has been proposed that this band be called a *photodesmotic* band (from Greek meaning link caused by

[122](a) S. Winstein, L. DeVries, and R. Orloski, *J. Am. Chem. Soc.,* **83,** 2020 (1961); (b) E. M. Kosower, W. D. Closson, H. L. Goering, and J. C. Gross, *ibid.,* **83,** 2013 (1961).

light) because the transition leads to a weak bend in the excited state.[122b] Also, this type of transannular interaction does not enhance the intensity of the carbonyl $n \rightarrow \pi^*$ band. These spectral characteristics are illustrated by the data for compounds XXIV.A-XXIV.E.

The second type of transannular orbital overlap, homoconjugation, allows a mixing of $\pi \rightarrow \pi^*$ and $n \rightarrow \pi^*$ transitions, and in addition to a photodesmotic band appearing, the $n \rightarrow \pi^*$ band undergoes an increase in intensity.[86,87] Compounds XXIV.F–XXIV.I are examples, and additional cases are given below.

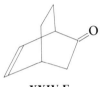

XXIV.F

$\lambda_m = 202, 290 \text{ m}\mu$
$\epsilon = 3000, 110$

XXIV.G

$\lambda_m = 308 \text{ m}\mu$
$\epsilon = 266$

XXIV.H

$\lambda_m = 213\text{–}4, 290 \text{ m}\mu$
$\epsilon = 5500, 562$

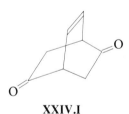

XXIV.I

$\lambda_m = 223, 296, 307 \text{ m}\mu$
$\epsilon = 2290, 267, 267$

It is noteworthy that the mixing of transitions does not affect the ground state of the molecule, as shown by the fact that the $\nu_{C=O}$ is usually in the normal frequency range, i.e., ν_{CO} for XXIV.I is at 1740 cm^{-1}. As to be expected, the saturated ketone XXIV.J does not exhibit a photodes-

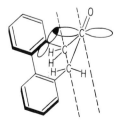

motic band nor an enhanced $n \longrightarrow \pi^*$ band. Models show that the phenyl ring and carbonyl group in XXIV.K, XXIV.M, and XXIV.N are almost perpendicular with π orbitals overlapping in a perpendicular direction. Note that XXIV.L has a typical single carbonyl absorption. A comparison of XXIV.S with XXIV.T reveals that there is only reduced π-type overlap of the C_7 carbonyl and the 1,2-benzo group in the latter compound.

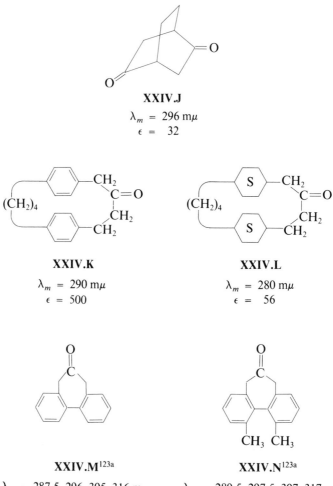

XXIV.J

$\lambda_m = 296$ mμ

$\epsilon = 32$

XXIV.K

$\lambda_m = 290$ mμ

$\epsilon = 500$

XXIV.L

$\lambda_m = 280$ mμ

$\epsilon = 56$

XXIV.M[123a]

$\lambda_m = 287.5, 296, 305, 316$ mμ

$\epsilon = 760, 646, 437, 174$

XXIV.N[123a]

$\lambda_m = 289.5, 297.5, 307, 317$ mμ

$\epsilon = 760, 760, 575, 257$

[123](a) K. Misıow, M. A. W. Glass, R. E. O'Brian, P. Rutkin, D. H. Steinberg, J. Weiss, and C. Djerassi, *J. Am. Chem. Soc.,* **84,** 1455 (1962); (b) R..C. Cookson, *et al., Chem. and Ind. (London)* 589 (1961); (c) 'P. D. Bartlett and W. P. Giddings, *J. Am. Chem. Soc.,* **82,** 1240 (1960).

XXIV.O

λ_m = 288.3 mμ
ϵ = 15

Plain carbonyl absorption.

XXIV.P

λ_m = 289.9 mμ
ϵ = 15

Hence, orbitals on C=C
and C=O do not over-
lap in any way.

XXIV.Q[122b]

λ_m = 214.5, 270–80 mμ
ϵ = 2300, 20

Hence, π orbitals on
C=C and C=O must
have some π-type overlap.

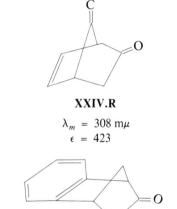

XXIV.R

λ_m = 308 mμ
ϵ = 423

XXIV.S[123a]

$\pi \longrightarrow \pi^*$	Benzene bands	$n \longrightarrow \pi^*$ bands
λ_m = 210	264, 273	300, 308, 321 mμ
ϵ = 10,700	575, 603	831, 795, 501

XXIV.T[123c]

$\pi \longrightarrow \pi^*$	Benzene bands
λ_m = 211,	257, 263, 271 mμ
ϵ = 6300	550, 831, 892

XXIV.U

	λ_m	ϵ	λ_m	ϵ
Hexane	220 mμ	3300	314 mμ	110
Alcohol	224	2500	313	126
Tetrahydro	XXIV.U	H	315 mμ	31
		A	313	32

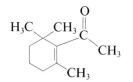

XXIV.V

$$\lambda_m = 243, 305 \text{ m}\mu$$
$$\epsilon = 1400, 90$$

Steric hindrance prevents coplanarity of
C=C—C=O system and only get
σ-type overlap.

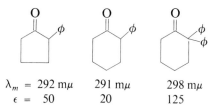

$$\lambda_m = 292 \text{ m}\mu \qquad 291 \text{ m}\mu \qquad 298 \text{ m}\mu$$
$$\epsilon = 50 \qquad\qquad 20 \qquad\qquad 125$$

Hence, one phenyl group in the diphenyl ketone is rotated
to give σ-type overlap.

Since the excited state of the α,β-enone system is more closely identified
with the polar resonance structure:

$$\text{>C=C—C=O,} \qquad \text{>}\overset{+}{\text{C}}\text{—C=C—O}^-$$

electron-withdrawing groups or positively charged groups near the γ carbon atom reduce the stability of the excited state and thereby lead to a blue-

shift of the $\pi \rightarrow \pi^*$ (N $\rightarrow$ V) band.[81]   Also, polar solvents preferentially stabilize the excited state and produce a red-shift of this band.   On the other hand, the solvent and substitution effects are just the opposite on the $n \rightarrow \pi^*$ band.   The excited state of the latter transition carries an excess of negative charge and is therefore stabilized by electron-withdrawing or positively charged groups near the γ carbon atom.   Hydroxylic solvents lower the energy of the oxygen lone-pair electrons through H bonding which increases the $n \rightarrow \pi^*$ transition energy to produce a blue-shift. This view accounts for the significant blue-shift of the $\pi \rightarrow \pi^*$ band of the α,β-enone system in compounds of type XXV.[80]   Electron-donating groups of course, have just the opposite effect on the two bands.

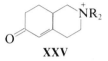

XXV

Summary. The spectral characteristics of the four types of carbonyls discussed in this Section can be summarized as follows:

	Absorption regions			
	Red-shift with increasing polarity of solvent		Blue-shift with increasing polarity of solvent	
Type	λ_m	ϵ	λ_m	ϵ
Isolated C=O	185 mμ	10^3–10^4	280 mμ	< 50
α,β-Enone	220–260	10^4	300–350	~ 50
Transannular π-type overlap	220–240	10^3	280–315	~ 50
Homoconjugated C=C and C=O	200–240	10^3	290–340	10^2–10^3

Infrared spectra. Ring compounds with very closely opposed C—H bonds exhibit C—H infrared frequencies at unusually high values (above 3018 cm^{-1}), and some examples are the following:[124]

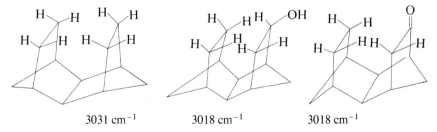

3031 cm^{-1} 3018 cm^{-1} 3018 cm^{-1}

[124]D. Kivelson, S. Winstein, P. Bruck, and R. L. Hanson, *J. Am. Chem. Soc.,* **83,** 2938 (1961); L. DeVries and P. R. Ryason, *J. Org. Chem.,* **26,** 621 (1961).

whereas,

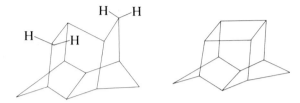

have no such band;

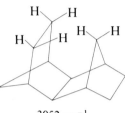

3052 cm⁻¹

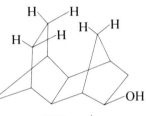

3049 cm⁻¹

whereas,

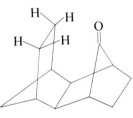

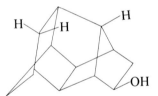

have no such band.

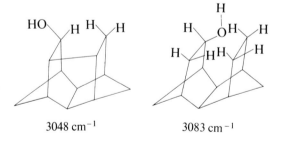

3048 cm⁻¹   3083 cm⁻¹

Nuclear magnetic resonance spectra. Deformed benzene rings, brought about by strong bond angle strain, exhibit proton signals at τ values outside of of the usual 2.0–3.5τ range:

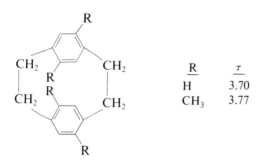

R	τ
H	3.70
CH$_3$	3.77

Whereas, for similar compounds having strainless benzene rings:

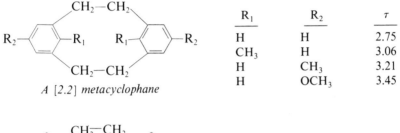

R$_1$	R$_2$	τ
H	H	2.75
CH$_3$	H	3.06
H	CH$_3$	3.21
H	OCH$_3$	3.45

A [2.2] metacyclophane

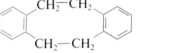

ArH $\tau = 3.10$

[2.2]Orthocyclophane

Consequently, n.m.r. spectra can be used to detect strained benzene rings as well as serving as a diagnostic tool for aromaticity in molecular rings (See Sec. 4.9.4).

5.4.3. H BONDING AND SPECTRA

In general, the effects of H bonding on ultraviolet spectra are studied by noting the spectral differences between corresponding hydroxy and ether compounds,[125] or between o- and m-hydroxy isomers, or even by observing solvent effects.[126]

Intramolecular H bonding has a marked visible effect on ultraviolet absorption whereas intermolecular H bonding has only small effects. For example, o-nitrophenol is yellow but the p-isomer is buff colored. Similarly, the chelated compound (XXVI) is yellow whereas its methyl ether

[125] J. C. Dearden and W. F. Forbes, Can. J. Chem., **38**, 1837, 1852 (1960).
[126] J. C. Dearden and W. F. Forbes, Can. J. Chem., **38**, 896 (1960).

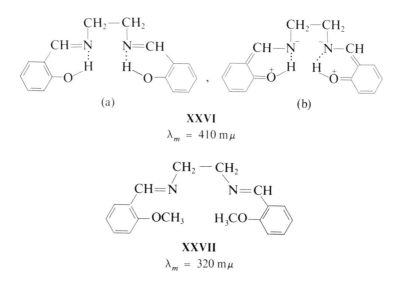

XXVI

$\lambda_m = 410\,m\mu$

XXVII

$\lambda_m = 320\,m\mu$

(XXVII) is pure white.[127] The bathochromic effect of the intramolecular H bond can be attributed to an increase in the H-bond strength in the excited state as a result of resonance among dipolar structures such as XXVI(b). This produces a net stabilization of the excited state, decreases $E_1 - E_0$, and leads to absorption at longer wavelengths. The bathochromic effect of intramolecular H bonding can be demonstrated in another way. Compounds which exhibit intermolecular H bonding normally undergo a red-shift upon methylation while compounds forming intramolecular H bonds undergo a blue-shift upon methylation.[128] Some examples are given below.

Parent Compound		Wavelength ($m\mu$) of primary band in hexane			
		CH_3O	OH	$\Delta\lambda$ para	$\Delta\lambda$ ortho
Benzaldehyde	4-	266.4	262.0	+4.4	
	2-	246.5	255.0		−8.5
Nitrobenzene	4-	292.0	287.0	+5.0	
	2-	248.3	271.0		−22.7

Recognition of the effects of inter- as well as intramolecular H bonding on infrared spectra has been particularly useful. When an O—H bond forms a H bond, the attraction of O_2 for the proton facilitates the O_1—H

$$O_1\text{—}H \cdots O_2$$

[127] L. N. Ferguson and I. Kelly, *J. Am. Chem. Soc.*, **73**, 3707 (1951).

[128] A. Burawoy, *Hydrogen Bonding*, ed. D. Hadzi and H. W. Thompson (New York: Pergamon, 1959), p. 259; B. Akermark, *Acta Chem. Scand.*, **15**, 985 (1961).

stretching vibration but makes it more difficult for the O_1—H bond to bend. This results in a lowering of the stretching frequency and a raise in the bending frequency. For example, the stretching frequencies of some single bonds and the respective H bonds are given in Table 5.17.

Table 5.17. INFRARED FREQUENCIES OF SOME SINGLE AND ASSOCIATED BONDS.

			Absorption frequencies (cm^{-1})	
Single	Associated	Substance	Dilute solns. (monomeric)	Conc. solns. (associated)
O—H	O—H $\cdots$ O	{Alcohols[129]	3620	3355
		{Carboxylic acids[130]	3520	3075
O—D	O—D $\cdots$ O	{D$_2$O[131]	2790	2500
		{CH$_3$OD[132]	2680	2500
N—H	N—H $\cdots$ N	{Pyrrole[133]	3500	3425
		{Dipeptides[134]	3450	3330

As already stated, H bonding raises the O—H bending frequency.[136]

Compound	Monomeric O—H bend	Associated O—H bend
CH$_3$OH	1340 cm^{-1}	1420 cm^{-1}
Cyclohexanol	1370	1430

Most often, however, the O—H bending frequency is hard to pick out because it is superimposed on C—H bending vibration frequencies. In the case of carboxylic acids, three spectral regions are affected by association which can be assigned to C=O and O—H stretching vibrations and the C—O bending vibration.[130] For acetic acid, the data are:

	Monomer	*Dimer*
C=O	1768 cm^{-1}	1701 cm^{-1}
O—H	3521	3073
C—O	1379	1425

[129] M. St. C. Flett, *Spectrochim. Acta,* **10,** 21 (1957); F. A. Smith and E. C. Creitz, *J. Res. Nat. Bur. Standards,* **46,** 145 (1951).

[130] M. M. Davies, *J. Chem. Phys.,* **16,** 274 (1948), and earlier papers.

[131] V. Thornton and F. E. Condon, *Anal. Chem.,* **22,** 690 (1950).

[132] W. Gordy, *J. Chem. Phys.,* **9,** 215 (1941).

[133] N. Fuson, M. L. Josien, and E. Utterback, Paper presented before Physics Section of the National Institute of Science, Greensboro, N. C., April, 1951.

[134] S. Mizushima, *et al., J. Am. Chem. Soc.,* **73,** 1330 (1951); A. M. Buswell, J. R. Downing, and W. H. Rodebush, *J. Am. Chem. Soc.,* **62,** 2759 (1940).

[135] J. J. Fox and A. E. Martin, *Proc. Roy. Soc.,* **A162,** 419 (1937).

[136] E. K. Plyler, *J. Res. Nat. Bur. Standards,* **48,** 281 (1952).

Note that the stretching frequency is lowered and the bending frequency is raised by H bonding.

In the liquid state and concentrated solutions, N—H and O—H compounds associate through H bonds. As the solutions are progressively diluted, the solute molecules are separated more and more, and the H bonds are gradually broken. The mean state of aggregation passes successively from the polymeric through the tetrameric, trimeric, dimeric states, until the solute is essentially monomeric.[135] This is illustrated by the spectra in Fig. 5.12. It is to be noted that as the concentration changes, ν_{OH} does not continuously change. Rather, the intensities of different bands change, depending upon the relative populations of the three different species, monomer, dimer, polymer.

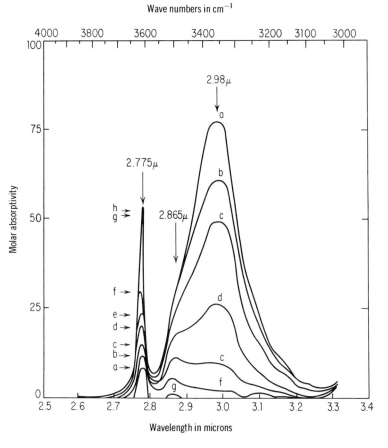

Fig. 5.12. Infrared absorption curves for t-butyl alcohol at various concentrations decreasing a to h.[129]

The degree of association of H-bonding substances is affected by temperature. As the temperature rises, the mean kinetic energy of the molecules is raised and the H bonds are less able to hold two or more molecules together. Thus, intermolecular H bonding decreases with increasing temperature, and this is reflected in the infrared spectra at different temperatures. An example, the spectrum of acetic acid at 18° and 74°, is shown in Fig. 5.13.

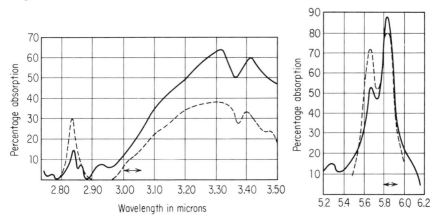

Fig. 5.13. Absorption spectrum of 0.01 M acetic acid in CCl_4 at 18° (solid curve) and at 74° (dotted curve.)[137]

In the case of an equilibrium involving essentially only two species, e.g., the monomer and the dimer, one may determine the approximate energy of the H bond involved by plotting the intensity of the band for one species vs. temperature. By this method, for example, the energy of the intermolecular H bond between cyclohexanol and dioxane was measured to be 3.2 ± 0.3 kcal/mole,[138] and the intramolecular H bond in o-methoxybenzoic acid was reported to be 3.3 kcal/mole.[139]

Intermolecular H bonding also lowers stretching frequencies. The fundamental O—H stretching vibration of phenol is at 3642 cm^{-1} and it has a first and second overtone at 7050 cm^{-1} and 10,331 cm^{-1} (1.42 and 0.968 μ, respectively). Some persons have measured the spectra of phenols in the fundamental vibrational range and others have worked in the first[140] or second[141] overtone regions. Experimental results in all three regions

[137] M. M. Davies, *J. Chem. Phys.,* **16,** 274 (1948).

[138] A. R. H. Cole and F. Macritchie, *Spectrochim. Acta,* 6 (1959).

[139] M. M. Davies, *Chem. and Ind.* (London), 614 (1953).

[140] O. R. Wulf, *et al., J. Am. Chem. Soc.,* **58,** 1991, 2287 (1936).

[141] O. R. Wulf, E. J. Jones, and L. S. Deming, *J. Chem. Phys.,* **8,** 745, 753 (1940); H. Kempter and R. Mecke, *Z. physik. Chem.,* **B46,** 229 (1940).

have been in accord with each other. Resonance of the OH group with the benzene ring restricts the molecule to one of two equivalent conformations

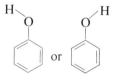

or

Consequently, the O—H bond exhibits only one absorption band in each of the harmonic regions. On the other hand, the two conformations of an *o*-substituted halophenol are not equivalent because the *cis* conformation is stabilized by an intramolecular H bond.

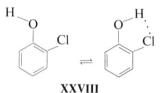

XXVIII

Whereas the *trans* isomer of *o*-alkylphenols is more abundant than the *cis,* the *cis* isomer of *o*-halophenols is more abundant than the *trans*.[142] It is no surprise then that *o*-chlorophenol has two absorption bands, one at the phenol wavelength of 1.42 μ and one at a slightly longer wavelength (1.45 μ). This latter band can be assigned to the *cis* isomer because 2,4,6-trichlorophenol, in which only the O—H $\cdots$ Cl bond occurs no matter to which side the H is oriented, has only one band at 1.45 μ. Similar results are obtained with other *o*-substituted phenols in which there are intramolecular H bonds.

2-Bromophenol	1.42 μ	1.46 μ
2,4,6-Tribromophenol		1.465
2-Iodophenol	1.424	1.47
2,4,6-Triodophenol		1.48
2-Fluorophenol	1.425	

The existence of an equilibrium between the *cis* and *trans* conformations of *o*-chlorophenol is confirmed by the fact that its electric dipole moment varies with temperature whereas the moments of the *m*-and *p*-isomers are temperature independent.[143] Also, the ratio of intensity of the two peaks in the spectrum of *o*-chlorophenol varies with temperature changes.[144] Although it is tempting to relate $\Delta\nu$ with H bond strength in these *o*-halophenols, it is risky to do so because several factors may be involved, such as

[142] K. U. Ingold and D. R. Taylor, *Can. J. Chem.,* **39,** 471 (1961).
[143] R. Linke, *Z. physik. Chem.,* **B46,** 251, 261 (1940); **47,** 194 (1940).
[144] L. R. Zumwalt and R. M. Badger, *J. Chem. Phys.,* **7,** 87 (1939).

the geometry of the O—H ⋯ X bonds, repulsions between nuclei and/or lone-pair electrons, resonance, electronegativities, etc.[145] As a result, there is considerable disagreement in the literature on the relative strengths of the H bonds in *o*-halophenols. In *α*-halohydrins, the order of increasing infrared frequency shifts is I > Cl > Br, suggesting that the proximity and/or polarizability of the halogen governs the strength of the O—H ⋯ X bond.[146]

Intramolecular H bonding has a marked effect on infrared O—H and C=O absorption frequencies in tropolones, *α*-hydroxyaromatic ketones, and the enols of *β*-diketones. The ν_{OH} frequency is lowered by several hundred wave-numbers and ν_{CO} is decreased by some 50–100 cm^{-1}. Some examples are given in Table 5.18. N.m.r. spectroscopy offers an advantage

Table 5.18. Infrared Absorption Frequencies in
Some Chelated Compounds

Compound	$\nu_{C=O}$	ν_{O-H}
Acetylacetone[147]	1610 cm^{-1}	2800 cm^{-1}
Benzoylacetone[147, 148]	1603	2640
Dibenzoylmethane[147]	1605	2604
1-Hydroxy-2-naphthaldehyde[149]	1637	3178

for studying the H bond in some of these compounds because the infrared bands sometimes overlap with C—H bands. There is a semiquantitative relationship between $\Delta\nu_{OH}$ and $\Delta\delta_{OH}$, where $\Delta\nu_{OH}$ is the shift in the infrared O—H frequency and $\Delta\delta_{OH}$ is the corresponding shift in the proton resonance signal upon H bond formation.[150] It is not surprising to find a parallel correlation of the double-bond character of the β bond in an enol

The β bond

with $\Delta\nu_{OH}$, $\Delta\delta_{OH}$, or even with $\Delta\nu_{CO}$.[151] (Cf. Sec. 1.4.4 concerning the correspondence between the double-bond character of the β bond and chelate stability.)

[145] A. W. Baker and W. W. Kaeding, *J. Am. Chem. Soc.*, **81**, 5904 (1959).

[146] A. Nickon, *J. Am. Chem. Soc.*, **79**, 243 (1957).

[147] S. Bratoz, D. Hadzi, and G. Rossmy, *Trans. Faraday Soc.*, **52**, 464 (1956).

[148] J. U. Lowe and L. N. Ferguson, unpublished results.

[149] I. M. Hunsberger, *J. Am. Chem. Soc.*, **72**, 5626 (1950).

[150] L. W. Reeves, E. A. Allan, and K. O. Stromme, *Can. J. Chem.*, **38**, 1249 (1960).

[151] A. L. Porte, H. S. Gutowsky, and I. M. Hunsberger, *J. Am. Chem. Soc.*, **82**, 5057 (1960).

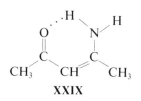

XXIX

Inter- and intramolecular H bonding are easily distinguished by infrared spectroscopy. Intramolecular H bonding is only slightly affected by dilution so that Beer's law would hold for the corresponding band. On the other hand, intermolecular H bonding is markedly decreased by dilution and the corresponding band does not follow Beer's law. For illustration, the spectrum of **XXIX** in carbon tetrachloride has several bands in the N—H stretch region (cf. Fig. 5.14).[152] Two of these bands, 2.86 μ and

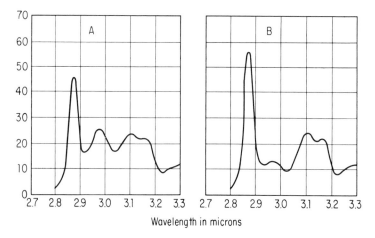

Wavelength in microns

Fig. 5.14. Spectra of **XXIX** in CCl_4 in the 3-μ region at a given concentration X (curve A) and $X/4$ (curve B).[152]

2.96 μ, vary in intensity with changing concentration. The band at 2.86 μ, whose intensity increases upon dilution of **XXIX**, can be assigned to the free N—H, and the 2.96-μ band, which decreases in intensity with dilution of **XXIX**, can be attributed to the intermolecularly bonded N—H bond. The absorptivity of the doublet at 3.09 and 3.15 μ is insensitive to the concentration of **XXIX** and is attributed to the intramolecular N—H $\cdots$ O bond. As to be expected, the 2.86-μ band disappears in the solid state. Similarly, o-nitrophenol has an O—H band at 3200 cm^{-1} in KBr pellets as well as in $CHCl_3$ solution, whereas the frequency of the O—H band of 3-nitrophenol shifts from 3330 cm^{-1} in the pellet to 3520 cm^{-1} in

[152] J. Weinstein and G. M. Wyman, *J. Org. Chem.*, **23**, 1618 (1958).

[153] B. Akermark, *Acta Chem. Scand.*, **15**, 985 (1961).

$CHCl_3$ solution, and the *para* isomer has a similar shift (3325 to 3530 cm^{-1}).[154]

Inter-and intramolecular H bonding in hydroxycarbonyl compounds have also been distinguished by noting a solvent effect on the carbonyl absorption. Those compounds which form intermolecular H bonds exhibit significantly higher carbonyl frequencies in dioxane than in the pure state, whereas the compounds which form intramolecular H bonds show only small changes.[153]

It has been shown that X=Y dipoles all tend to exhibit a common pattern of solvent behavior such that $\Delta\nu/\nu$ values of any one compound in a series of different solvents can be plotted against the corresponding values of another compound to give a straight line.[155] This provides a method of identifying polar group frequencies.[156] For example, tropolones give two prominent bands in the 1570–1650 cm^{-1} region, and most authors have assigned the higher band to the carbonyl group. However, if one compares the frequency shift produced by a series of solvents on the tropolones and acetone bands, it is readily noted that the lower-frequency band is actually the carbonyl band.[157] Only the 1590-cm^{-1} band exhibits the steady shift shown by acetone.

Solvent	ν_{CO} Acetone	ν_{CO} Tropolone		
Hexane	$1726 \, cm^{-1}$	1647	1637	$1597 \, cm^{-1}$
Tetrachloroethylene	1722	1646	1633	1597
Benzene	1718	1645	1635	1591
Acetonitrile	1716	1650	1634	1583
Chloroform	1713	1650	1635	1577
1,1,2,2-Tetrabromoethane	1709	. .	1633	1572

This solvent-effect technique can also be used to distinguish inter- and intramolecular H bonding. For illustration, when there is inter- but no intramolecular H bonding, the relative $\Delta\nu/\nu$ values produced by intermolecular H bonding to the solvents will be linearly related to the $\Delta\nu/\nu$ values for most other intermolecular H-bonded solutes, and such a plot would pass through the origin. However, if a given solute forms intramolecular H bonds as well, the weak proton-accepting solvents will depress the ν_{N-H} or ν_{O-H} values of the solute very little if at all, and frequency depressions will not be observed until sufficiently strong proton-acceptor solvents are used. The plot of $\Delta\nu/\nu$ for this solute when plotted against

[154] P. M. Boll, *Acta Chem. Scand.*, **12**, 1777 (1958).

[155] L. J. Bellamy, *et al., Trans. Faraday Soc.*, **55**, 220 (1959); *Spectrochim. Acta*, **14**, 192 (1959).

[156] L. J. Bellamy and P. E. Rogasch, *J. Chem. Soc.*, 2218 (1960).

[157] H. Götz, E. Heilbronner, A. R. Katritzky, and R. A. Jones, *Helv. Chim. Acta*, **44**, 387 (1961).

$\Delta \nu / \nu$ for a nonintramolecular H-bonding solute will not be linear nor pass through the origin. This technique was employed to offer convincing evidence for the lack of intramolecular H bonding in o-nitroaniline.[158] Previous workers had attributed some of the spectral properties of o-nitro-aniline to the formation of an intramolecular H bond, and such a bond would be expected, but apparently this is not the case.[159] Using the solvent-variation technique, evidence was presented to show that there is no intra-molecular H bond in 2-nitroaniline, 2,4-dinitroaniline, and 6-chloro-2-nitroaniline but that there is in 2,6-dinitroaniline and 2,4,6-trinitroaniline.[158] It would be interesting to apply this solvent-effect technique to o-nitro-benzaldehyde, because a comparison of melting points of the *ortho* and *para* nitrobenzaldehydes suggests that intramolecular H bonding exists in the former compound, whereas the infrared spectrum of the *ortho* isomer has been interpreted to refute the presence of an intramolecular H bond (in CCl_4 solution).[160]

As with ultraviolet spectra, spatial crowding has a marked effect on infrared spectra, particularly the spectra of H-bonded compounds. In o-substituted phenols, for example, as the sizes of the *ortho* groups increase, a molecular shield is built up around the hydroxyl group which hinders the close approach of the OH groups of other molecules for H bonding. Consequently, the infrared band attributed to the H bond gradually dis-appears.[161] For example,[162] p-t-butylphenol has a single OH band at 3608 cm^{-1} which can be assigned to the associated state. The *ortho* isomer has

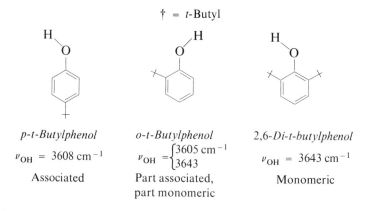

† = t-Butyl

p-t-Butylphenol	o-t-Butylphenol	2,6-Di-t-butylphenol
ν_{OH} = 3608 cm^{-1}	$\nu_{OH} = \begin{cases} 3605 \text{ cm}^{-1} \\ 3643 \end{cases}$	ν_{OH} = 3643 cm^{-1}
Associated	Part associated, part monomeric	Monomeric

[158] L. K. Dyall, *Australian J. Chem.,* **13**, 230 (1960); *Spectrochim. Acta,* **17**, 291 (1961).

[159] A. N. Hambly, *Revs. Pure and Applied Chem.,* **11**, 212 (1961).

[160] R. West and L. S. Whatley, Chem. and Ind. (London), 333 (1959).

[161] N. D. Coggeshall, *J. Am. Chem. Soc.,* **69**, 1620 (1947); **73**, 5414 (1951); R. A. Freidel, *J. Am. Chem. Soc.,* **73**, 2881 (1951); E. E. Pickett aad H. E. Ungnade, *J. Am. Chem. Soc.,* **71**, 1311 (1949); R. E. Richards and H. W. Thompson, *J. Chem. Soc.,* 1260 (1947).

[162] R. F. Goddu, *J. Am. Chem. Soc.,* **82**, 4533 (1960).

two bands, one at 3605 and one at 3643 cm^{-1}. This indicates that some of the molecules are associated and some are monomeric. 2,6-Di-t-butyl-phenol, on the other hand, has only one band at 3642 cm^{-1}, which shows that none of the molecules is associated. Smaller groups offer less hindrance to H bonding such that two o-methyl groups are about as effective as one t-butyl group.[163] However, if there are also groups in the *meta* position, a buttressing effect sets in. For example, the degree of association of 2,3,5,6-tetramethylphenol (XXX) is about the same as for 2-methyl-6-t-butylphenol (XXXI).[163] A shielding of the OH group may occur in alcohols too. For example, 3-pentanol (XXXII) exists in the monomeric and polymeric states, chiefly the latter, tri-isopropylcarbinol (XXXIII) exists about equally in the dimeric and polymeric states, and di-t-butyl-isopropyl-carbinol (XXXIV) is all monomeric.[129]

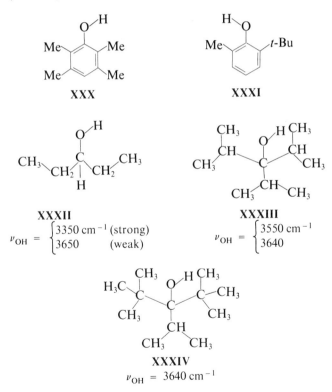

As stated in Sec. 1.6.2, for a long period it was believed that H bonds of the S—H $\cdots$ S type were unlikely for thioalcohols. Even infrared spectroscopy was slow in providing evidence for such bonds.[164] Later, n.m.r.

[163] W. C. Sears and L. J. Kitchen, *J. Am. Chem. Soc.*, **71**, 4110 (1949).
[164] R. A. Spurr and H. F. Byers, *J. Phys. Chem.*, **62**, 425 (1958).

spectroscopy confirmed their existence in ethyl mercaptan[165(a)] and other thiols.[165(b)]

Infrared spectroscopy has been used in an empirical method to provide information about the characteristics of H bonds. Particular attention has been given to relationships between frequency shifts and the strength or length of a H bond. The infrared absorption frequency of a given bond is directly related to the force constant, which in turn is affected by the dielectric constant of the medium. Hence, frequency shifts ($\Delta \nu$) of bands attributed to H bonding should not be used indiscriminately as a measure of relative H-bond strengths.[166] However, it is reasonable to relate frequency shifts and H-bond energies for a series of compounds in the same environment.[167-169] For illustration, the ν_{CO} frequency shifts of some substituted acetic acids in CCl_4 are given in Table 5.19.[170] The 1721 cm^{-1} band of acetic acid is affected by the strength of the H bond in the dimer, and the absorption frequency decreases with increasing strength of the H bond. As noted earlier in Sec. 1.6.2(ii), it is observed in Table 5.19 that the H-bond strength in aliphatic acid dimers decreases in strength as the ionization constants of the acids increase.

Table 5.19. INFRARED FREQUENCY SHIFTS OF THE C=O BOND OF SOME SUBSTITUTED ACETIC ACIDS

Acid	$\Delta \nu$ (cm^{-1}) (for the 1721-cm^{-1} band)
Trichloroacetic	43
Dichloroacetic	30
Monochloroacetic	15
Monobromoacetic	9
Monoiodoacetic	0
Acetic	0
Dimethylacetic	−6
Diethylacetic	−15
Trimethylacetic	−17

[165] (a) S. Forsen, *Acta Chem. Scand.,* **13,** 1472 (1959); (b) L. D. Colebrook and D. S. Tarbell, *Proc. Nat. Acad. Sci. U. S.,* **47,** 993 (1961).

[166] M. M. Davies, *Ann. Repts. Chem. Soc.,* **43,** 5 (1946).

[167] R. M. Badger, *J. Chem. Phys.,* **8,** 288 (1940).

[168] It is noteworthy that the OH stretching frequency for dimethylglyoxime is at 1800 cm^{-1}, which is very much lower than the normal value (L. E. Godycke and R. E. Rundle, *Acta Cryst.,* **6,** 487 (1953).

[169] E. D. Becker, *Spectrochim. Acta,* **17,** 436 (1961).

[170] For a study of the variation of the OH frequency with acid strengths of carboxylic acids and phenols, respectively, see J. D. S. Goulden, *Spectrochim. Acta,* **6,** 129 (1953–54), and P. M. G. Bavin and W. J. Canady, *Can. J. Chem.,* **35,** 1555 (1957).

Hydroxyl group frequency shifts provide evidence that intermolecular[171] and intramolecular[172] O—H $\cdots$ N bonds are stronger than O—H $\cdots$ O bonds. Thus, in the several examples given below, the O—H $\cdots$ N bond frequencies are at lower frequencies than the frequencies for similar O—H $\cdots$ O bonds.

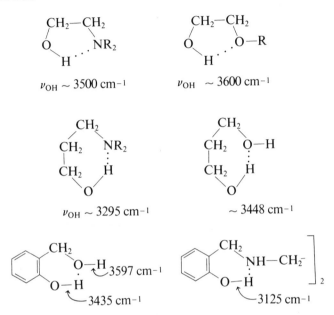

A useful extension of this practice of relating the variation of $\Delta \nu$ to the strengths of H bonds is to use the relationship as a measure of the relative basicity of Lewis bases.[173-176] For example, with phenol as a reference acid, the shift of the phenol O—H stretching frequency upon forming a H bond with various bases in a common solvent has been used to ascertain the relative strengths of the Lewis bases. Several proton donors have been used as a probe in this method, such as $CHCl_3$, alcohols, acetylenes, amines, and HCl, but phenol appears to be the best of these compounds to use.[175] The relative base strengths of several compounds as determined by this technique are given in Table 5.20. The relative basicity of some arenes towards

[171] J. W. Baker, M. M. Davies, and J. Gaunt, *J. Chem. Soc.*, 25 (1949).

[172] H. H. Freedman, *J. Am. Chem. Soc.*, **83**, 2900 (1961).

[173] D. Cook, *J. Am. Chem. Soc.*, **80**, 49 (1958).

[174] A. W. Baker and G. H. Harris, *J. Am. Chem. Soc.*, **82**, 1923 (1960).

[175] R. West, *J. Am. Chem. Soc.*, **81**, 1615 (1959); A. W. Baker and A. T. Shulgin, *J. Am. Chem. Soc.*, **81**, 1523 (1959).

[176] M. L. Josien and G. Gourisseau, in *Hydrogen Bonding*, ed. D. Hadzi and H. W. Thompson (New York: Pergamon, 1959), p. 129.

Table 5.20. RELATIVE BASICITIES OF SEVERAL SERIES OF LEWIS BASES
AS DETERMINED BY H-BOND FREQUENCY SHIFTS

Compound	Relative basicity $\Delta \nu_{OH}$ phenol[178]	Compound	Relative basicity $\Delta \nu_{OD}$ CH_3OD[179]
n-Butyl ether	1.0	Acetone	1.0
n-Butyl iodide	0.27	Ethyl ketone	0.96
n-Butyl bromide	0.25	Cyclobutanone	0.91
n-Butyl chloride	0.21	Cyclopentanone	1.12
n-Butyl fluoride	0.14	Cyclohexanone	1.22
		Cycloheptanone	1.4

	Relative basicity as determined by	
Compound	$\Delta \nu_{OH}$ (phenol)[175, 180]	CT complex stability towards HCl[181]
Fluorobenzene	0.08	0.97
Chlorobenzene	0.60	0.87
Bromobenzene	0.79	0.85
Iodobenzene	0.96	0.84
Benzene	1.0	1.00
Toluene	1.22	1.51
p-Xylene	1.4	1.64
Mesitylene	1.55	2.61
1-Hexene	1.47	
1-Hexyne	2.0	
Cyclohexene	2.01	

HCl are given in the far right column for comparison of the results of the two methods. At the same time, the method can provide a measure of the relative acidity of proton-donor H-bonding substances.[177] For example, by measuring the C—H infrared frequency shifts for a series of substituted acetylenes in a common solvent, the relative strengths of the corresponding H bonds can be determined and the sequence taken as a reflection of the relative acidities of the acetylenic hydrogen atoms.

R in R—C≡C—H	$\Delta \nu_{C-H}$[177] (in dimethylacetamide)
n-C_4H_9—	74 cm^{-1}
C_6H_5—	91
$BrCH_2$—	94
$C_2H_5CO_2$—	123

[177] R. West and C. S. Kraihanzel, *J. Am. Chem. Soc.*, **83**, 765 (1961), and references cited therein.

[178] P. R. Schlayer and R. West, *J. Am. Chem. Soc.*, **81**, 3164 (1959).

[179] M. Tamres and S. Searles, Jr., *J. Am. Chem. Soc.*, **81**, 2100 (1959).

[180] G. A. Olah, S. J. Kuhn, and S. H. Flood, *J. Am. Chem. Soc.*, **83**, 4581 (1961).

[181] H. C. Brown and J. D. Brady, *J. Am. Chem. Soc.*, **74**, 3570 (1952).

From the foregoing discussion it can be expected that as the $C=O$ stretching frequency increases, its donor character should decrease and its ionization potential should increase. An increase in ν_{CO} signifies a greater double-bond character, and the smaller the contribution from the ionic structure $\overset{+}{C}-O^-$, the less is its donor character and the more difficult it is to extract one of the nonbonding lone-pair electrons from the group. These expectations have been substantiated.[171] It was found that for a series of carbonyl compounds, as ν_{CO} increases, so does the ionization potential and also the $\Delta\nu_{C-H}$ for phenylacetylene dissolved in the carbonyl compound.

Equally valuable to the frequency shift-bond strength correlations have been frequency shift-bond length relationships. These three bond characteristics—bond strength, length, and infrared absorption frequency—are closely related, and it is not surprising that a smooth curve is obtained when the shift in frequency from the "normal" value for the bond $X-H$ is plotted against the $A\cdots B$ distance or against the $H\cdots B$ distance in $A-H\cdots B$ bonds.[182] This means that the $A\cdots B$ or $H\cdots B$ distance of an intramolecular bond may now be estimated from a measure of the frequency shift for the specific $A-H$ bond.[183] This observation is very helpful in the elucidation of spatial configurations.[184]

It can be expected that in a 1,2-diol, $R_2CHOH-CH_2OH$, as the sizes of the R groups increase, steric repulsion spreads the distance between R groups, strengthens the bond, and produces a larger $\Delta\nu$.[185]

R in $R_2COH-CH_2OH$	$\Delta\nu$
Me	51 cm^{-1}
Et	54
i-Pr	70
t-Bu	97

5.4.4. ELECTRONEGATIVITY AND SPECTRA

It has already been stated that the infrared absorption frequency for a bond $A-B$ is directly related to the bond force constant, and the absorption intensity is proportional to the square of the change in dipole moment during excitation. Thus, both spectral parameters have a relationship to the electronegativities of the atoms A and B of the bond $A-B$, and indeed, the chapter on electronegativities (Sec. 2.3) discussed attempts to establish

[182] R. E. Rundle, *et al., J. Chem. Phys.,* **20,** 1487 (1952); *J. Am. Chem. Soc.,* **77,** 6480 (1955); L. P. Kuhn, *J. Am. Chem. Soc.,* **74,** 2492 (1952); R. C. Lord and R. E. Merrifield, *J. Chem. Phys.,* **21,** 166 (1953); R. Schroeder and E. R. Lippincott, *J. Phys. Chem.,* **61,** 921 (1957).

[183] P. von R. Schleyer, *J. Am. Chem. Soc.,* **83,** 1368 (1961); H. J. Bernstein, *Spectrochim. Acta,* **18,** 161 (1961).

[184] Cf. H. Kwart and W. G. Vosburgh, *J. Am. Chem. Soc.,* **76,** 5400 (1954).

[185] L. P. Kuhn, *J. Am. Chem. Soc.,* **80,** 5950 (1958).

a table of relative group electronegativities from infrared absorption frequencies and intensities. Also, Sec. 4.11.6 discussed qualitative relationships between polar effects of groups and infrared frequencies and intensities as expressed by Hammett- and Taft-type substituent constants.

The effects of electronegativity on infrared frequencies have been observed in other ways too. For example, as the electronegativity of the carbon atom in a carbonyl group increases, the bond acquires less single-bond character and the larger bond force constant leads to increased infrared frequencies. This may be brought about by increasing the electronegativity of the groups attached to the carbonyl carbon or by increases in the s character of the carbonyl carbon through hybridization changes. For illustration, it can be seen in Table 5.21 that as the electronegativities of the attached groups increase, there is an increase in infrared absorption frequency. Thus, F_2C=O has one of the highest carbonyl frequencies known, namely, 1940 cm^{-1}.[186]

Table 5.21. INFRARED ABSORPTION FREQUENCIES OF SOME SUBSTITUTED CARBONYL COMPOUNDS

α-Haloesters[187]			α-Haloacids[188]	
R in RCOOEt	$\nu_{C=O}$	ν_{C-O}	R in RCOOH	$\nu_{C=O}$
CH$_3$	1740 cm^{-1}	1236 cm^{-1}	CH$_2$I	1721 cm^{-1}
CH$_2$Br	1740	1281	CH$_2$Br	1730
CH$_2$Cl	1753	1288	CH$_2$Cl	1736
CH$_2$F	1778	1290	CHCl$_2$	1750
CHF$_2$	1770	1301	CCl$_3$	1784
CF$_3$	1789	1319		

Several studies have shown that the s character of carbon bonding orbitals increases with decreasing ring size.[189] This could account for the increasing carbonyl infrared frequency of small-ring cyclanones with decreasing ring size (Table 5.22). It has been pointed out that this relationship is determined by the hybridization of the carbonyl carbon atom (s character) and not by the increased bond angle strain in the cyclanones. In support of this view is the observation that carbonyl infrared frequencies show no relationship to the tendency of the compounds to polymerize (i.e., an attempt to relieve bond strain) but there is a correlation with their

---

[186] Cf. R. N. Jones and C. Sandorfy, *Techniques of Organic Chemistry,* ed. A. Weissberger, vol. IX (New York: Interscience, 1956), chap. 4.

[187] E. T. McBee and D. L. Christman, *J. Am. Chem. Soc.,* **77,** 755 (1955).

[188] R. H. Gillette, *J. Am. Chem. Soc.,* **58,** 1143 (1936).

[189] A. D. Walsh, *Trans. Faraday Soc.,* **45,** 179 (1949); C. A. Coulson and W. E. Moffitt, *J. Chem. Phys.,* **15,** 151 (1947); J. D. Roberts and V. C. Chambers, *J. Am. Chem. Soc.,* **73,** 5030 (1951); P. D. Bartlett and M. Stiles, *J. Am. Chem. Soc.,* **77,** 2810 (1955).

Table 5.22. INFRARED CARBONYL FREQUENCIES OF SOME CYCLANONES[186, 191]

Ring size	$\nu_{C=O}$	Ring size	$\nu_{C=O}$
3	ca. 1815 cm^{-1}	7	1703 cm^{-1}
4	1788	8	1692*
5	1746	9	1698
6	1715	10	1694
Et$_2$CO	1720	11	1700

*1702 and 1701 cm^{-1} according to Refs. 190 and 191.

reactivities towards nucleophilic reagents.[191(c)] Nevertheless, it is not clear why there is an alternation in ν_{CO} with ring size for the cyclanones above C_7 (Table 5.22). As stated in Sec. 4.8.4, many chemical and physical properties of medium-sized ring compounds show this alternation with ring size. In the case of the carbonyl infrared frequencies of the cyclanones, this may be related in some way to their conformations, which affect the hybridization of the carbonyl carbon atom or the coupling of carbonyl with other vibrations. For instance, the C=C infrared stretching frequencies of cycloalkenes decrease with decreasing ring size to a minimum for cyclobutene.

Cycloalkene	$\nu_{C=C}$
C_8	1673 cm^{-1} (1648)
C_7	1651
C_6	1646
C_5	1611
C_4	1566
C_3	1640

This trend was first attributed to increasing strain in the double bond, the idea being that as the bond angles are distorted the C=C force constants decrease.[192] However, this view does not hold for cyclopropene. Alternately, it has been shown that the relationship of $\nu_{C=C}$ to ring size can be accounted for by regarding the observed frequency as a coupled molecular frequency of the olefin bond with neighboring bonds.[193] Consequently, there are several factors which may contribute to the alternation of $\nu_{C=O}$ with ring size in the medium-sized ring cyclanones.

It is of interest to note that the resonance and inductive effects in acrylate esters would have opposite effects on the infrared carbonyl frequency. The inductive effect of the vinyl group should make $\nu_{C=O}$ larger than for ethyl

[190] N. J. Leonard and F. H. Owens, J. Am. Chem. Soc., **80**, 6039 (1958).
[191] (a) K. B. Wiberg and B. J. Nist, J. Am. Chem. Soc., **83**, 1226 (1961); P. D. Bartlett and M. Stiles, J. Am. Chem. Soc., **77**, 2806 (1955); (b) M. Tamres and S. Searles, Jr., J. Am. Chem. Soc., **81**, 2100 (1959); (c) H. K. Hall and R. Zbinden, J. Am. Chem. Soc., **80**, 6428 (1958).
[192] K. W. F. Kohlrausch, R. Seka, and O. Tramposch, Ber., **75**, 1385 (1942).
[193] C. F. Wilcox, Jr., and R. R. Craig, J. Am. Chem. Soc., **83**, 3866 (1961).

propionate. The contribution of the ionic forms to the resonance hybrid should lower $\nu_{C=O}$.

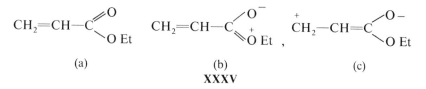

(a)   (b)   (c)

XXXV

Since $\nu_{C=O}$ for ethyl acrylate (1728 cm^{-1}) is lower than that for ethyl propionate (1738 cm^{-1})[194] we can conclude that the resonance effect outweighs the inductive effect by a small amount.

We have already observed (Secs. 1.2.9 and 2.3.1) that as the electronegativity of X in X—C—Y increases, it increases the electronegativity of C, which in turn affects the C—Y bond in various ways. The C—Y bond distance, for example, is decreased, and the C—Y force constant and hence the infrared stretching frequency is increased. It is found also that the n.m.r. chemical shift and J_{CH} coupling constant increase with increasing electronegativity of X in X—C^{13}—H (Table 5.23). In general, n.m.r. proton chemical shifts (δ) get more positive (to lower fields) with increasing ionic character of a bond X—H, and the acidity of the proton normally follows the same order. For example, relative to water, δ values for the OH group of CH_3OH, C_6H_5OH, CH_3CO_2H, and CH_3SO_3H are +0.01, 0.27, 0.63, and 0.70.[196] A complete relationship with acid strength will not hold for all compounds because δ also depends on the nature of the atom to which the proton is attached. Other empirically drawn relationships between coupling constants, electronegativity, and bond distance have been found.[197]

Table 5.23. EFFECT OF ELECTRONEGATIVITY ON C^{13}—H
COUPLING CONSTANTS[195]

X in X—CH$_3$	J_{CH}
H	125 sec^{-1}
CHO	127
CO$_2$H	130
C≡CH	132
CCl$_3$	134
OH	141
NO$_2$	147
F	149

[194] G. W. Cannon, A. A. Santilli, and P. Shenian, *J. Am. Chem. Soc.*, **81**, 1660 (1959).
[195] N. Muller and D. E. Pritchard, *J. Chem. Phys.*, **31**, 1471 (1959).
[196] L. H. Meyer, A. Saika, and H. S. Gutowsky, *J. Am. Chem. Soc.*, **75**, 4567 (1953).
[197] G. S. Hundler and J. H. Anderson, *Tetrahedron*, **2**, 345 (1958).

5.4.5. POLARIZABILITY AND SPECTRA

We have seen in Sec. 5.4.1 that resonance stabilization of the electronic ground states of molecules tends to shift λ_m to shorter wavelengths and resonance stabilization of the excited state produces bathochromic shifts.[198] However, in several places (cf. Secs. 4.10 and 5.3.3) it was shown that polarization in excited states of molecules markedly lowers the transition energies to shift λ_m to smaller values.   In essentially all *p*-substituted

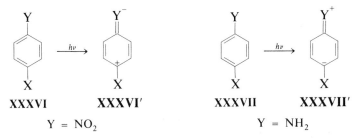

XXXVI   XXXVI′   XXXVII   XXXVII′

Y = NO$_2$ Y = NH$_2$

halobenzenes, for example, λ_m of the primary band increases with increasing polarizability of the substituent (Table 5.24).   With electron-withdrawing substituents (XXXVI), absorption of light is accompanied by a migration away from the halogen (or H) and increases with the polarizability of the halogen.   When Y is an electron-donor (XXXVII), the polarization is towards the halogen.   The fluorine atom, which has a polarizability close to that of H but has a large *p*-donor resonance,

Table 5.24. λ_m (First Primary Band, mμ) of Some
p-Substituted Halobenzenes, *p*-X—C$_6$H$_4$—Y

X	Y				
	H[199] (in hexane)	NO$_2$[199] (in hexane)	COOH[200] (in EtOH)	CHO[201] (in hexane)	NH$_2$[199] (in hexane)
F	206.8	256.9	227	244	230.5
H	202	251.3	228	241	234.0
Cl	215.2	265.2	234	253	241.4
Br	216.0	269.7	238.5	257.5	241.8
I	230.0	286.5	252	274	246.3

[198] For an alternative theory, see E. Spinner, *Spectrochim. Acta.* **17**, 545, 558 (1961).
[199] A. Burawoy, *Tetrahedron,* **5**, 340 (1959) and earlier papers in this series.
[200] W. F. Forbes and M. B. Sheratte, *Can. J. Chem.,* **33**, 1829 (1955).
[201] J. C. Dearden and W. F. Forbes, *Can. J. Chem.,* **36**, 1362 (1958).

varies in its position relative to H depending upon the nature of the substituent. It is found that similar trends are observed for *m*-substituted halobenzenes, in which the effect of resonance between the halogen atom and the substituent is insignificant. Other examples of the effect of polarizability on ultraviolet spectra are found in some properties of substituted anilines. In Table 5.25 are listed the spectral characteristics of the first primary band and pK_a's of several nuclear alkylated anilines. We saw in Sec. 4.7.5 on the basis of dipole moments that one *o*-alkyl group produces little steric inhibition of the aniline resonance. However, the resonance of the alkyl group (C—H or C—C hyperconjugation) opposes that of the

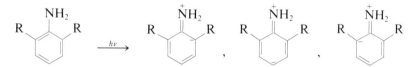

amino group, and this competitive resonance would be destablizing. On the other hand, it is observed that the introduction of methyl or *t*-butyl groups *ortho* (or *para*) to the amino group shifts the λ_m of aniline to longer wavelengths. This can be attributed to a stabilization of the excited state as a result of polarization of the alkyl groups. It must be pointed out that such stabilization is equally accounted for in terms of induction. At the same time, the steric effect of the *ortho* alkyl groups decreases the basicity of the amines as shown by the pK_a values listed in Table 5.25. This steric hindrance develops from the steric inhibition to solvation of the ion as well as some steric strain in the ion (cf. Sec. 4.8.1). It is surprising to find that even the *t*-butyl groups produce little steric inhibition of the aniline resonance.

Table 5.25. SPECTRAL CHARACTERISTICS (IN ISOOCTANE) AND pK_a'S (IN 50% EtOH) OF SOME NUCLEAR-ALKYLATED ANILINES[202]

R in R—$C_6H_4NH_2$	λ_m	ϵ_m	pK_a
H	234 mμ	9130	4.26
2-Me	234	8800	4.09
2,4,6-Tri-Me	237	8600	4.00
2-*t*-Bu	237	7850	3.38
2,6-Di-*t*-Bu	240	6900	1.80
2,4,6-Tri-*t*-Bu	242	8750	2.20

5.4.6. FUNDAMENTAL BOND CHARACTERISTICS AND SPECTRA

The several descriptive parameters of chemical bonds have been discussed in various places in this book. We have seen that experimental observations provide measures of bond lengths, bond energies, and vibrational

[202] B. M. Wepster, symposium on "Steric Effects in Conjugated Systems," held at The University, Hull, July, 1958.

frequencies, and yield derived quantities such as bond moments, bond orders, and force constants. These data provide a vast amount of information about the charge distribution in chemical bonds, and it is quite apparent that many of the required data are obtained through spectroscopy. Thus, the determinations of bond lengths and bond energies from absorption spectra are briefly described in Secs. 5.3.1, 5.5.7, and 1.2.10. Group vibrational frequencies are taken up in Sec. 5.3.1. In a few cases, when there might be some advantage in doing so, bond moments have been determined from spectroscopically measured dipole moments (Sec. 5.5.7). Force constants can be derived through empirical correlations and through detailed mathematical analyses of spectra. This latter method is called *normal coordinate analysis.* In recent years many empirical correlations between bond length and force constants[203] and between bond lengths and group frequencies[204] have been drawn. The first such generalization was that of Badger (Sec. 5.3.2), and in recent years, several persons have shown that a smooth curve is obtained when one plots bond force constants or infrared band frequencies vs. bond lengths of a given bond-type in different molecules.[203]

5.5. Applications of spectroscopy

5.5.1. QUALITATIVE AND QUANTITATIVE ANALYSIS[205]

The oldest form of spectroscopy is the identification or distinction of compounds by their visible colors. Many, many qualitative analytical procedures are based on the formation of a colored solution or precipitate, and this fact is familiar to all students who have taken analytical chemistry. A step up in refinement is to use a colorimeter in the measurement. This leads to a quantitative level, because the intensity of color may be measured and, since the intensity is directly proportional to the concentration of the colored constituent, one may compute the amount present.

Similarly, in other regions of the spectrum, qualitative analyses are based on easily recognized spectral differences. Isomers, for instance, are frequently distinguishable by their infrared spectra. Many examples may be found in the general reference books listed at the opening of this chapter. Just to mention a few random cases for illustration, it has been found that *para* sulfonates of primary alkylbenzenes, $R—C_6H_4SO_3Na$, exhibit a doublet infrared absorption band at 815 and 840 cm^{-1} whereas the *ortho*

[203] Cf. G. C. Pimentel, *J. Chem. Educ.,* **37,** 651 (1960), and references cited therein; N. B. H. Jonathan, *J. Mol. Spectroscopy,* **4,** 75 (1960).

[204] W. J. Orville-Thomas, *Chem. Revs.,* **57,** 1182 (1957), and references cited therein; A. D. Walsh, *Trans. Faraday Soc.,* **43,** 60, 158 (1947).

[205] L. N. Ferguson, in *Organic Analysis,* Vol. 5, edited by J. Mitchell, Jr., (New York: Interscience, in press).

isomers exhibit a single band at 749 cm^{-1}, and thus the two isomers may be distinguished.[206]   Primary, secondary, and tertiary alcohols have O—H bands close to 3637, 3627, and 3617 cm^{-1}, respectively, which fact can sometimes be used in the classification of an alcohol.   The absorption ranges of lactones, lactams, and cyclic acetals normally differ for five- and six-membered rings and can generally be used to confirm the size of the ring in a sample.   The infrared spectrum of a heteroannular disubstituted ferrocene is the sum of the spectra of the respective monosubstituted ferrocenes minus two peaks at 1000 and 1111 cm^{-1} [207]

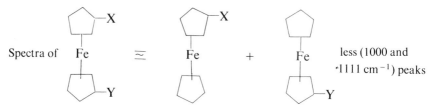

Metal chelates of type **XXXVIII** have two bands in the double-bond region, one at 1480–1600 cm^{-1} attributed to the perturbed chelated carbonyl group and one at 1540 cm^{-1} for the C=C bond.   They also have a band near 823 cm^{-1} which is assigned to the C=C—H group containing the α-H atom. Those chelates substituted in the α position have only a single band in the 1480–1600 wave number region and lack the 823-cm^{-1} band.[208, 209]

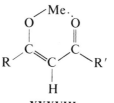

XXXVIII

The same quantitative analytical principles apply for all of the types of spectroscopy.   In the absence of interactions between components of a mixture or with the solvent, the spectrum of a mixture is the additive sum of the spectra of the individual components.   For illustration, the infrared spectra of *o*- and *p*-ethylchlorobenzene and of two mixtures of the two isomers are given in Fig. 5.15.   It can be seen that as the concentration of

[206] F. W. Gray and I. J. Krems, *J. Org. Chem.,* **26**, 209 (1961).

[207] M. Rosenblum, *Chem. and Ind. (London),* 953 (1958); W. F. Little and R. Eisenthal, *J. Am. Chem. Soc.,* **82**, 1577 (1960).

[208] R. W. Kluiber, *J. Am. Chem. Soc.,* **82**, 4839 (1960); H. F. Holtzclaw, Jr., and J. P. Collman, *J. Am. Chem. Soc.,* **79**, 3318 (1957); R. P. Dryden and A. Winston, *J. Phys. Chem.,* **62**, 635 (1958).

[209] This empirical rule does not hold for the α-substituted chelates when the substituent possesses a double bond (J. P. Collman, R. A. Morse, S. D. Goldby, and W. S. Trahanovsky, *Chem. and Ind. (London),* 1213 (1960).

[210] Descriptive bulletin of Dow Chemical Co., Midland, Mich.

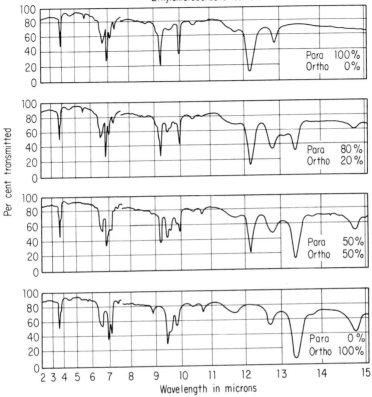

Fig. 5.15. Infrared absorption spectra of o- and p-ethylchloroben-
zene.[210]

the *para* isomer increases from zero to 100 per cent, the intensity of its
12.2-μ band increases and simultaneously the 13.3-μ band of the *ortho*
isomer decreases.

The basic equation for quantitative analysis is

$$A = \sum_{i}^{n} \epsilon_i c_i = \epsilon_1 c_1 + \epsilon_2 c_2 + \cdots + \epsilon_n c_n \qquad (5\text{-}8)$$

where A is absorbance of the mixture and ϵ_i and c_i are the molar
absorptivities and molar concentrations of the ith component in a
mixture of n components. This equation is applicable at any wavelength
provided the solution obeys Beer's law. This will normally be true if there
is no appreciable change in degree of dissociation or association with a
change in concentration. Usually, one works at wavelengths where absorption by other components is small. The ϵ values are determined at the
chosen wavelengths on pure single components. Then, for a mixture,
A is measured at these wavelengths. It can be seen that from Eq. (5-8), a
calculation of the concentrations of the components in an n-component

mixture requires the solution of n simultaneous equations. This is a tremendous task for five or more components even with an electric desk calculator. Several short-cut methods such as inverted matrices and other techniques have been used.[211] Also, electronic computors facilitate the computations. However, if one is able to choose working wavelengths where the ϵ_i's are nearly zero for all of the components except that with a λ_m at a given wavelength, then these $\epsilon_i c_i$ products can be neglected and the calculations are simplified. Using the general spectroscopic method, infrared analysis of mixtures containing up to 11 components[212] and Raman analysis of mixtures containing 10 components[213] have been made in reasonably high accuracy. At the present time, these analyses could hardly be matched by any other method.

Infrared spectra are more precise for multicomponent mixtures than ultraviolet because the infrared bands are much narrower and there is considerably less overlapping of the bands of each component. Nevertheless, ultraviolet as well as other forms of spectroscopy are often used for quantitative analysis of mixtures.[205]

In general, the longer is the wavelength the more the spectrum is related to segments of a molecule and becomes a "fingerprint" of a particular molecule. For examples, the structures of XXXIX and XL differ only in the positions of a double bond; XLI and XLII differ merely in the *cis* and *trans* orientation of OH and H; and α- and β-pinene are tautomers differing in the location of a proton and double bond. In each case, marked differences appear in their spectra (Figs. 5.16–5.18), and the spectra are as

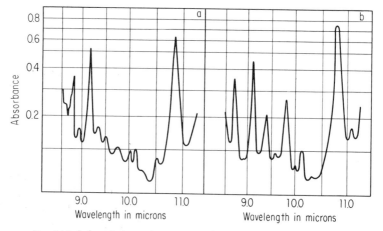

Fig. 5.16. Infrared absorption spectra of the benzenesulfonate esters of XXXIX(a) and XL (b).[214]

[211] P. D. Croit, *Trans. A.I.C.E.*, **60**, 1235 (1941).

[212] M. E. Griffing and R. L. Hudson, *Anal. Chem.*, **23**, 684 (1951); J. W. Kent and J. Y. Beach, Anal. Chem., **19**, 290 (1947).

[213] M. R. Fenske, *et al.*, *Anal. Chem.*, **19**, 700 (1947).

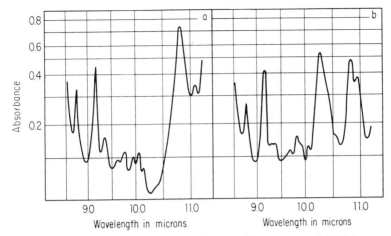

Fig. 5.17. Infrared spectra of the benzenesulfonate esters of XLI(a) and XLII(b).[214]

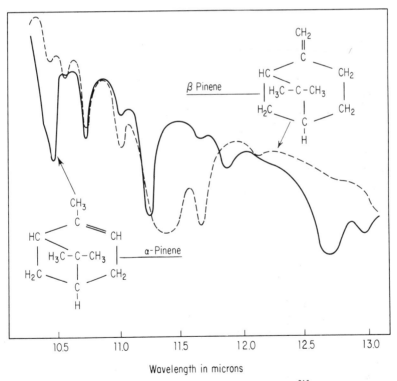

Fig. 5.18. Infrared spectra of α- and β-pinene.[215]

[214] J. Carol, *J. Am. Pharm. Assoc., Sci. Ed.,* **39,** 425 (1950).

[215] J. E. Tyler, *Interchem. Rev.,* Winter, 1950, p. 91.

unique as the fingerprints of twins. Thus, spectroscopy is a powerful tool for the qualitative and quantitative analysis of mixtures, and many examples are found of its use in almost every issue of any chemical journal.

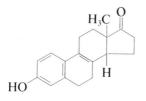

XXXIX
8-Dehydro-14-isoestrone

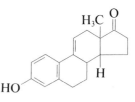

XL
9-Dehydro-14-isoestrone

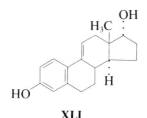

XLI
9-Dehydro-14-isoestradiol-17-α

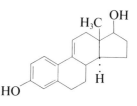

XLII
9-Dehydro-14-isoestradiol-17-β

It hardly needs mention that physical methods, particularly spectroscopy, offer the advantages for quantitative analysis of speed, accuracy, small sample size, and often preservation of the sample. Thus, spectroscopy is often used for the analysis of superfast reactions[216] or complex biological mixtures.[217] Spectroscopy, like all physical methods, is especially suited for studying equilibria because the measurement does not disturb an equilibrium. For instance, n.m.r. and infrared spectroscopy have been used to measure the percent of enol in enol-keto equilibria.

The classical Kurt-Meyer bromine titration method or some modification of it frequently gives values over 100 per cent enol for highly enolic systems.[218] In these cases, n.m.r. and infrared spectroscopy offer a distinct

[216] R. S. Berry, G. N. Spokes, and R. M. Stiles, *J. Am. Chem. Soc.,* **82,** 5240 (1960).

[217] Cf. the bibliography of infrared spectra of biochemicals, C. Clark and M. Chianta, *Ann. N. Y. Acad. Sci.,* **69,** 205 (1957).

[218] Cf. R. Filler and S. M. Naqvi, *J. Org. Chem.,* **26,** 2571 (1961).

advantage. Different proton n.m.r. signals arise from the nonequivalent protons in the enol and keto forms of, for example, ethyl acetoacetate.

Group	Chemical shift ppm (to lower fields)[219]
Enol CH_3	0
Keto CH_3	0.17
Keto CH_2	1.65
Enol C=C—H	3.58
Enol OH	13.58

From the relative areas under the respective peaks one may determine the ratio of the two tautomers present.[220] In the infrared region, one may use the chelated carbonyl band (ca. 1625 cm^{-1}) and the keto carbonyl band (ca. 1690 cm^{-1}). Values of keto-enol ratios by these physical methods generally agree with values obtained by the Kurt-Meyer method for compounds less than 90 per cent enolic (Table 5.26). Ultraviolet spectroscopy has not been as useful for measuring keto-enol equilibria.[221] From the temperature coefficient of the equilibrium constant, the heat of tautomerization at 25° for ethylacetoacetate as measured by several methods can be compared:

	$-\Delta H_{gas}$ (kcal/mole)	$-\Delta H_{sol'n}$ (kcal/mole)
Bromine titration[222]	~ 3.5	
Infrared spectroscopy[223]	2.4	2.0
N.m.r. spectroscopy[219]		2.7

N.m.r. spectroscopy is not as sensitive as infrared spectroscopy for some of these systems. For instance, n.m.r. failed to detect any non H-bonded enol (XLIII) in ethyl thiobenzoylacetate (XLIV) whereas the infrared spectrum and other data indicate that thioenol (XLIII) is present in the equilibrium mixture to about 1 per cent.[224] Similarly, n.m.r. spectra of benzoylacetones fail to detect the small amount of *diketone* present, which is revealed by the infrared spectra.[225]

[219] L. W. Reeves, *Can. J. Chem.*, **35**, 1351 (1957).

[220] C. Y. Hopkins and H. J. Bernstein, *Can. J. Chem.*, **37**, 775 (1959); H. S. Harrett, M. S. Sadler, and J. N. Shoolery, *J. Chem. Phys.*, **21**, 2092 (1953).

[221] R. D. Campbell and H. M. Gilow, *J. Am. Chem. Soc.*, **82**, 5426 (1960); compare G. S. Hammond, *et al.*, *J. Am. Chem. Soc.*, **81**, 4682 (1959).

[222] G. Briegleb and W. Strohmeier, *Z. Naturforsch.*, **6b**, 1 (1951).

[223] J. Powling and H. J. Bernstein, *J. Am. Chem. Soc.*, **73**, 4353 (1951).

[224] Z. Reyes and R. M. Silverstein, *J. Am. Chem. Soc.*, **80**, 6367 (1958).

[225] J. U. Lowe and L. N. Ferguson, unpublished results.

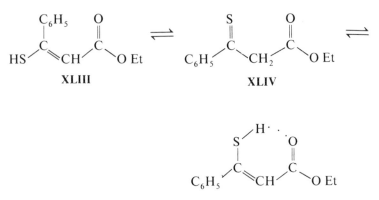

XLIII   XLIV

XLV

5.5.2. STRUCTURE ASSIGNMENT

Having empirically established several correlations between structure and absorption spectra (Sec. 5.4), one may use these relationships to provide evidence for a proposed structure of a given compound. For example, XLVI and XLVII can hardly be distinguished chemically because under the conditions for preparing derivatives, XLVII readily isomerizes into XLVI to give the same derivative.[226] However, the infrared and ultraviolet spectra readily distinguish the two compounds, and structures may be assigned on the basis that the infrared and ultraviolet bands of XLVI are in the region for an α,β-enone system and those for XLVII are characteristic of an isolated C=O group. Similarly, ketone XLVIII can readily be distinguished from XLIX because the former has a band in the isolated carbonyl region and also has a band in the OH region due to the presence of enol, whereas XLIX has a band in the α,β-enone region.[227]

Table 5.26. ENOL CONTENT IN SOME β-DIKETONES

Compound	Per cent enol by	
	Br_2 titration	N.m.r.[220]
Acetylacetone	76	85 (81)[219]
β-Methyl-acetylacetone	31.5	30

[226] M. S. Kharasch and P. O. Tawney, *J. Am. Chem. Soc.*, **67**, 128 (1945); M. S. Kharasch and B. S. Joshi, *J. Org. Chem.*, **22**, 1435, 1439 (1957).

[227] J. D. Park, R. E. Noble, and J. R. Lacher, *J. Org. Chem.*, **23**, 1396 (1958).

[228] L. F. Fieser and M. Fieser, *Advanced Organic Chemistry* (New York: Reinhold Publishing Corp.), 1961.

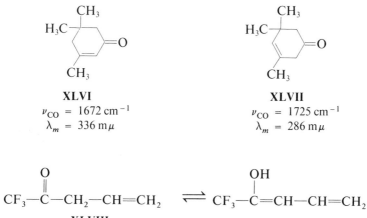

XLVI
$\nu_{CO} = 1672 \text{ cm}^{-1}$
$\lambda_m = 336 \text{ m}\mu$

XLVII
$\nu_{CO} = 1725 \text{ cm}^{-1}$
$\lambda_m = 286 \text{ m}\mu$

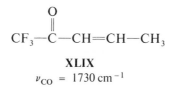

XLVIII
$\nu_{CO} = 1775 \text{ cm}^{-1}; \nu_{OH} = 3510 \text{ cm}^{-1}$

$$CF_3-\overset{\overset{\displaystyle O}{\|}}{C}-CH{=}CH-CH_3$$

XLIX
$\nu_{CO} = 1730 \text{ cm}^{-1}$

The spectra of hindered phenols and some of their oxidation products correlate well with their assigned structures.[226] For examples, the ultraviolet and infrared spectral characteristics of some of these compounds are in accord with the following structures:

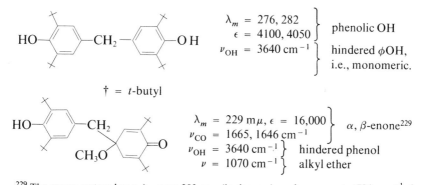

$$\lambda_m = 276, 282 \\ \epsilon = 4100, 4050 \left.\right\} \text{ phenolic OH}$$
$$\nu_{OH} = 3640 \text{ cm}^{-1} \left.\right\} \begin{array}{l}\text{hindered } \phi\text{OH,}\\ \text{i.e., monomeric.}\end{array}$$

† = *t*-butyl

$$\lambda_m = 229 \text{ m}\mu, \epsilon = 16,000 \left.\right\} \alpha, \beta\text{-enone}^{229}$$
$$\nu_{CO} = 1665, 1646 \text{ cm}^{-1}$$
$$\nu_{OH} = 3640 \text{ cm}^{-1} \left.\right\} \text{ hindered phenol}$$
$$\nu = 1070 \text{ cm}^{-1} \left.\right\} \text{ alkyl ether}$$

---

[229] The enone system has a λ_m near 203 mμ (in hexane) and a ν_{CO} at 1704 cm^{-1} in (CCl$_4$). Substitution of carbon-attached groups to the enone system raises λ_m about 10–15 mμ per attachment and decreases ν_{CO} by approximately 10 wave numbers per attachment (cf. W. F. Forbes and R. Shilton, *J. Org. Chem.*, **24**, 436 (1959) for leading references). Of course, other effects such as electronegativity of the attached groups also have pronounced effects on λ_m and ν_{CO}.

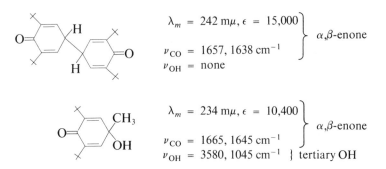

$$\lambda_m = 242 \text{ m}\mu, \epsilon = 15{,}000$$

$$\nu_{CO} = 1657, 1638 \text{ cm}^{-1}$$

$$\nu_{OH} = \text{none}$$

α,β-enone

$$\lambda_m = 234 \text{ m}\mu, \epsilon = 10{,}400$$

$$\nu_{CO} = 1665, 1645 \text{ cm}^{-1}$$

$$\nu_{OH} = 3580, 1045 \text{ cm}^{-1} \text{ } \} \text{ tertiary OH}$$

α,β-enone

Ultraviolet spectra have been helpful in the characterization of terpenes and unsaturated steroids. The resonance of a polyenone system

$$C{=}C{-}C{=}C{-}C{=}O, \qquad \overset{+}{C}{-}C{=}C{-}C{=}C{-}O^-$$

tends to increase λ_m because it stabilizes excited states with respect to ground states (more dipolar structures may be written which make their major contributions to the excited states). Bond angle strain also increases λ_m by decreasing the thermodynamic stability of the compound (primarily destabilizes the ground state) and, hence, decreases the difference in energies of the ground and excited states. For example, λ_m of cyclopentadiene is larger than that of butadiene (at most, the methylene group would increase λ_m by 10 mμ if it were regarded as two alkyl groups substituted on the 1 and 4 carbon atoms of the diene system).

$$\lambda_m = 238.5 \text{ m}\mu$$
$$\epsilon = 3{,}400$$

$$\lambda_m = 217 \text{ m}\mu$$
$$\epsilon = 20{,}900$$

The absorptivity is normally much smaller for the cisoid diene because, among other reasons, it has a shorter transition moment. Similarly, an exocyclic double bond increases λ_m more than an endocyclic double bond, which is in accord with the observation that an endocyclic double bond is about 1–2 kcal/mole more stable than an exocyclic double bond (for small and normal-size rings). The approximate positions of absorption maxima for polycyclic systems can be calculated in quite good agreement with observed data by taking these structural effects into consideration.[228]

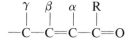

Parent α,β-enone
$\lambda_m^{\text{EtOH}} = 215\ m\mu$

		Increment
Cisoid diene system		39 $m\mu$
Additional conjugated C=C		30
Exocyclic position of C=C		5
Substituent (alkyl or ring		
residue);	α	10
	β	12
	γ (or higher)	18

For examples, the calculated and observed λ_m values for some steroids in ethanol are as follows (calculated values and structural increments in parentheses; only relevant fragments shown):

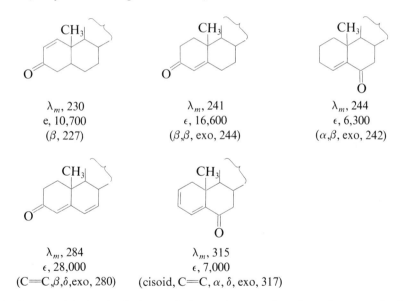

λ_m, 230
e, 10,700
(β, 227)

λ_m, 241
ϵ, 16,600
(β,β, exo, 244)

λ_m, 244
ϵ, 6,300
(α,β, exo, 242)

λ_m, 284
ϵ, 28,000
(C=C,β,δ,exo, 280)

λ_m, 315
ϵ, 7,000
(cisoid, C=C, α, δ, exo, 317)

Similar empirical calculations of absorption maxima have been made for terpenes and unsaturated steroids with equal success.

A classical example of structure assignment based on spectra was the case of the penicillins. Ten or more years had elapsed following its discovery before much interest was shown in securing information about the chemical structure of penicillin. Recognition of its potential military importance at the start of World War II led to a vast restricted international experimental and theoretical investigation of its chemical constitution and of methods of synthesizing it.   About 39 American and British scientific groups collaborated on this project, and the results have been described in a monograph.[230]

The usual methods of organic chemistry were entirely adequate for determining the structures of the degradation products of the penicillins, and although physical methods were employed in characterizing the degradation products, the latter methods were largely confirmatory in nature.   On the basis of the information at hand by early 1944, primarily chemical data, two alternative structures were held possible by most of the collaborating groups.   These were referred to as the oxazolone (L) and the β-lactam (LI) structures.   It was not possible to make an unequivocal

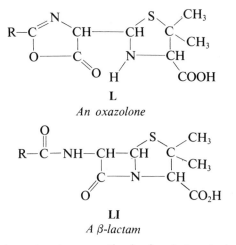

L

An oxazolone

LI

A β-lactam

selection from the two structures on the basis of chemical evidence alone because as a result of chemical rearrangements during chemical reactions, either structure might give the recovered degradation products.   Hence some knowledge was necessary concerning the penicillin molecules while intact.   This is precisely the advantage offered by physical methods, for usually chemical changes do not occur during the experimental observations.

In examining the spectra of the penicillins, the 3-μ and 5–8 μ regions provide the most information.   The absorption bands of methyl penicillinate and of sodium penicillinate are typical of the significant absorption bands of penicillins in these regions of the spectrum.[231]

[230] *The Chemistry of Penicillin,* ed. H. T. Clarke, J. R. Johnson, and R. Robinson (Princeton, N.J.: Princeton U. P.), 1949.

[231] For an infrared spectroscopic procedure for a quantitative analysis of mixtures of the five most common penicillins see R. B. Barnes, R. C. Gore, E. F. Williams, S. G. Linsley, and E. M. Petersen, *Anal. Chem.,* **19,** 620 (1947).

| Methyl benzylpenicillinate | 3.00 μ | 5.65 | 5.72 | 5.94 | 6.64 |
| Sodium benzylpenicillinate | 3.00 | 5.65 | 6.20 | 5.95 | 6.60 |

The 3-μ bands are immediately assigned to the N—H bonds, and the 5.72-μ band of the ester and the 6.2-μ band of the salt can be assigned to the respective C=O bonds. This leaves three bands to be accounted for, two of which are in the double-bond region.

A survey of the spectra of a large number of model 5(4)-oxazolones of the type

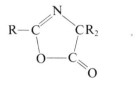

revealed that they are typified by two bands, one at 5.48 μ for the C=O group and one at 5.97 μ for the C=N group. Then, too, an examination was made of the spectra of a large number of thiazolidine compounds of the type

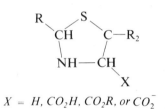

$$X = H, CO_2H, CO_2R, \text{ or } CO_2^-$$

These compounds exhibited no absorption in the double-bond region. Hence, the oxazolone structure (L) could account for the 5.95-μ band of penicillins but not the 5.62-μ and the 6.6-μ bands. It remained to be shown that the β-lactam structure is in accord with the spectral data.

Inspection of the spectra of a large number of amides established the fact that they all have bands near 6.0 μ which can be attributed to the C=O bond. In addition, unsubstituted amides have a second band near 6.2 μ and monosubstituted amides have a second band near 6.6 μ.

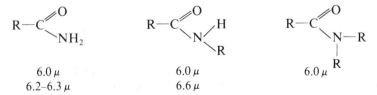

The two typical bands of monosubstituted amides correspond well to the 5.95-μ and 6.6-μ bands of the penicillins and provide evidence of an amide-type linkage in the molecules. Moreover, deuterization of benzylpenicillin causes exactly the same shift of its 6.6-μ band as does deuterization of simple monosubstituted amides. The 6.6-μ band is assigned to a bending vibration of the N—H bond which shifts to 6.8 μ for an N—D bond.

The only absorption band of the penicillins unaccounted for now is the 5.65-μ band. Simple β-lactams with fused thiazolidine rings were synthesized and each was found to have a band at 5.65 μ. This completes the picture, with all important absorption bands of the penicillins being interpreted in terms of the β-lactam (LI) structure.

Compound	N—H	β-lactam thiazolidine	CO_2^- or COOR	Amide	
Methyl benzylpenicillinate	3.00 μ	5.65	5.72	5.94	6.64
Sodium benzylpenicillinate	3.00	5.65	6.20	5.95	6.60

Although the infrared spectra of the penicillins provided strong evidence for their structure assignment, other physical methods such as ultraviolet spectra and dissociation constant data were used to supplement the evidence. However, the conclusive evidence came from the X-ray diffraction patterns which made it possible to make indisputable structure assignments to the penicillins.

In general, the two features sought in an n.m.r. spectrum are the chemical shift for the particular resonance observed and the spin-spin coupling interaction derived from the fine structure. The chemical shift-of proton resonance for example-provides information about the type of chemically different protons present. The proton frequencies when attached to various types of functional groups have been tabulated,[232,233] and regions for some functional groups are given in Fig. 5.19. Proton chemical shifts are very helpful, sometimes uniquely, for structure characterization. For illustration, Feist's acid was long thought to have the structure LII since it yields LIII upon ozonolysis of the ester.

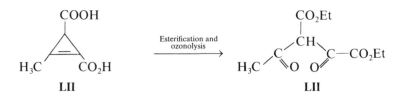

Later, it was pointed out that the structure could also be *trans*-3-methylene-cyclopropane-1,2-dicarboxylic acid (LIV). When the n.m.r. spectrum

[232] N. F. Chamberlain, *Anal. Chem.*, **31**, 56 (1959).

[233] L. M. Jackman, *Applications of NMR Spectroscopy in Organic Chemistry* (New York: Pergamon, 1959).

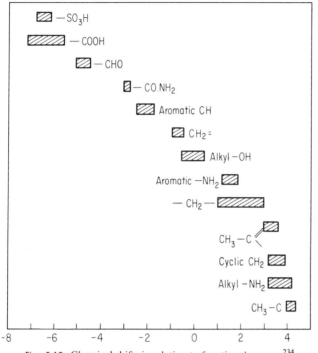

Fig. 5.19. Chemical shifts in relation to functional groups.[234]

was measured, there was found a proton signal for vinyl hydrogens and a peak for a tertiary C—H hydrogen with an intensity corresponding to two such groups.[235] This confirms structure LIV for Feist's acid.

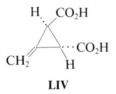

LIV

The number and relative intensities of peaks in a resonance signal are related to the number of protons in each group of chemically equivalent protons. Such details are useful for structure assignment too.[236] For examply, five conceivable structures for diketene can readily be distinguished by the n.m.r. spectrum on the basis of the number of equivalent hydrogen atoms. The p.m.r. spectrum of diketene should have two bands with

[234]L. H. Meyer, A. Saika, and H. S. Gutowsky, *J. Am. Chem. Soc.,* **75,** 4567 (1953).
[235]A. T. Bottini and J. D. Roberts, *J. Org. Chem.,* **21,** 1169 (1956).
[236]M. T. Rogers, *Rec. Chem. Progress,* **21,** 197 (1960).

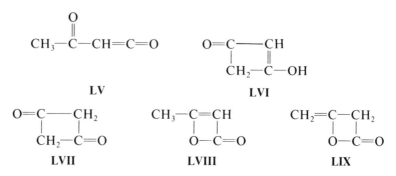

LV   LVI

LVII   LVIII   LIX

relative peak intensities of 3:1 for LV, 2:1:1 for LVI, 4 for LVII; 3:1 for
LVIII; and 2:2 for LIX. On this basis it was concluded that the structure
in the liquid state is LIX, which is in accord with X-ray diffraction data.[237]

In another case, three structures were proposed for the product obtained from the reaction of diketene and acetone, LX, LXI, and LXII.
In the p.m.r. spectrum there are three bands with relative intensities ap-

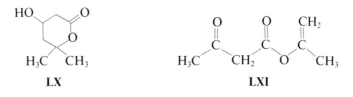

LX   LXI

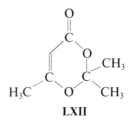

LXII

proximately 6:3:1 in ranges expected for $C(CH_3)_2$, CH_3—C=C, and
C=C—H groups.[238] This is in accord for structure LXII only, for structure LXI should give four lines with relative intensities 3:3:2:2 and structure LX four lines, 6:2:2:1. The fine structure in high-resolution spectra
can be helpful for conformational analysis.[239] For illustration, in the isomer
LXIII proton H_x is strongly coupled with the two axial H_y atoms, and

[237] A. R. Bader, H. S. Gutowsky, G. A. Williams, and P. E. Yankwich, *J. Am. Chem.
Soc.*, **78**, 2385 (1956).

[238] A. R. Bader, H. S. Gutowsky, and J. P. Heeschen, *J. Org. Chem.*, **21**, 821 (1956).

[239] J. Musher and R. E. Richards, *Proc. Chem. Soc.*, (London), 230 (1958); S. Brownstein
and R. Miller, *J. Org. Chem.*, **24**, 1886 (1959); P. M. Nair and J. D. Roberts, *J. Am.
Chem. Soc.*, **79**, 4565 (1957).

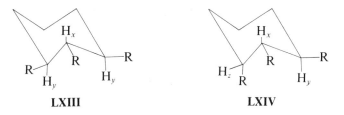

LXIII   **LXIV**

the H_x signal should therefore consist of a triplet with the center band at approximately twice the intensity of the two outer bands (see Fig. 5.20). In isomer LXIV, the H_x signal should be a quartet because coupling between cis protons is less than between *trans* protons.[240] On this basis, the configurations of two 1,3-dimethoxy-2-acetoxycyclohexanes were established.[241]

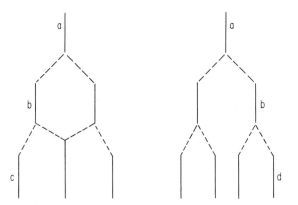

Fig. 5.20.[241] Graphic representation of n.m.r. signals for H_x atoms in LXIII and LXIV: (a) represents the signal for H_x if not coupled with other hydrogen atoms; (b) signal of H_x if coupled with H_y only; (c) signal of H_x if coupled with two H_y atoms as in LXIII (cf. Ref. 233); (d) signal of H_x if coupling with two H atoms is of different strengths.

In another example of structure assignment, it has been shown that crotyl bromide and α-methylallyl bromide each react with magnesium in ether to yield the same butenyl Grignard reagent. The Grignard could conceivably be crotylmagnesium bromide (LXV), α-methyl-allylmagnesium bromide (LXVI), a fluid equilibrium mixture of the two, or an intermediate nonclassical bridged structure such as LXVII. On the basis of the proton n.m.r. chemical shifts, it was concluded that the Grignard consists of almost 100 per cent LXV.[242] The spin-spin splitting pattern is in accord with

[240] A. C. Huitric and J. B. Carr, *J. Org. Chem.*, **26**, 2648 (1961).
[241] R. U. Lemieux, R. K. Kullnig, and R. Y. Moir, *J. Am. Chem. Soc.*, **80**, 2237 (1958)
[242] J. E. Nordlander, W. G. Young, and J. D. Roberts, *J. Am. Chem. Soc.*, **83**, 494 (1961).

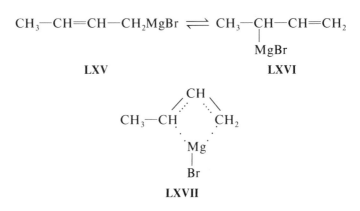

LXVII

LXV; i.e., the CH_2 signal is a doublet, the β-CH is a quartet, the γ-CH is a quintet, and the CH_3 signal is a doublet. The conclusion was in agreement with infrared evidence.

5.5.3. IDENTITY CONFIRMATION

A third way in which spectra are used in the characterization of compounds is the confirmation of identity of substances. As stated previously, infrared, microwave, and n.m.r. spectra serve as "finterprints" of molecules because they reveal very minor differences in molecular structure. Even large molecules with small hydrogen atoms differing in *cis* or *trans* positions exhibit unique infrared and n.m.r. absorption bands. Some of the strongest evidence available that two samples are identical is for them to have infrared or n.m.r. spectra which are identical in all respects. On this basis, for example, natural and synthetic vitamin K were shown to be identical. Also, natural and synthetic oxytocin, the first natural protein ever to be synthesized, were shown to be identical on the basis that not only did they have the same biological behavior but they had the same spectra and other physical properties. When the first successful attempt to synthesize penicillin G yielded only about one gram of product, a portion of this yield was immediately used for an infrared measurement to establish its identity with the natural material. An infrared spectrum is now accepted as proof of identity in patent claims.

5.5.4. STUDY OF COMPLEXES

(i) **Structure.** Absorption spectra have been particularly useful in the elucidation of the structures of chelates, metallocenes, charge-transfer complexes, and other types of molecular aggregates. The success of ligand field theory in accounting for visible absorption spectra of chelates and metallocenes has been largely responsible for its recent rise in popularity. Although all forms of spectroscopy can provide some information about any of the several different types of complexes, it has been applied in the past in particular as follows:

Chelates and metallocenes: Electronic spectra to determine energy states of the metal component and relative stabilities. Infrared and n.m.r. spectroscopy to study the organic portions.

Charge-transfer complexes and sigma complexes:[243] Electronic spectra to determine formation constants and relative stabilities.[244] Infrared spectra to study bonding within the components.

The use of spectroscopy in the study of these several types of complexes was illustrated in the discussion of the complexes in Chap. 1; additional examples need not be presented here.

(ii) Empirical formula determination. Several procedures are now in use for the determination of empirical formulas of complexes in solution.[245] The procedures are based on the expectation that two substances A and B react to give one or more complex compounds in solution. In the *method of continuous variations*, mixtures of various mole fractions of A and B are prepared with the total number of moles of A and B held constant. Then, the absorbances for the solutions at a given wavelength are plotted against the mole fraction of either component, and the point of maximum absorbance indicates the mole fraction of that component in the complex.[246] In the *slope ratio method*[247] the concentration of one component in a large, fixed excess of the other is varied, while the ionic strength is held fixed. Then, the absorbance is plotted against the concentration of the variable component and the slope of the expected straight line gives the ratio of the components in the complex. In the *molar ratio method*,[247,248] the absorbance is plotted against the molar ratio of A to B while the concentration of one is held constant. Frequently, there will be a sharp maximum at the

[243]The theory of charge-transfer spectra has been reviewed by J. N. Murrell, *Quart. Revs.*, **15**, 191 (1961).

[244]One unique application is to use the position of c-t bands as a measure of solvent polarity (E. M. Kosower, *J. Am. Chem. Soc.*, **80**, 3253 (1958).

[245]Cf. A. E. Harvey, Jr., and D. L. Manning, *J. Am. Chem. Soc.*, **73**, 4744 (1952); E. I. Stearns, *Anal. Chem.*, **25**, 1004 (1953); W. Liptay, *Z. Elektrochem.*, **65**, 375 (1961).

[246]C. V. Banks and E. K. Byrd, *Anal. Chim. Acta*, **10**, 134 (1954); W. C. Vosburgh and G. R. Cooper, *J. Am. Chem. Soc.*, **63**, 437 (1941); M. M. Jones, *J. Am. Chem. Soc.*, **81**, 4485 (1959); J. H. Yoe and A. E. Harvey, *J. Am. Chem. Soc.*, **70**, 648 (1948).

[247]A. E. Harvey, Jr., and D. L. Manning, *J. Am. Chem. Soc.*, **72**, 4488 (1950).

[248]S. M. Edmonds and N. Birnbaum, *J. Am. Chem. Soc.*, **63**, 1471 (1941); R. W. Shellman, *J. Org. Chem 22*, 818 (1957).

[249]W. D. Kingery and D. N. Hume, *J. Am. Chem. Soc.*, **71**, 2393 (1949); H. E. Bent and C. L. French, *J. Am. Chem. Soc.*, **63**, 568 (1941).

molar ratio corresponding to that in the complex. In the *logarithmic method*,[249] the concentration of one component, say for example A, is kept constant and then a plot of the log of the concentration of A vs. the log of the concentration of B may yield a straight line whose slope gives the ratio of the components in the complex.

The applicability of these methods depends on whether or not the absorption bands for A, B, and the complex overlap significantly, and whether more than one complex is formed. Often, modifications or combinations of these methods are found to be more effective.[250]

(iii) **Association and ionization constants.** Spectroscopy has been used for the measurement of ionization constants of acids and bases with essentially the same principles as used in the determination of empirical formulas of complexes in solution. The logarithmic method, for example, has been particularly successful for the determination of association constants between weak acids and bases in organic solvents.[251,252] As an illustration, consider the equilibrium reaction between an acid (A), a base (B), and its salt (S), whose equilibrium constant is given by Eq. (5-10), where K_a is the

$$A + B = S \tag{5-9}$$

$$K_a = \frac{(S)}{(B)(A)} \tag{5-10}$$

association constant and quantities in parentheses are the respective activities. At low concentration, activity constants are normally taken as unity so that the concentrations of S, B, and A approximate their activities. With a given reference acid, the order of K_a's for a series of bases should be the same as their relative basicities. Taking the logarithms of both sides of Eq. (5-10), one can write

$$\log K_a = \log \frac{(S)}{(A)} - \log (B)$$

When the ratio $(S)/(A)$ is unity, $\log K_a = -\log (B)$. Hence, if $\log (S)/(A)$ is plotted against $-\log (B)$, when the former becomes zero, the value of $-\log (B)$ can be used to calculate $\log K_a$, or the equilibrium constant, K_a. The values of (S), (A), and (B) can be determined from spectroscopic measurements. Separate spectra of the salt, acid, and base are measured, and an absorption band of the salt is selected in a region where the base and acid have little absorption. Then, at this wavelength, the ratio of the absorbance for a given concentration of base to the absorbance of the

[250]C. Eaborn, *J. Chem. Soc.*, 4154 (1953).

[251]S. W. Tobey, *J. Chem. Educ.*, **35**, 515 (1958).

[252]Cf. M. M. Davis, *et al.*, *J. Res. Nat. Bur. Stand.*, **42**, 595 (1949).

pure salt multiplied by the original molar concentration of the acid C_a gives the molar concentration of the salt (S). The concentration of the unreacted acid (A) is $C_a - (S)$. If C_b is the original molar concentration of the base added to the mixture, the concentration of base (B) in the equilibrium mixture equals $C_b - (S)$. Hence, from a series of values of (S), (A), and (B), calculated in this way for solutions containing the same initial concentration of acid but with different amount of a given base, graphs of log $(S)/(A)$ versus $-$log (B) can be drawn, from which at the point log $(S)/(A)$ equal to zero, the value of $-$log K_a may be obtained. In this manner, for example, the value of $K_b = 1.6 \times 10^{-11}$ has been obtained for p-aminobenzophenone in aqueous dioxane.[253] Very often, this general procedure uses a somewhat different equation.[254]

Of course, intermolecular H bonding is a form of association which occurs in solution. Nevertheless, spectroscopy of H bonding has been discussed extensively already in several sections of this book, and more need not be said about it here.

5.5.5. DETECTION OF TRANSIENT PRODUCTS AND STUDY OF REACTION KINETICS

Spectroscopy has been a useful tool for studying the kinetics of reactions and a powerful probe for detecting short-lived intermediates[255] or for measuring the rates of extremely fast reactions. This, of course, is the basis of acquiring information about the mechanisms of reactions. For examples, in the study of the rate of reaction of o-mercaptobenzoic acid with p-nitrophenol acetate,[256] the rate of reaction may be followed by periodically withdrawing a sample from the reaction mixture and measuring the

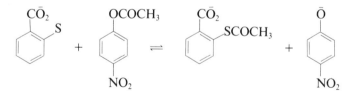

absorbance at 410 mμ. At this wavelength, essentially all of the absorption is by the p-nitrophenoxide ion. With the measured absorbance (A) and the known molar absorptivity (ϵ) of the nitrophenoxide ion, its concentration C is calculated from the relationship $A = C \cdot \epsilon$. The results were found to agree with the much slower analytical method of titrating the

[253]E. E. Sager and I. J. Siewers, *J. Res. Nat. Bur. Stand.*, **45**, 489 (1950).

[254]Cf. A. R. Lawrence and L. N. Ferguson, *J. Org. Chem.*, **25**, 1220 (1960), and D. S. Noyce and M. J. Jorgenson, *J. Am. Chem. Soc.*, **84**, 4312 (1962), for key references.

[255]R. S. Berry, G. N. Spokes, and R. M. Stiles, *J. Am. Chem. Soc.*, **82**, 5240 (1960).

[256]G. R. Schonbaum and M. L. Bender, *J. Am. Chem. Soc.*, **82**, 1900 (1960).

unreacted *o*-mercaptobenzoic acid in aliquote samples. In a similar fashion, one could follow the rate of dehydration of β-hydroxyketones

$$R\!-\!CO\!-\!CH_2\!-\!CHOH\!-\!R \xrightarrow{-H_2O} R\!-\!CO\!-\!CH\!=\!CH\!-\!R$$

by observing the increase in intensity of an absorption band in the 225–240 mμ region corresponding to the formation of the α,β-enone product as the reaction proceeds. In other examples, the mechanism of oximation of ketones was confirmed by ultraviolet spectroscopic measurements,[257a] and the rate of reduction of nitrobenzene to aniline was followed by measuring the nitrobenzene absorption at 265 mμ.[257b]

Normally n.m.r. spectroscopy is not as sensitive as other spectroscopic methods for quantitative analysis because fairly concentrated solutions must be used and peak intensities cannot be measured as accurately. However, there are times when n.m.r. spectroscopy can be used to an advantage. For example, the rearrangement of LXVIII to LXIX can readily be followed by n.m.r.[258] The equilibrium is attended by an increase in the

$$CH_2\!=\!CH\!-\!CH_2\!-\!CD_2\!-\!MgBr \qquad CH_2\!=\!CH\!-\!CD_2\!-\!CH_2\!-\!MgBr$$
LXVIII **LXIX**

$$\underset{\underset{CD_2}{\diagdown\diagup}}{CH_2\!-\!CH\!-\!CH_2\!-\!MgBr}$$

—CH$_2$— peak for the 1-position and a corresponding decrease for this group in the 2-position.

Spectroscopy has been particularly amenable to the study of the kinetics of biological systems. For instance, in the study of respiration in mammalian tissue cells, the sequence of six respiratory enzymes can be studied in detail through ultraviolet spectrophotometric measurements at the six different characterizing wavelengths:[259]

Substrate $\longrightarrow$ reduced pyridine nucleotide $\longrightarrow$ flavoprotein
(340 mμ) (465 mμ)

cytochrome *a* $\longleftarrow$ cytochrome *c* $\longleftarrow$ cytochrome *b*
(605 mμ) (550 mμ) (564 mμ)

cytochrome *a*$_3$ $\longrightarrow$ O$_2$
(445 mμ)

[257](a) W. P. Jencks, *J. Am. Chem. Soc.*, **81**, 475 (1959); (b) O. J. Cope and R. K. Brown, *Can. J. Chem.*, **39**, 1695 (1961).

[258]M. S. Silver, P. R. Shafer, J. E. Nordlander, C. Ruchardt, and J. D. Roberts, *J. Am. Chem. Soc.*, **82**, 2646 (1960).

[259]B. Chance, *Science*, **120**, 767 (1954).

5.5.6. STUDY OF ISOMERISM AND CONFORMATIONAL ANALYSIS

Section 3.3 discussed the use of spectra for determining potential energy differences between acyclic conformations and for distinguishing alicyclic conformations. Usually infrared, Raman, microwave, or n.m.r.[260] spectroscopy is most effective for this. Several examples of the use of spectroscopy in conformational analysis were given in Secs. 3.3.3 and 5.4.2 so that only two will be given here. Of particular interest in conformational analysis has been the energy of the chair-chair inversion of cyclohexane. Estimates have ranged from 2 to 14 kcal/mole, but n.m.r. spectroscopy has provided a reasonably reliable energy value for this process. At high temperatures the n.m.r. spectrum obtained for a sample is the weighted time average of the two conformers; at low temperatures, however, the spectrum is the summation for the individual conformers. Thus at room temperature the proton signal of cyclohexane appears as a single, sharp peak; at $-70°$ it separates into two clear peaks, each of which shows a fine structure.[260b] The peak at low field is assigned to the equatorial protons and that at high field to the axial. The axial peak is broader because axial-axial coupling is greater than e-a or e-e coupling. This separation into two bands is evidence that the rate of the chair-chair interconversion has been slowed sufficiently at low temperature so that the mean lifetime in any given conformation is larger than the inversion frequency separation due to the two kinds of hydrogens. Assuming the boat conformer to be the less stable form of cyclohexane, the energy differences between the chair and twisted boat conformations can now be represented by the accompanying diagram.[260b]

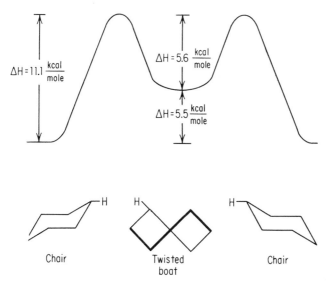

$$\Delta H = 11.1 \frac{kcal}{mole} \qquad \Delta H = 5.6 \frac{kcal}{mole} \qquad \Delta H = 5.5 \frac{kcal}{mole}$$

Chair   Twisted   Chair
                          boat

Simple monosubstituted cyclohexanes undergo rapid chair-chair inversions too. At room temperature the C_1 proton n.m.r. signal is seen in an average position rather than the position for pure axial or equatorial proton. If δ is the chemical shift of the C_1 proton, δ_e is the corresponding shift for an axial proton on an equatorially substituted cyclohexane $C_6H_{11}X$, and δ_a is the shift for an equatorial proton on an axially substituted cyclohexane, then

$$\delta = N_e\delta_e + N_a\delta_a$$

and

$$K = \frac{\delta_a - \delta}{\delta - \delta_e}$$

where N_e and N_a are the mole fractions of $C_6H_{11}X$ in equatorial or axial conformation, respectively, and K is the equilibrium constant between the two conformers. Two methods have been used to obtain δ_e and δ_a. One is to make measurements at very low temperatures as discussed in the preceding example. In the second method, the shifts are measured in a 4-t-butyl substituted cyclohexyl compound, 4-t-Bu-CH—$(CH_2)_4$—CHX-1.[260c] The *cis* isomer gives δ_a and the *trans* isomer gives δ_e. In this technique it is assumed that the 4-t-butyl group does not affect the chemical shifts in any way other than to hold the molecule in one conformation. Thus, it is not as sound theoretically as the low-temperature technique. Nevertheless, the results from the two procedures are in general accord with each other.

5.5.7. DATA FOR CALCULATION OF THERMODYNAMIC FUNCTIONS, BOND DISTANCES, AND DIPOLE MOMENTS

In statistical mechanics, the quantity denoted by Q

$$Q = \sum_i p_i e^{-\epsilon_i/kT} \tag{5-11}$$

is called the *partition function*, where p_i is the statistical number of quantum states i, k is Boltzmann's constant, T is the absolute temperature, and ϵ_i is the energy of a quantum state, i. Also, the total internal energy E per mole of a gas is expressed as

[260](a) J. Lee and L. H. Sutcliffe, *Trans. Faraday Soc.,* **55,** 880 (1959); J. C. Schug, P. E. McMahon, and H. S. Gutowsky, *J. Chem. Phys.,* **33,** 843 (1960); R. J. Abraham and H. J. Bernstein, *Can. J. Chem.,* **39,** 39 (1961); S. Brownstein and R. Miller, *J. Org. Chem.,* **24,** 1886 (1959); (b) F. R. Jensen, D. S. Noyce, C. H. Sederholm, and A. J. Berlin, *J. Am. Chem. Soc.,* **84,** 386 (1962); (c) E. L. Eliel and M. N. Gianni, *Tetrahedron Letters* no. 3, 97 (1962).

$$E = \frac{N \sum_i p_i \epsilon_i e^{-\epsilon_i/kT}}{\sum_i p_i e^{-\epsilon_i/kT}} \tag{5-12}$$

where N is Avogadro's number and the other symbols have the same meaning as in Eq. (5-11). Since the heat capacity and entropy S of a gas are related to its energy

$$C_V = T \frac{dS}{dT} = \frac{\partial E}{\partial T}$$

both can be derived from Eq. (5-12), where the right-hand side is summed over all rotational, vibrational, and electronic energy states. To this must be added the translational energy.

Calculation of thermodynamic quantities from Eq. (5-12) is a tedious, complex process, of no special interest here. The topic is mentioned, however, because the energies of the various energy levels for the partition functions are obtained from infrared spectra. Once the vibrational frequencies of a molecule are determined, the heat capacity, enthalpy, free energy, and entropy may be calculated through the methods of statistical mechanics, sometimes beyond the limits of precise experimental measurements (e.g., extremely high pressures).

Mention was made in Sec. 3.3.1 that microwave spectroscopy is particularly good for the determination of bond distances in small molecules. A good example of the value of infrared spectroscopy for structure determination is the case of nitrous acid.[261] Moments of inertia were calculated from the fine structure frequencies from which bond distances and bond angles were computed (Fig. 5.21). This study has provided the most accurate measure of the structure of nitrous acid yet made.

There have been scattered attempts to determine dipole moments from infrared absorption intensities.[262] The procedure is based on the relationship

$$I \alpha f \left(\frac{\partial \mu}{\partial r} \right)^2$$

where I is the band intensity, μ is the change in dipole moment during excitation, and r is a space coordinate, usually taken as the distance of atomic oscillation from the equilibrium interatomic distance. The method yields what are called dynamic moments rather than static moments. However, it

[261] L. H. Jones, R. M. Badger, and G. E. Moore, *J. Chem. Phys.*, **19**, 1599 (1951).

[262] See the excellent review on applications of infrared intensities by T. L. Brown, *Chem. Revs.*, **58**, 581 (1958); R. J. Lovell and E. A. Jones, *J. Mol. Spectroscopy*, **4**, 173 (1960).

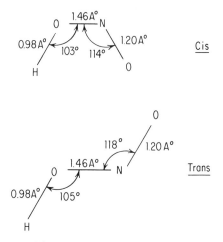

Fig. 5.21. The structures of *cis* and *trans*-nitrous acid.[261]

has proved useful in certain instances, where, for example, the compound is too unstable to be studied by the usual methods.[263]

5.5.8. MOLECULAR WEIGHT DETERMINATIONS

Many amine-picrates have a strong absorption band near 380 mμ and of the same intensity (ϵ = 38,440).[264] Hence, by the use of the Bouguer-Beer law, where A is the observed absorbance,

$$A = c \cdot d \cdot \epsilon$$

c is the molar concentration of the picrate, d is the cell thickness, and ϵ = 38,400, the molecular weight of the picrate may be calculated and the molecular weight of the amine determined therefrom. The procedure is quite simple and yields acceptable results.[265]

5.5.9. PROCESS CONTROL

It is standard procedure for chemical plants to continuously monitor the compositions of reaction mixtures by following in the spectrum of the reaction mixture the changing intensities of certain constituents. A good example is found in the case of the production of synthetic rubber. In 1941, the U.S. was importing 90 per cent of its natural rubber from the East Indies when Japan cut off this supply. Immediately a crash program

[263] F. A. Andersen, B. Bak, and J. Rastrup-Andersen, *Acta Chem. Scand.*, **7**, 643 (1953).

[264] K. G. Cunningham, G. W. Dawson, and F. S. Spring, *J. Chem. Soc.*, 2304 (1951).

[265] V. Boekelheide and J. C. Godfrey, *J. Am. Chem. Soc.*, **75**, 3679 (1953); J. C. Godfrey, *Anal. Chem.*, **31**, 1087 (1959).

was initiated to synthesize rubber. One of the key monomers was buta-diene, which may polymerize either by *cis*-1,4-, *trans*-1,4-, or by 1,2-addition. From the spectra of simple *cis* and *trans* olefins of the type RCH=CHR, and of simple vinyl RCH=CH$_2$ compounds, it was found that there are characteristic infrared absorption bands for these stereoiso-mers.

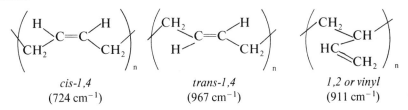

cis-1,4	*trans*-1,4	1,2 or vinyl
(724 cm^{-1})	(967 cm^{-1})	(911 cm^{-1})

On the basis of the absorbances at these wavelengths, quantitative mea-surements were made of the relative amounts of *cis*-1,4-, *trans*-1,4-, and 1,2-addition along the polymer chain. The configuration of the polymer is important because it largely determines the elasticity, tensile strength, and other properties of the product. Thus, it was fortunate that quick, accurate analyses of the polymerization products could be made, expediting the research to find the experimental conditions for producing a synthetic rubber with the optimum desired properties.

STUDY QUESTIONS

1. The λ_m for the C=O and C=C—C=O systems are 280 mμ and 310–330 mμ, respectively. Predict λ_m for the $\overset{\displaystyle C}{\overset{\textstyle |}{C-C}}$—C=O system.

2. How would you account for the relative λ_m's for the three species:

$(C_6H_5)_3CH$	$(C_6H_5)_3C^-$	$(C_6H_5)_3C \cdot$
$\lambda_m = 264$ mμ	$\lambda_m = 282,480$ mμ	$\lambda_m = 339,512$ mμ
$\epsilon = 900$	$\epsilon = 3800, 5600$	$\epsilon = 8900, 15$

3. Explain the fact that *trans*-2,2',4',6,6'-pentamethyl-4-hydroxyazobenzene is red while the *cis* isomer is essentially colorless.

4. Predict the order of λ_m's for the compounds[266]

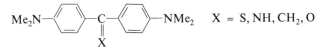

X = S, NH, CH$_2$, O

[266]A. Burawoy, *Ber.*, **63**, 3155 (1930).

5. To what extent will the ultraviolet spectra of the compounds

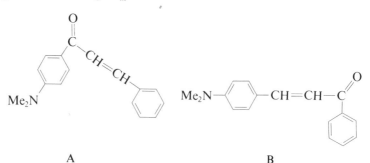

resemble one another? Give the basis for your prediction.[267]

6. What resemblance would you expect in the ultraviolet spectra of the compounds C_6H_5—CH_2CH_3, $(C_6H_5)_2CH_2$, and $(C_6H_5)_4C$?

7. What relationships would you expect between the ultraviolet spectra[268] of the compounds R—CH_3, R—CH_2—R, and R—R, where R represents

$$Me_2N\text{—}\langle\ \rangle\text{—}N\text{=}N\text{—}\langle\ \rangle\text{—}$$

8. It is observed that λ_m of an unsymmetrical cyanine dye R_2N—$(CH\text{=}CH)_n$—$CH\text{=}\overset{+}{N}R_2'$ is less than the arithmetic mean of the λ_m's of the two related symmetrical dyes, R_2N—$(CH\text{=}CH)_n$—$CH\text{=}\overset{+}{N}R_2$ and $R_2'N$—$(CH\text{=}CH)_n$—$CH\text{=}\overset{+}{N}R_2'$. Why should this deviation of λ_m from the mean be related to the relative basicities of the two symmetrical dyes?[269]

9. Since *cis*-stilbene has a smaller λ_m than *trans*-stilbene, how do you account for tetraphenylethylene having a λ_m close to that of *trans*-stilbene?[270]

10. If A and B each have two absorption bands, which should have the larger λ_m and which the larger λ_m'?[271]

A

B

11. Which halobenzene should exhibit the least fine structure in its ultraviolet spectrum?

[267] For the ultraviolet spectra, see E. Mayer-Pitsch, *Z. Elektrochem.*, **49**, 368 (1943).

[268] J. D. Piper and W. R. Brode, *J. Am. Chem. Soc.*, **57**, 135 (1935); W. R. Brode and L. E. Herdle, *J. Org. Chem.*, **6**, 713 (1941).

[269] Cf. L. G. Brooker, *et al.*, *J. Am. Chem. Soc.*, **67**, 1889 (1945).

[270] R. N. Jones, *J. Am. Chem. Soc.*, **65**, 1818 (1943).

[271] E. R. Katzenellenbogen and G. E. K. Branch, *J. Am. Chem. Soc.*, **69**, 1615 (1947).

12. How do you explain the fact that the infrared C=O frequency of (I) is 15 cm^{-1} lower than that of (II)?[272]

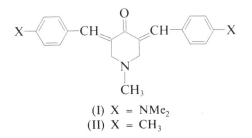

(I) X = NMe$_2$
(II) X = CH$_3$

13. The infrared O—H frequencies in ethanol, acetic acid, and trichloroacetic acid are 3640, 3521, and 3495 cm^{-1}, respectively. How do you account for this trend in their infrared frequencies?

14. Why should catechol have two infrared absorption bands at 7060 and 6970 cm^{-1}, whereas resorcinol only has one at 7050 cm^{-1}?

15. How would you explain the fact that o-chloro, o-bromo, and o-iodophenol all have two infrared absorption bands, one at the phenol frequency 7050 cm^{-1} and one at a lower frequency, but o-fluorophenol only has one band at 7015 cm^{-1}?

16. The O—H infrared absorption band usually shifts to longer wavelengths upon passing from the vapor or solution to the solid state. Why should this be so?

17. How many modes of vibration should there be for HCN?

18. Predict the order of λ_x and λ_y for 4-substituted malachite green dyes with the substituents CH$_3$, NMe$_2$, and OCH$_3$.

19. Compounds of the type

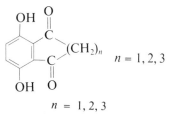

$n = 1, 2, 3$

do not react with diazomethane. On this basis, predict the approximate infrared absorption frequencies for the OH and C=O groups.

20. Offer an explanation for the frequency and number of infrared OH absorption bands for the following set of compounds:[273]

[272] N. J. Leonard and D. M. Locke, J. Am. Chem. Soc., 77, 1852 (1955).
[273] S. A. Barker, et al., Tetrahedron, 7, 10 (1959).

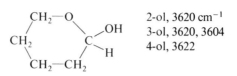

2-ol, 3620 cm^{-1}
3-ol, 3620, 3604
4-ol, 3622

tetrahydropyran-2-ol

21. What spectral characteristics would you look for in trying to assign structure A or B to an isoxazole?

A   B

22. Which infrared absorption band of the benzenediazonium ions should shift to higher frequencies upon the introduction of an electron-donating group into the *para* position?[274]

23. Make the following predictions and give the basis for each prediction:
    (a) The order of infrared OH frequency shifts in the β-substituted compounds, $X-CH_2CH_2OH$, with X = F, Cl, Br, I.[275]
    (b) The infrared carbonyl frequency in CCl_3CO_2Et on the basis of the data in Table 5.21 [cf. Ref. 173].
    (c) The order of infrared O—H stretching frequencies for monomeric acetic, chloroacetic, and trichloroacetic acids.[276]
    (d) The order of λ_m of the first primary band of *p*-haloacetanilides, *p*-X—$C_6H_4NHCONH_2$, for X = F, Cl, Br, I, and H.[277]
    (e) The order of infrared carbonyl frequencies of alkyl benzoates, $C_6H_5CO_2R$, for R = Me, Et, *i*-Pr, and *t*-Bu.[278]
    (f) Which should have the larger infrared carbonyl frequency, γ- or δ-lactones?[279]

24. The mono ester of a diaxial 1,3-diol of a six-membered ring has a single infrared band in the 3594 cm^{-1} region whose extinction coefficient is concentration independent. On the other hand, the axial-equatorial isomer of the mono ester has a sharp peak at 3607 cm^{-1} and a broad band with a maximum at 3450 cm^{-1}, and the relative intensities of the two bands change with concentration.[280] Offer an explanation for these observations. Which band of the axial-equatorial isomer will decrease in intensity as the concentration increases?

[274]K. B. Whetsel, G. F. Hawkins, and F. E. Johnson, *J. Am. Chem. Soc.,* **78,** 3360 (1956).
[275]P. R. Schleyer and R. West, *J. Am. Chem. Soc.,* **81,** 3164 (1959).
[276]J. T. Harris and M. E. Hobbs, *J. Am. Chem. Soc.,* **76,** 1419 (1954).
[277]H. E. Ungnade, *J. Am. Chem. Soc.,* **76,** 5133 (1954).
[278]C. J. W. Brooks, G. Eglinton, and J. F. Morman, *J. Chem. Soc.,* 661 (1961).
[279]S. A. Barker, E. J. Bourne, R. M. Pinkard, and D. H. Whiffen, *Chem. and Ind.,* (London), 658 (1958).
[280]R. West, J. J. Korst, and W. S. Johnson, *J. Org. Chem.,* **25,** 1976 (1960).

25. Offer an accounting for the fact that in the spectrum of *o*-allylphenol in the OH stretch region, that at a certain concentration there are three bands (3605, 3542, and 3360 cm^{-1}), and the intensities of the first two are concentration independent but the intensity of the third is concentration dependent.[281]

26. Cholesterol and epicholesterol have infrared O—H absorption bands at 3590 and 3630 cm^{-1}, respectively. Offer an explanation for the difference in positions of these two bands.

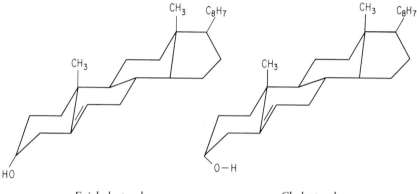

Epicholesterol   *Cholesterol*

27. α-Ferrocenylethanol in CCl$_4$ has an absorption band at 3617 cm^{-1} and another more intense concentration-independent but temperature-dependent band at 3574 cm^{-1}. β-Phenylethanol exhibits similar bands at 3630 and 3601 cm^{-1}, but with reversed relative intensities. Offer an explanation for these data in terms of H bonding. Is the bonding inter- or intramolecular, and in which compound is there the stronger H bond?[282]

28. The fact that C$_6$H$_5$C≡C—H exhibits H bonding supports the idea that *sp*-hybridized carbon atoms are much more electronegative than *sp*^{2} or *sp*^{3} hybridized carbons. What other types of data support this view?

29. Pentafluorophenol has two infrared OH absorption bands, 3630 and 3450 cm^{-1}. Its boiling point is 144–6°. What can be said about the H bond in this compound, is it inter- or intramolecular?[283]

30. An overtone of the C—Cl stretching frequency (13.3–14.3 μ) occurs at 1.86 μ. Which overtone must it be?

31. Why should the frequency of the salicylaldehyde infrared carbonyl band (1666 cm^{-1}) be lower than that of *m*-hydroxybenzaldehyde (1700 cm^{-1})?

32. Offer an explanation for the bathochromic shifts of the following substituents on the azobenzene and *p'*-ferrocenylazobenzene systems:[284]

[281]A. W. Baker and A. T. Shulgin, *J. Am. Chem. Soc.,* **80,** 5358 (1958).
[282]D. S. Trifan, *et al., J. Am. Chem. Soc.,* **79,** 6566 (1957).
[283]W. J. Pummer and L. A. Wall, *Science,* **127,** 643 (1958).
[284]W. F. Little and A. K. Clark, *J. Org. Chem.,* **25,** 1979 (1960).

Group	$\Delta\lambda_m$ in azobenzene spectrum (mμ)	$\Delta\lambda_m$ in p'-ferro-cenylazobenzene spectrum (mμ)
p-Cl	6	7
p-Br	8	8
p-I	13	11
p-CH$_3$	7	3
p-NO$_2$	15	26

Predict the shift for the p-F atom.

33. Offer an explanation for the observation that a fluorine atom produces a small hypsochromic effect on the first primary bands of aniline, anisole, and iodobenzene whereas the other halogens produce bathochromic shifts.

34. Most of the di-t-butylphenol free radicals such as (I) have two infrared carbonyl bands near 1650 cm^{-1} but (II) has only one at 1570 cm^{-1}. Offer an explanation for the single band at the unusually low frequency for the latter compound.

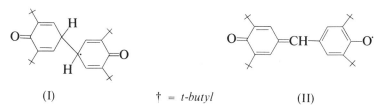

(I)   † = t-butyl   (II)

35. Among the most probable structures for biuret are (I)–(V):

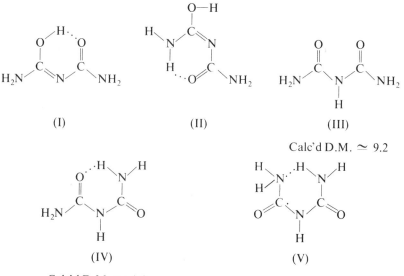

(I)   (II)   (III)

Calc'd D.M. $\simeq$ 9.2

(IV)   (V)

Calc'd D.M. $\simeq$ 4.6

Biuret is observed to have the following properties: neutral to aqueous alkali; two infrared N—H absorption bands, 3380 cm^{-1} (free NH) and 3185 cm^{-1} (H-bonded NH); two carbonyl bands at about 1610 and 1700 cm^{-1}; and a dipole moment in dioxane of 3.27 D.[285] Propose a structure for biuret from among (I)–(V) which is in the best accord with the above properties.

36. The observed order of decreasing infrared N=O frequencies in p-substituted nitrosobenzenes p-X—C$_6$H$_4$NO, is X = NO$_2$, Cl, CH$_3$, Br, I, NMe$_2$.[286] Does this order parallel that expected on a basis of resonance or on a basis of polarizability of the substituent X?

37. How would you attempt to distinguish between mechanical coupling of infrared vibrational frequencies and conformational isomerism for a substance that exhibits a carbonyl doublet?

38. How many peaks would you observe in the nuclear magnetic resonance spectrum of CH$_3$—CH(OCH$_3$)$_2$ for the three groups of chemically equivalent protons?

39. According to the A$_x$B$_y$C$_z$ spin system of classification, in what class do monosubstituted benzenes fall? Predict the classification for cyclopentanone.[287]

40. Consider an explanation for the observation that electronegative groups such as halogen, nitro, and methoxy, when situated *ortho* to the formyl group of benzaldehyde, increase the aldehydic C—H stretching frequency, and although one *ortho* methyl group does not, two *ortho* methyl groups do.[288] [Note. Although explanations have been proposed in the literature,[288] this author does not believe a satisfactory explanation has yet been advanced.]

41. What effect would you predict N-methylation would have on $\nu_{C=O}$ for a cyclic imide?[289]

42. On the basis of the following data, propose a structure for *trans*-1,2-diphenyl-1,2-cyclohexanediol:[290]

	ν (cm^{-1})
trans-isomer	3607, 3571
cis-isomer	3606

43. Predict λ_m for the steroidal system

[285] W. D. Kumler and C. M. Lee, *J. Am. Chem. Soc.*, **82**, 6305 (1960).
[286] K. Nakamoto and R. E. Rundle, *J. Am. Chem. Soc.*, **78**, 1113 (1956).
[287] Compare F. A. L. Anet, *Can. J. Chem.*, **39**, 2316 (1961).
[288] Cf. R. West and L. S. Whatley, *Chem. and Ind. (London)*, 333 (1959).
[289] Cf. C. M. Lee and W. D. Kumler, *J. Am. Chem. Soc.*, **83**, 4586 (1961).
[290] P. Tomboulian, *J. Org. Chem.*, **26**, 2653 (1961).

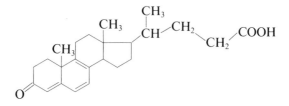

44. In a study of *cis* and *trans* p-tolylmercapto-(Ar—S—CH=CH—S—Ar) and p-tolylsulfonyl-ethenes (ArSO$_2$CH=CHSO$_2$Ar), it was found that the *trans* isomers have appreciable dipole moments, resulting from rotation of the sulfur groups, and the moments are too close to the *cis* values for valid isomer characterization. Also, the infrared spectra are too complex for *cis* and *trans* assignments. The proton coupling constants from their n.m.r. spectra are 9.7 and 15.4 c.p.s. for the mercapto compounds and 10.4 and 14.9 c.p.s. for the sulfonyl pair. For each pair, which coupling constants would you assign to the *cis* isomer?[291]

[291]W. E. Truce and B. Groten, *J. Org. Chem.*, **27**, 128 (1962).

AUTHOR INDEX

Abel, E. W., 100
Abraham, R. J., 232, 570
Abrahams, S. C., 20
Abramovitch, R. A., 372
Acker, D. S., 113
Adamcik, J. A., 250
Adams, E., 88
Adams, R., 277, 280
Adamson, A. W., 67
Addes, H. W., 397
Addison, C. C., 105
Addlebury, J. W., 149
Adelfang, J. L., 495, 501
Adkins, H., 296
Adolph, H. G., 483
Aggarwal, S. L., 108
Agliardi, N., 365
Ahrland, S., 77
Ainsworth, S., 119
Akamatsu, H., 108, 110, 112
Akermark, B., 528, 534
Albert, A., 485
Albinak, M. J., 55
Albrecht, A. G., 408, 411
Alder, B. J., 129
Alewaeters, R., 107
Alford, D., 130
Alfrey, Jr., T., 296
Ali, M. A., 452
Allan, E. A., 533
Allen, G., 131, 142
Allen, M., 279
Allen, T. L., 174
Allinger, J., 241, 263
Allinger, N. L. 236, 240, 241, 242,
    245, 250, 256, 263, 266, 517
Allred, A. L., 176, 178, 181, 190
Almennigen, A., 243
Alt, G. H., 263
Amiel, Y., 390
Amstutz, E. D., 145, 146, 375
Amy, J. W., 36
Andersen, F. A., 572
Anderson, A. G., 384
Anderson, E. K., 124
Anderson, H. D., 115, 378
Anderson, J. H., 544
Anderson, J. S., 79
Andrew, E. R., 486, 492
Andrews, D. H., 464
Andrews, L. J., 104, 115, 117,
    401
Anet, F. A. L., 579
Angla, B., 162
Angus, H. J. F., 367
Angyal, S. J., 240, 253
Anzilotti, W. F., 157
Arnett, E. M., 298
Arnold, R. T., 265, 295, 454, 502
Astle, M. J., 151
Aston, J. G., 226, 231, 319

Atkinson, V. A., 258
Audrieth, L. F., 112
Audsley, A., 395
Auwers, K. von, 263
Avram, M., 391
Axford, D. W. E., 223, 224
Aynsley, E. E., 168, 398
Ayton, M. Y., 461

Baba, H., 323
Bablitz, O. E., 433
Bacon, G. E., 33
Bacskai, R., 134
Baddeley, G., 393
Bader, A. R., 562
Badger, G. M., 156, 429
Badger, R. M., 476, 532, 538, 571
Baevsky, M. M., 424
Bailar, J. C., 65, 71, 84
Bailes, R. H., 80, 85
Bailey, A. S., 113
Bak, B., 38, 572
Baker, A. W., 130, 134, 145, 157,
    158, 429, 533, 539, 577
Baker, J. W., 320, 321, 406, 407,
    453, 539
Baker, W., 379, 453
Baliah, V., 396
Ballhausen, C. J., 72, 99
Ballinger, P., 458
Banes, F. W., 142
Banks, C. V., 154, 565
Banks, L. J., 133
Barb, W. G., 104
Barclay, L. R. C., 298
Barker, C. C., 507, 508
Barker, S. A., 575, 576
Barlow, G. B., 166
Barnard, Jr., A. J., 62
Barnard, D., 131
Barnes, R. A., 265, 454
Barnes, R. B., 558
Barnes, R. G., 394, 414, 424, 428
Barr, S. J., 232, 254
Bartell, L. S., 36, 58, 257
Bartholomay, H., 284
Bartlett, P. D., 295, 302, 327,
    404, 426, 456, 522, 542, 543
Barton, D. H. R., 217, 219, 225,
    228, 234, 253, 254, 263
Basolo, F., 69, 71, 87
Bassin, M., 115
Basso, A. J., 124
Bastiansen, O., 32, 151, 243, 252,
    275, 302, 334
Bauer, E., 129
Bauer, L., 125
Bauer, R. H., 107
Bauer, S. H., 224
Bauer, V. J., 233
Bavin, P. M., 496, 538
Bayles, J. W., 291
Beach, J. Y., 222, 443, 550
Becker, E. D., 538
Becker, E. I., 506

Becker, F., 423
Becker, H. J., 61
Becker, R. S., 478
Beckering, W., 134
Beckett, C. W., 235
Beeven, C. W., 34
Bekkum, H. V., 263, 424
Bell, J. V., 188, 189
Bell, R. P., 186
Bellamy, L. J., 67, 254, 461, 535
Bellanato, J., 430
Belluque, J., 181
Bender, M. L., 567
Bender, P., 197, 301
Ben-Efraim, D. A., 390
Benfey, O. T., 148
Benkeser, R. A., 405, 427, 428
Bennett, G. M., 393, 397
Bennett, M. A., 100
Benson, Jr., A. M., 129
Benson, R. E., 99, 389
Bent, H. A., 25, 37, 308
Bent, H. E., 357, 565
Bentley, J. B., 227
Berchtold, G. A., 245
Bergman, J. G., 55
Bergmann, E. D., 302
Bergmann, F., 296
Beringer, F. M., 399
Berlenback, B. E., 508
Berlin, A. J., 235, 240, 570
Berliner, E., 327, 330, 403
Bernhard, C., 384
Bernstein, H. J., 38, 220, 223,
    226, 256, 486, 541, 553, 570
Berry, R. S., 552, 567
Berson, J. A., 486
Bertelli, D. J., 392
Bethe, H., 72
Bettman, B., 393, 412
Bevan, C. W. L., 403
Bhalnager, S. S., 108
Bieber, T. I., 384
Bigeleisen, J., 506
Biggs, A. I., 397
Bijvoet, J. M., 33
Bilbo, A. J., 278
Biltz, W., 69
Bird, C. W., 242
Birks, J. B., 116
Birmingham, J. M., 94
Birnbaum, N., 565
Birr, E. J., 112
Bjerrum, J., 66, 81
Blinc, R., 133
Block, B. P., 85
Blomquist, A. T., 280, 517
Bloomfield, J. J., 321
Blout, E. R., 518
Bobko, E., 298
Boden, H., 456
Boekelheide, V., 124, 388, 449,
    572
Boggus, J. D., 118
Bohlmann, F., 390, 500

Boll, P. M., 535
Bolto, B. A., 402
Bondhus, F. J., 327
Bondi, A., 151
Bonham, R. A., 257
Bonner, W. A., 498
Bonner, W. H., 299, 403, 404
Booth, J., 162
Borduin, W. G., 302, 377
Bordwell, F. G., 427
Bornstein, J., 327
Bose, A. K., 264
Boston, A., 254
Bothner-By, A. A., 390, 430
Bottini, A. T., 561
Bouck, J. B., 209
Boulton, A. J., 498
Bourne, E. J., 576
Boutan, P. J., 427
Bowden, E., 399, 409
Boyland, E., 162
Brackman, W., 103
Bradacs, K., 227
Bradbury, W. C., 216
Bradley, A., 295
Bradley, W., 167
Brady, J. D., 109, 110, 115, 403, 404, 540
Branch, G. E. K., 187, 205, 357, 393, 412, 508, 574
Branch, R. F., 67
Brandon, M., 120
Brandon, R. L., 115
Brandt, J. L., 36
Branson, H. R., 149
Bratoz, S., 533
Brattain, R. R., 227
Braude, E. A., 32, 53, 196, 213, 221, 319, 344, 353, 395, 399, 409, 461, 478, 482, 512, 516
Bray, P. J., 394, 399, 414, 424, 428
Brealey, G. J., 119
Bresolow, R., 315, 386
Breuer, E., 321
Brewster, J. H., 264
Brickwedde, F. G., 226
Briegleb, G., 104, 108, 115, 116, 118, 120, 401, 553
Briggs, E. R., 120
Brigham, H. R., 484
Brill, R., 126
Brock, F. H., 426
Brockman, R. W., 433
Brockway, L. O., 36, 58, 443
Brode, W. R., 148, 574
Brook, A. G., 457, 496
Brooker, L. G. S., 503, 516, 574
Brooks, C. J. W., 576
Brooks, G. L., 397
Brown, C. R., 461
Brown, H. C., 109, 110, 111, 115, 147, 183, 231, 243, 284, 286, 287, 298, 299, 327, 353, 394, 402, 403, 404, 414, 416, 425, 511, 540
Brown, J. F., 171
Brown, M. G., 37, 331

Brown, R. D., 449
Brown, R. F., 302
Brown, R. K., 568
Brown, T. L., 187, 200, 406, 407, 429, 430, 456, 571
Brown, W. G., 321, 514
Brownstein, S., 302, 562, 570
Brubacker, L. J., 55
Brück, D., 433, 461
Bruck, P., 525
Bruehlman, R. J., 81
Bruhl, J. W., 321
Brunnings, K. J., 516
Bruson, H. A., 298
Brutcher, Jr., F. V., 232, 254
Bryce-Smith, D., 367
Bryson, A., 427
Buck, F. R., 296
Buckles, R. E., 107, 112, 131
Buckley, F., 201
Buehler, C. A., 113, 149, 158
Bunnenberg, E., 262
Bunnett, J. F., 334
Burawoy, A., 400, 405, 528, 545, 573
Burbach, J. C., 104
Bürer, Th., 237
Burg, A. B., 287
Burke, H. J., 241, 254
Burr, M., 386
Burstall, H. F., 69, 84
Burt, C. P., 321
Burton, R., 100
Busch, D. H., 71, 84
Bushick, R. D., 95
Buswell, A. M., 529
Byers, H. F., 130, 537
Byrd, E. K., 565
Byrne, F. P., 237

Cabana, A., 188, 429, 496
Cahn, A., 353
Cairns, T. L., 367
Calden, E. F., 142
Calvin, M., 64, 66, 79, 80, 81, 85, 88, 147, 155, 187, 205, 283, 485, 506
Campaigne, E., 3
Campbell, A. N., 128
Campbell, R. D., 553
Campbell, R. W., 499
Campbell, W. A., 168
Canady, W. J., 538
Cannon, C. G., 127
Cannon, G. W., 544
Carboni, R. A., 269
Cardwell, H. M. E., 133, 378
Carlisle, C. H., 34
Carlson, A. H., 67
Carlton, J. K., 216
Carol, J., 551
Carr, E. P., 321
Carr, J. B., 563
Carroll, B., 11
Casabella, P. A., 399
Case, J. R., 113
Caserio, F. F., 503
Caserio, M. C., 391

Cass, R. C., 319
Castro, A. J., 366
Catalano, E., 135
Cavanaugh, J. R., 190
Cerfontain, H., 394
Cetina, R., 429
Chamberlain, N. F., 560
Chambers, V. C., 209, 456, 542
Chance, B., 568
Chang, H. W., 315
Chaplin, H. O., 145, 152
Charbonnier, E., 122
Charette, G., 67
Charney, E., 262
Charton, M., 424
Chatt, J., 71, 77, 106, 125
Chen, Y. T., 87
Chessick, J. J., 146
Chianta, M., 552
Chiwzcloglu, G., 250
Choake, R. L., 410
Christ, H. A., 488
Christian, C. G., 169
Christman, D. L., 189, 542
Chu, C., 256
Cilento, G., 149
Clamp, A. C., 166
Clark, A. K., 577
Clark, C., 552
Clark, G. L., 275, 461
Clark, H. C., 70
Clark, J. R., 124
Clarke, H. T., 34, 558
Clement, R. A., 354, 404, 405
Cleveland, F. F., 106
Clifford, A. F., 191
Close, W. J., 124
Closson, W. D., 520
Coan, S. B., 506
Coburn, Jr., W. C., 142
Coggeshall, N. D., 131, 536
Cohen, A. D., 135
Cohen, I., 7
Cohen, L. A., 292
Cohen, M. D., 154
Colclough, R. O., 131
Cole, A. R. H., 531
Cole, L. G., 362
Cole, R. H., 130
Colebrook, L. D., 538
Collin, J., 107, 323, 456
Collman, J. P., 67, 82, 548
Colthup, N. B., 465
Comyns, A. E., 122
Conant, J. B., 317, 321, 357
Condon, F. E., 529
Connolly, J. W., 169
Connor, T. M., 131
Cook, C. D., 299
Cook, D., 104, 457, 539
Cook, J. W., 385, 455
Cooke, A. H., 168
Cookson, R. C., 217, 242, 253, 255, 381, 441, 442, 503, 522
Coolidge, A. S., 142
Cooner, T. M., 461
Cooper, G. R., 565
Coops, J., 230

Cope, A. C., 244, 245
Cope, O. J., 568
Corey, E. J., 241, 254
Corey, R. B., 149
Corio, P. L., 430
Corwin, A. H., 516
Coryell, C. D., 229, 301
Cosgrove, W. R., 169
Costain, C. C., 38
Cotter, R. J., 245
Cotton, F. A., 67, 82, 88, 94, 95
Cottrell, T. L., 42, 43
Coulson, C. A., 21, 37, 38, 131,
    135, 201, 207, 315, 335, 388,
    390, 392, 444, 446, 447, 449,
    452, 542
Courty, C., 108
Cox, E. G., 141
Craig, D. P., 70, 387, 392
Craig, R. R., 472, 543
Cram, D. J., 107, 215, 225, 250,
    280, 517
Cramer, F. D., 104, 160, 163, 165,
    168
Craven, J. M., 410
Crawford, B. L., 467
Crawford, V. A., 20, 320
Creitz, E. C., 529
Crick, F. H. C., 149
Croit, P. D., 550
Cromwell, N. H., 495, 501
Cromwell, T. M., 120
Crowfoot, D., 34
C. S. C., 82
Cuckler, A. C., 124
Cummins, E. G., 254
Cunningham, K. G., 124, 572
Curran, B. C., 157
Curry, N. A., 33
Curtin, D. Y., 227
Czekalla, J., 108, 116, 118, 500

Dahlgren, Jr., G., 148, 156
Dahn, H., 488
Daignault, R., 181
Dailey, B. P., 190, 191, 430
Dainton, F. S., 118
Dallinga, G., 112
Daniels, R., 125
Danielsson, U., 135
Danish, A. A., 454
Danyluk, S. S., 384
Dauben, Jr., H. J., 101, 384, 386,
    392
Dauben, W. G., 217, 254, 272
Daudel, R., 181, 444, 445
Davies, M., 106
Davies, M. M., 128, 199, 529,
    531, 538, 539
Davies, N. R., 77
Davis, M. M., 566
Davis, N. C., 88
Davis, W. C., 397
Dawson, G. W., 124, 572
Day, J. H., 382
Day, Jr., R. A., 433
Dearden, J. C., 152, 527, 545
Dekker, H., 230

De la Mare, P. B. D., 32, 215,
    245, 350, 394, 402, 403, 454,
    514
Deming, L. S., 531
Denney, D. B., 301
Deno, N. C., 414, 421
DePuy, C. H., 267, 383, 384, 438
Derby, T. J., 461
Detert, F. L., 386
DeVault, D., 10
DeVries, L., 439, 520, 525
Dewar, J., 29
Dewar, M. J. S., 37, 103, 286, 331,
    379, 385, 450, 510
Diehl, P., 430, 488
Dinerstein, R. A., 169
Dippy, J. F. J., 412
Djerassi, C., 242, 250, 259, 262,
    263, 303, 464, 522
Doak, G. O., 148, 424, 427
Dobriner, K., 254
Dodd, R. E., 148, 168
Doehaerd, Th., 250
Doering, W. von E., 380, 384,
    385, 386
Dolby, L. J., 240
Donahue, W. E., 145, 375
Donath, W. E., 232
Donohue, J., 332, 342
D'Or, L. 107
Dorsey, W. S., 104, 169
Doty, P. M., 231
Doub, L., 409, 430, 480
Douglas, B. E., 109
Downing, J. R., 529
Dows, D. A., 468
Drago, R. S., 120
Dreger, L. H., 233
Dreiding, A. S., 219
Drickamer, H. G., 129
Dryden, R. P., 548
Drysdale, J. J., 354, 404
Dudek, G. O., 372
Duncanson, L. A., 106, 125
Dunitz, J. D., 89, 99, 133, 243,
    244, 257
Dunn, T. M., 77
Dyall, L. K., 536

Eaborn, C., 394, 402, 403, 405,
    566
Eastman, R. H., 326, 498
Ebelke, W. H., 296
Eda, B., 151
Edgell, W. F., 36, 221
Edmonds, S. M., 565
Eggers, D. F., 200
Eglinton, G., 576
Ehrenson, S., 338, 420
Ehrenson, S. E., 404
Eisenbraun, E. J., 262
Eisenthal, R., 548
Ekwall, P., 171
Elbe, G. von, 142
Elhafez, F. A. A., 225
Eliel, E. L., 217, 240, 254, 265,
    273, 570
El-Sayed, M. F. A., 398

Elschneg, G. H., 104
Emeleus, H. J., 79, 88
Emerson, M. E., 291
Ens, A., 141
Erickson, R. E., 107, 131
Eschenmoser, A., 273, 518
Evans, D. F., 104, 118, 168
Evans, H. D., 515
Evarard, K. B., 227
Ewald, L., 356
Eyring, G., 279
Eyring, H., 24, 201, 220

Fabian, J. M., 131
Fainberg, A. H., 486
Fairbrother, F., 108, 110
Fajans, K., 67, 77, 195
Faleley, W. G., 382
Falls, C. P., 424
Farber, M., 254
Farnum, D. G., 386
Farthing, A. C., 414
Fassel, V. A., 49, 106, 154, 180,
    188, 430, 494
Faust, W., 259
Fawcett, F. S., 268
Feilchenfeld, H., 49
Felder, E., 378, 383
Fenske, M. R., 550
Fenton, S. W., 244
Fenton, T. M., 142
Ferguson, E. E., 106
Ferguson, G., 215
Ferguson, L. N., 115, 136, 146,
    147, 191, 394, 411, 433, 480,
    498, 502, 503, 528, 533, 547,
    553, 567
Fernelius, W. C., 74, 79, 85, 372,
    376
Ferreira, R., 175
Ferreira, R. C., 407
Ferrett, D. J., 63
Ferroni, E., 105
Fessenden, R. W., 490
Field, F. H., 43
Fierens, P. J. C., 424
Fieser, L. F., 162, 554
Fieser, M., 554
Fife, W. K., 426
Filler, R., 376, 552
Finch, N., 242
Fineman, M. A., 177, 181, 191
Fink, H. J., 231
Finkelstein, H., 296
Finkelstein, R., 72
Fischer, E. O., 88, 92, 96, 97, 100
Fischer, H., 457
Fisher, N. I., 503
Flascha, H. A., 62
Flett, M. St. C., 135, 494, 529
Flood, S. H., 115, 540
Floss, E., 122
Flowers, D. L., 301
Fohlen, G. M., 342
Fonken, G. J., 272
Forbes, W. F., 152, 399, 430, 483,
    494, 503, 510, 512, 527, 545, 555
Forman, E. J., 291

Forsén, S., 130, 538
Foster, R., 113, 115, 116, 118
Fox, C. J., 185
Fox, I., 338, 433
Fox, J. J., 529
Foz, O. R., 142
Fraenkel, G. K., 487
France, H., 518
Frank, R. L., 495
Franklin, J. L., 43, 118, 318
Franzen, J. S., 130
Fraser, R. R., 256, 422
Freedman, H. H., 130, 131, 391, 495, 539
Freedman, L. D., 148, 427
Freeman, N. K., 254
Freeman, S. K., 326
Freidel, R. A., 536
Freiser, H., 79
French, C. L., 565
French, D., 163
Freudenberg, K., 163
Fridrichson, J., 34
Friess, S. L., 494
Frisch, M. A., 233
Fritz, H. P., 88, 92, 96, 391
Fritz, J. S., 124
Frolen, L. G., 397
Fuchs, O., 206
Fuchs, R., 321
Fujita, J., 133
Fukui, K., 450
Fuller, W., 133
Furst, A., 254
Fuson, N., 497, 529
Fuson, R. C., 455

Gabrielli, G., 105
Gane, R., 237
Gaoni, Y., 390
Garcia, P., 158
Gardner, P. D., 115, 117, 401
Garner, A. Y., 115, 394
Garner, W. E., 142
Garrett, E. R., 104
Gaunt, J., 539
Gaydon, A. G., 43
Geiseler, G., 473
Geisenfelder, H., 319
Geller, L. E., 262, 263
Gent, W. L. G., 200, 201
George, P., 74
Gerdie, R., 213, 510
Gerding, H., 223, 224
Gergely, E., 395, 433
Gero, A., 369, 377
Gerrard, W., 86
Gerstein, M., 284
Gianni, M. N., 570
Gibb, A. R., 385
Gibson, R. E., 118
Giddings, W. P., 522
Gilbert, E. C., 362
Gilby, Jr., R. F., 424
Giles, C. H., 105, 139, 149, 151
Gillam, A. E., 461
Gillespie, R. J., 68
Gillette, R. H., 142, 542

Gilman, H., 457
Gilow, H. M., 553
Gilson, D. F. R., 161
Ginsberg, A. P., 177
Ginsburg, D., 250, 379
Ginsburg, E., 359
Glass, B., 79, 88
Glass, M. A. W., 522
Glasstone, S., 393, 397
Glenn, D. M., 149
Glick, R. E., 338, 420, 430
Glockler, G., 42, 49, 221
Glusker, D. L., 106, 120
Go, Y., 162
Goddu, R. F., 536
Godfrey, J. C., 124, 572
Godfrey, M., 479
Godshalk, S., 499
Godycki, L. E., 133, 538
Goering, H. L., 301, 520
Gold, V., 111
Goldby, S. D., 548
Goldenson, J., 188, 189
Goldish, E., 230
Goldschmidt, H., 294
Golebiewski, A., 390
Gomberg, M., 355
Goodman, L, 397
Goodwin, T. C., 461
Goodwin, T. H., 141
Gordy, W., 32, 131, 177, 180, 371, 529
Gordy, W. J., 194
Gore, R. C., 558
Goss, F. R., 381, 395
Götz, H., 535
Goulden, J. D. S., 538
Gourisseau, G., 539
Gouterman, M., 129
Govindarajan, S. R., 108
Gowenlock, B. G., 482
Graebe, C., 482
Graham, P. J., 93
Graham, W. A. G., 301
Grahn, R., 135
Grant, D. M., 220
Grant, F. W., 298
Gray, F. W., 548
Gray, G. W., 216, 414, 510
Grayson, M., 403, 404
Green, A. A., 287
Green, M., 122
Green, M. L. H., 100
Greenburg, S., 250, 256
Greene, F. D., 256
Greer, F., 296
Gregory, N. W., 17
Gregory, T. M. 497
Griffing, M. E., 550
Griffith, J. S., 70
Griffiths, J. M. M., 87
Gross, J. C., 520
Gross, P. M., 142
Groten, B., 580
Groves, L. G., 344, 395, 406
Grunwald, E., 142, 269, 291, 424, 486
Gubeau, J., 61

Guile, R. L., 104
Günthard, H. H., 237, 254
Guter, G. A., 88, 302, 377
Guthrie, G. B., 319
Gutowsky, H. S., 190, 226, 334, 394, 430, 533, 544, 561, 562, 570
Guy, J., 275
Gwinn, W. D., 220, 223

Haas, C. G., 85
Haber, R. G., 265
Hadzi, D., 33, 125, 133, 154, 166, 528, 533, 539
Hafliger, O., 353
Hafner, K., 384
Hairn, J. L., 409
Hakala, R. W., 11
Hale, J. B., 280
Halevi, E. A., 186
Halford, J. O., 226
Hall, H. K., 290, 472, 543
Hall, L. D., 232
Hall, Jr., L. W., 428
Hall, N. D., 298
Hallam, H. E., 106
Halmann, M., 469
Halpern, O., 250
Halverstadt, I. F., 198, 206
Ham, J., 119
Ham, J. S., 118
Ham, N. S., 37
Hambly, A. N., 536
Hamer, F. M., 503
Hamlet, Z., 486
Hammer, C. F., 201
Hammett, L. P., 412
Hammick, D. L., 104, 113, 115
Hammick, D. L1., 378
Hammond, G. S., 88, 292, 297, 302, 377, 379, 458, 553
Hammond, V. J., 409
Hancock, C. K., 424, 428
Hannaert, H., 424
Hannay, N. B., 194
Hansen, M. W., 209
Hansen-Nygaard, L., 38
Hanson, R. L., 525
Harmelin, M., 462
Harms, H., 129
Harrett, H. S., 553
Harris, F. E., 129
Harris, G. H., 130, 539
Harris, J. T., 576
Harris, M. M., 281
Harris, R. K., 235
Harrison, A. G., 457
Hartman, H., 72
Hartman, L., 3
Harvey, Jr., A. E., 565
Harvey, J. T., 403
Hässel, O., 106, 112, 233, 234, 235, 236, 252, 258, 334
Hastings, H., 118
Haszeldine, R. N., 106
Hatch, L. F., 321
Hauser, K. W., 485
Havinga, E., 511

Hawkins, G. F., 576
Hawthorne, M. F., 297, 501
Haynes, L. J., 455
Hazebroek, P., 233
Hearon, J., 71
Heath, D. F., 212
Hecht, H., 220
Hedberg, K., 385
Heeks, J. S., 60
Heeschen, J. P., 562
Heffernan, M. L., 449
Heilbronner, E., 213, 385, 510, 518, 535
Heindel, C. C., 82
Heisler, J., 188, 189
Henbest, H. B., 155
Hendrickson, J. B., 262
Henne, A. L., 185
Hensley, A. L., 181
Hepworth, M. A., 77
Herdle, L. E., 574
Herling, F., 254
Herman, R. C., 142
Hermans, Jr., J., 155
Hermans, P. H., 219, 229
Herwig, W., 122
Herzberg, G., 16, 37, 43
Herzog, H. L., 518
Hesatsune, I. C., 200
Hess, P. H., 495
Higasi, K., 223, 323
Higgins, W., 4
Hill, E. A., 92
Hill, M. E., 295
Hill, R. R., 441
Hill, T. L., 280
Himel, C. M., 359
Himoe, A., 402
Hindman, J. O., 66
Hine, J., 418, 424
Hinman, R. L., 480
Hinze, J., 177
Hirayama, K., 503
Hirota, M., 150, 429
Hirshberg, Y., 154
Hiskey, C. F., 67
Ho, B. T., 123
Hobbs, M. E., 142, 576
Hodgkin, D. C., 34
Hoerger, E., 254
Hoffsommer, J. C., 483
Hogland, J. R., 397
Hogle, D. H., 292
Hoh, G., 433
Holleck, L., 433
Hollo, J., 165
Holm, C. H., 334
Holm, R. H., 67, 82, 372
Holman, R. T., 170
Holmes, R. R., 301
Holmyard, E. J., 2
Holness, N. J., 240
Holst, E. H., 376
Holtzclaw, H. F., 67, 548
Honnen, L. R., 384
Hoogzand, C., 298
Hopkins, C. Y., 553
Hopp, R., 302

Hossenlopp, I. A., 232
Hough, L., 232
Howell, M. G., 254
Hu, S-E., 240
Hubbard, W. N., 233, 319
Hübel, W., 122, 298
Hückel, E., 380
Hückel, W., 151, 252, 254, 267
Hudec, J., 381, 441
Hudson, R. F., 122
Hudson, R. L., 550
Huggins, C. M., 134
Huggins, M. L., 35, 49, 143, 149
Hughes, E. D., 403
Huisgen, R., 252
Huitric, A. C., 563
Hume, D. N., 291, 565
Hundler, G. S., 544
Hunsberger, I. M., 83, 146, 533
Hunt, C. K., 292
Hunt, J. P., 57
Hunter, L., 139, 145, 148, 152
Hunter, W. H., 116
Huse, G., 334
Hutchison, C. C., 53
Hyne, J. B., 141

Ichikawa, K., 243
Iczkowski, R. P., 181
Iffland, D. C., 512
Illuminati, G., 394
Imanishi, S., 478
Ingold, C. K., 111, 237, 294, 381, 403, 419
Ingold, K. U., 532
Ingraham, L. L., 85, 269
Inokuchi, H., 108, 110
Inuzuka, K., 478
Ioffe, S. T., 377
Iredale, T., 395, 433
Irvine, J. W., 71
Irving, H., 63, 79, 87
Israelashwile, S., 296
Ito, K., 151, 233
Ito, M., 478
Ives, D. J. G., 185
Ivin, K. J., 118
Iwamura, H., 158
Iwasaki, M., 226
Izatt, R. M., 85

Jack, K. H., 77
Jackman, L. M., 486, 492, 560
Jaffe, H. H., 18, 70, 99, 127, 148, 177, 417, 424
Janke, W., 362
Jencks, W. P., 568
Jenkins, H. O., 49
Jensen, F. R., 235, 240, 402, 570
Jensen, M. B., 186
Jerslev, B., 126
Johannesen, R. B., 287
Johnson, E. A., 216
Johnson, E. W., 142
Johnson, F. E., 576
Johnson, J. R., 34, 558
Johnson, W. S., 233, 576
Johnston, M. B., 62

Jonathan, N. B. H., 547
Jones, B., 393
Jones, E. A., 571
Jones, E. J., 531
Jones, H. W., 424
Jones, L. H., 571
Jones, M. M., 79, 178, 565
Jones, R. A., 535
Jones, R. G., 457
Jones, R. N., 254, 430, 465, 485, 494, 495, 542, 574
Jorgenson, M. J., 567
Joshi, B. S., 300, 363, 554
Josien, M. L., 497, 529, 539
Jubota, M., 456
Julia, S., 237

Kabachnik, M. I., 377
Kaeding, W. W., 297, 533
Kaesz, H. D., 301, 457
Kagarise, R. E., 104, 142, 189, 223, 224
Kahovec, L., 227
Kamlet, M. J., 483
Kanathil, A. J., 82
Kaplan, C. A., 321
Kaplan, M. L., 291
Karagounis, G., 122
Karle, I. L., 32, 36, 332
Karle, J., 32, 36
Kartzmark, E. M., 128
Kasha, M., 119
Katayama, M., 223
Katritzky, A. R., 498, 535
Katz, C., 319
Katz, S., 95
Katz, T. J., 388
Katzenellenbogen, E. R., 574
Kaufman, J. J., 429
Kealy, T. J., 89
Kebarle, P., 457
Keefer, R. M., 104, 115, 117, 401
Kehres, P. W., 154
Kehrmann, F., 215
Kelb, R. W., 327
Keldner, L., 342
Kelly, I., 146, 528
Kelly, R. B., 263
Kemp, J. D., 221
Kempter, H., 531
Kent, J. W., 550
Kerlinger, H. O., 151
Kern, D. M., 47
Ketelaar, J. A. A., 199
Kettering, C. F., 464
Kewin, A. H., 256
Kharasch, M. S., 182, 300, 363, 554
Kice, J. L., 426
Kierstead, R. W., 280
Kilner, H. E., 378
Kilpatrick, M., 115, 209, 237
Kimball, G. E., 24
King, E. J., 186, 294
King, R. B., 100
King, R. W., 267
King, W. T., 467
Kingery, W. D., 565

Kirby, A. F., 511
Kirschner, S., 55
Kistiakowsky, G. B., 277, 317, 322
Kitchen, L. J., 284, 537
Kittleman, E. T., 82
Kivelson, D., 331, 525
Klages, F., 318
Klein, H. S., 186, 210
Klemm, L. H., 117, 123, 216
Klevens, H. B., 409
Klit, A., 111
Klotz, I. M., 88, 130
Klove, M. S., 95
Kluiber, R. W., 82, 548
Klyne, W., 32, 148, 213, 215, 219, 234, 245, 259, 262, 350, 454, 512, 514
Knipe, R. H., 396
Knox, B. E., 39
Knox, G. R., 94
Kobayashi, K., 216, 457
Kobe, K. A., 160
Koch, H. P., 131
Kogon, I. C., 470
Kohler, E. P., 321
Kohlrausch, K. W. F., 233
Kornblum, N., 293
Korst, J. J., 576
Kortum, G., 108
Koski, W. S., 398, 429
Kosower, E. M., 104, 116, 119, 381, 409, 486, 500, 520, 565
Kozikowski, J., 95
Kozima, K., 120, 237, 255, 471
Kraihanzel, C. S., 540
Kratky, O., 162
Kreevoy, M. M., 330
Kreiter, V. P., 498
Krems, I. J., 548
Krespan, C. G., 367
Kromhout, R. A., 291
Kross, R. D., 49, 106, 180, 188, 430, 494
Krysiak, H. R., 427
Kubo, M., 386
Kuboyama, A., 120
Kuchitsu, K., 257
Kuhn, H. H., 254
Kuhn, L. P., 134, 237, 240, 302, 541
Kuhn, M., 227
Kuhn, R., 457, 485, 499
Kuhn, S. J., 115, 299, 540
Kullnig, R. K., 256, 563
Kumler, W. D., 198, 206, 210, 342, 472, 480, 579

Leonard, N. J., 518
Leutner, R., 497
Levine, H. B., 226
Levy, H. A., 133
Levy, S., 341, 381, 384
Lewis, E. S., 458
Lewis, F. M., 296
Lewis, G. N., 485, 506
Lewis, I. C., 327, 338, 404, 419
Lewis, J., 77
Li, C. C., 277

Li, S. T., 180
Liddell, V., 470
Lide, Jr., D. R., 38, 226, 255, 326, 330
Liebermann, C., 482
Liehr, A. D., 99
Lien, A. P., 115, 328
Lillien, I., 399
Lin, C. C., 327
Lind, C. D., 216
Linden, S., 499
Lindsey, R. V., 93, 99
Linke, R., 532
Linnett, J. W., 71, 96, 99, 212, 312, 476
Linsley, S. G., 558
Linstead, R. P., 84
Lippincott, E. R., 49, 90, 131, 134, 332, 382, 468, 541
Lipscomb, W. J., 104
Liptay, W., 565
Liston, T. V., 405
Little, Jr., E. J., 178
Little, R., 398
Little, W. F., 548, 577
Liu, C. F., 148
Liu, C. H., 148
Liu, T. H., 180
Livingston, R. L., 36, 37, 243
Llewellyn, F. J., 141
Lloyd, D., 381
Lloyd, L. L., 294
Locke, D. M., 575
Locket, G. H., 105
Loeffler, O. H., 118
Lombardo, G., 85, 290
Long, F. A., 111, 148, 156, 208, 458
Longuet-Higgins, H. C., 445, 446, 447, 514
Lord, R. C., 332, 541
Lossing, F. P., 323, 456, 457
Lovell, B. J., 155
Lovell, R. J., 571
Lowe, J. U., 533, 553
Lu, C., 207
Luborsky, F. E., 115
Lucas, H. J., 104, 115, 122
Luder, W. R., 312
Lupien, Y., 104
Luther, H., 111
Lüttke, W., 227, 470
Lüttringhaus, A., 279
LuValle, J. E., 227
Lwowski, W., 434
Lyle, R. E., 234

Maccoll, A., 22, 70, 392, 504
MacDougall, F. H., 142
Mack, J. L., 394
MacKenzie, S., 442
Mackle, H., 227, 338
MacLean, J. W., 298
Macritchie, F., 531
Magat, M., 129
Maginn, R. E., 95
Maguire, M. M., 143
Marrin, D. L., 126

Mak, T. C. W., 451
Maki, A. H., 82
Malanga, C. M., 124
Maley, L. A., 66
Maltz, H., 82
Mamalis, P., 414
Mandelcorn, L., 160, 165, 168
Maneh, W., 74
Mann, D. E., 326, 327
Mannhardt, H. J., 500
Manning, D. L., 565
Manuel, T. A., 100
Marcillo, J., 142
Marcus, E., 502
Margoshes, M., 132, 135
Margrave, J. L., 181, 233
Markby, R., 122
Marica, E., 391
Marino, G., 394
Marschner, R. F., 162, 169
Marsden, R. J. B., 227
Marsen, H., 433
Marsh, R. E., 166
Martell, A. E., 64, 65, 66, 82, 472
Martin, A. E., 529
Martin, D. F., 372
Martin, J. C., 486
Marvel, C. S., 359
Maryott, A. A., 142, 201
Mason, J. G., 98
Mason, S. F., 461, 503, 510
Massingill, J. L., 226
Mateos, J. L., 429
Mather, J. G., 425
Mathews, F. S., 104
McL. Mathieson, A., 33, 34
Matsen, F. A., 118, 410
Matsunaga, Y., 108, 110, 112
Mayer, J. E., 280
Mayer-Pitsch, E., 574
Mayo, F. R., 120, 296
McAlpine, K. B., 212
McArnett, E., 95
McBee, E. T., 189, 296, 542
McCall, D. W., 430
McCarthy, P. J., 82, 472
McCaulay, D. A., 115, 328
McClellan, A. L., 125
McClure, D. S., 74
McConnell, H., 118
McConnell, W. V., 151
McCullough, J. D., 222
McCullough, J. P., 232
McDaniel, D. H., 147, 291, 353, 414, 511
McDaniel, J. C., 438
McDonald, R. S., 332
McDowell, C. A., 161
McElhill, E. A., 341
McElhill, E. Am., 454
McElroy, W. D., 79, 88
McGarvey, B. R., 82, 430
McGlynn, S. P., 109, 118
McHugh, D. J., 240
McIninch, E., 424
McKie, D., 3
McKinnie, J. M., 78
McKusick, B. C., 367

McLauchlan, K. A., 232
McLean, D. C., 245
McLure, E. C., 105
McMahon, P. E., 570
McMillan, J. A., 487
McMillan, W. G., 442
McNulty, P. J., 403
McOmie, J. F. W., 379, 453
Meador, W. R., 442
Mecke, R., 227, 470, 531
Meerman, P. G., 223, 224
Meinwald, J., 206, 441
Meinwald, Y. C., 280
Meisenheimer, J., 62
Meister, A., 154
Melchoir, N., 79
Mellor, D. P., 66
Melzer, M. S., 424
Menefee, A., 130
Mergenthaler, E., 252
Merkel, E., 275
Merrifield, R. E., 104, 541
Metlesics, W., 122
Meyer, K. H., 126
Meyer, L. H., 430, 544, 561
Meyer, V., 215
Meyers, E. A., 424
Meza, S., 429
Michel, R. H., 424
Milhorat, A. T., 254
Miller, D. I., 125
Miller, E., 228
Miller, E. C., 149
Miller, J. A., 149
Miller, J., 417
Miller, J. M., 177
Miller, L. A., 123
Miller, L. J., 251
Miller, M. A., 236
Miller, N. E., 287
Miller, R., 562, 570
Miller, R. E., 148
Miller, S. I., 424
Millich, F., 112
Mills, J. A., 253
Mills, J. M., 467
Minton, R. G., 410
Mislow, K., 262, 281, 390, 512, 522
Mitchell, A. D., 154
Mitchell, J., 547
Mithoff, R. C., 357
Mizushima, S., 223, 529
Mladeck, M. H., 257
Moffitt, W., 259
Moffitt, W. E., 99, 182, 542
Moir, R. Y., 279, 563
Monack, L. C., 403
Montheard, P., 155
Moodie, R. B., 411
Moore, B., 100
Moore, G. E., 571
Moore, T. S., 126
Moreland, Jr., W. T., 418
Morgan, G. T., 84
Morgan, K. J., 482
Moriconi, E. J., 503
Morino, Y., 223, 226, 257

Moritz, A. G., 429
Morman, A., 171
Morman, J. F., 576
Morrison, J. D., 401
Morrow, D. F., 250
Morse, J. G., 209, 237
Morse, R. A., 548
Mortensen, E. M., 396
Moscowitz, A., 259, 262
Moser, C., 445
Moss, R. A., 82
Mottl, J. R., 210
Motz, K. L., 99
Mueller, C. R., 201
Mueller, M. B., 359
Mueller, W. A., 430, 486, 494, 512
Müller, E., 299, 357, 360, 362, 365, 366
Müller, R., 384
Müller-Rodloff, I., 357, 360
Muller, E., 461
Muller, G. P., 36
Muller, N., 493, 544
Mulliken, R. S., 25, 38, 103, 108, 110, 112, 118, 135, 177, 199, 227, 310, 315, 331, 396
Murmann, R. K., 87
Murphy, R. B., 410
Murray, F. E., 141
Murray, M. J., 106
Murrell, J. N., 118, 479, 514, 565
Musher, J., 562
Mysels, K., 197

Nachod, F. C., 32, 53, 196, 221, 319, 344, 395, 461, 478, 487
Nagakura, S., 112, 118, 120, 129, 495
Nagato, C., 450
Naghizadeh, J. N., 405
Nair, P. M., 256, 562
Nakagawa, N., 296
Nakagawa, T. W., 115
Nakahara, A., 133
Nakamoto, K., 82, 107, 132, 135, 472, 579
Nam, B., 414
Naqvi, S. M., 376, 552
Nash, L. K., 142
Nathan, W. S., 321
Neirynck, G., 67
Neiswender, D. D., 161
Nelson, J. A., 384
Nelson, N. A., 245
Nelson, R. D., 90, 382
Nenitzescu, C. D., 391
Nesmeyanov, A. N., 94
Neuhoff, H., 365
Newman, A. C. D., 170
Newman, M. S., 117, 186, 216, 217, 219, 280, 292, 294, 295, 379, 406, 419, 456
Nickon, A., 533
Nigam, S. S., 100
Nist, B. J., 255, 543
Nix, N. J., 115
Noble, R. E., 376, 554

Noethey, E. H., 116
Nordlander, J. E., 563, 568
Novak, A., 133
Nowacki, W., 257
Noyce, D. S., 235, 240, 272, 301, 567, 570
Nozoe, T., 381, 386
Nugent, L. J., 327
Nyholm, R. S., 69, 70, 77, 88, 100

O'Brian, R. E., 522
Ochs, C., 360
O'Connor, R. O., 368
O'Connor, W. F., 503
Oddu, G., 126
Odell, A. L., 70
Odian, G., 426
Öfele, K., 100
Oestreich, C., 382
Ogawa, I. A., 438
Ogg, R. A., 325
Ogilvie, A., 105
Ohlson, R., 123
Okamoto, Y., 416, 425
Oki, M., 150, 158, 429
Olah, G. A., 115, 299, 540
Olivera, E., 429
Omura, I., 323
O'Neill, R. C., 124
Onsager, L., 223
Oosterhoff, L. J., 233
Orchin, M., 117, 122
Orgel, L. E., 70, 72, 89, 99, 118, 133
Oriani, R. A., 194
Orloff, H. D., 234, 252
Orloski, R., 520
Orr, S. F. D., 162
Orville-Thomas, W. J., 547
O'Shaughnessy, M. T., 512
Oster, G., 112
O'Sullivan, D. G., 430, 434
Owens, F. H., 543

Pace, E. L., 226
Page, J. F., 254
Palmer, H. B., 39
Palmer, K. J., 38
Palmer, K. Y., 222
Panouse, J. J., 503
Paoletti, P., 85
Paoloni, L., 131
Pappas, S. P., 458
Park, J. D., 376, 554
Parry, R. W., 85
Parshall, G. W., 93
Parsons, B. N., 115
Partingion, J. R., 2
Patenaude, J. L., 496
Pauling, L., 22, 35, 38, 42, 49, 69, 70, 135, 149, 166, 174, 209, 212, 227, 296, 316, 319, 336, 398, 443, 444, 447
Paulsen, P. T., 78
Pauncz, R., 250
Pauson, P. L., 89, 92, 99

Pavelich, W. A., 424
Pearson, D. E., 296, 403, 433
Pearson, E. G., 148
Pearson, N., 232, 254
Pearson, R. G., 8, 69, 72, 73, 291
Pearson, W. B., 131
Peddle, G. J. D., 496
Pederson, E. E., 223
Peerdemann, A. F., 34
Pegg, J. A., 135, 151
Peirce, G., 265, 454
Penney, W. G., 72, 336
Pennington, R. E., 232
Pepinsky, R., 33
Person, W. B., 107, 120, 332
Pestemer, M., 461
Peters, D., 379
Peters, E. D., 454
Petersen, E. M., 558
Peterson, M. L., 93
Peterson, P. E., 245
Peterson, S. W., 133
Petro, A. J., 201
Pettit, R., 440
Pfab, W., 97
Pfanz, H., 366
Pfeiffer, P., 127
Pfrommer, J. F., 37
Phillips, W. D., 104, 334, 343, 487
Pickering, R. A., 236, 254
Pickett, E. E., 536
Pickett, L. W., 275, 518
Piette, L. H., 342
Pilato, L. A., 273
Pimentel, G. C., 125, 132, 134, 332, 547
Pinchas, S., 469
Pinckard, J. H., 503
Pinkard, R. M., 576
Pino, L. N., 146
Piper, J. D., 574
Piper, T. S., 95
Pitzer, K. S., 47, 128, 133, 135, 141, 217, 220, 221, 226, 232, 234, 235, 290, 332
Placito, P. J., 113
Plant, D., 130
Platt, J. R., 118, 397, 409, 431
Plesske, K., 92
Plimmer, J. R., 455
Plyler, E. K., 112, 529
Pockels, G., 111
Pohl, H. A., 142
Pople, A., 129
Pople, J. A., 256, 486, 489
Popov, A. I., 120
Popov, E. M., 377
Porte, A. L., 533
Porter, W. C., 142
Powell, H. M., 160, 165, 166, 167, 169, 170, 334
Powers, R. M., 433
Powling, J., 223, 553
Preckel, R. F., 357
Prelog, V., 219, 231, 234, 243, 244, 250, 378

Pressman, D., 229, 301
Preston, D. R., 453
Price, C. C., 236, 424
Price, W. C., 401, 408, 409
Prier, C. C., 254
Priest, W. J., 325
Pritchard, D. E., 493, 544
Pritchard, H. O., 174
Pullman, A., 444, 446
Pullman, B., 446
Pummer, W. J., 577
Puxeddu, E., 126

Quigley, M. A., 496

Rabinowitch, E., 119
Rabinowitz, J. L., 139
Radell, J., 169
Raisin, C. G., 111
Ramirez, F., 341, 381, 384, 511
Ramsay, D. A., 254
Ramsey, B. G., 381
Ramsperger, H. C., 142
Rank, D. H., 223, 224
Rao, C. N. R., 37, 429, 432
Rao, N. S., 108
Rapala, R. T., 518
Raphael, R. A., 245, 385
Rapp, W., 252
Rapson, B. W., 162
Rasmussen, R. S., 227, 233
Rastrup-Andersen, J., 572
Rausch, M. D., 88
Rayner, J. H., 167
Reagen, H., 514
Records, R., 262
Reed, D., 123
Reeves, L. W., 104, 134, 240, 533, 553
Regan, C. M., 381, 389
Reid, C., 118, 131, 135
Reid, D. H., 384
Reid, J. C., 147
Reillay, C. N., 62
Reinhard, L. R., 160
Remington, W. R., 514
Remy, D. C., 500
Reyes, Z., 375, 553
Reynolds, L. T., 94, 95
Riad, Y., 254
Rich, A., 89
Richards, J. H., 92
Richards, R. E., 168, 536, 562
Richards, W. T., 142
Richer, J. C., 273
Richter, P., 473
Rieger, M., 283
Riezebos, G., 511
Rinehart, K. L., 99
Ringold, H. J., 386
Ritchie, C. D., 458
Ro, R. S., 240
Roberts, J. D., 99, 209, 256, 269, 341, 342, 354, 381, 389, 391, 394, 396, 404, 418, 445, 454, 456, 457, 486, 503, 542, 561, 562, 563, 568

Roberts, T., 232, 254
Robertson, J. M., 32, 385
Robertson, P. W., 402
Robertson, W. W., 410
Robind, J., 409
Robinson, D. Z., 194
Robinson, R., 34, 225, 320, 558
Robinson, R. A., 397
Rochow, E. G., 178, 190
Rodebush, W. H., 127, 512, 518, 529
Rodionov, A., 136
Rogers, M. T., 187, 250, 325, 342, 396, 429, 561
Rogers, V., 453
Rogers-Low, B. W., 34
Rogasch, P. E., 535
Rollefson, R., 201
Roller, G. G., 245
Romming, Chr., 106
Rondestvedt, E., 295
Roof, Jr., R. B., 82
Rose, N. J., 120
Rose, T. J., 105
Rosenberger, M., 388
Rosenblum, M., 89, 95, 98, 99, 548
Rosenkrantz, H., 254
Ross, S. D., 115, 117, 120
Rossmy, G., 533
Rossotti, F. J. C., 65, 66, 126
Rossotti, H., 65, 66
Rouse, P. E., 142
Ruby, A., 472
Ruchardt, C., 568
Rundle, R. E., 106, 132, 133, 135, 163, 538, 541, 579
Rushbrooke, R. S., 392
Rutkin, P., 522
Rutner, E., 224
Ryason, P. R., 525
Rydon, H. N., 414

Sacconi, L., 85, 290
Sadek, F. S., 62
Sadler, M. S., 553
Sadler, P. W., 430, 434
Sager, E. E., 567
Sahney, R. C., 108
Saika, A., 544, 561
Saksena, B. D., 104
Saltrit, J. D., 458
Sam, A., 82
Samres, K., 185
Samuel, D., 469
Sand, D. M., 163, 170
Sanderson, R. T., 178
Sandorfy, C., 188, 496, 542
Sanford, J. K., 394
Sanford, R. A., 296
Santilli, A. A., 544
Sarel, S., 321
Sato, Y., 129
Saunder, D., 162
Saunders, M., 141
Saunders, Jr., W. H., 388, 449
Savard, K., 263
Sawyer, D. T., 78

Sawyer, D. W., 292
Schaeffer, W. D., 169
Schatz, P. N., 194
Schawlow, A. L., 201, 461
Scheibe, G., 433, 449
Schempf, J. M., 433
Schenker, K., 244
Scheraga, H. A., 155
Schiessler, R. W., 161
Schiller, J. C., 118
Schindler, R., 433
Schlapp, R., 72
Schlayer, P. R., 540
Schlenk, H., 163, 170
Schlenk, Jr., W., 161, 170
Schleyer, P. R., 134, 541, 576
Schmeising, H. N., 37, 331
Schmid, E. D., 430
Schmid, R. W., 62
Schmidt, G. M. J., 154
Schmiedel, K., 473
Schneider, H. R., 488
Schneider, W. G., 104, 134, 256, 342, 384, 394, 422, 449, 486
Schomaker, V., 207, 222, 227, 243, 451
Schonbaum, G. R., 567
Schreiber, J., 273
Schreiber, K., 436
Schroeder, R., 49, 131, 134, 468, 541
Schubert, W. M., 399, 405, 409, 410
Schug, J. C., 570
Schuler, D. E., 119
Schuler, R. H., 119
Schultz, R. F., 357
Schumacher, F. A., 501
Schumann, S. C., 231
Schwab, G. M., 365
Schwartz, N. V., 496
Schwarzenbach, G., 62, 378, 383
Schweitzer, G. K., 84
Scoggins, L. E., 428
Scotoni, R., 254
Scott, C. B., 130
Scott, D. W., 301
Scott, R. L., 120
Searcy, A. W., 128
Searles, S., 120, 540, 543
Sears, W. C., 284, 537
Sederholm, C. H., 132, 235, 570
Sehnnert, M. F., 117
Sehon, A. H., 39, 44
Seibold, E. A., 89
Seiffert, W., 449
Seltzer, R., 293
Selwood, P. W., 53, 356, 357
Semenow, D. A., 99
Serres, C., 301
Seshadri, S., 155
Seubold, Jr., F. H., 456
Shackleton, J. W., 359
Shafer, P. R., 568
Shafferman, R., 86
Shah, H. A., 155
Shah, R. C., 155

Shamma, M., 372
Sharman, S. H., 245
Sharpe, A. G., 88, 106
Sharpe, A. N., 407
Shearer, H. M. M., 244
Sheldon, J. C., 105
Sheline, R. K., 189, 398
Shellman, R. W., 565
Shenian, P., 544
Sheppard, N., 223, 235
Sheppard, S. E., 484
Sheratte, M. B., 545
Sheridan, J., 60, 399
Sherman, J., 22, 296
Shilton, R., 483, 555
Shimanouchi, T., 385
Shiner, V. J., 405
Shingu, H., 450
Shoolery, J. N., 190, 493, 553
Shoppee, C. W., 254
Short, D. J., 498
Shorter, J., 425
Shulgin, A. T., 134, 151, 158, 429, 539, 577
Shutts, L. W., 464
Sicher, J., 244, 245
Sidgwick, N. V., 145, 357
Sidman, J. W., 478
Siegel, H., 512
Siegel, S., 301
Siewers, I. J., 567
Sillen, L. G., 66
Silver, M. S., 568
Silverstein, R. M., 375, 553
Sim, G. A., 215
Simkin, D. J., 151
Simonetta, M., 434
Simmons, L. M., 11
Simpson, W. T., 408, 411
Singh, M., 108
Sipos, J. C., 207
Sisler, H. H., 151
Sixma, F. J. L., 394
Skancke, P. N., 32
Skell, P. S., 414, 421
Skinner, D. A., 169
Skinner, H. A., 174
Skita, A., 259, 263
Skorcz, J. A., 116, 409
Slater, J. C., 178
Slifkin, M. A., 116
Sloan, G. L., 365
Smakula, A., 485
Smid, J., 155
Smith, A. E., 161
Smith, B., 123
Smith, B. H., 280
Smith, C., 154
Smith, E. L., 88
Smith, F. A., 529
Smith, H. D., 237
Smith, H. G., 106
Smith, J. C., 232
Smith, J. W., 160, 196, 346
Smith, N. H., 115, 117
Smith, R. P., 396
Smith, S. G., 486

Smith, W. B., 226
Smith, W. R. 277
Smith, W. V., 32
Smutny, E. J., 391
Smyth, C. P., 194, 196, 199, 212. 338
Sneen, R. A., 254
Sneezum, N. S., 381
Sokolov, N. D., 136
Soloway, A. H., 494
Somerbille, A. R., 385
Sondheimer, F. J., 390, 516
Sone, K., 67, 87
Sonnenberg, J., 273, 438, 439
Spackman, D. H., 88
Speakman, J. C., 32, 133
Spence, J. T., 216
Spencer, C. F., 244
Spiesecke, H., 394, 422, 449
Spike, C. G., 85
Spinner, E., 405, 495, 545
Spitzer, R., 235, 290
Spokes, G. N., 552, 567
Sprague, J. W., 117
Spring, F. S., 124, 572
Springall, H. D., 38, 319
Spurr, R. A., 130, 537
Stackelberg, M. von, 165, 166
Stafford, F. E., 55
Stahl, R. E., 280
Stamford, S. C., 131
Staveley, L. A. K., 151
Stearns, E. I., 565
Steckler, B. M., 384
Steel, G., 414, 429
Steinberg, D. H., 522
Steinberg, H., 517
Sten, A., 171
Stern, E. S., 461
Sternberg, H. W., 122
Stevenson, D. P., 222
Stewart, R., 210, 411, 458
Stiles, M., 542, 543, 552, 567
Stillson, G. H., 292
Stock, A. M., 145, 375
Stock, L. M., 394, 402, 403
Stoicheff, B. P., 37, 38
Stolow, R. D., 233
Stone, F. G. A., 100, 301, 457
Straley, J. W., 200
Streitwieser, Jr., A., 116, 186, 210, 381, 389, 434, 445
Strem, M. E., 298
Strohmeier, W., 553
Strömme, K. O., 240, 533
Strother, C. O., 142
Stump, W. E., 401
Sudnorough, J. J., 294
Sugden, S., 344, 395
Sullivan, J. C., 66
Sun, C. E., 180
Sunners, B., 342
Surrey, A. R., 155
Sutcliffe, L. H., 570
Sutherland, G. B. B., 142
Sutton, L. E., 70, 71, 89, 135, 151, 196, 227, 327, 338, 343, 344, 395

Svoboda, M., 244
Swain, C. G., 425
Swedlund, B. E., 402
Sweeney, W. A., 405, 409
Swern, D., 157, 169
Szasz, G. J., 223, 226
Szejtli, J., 165
Szwarc, M., 39, 42, 44, 155

Ta, Y., 11
Taft, Jr., R. W., 151, 186, 327, 338, 394, 404, 406, 414, 419, 420, 421, 424, 427, 433, 515
Tamres, M., 120, 540, 543
Tan, T-L., 455
Tanaka, J., 495
Tannenbaum, H., 189
Tappe, W., 267
Tarbell, D. S., 130, 538
Taube, H., 57, 69
Taufen, H. J., 106
Taylor, A. F., 291
Taylor, D. R., 532
Taylor, M. D., 128, 142, 284
Taylor, P. F., 151
Taylor, R., 394, 405
Tawney, P. O., 554
Tazuma, J. J., 384
Teegan, J. P., 409
Teyssie, Ph., 67
Thael-Stewart, N., 162
Theilacker, W., 302
Thiele, J., 380
Thomas, J. R., 223
Thomas, L. F., 60
Thomas, W. J. O., 180
Thompson, A. R., 400
Thompson, H. B., 276
Thompson, H. W., 33, 106, 120, 125, 154, 166, 254, 414, 429, 528, 536, 539
Thorndike, A. M., 200
Thornton, V., 529
Tiers, G. V. D., 487
Tietz, E., 365
Tildesley, B. D., 106
Tillotson, J. A., 170
Tipper, C. F. H., 326
Titov, E. V., 430
Tkachuk, R., 381
Tobey, S. W., 566
Todd, A. 379
Tolberg, W. E., 111
Tolbert, B. M., 508
Tomboulian, P., 579
Townes, C. H., 191, 201, 461
Trachtenberg, E. N., 426
Trahanovsky, W. S., 548
Trambarula, R. F., 32
Tramposch, O., 543
Traynham, J. G., 117
Trifan, D. S., 134, 577
Trivedi, P. L., 155
Trotter, J., 99, 215, 275, 332, 333, 451, 454
Truce, W. E., 580
Trucker, D. E., 506
Trueblood, K. N., 115, 332

Truter, E. V., 169
Tschamier, H., 497
Tschitschibabin, A. E., 364
Tschugaeff, T., 321
Tsuboi, M., 385
Tsubomura, H., 108, 111, 117, 135
Tsuchida, R., 77, 133
Tsuno, Y., 417
Tuemmler, W. B., 480
Tunnicliff, D. D., 227
Turner, E. E., 277
Turner, R. B., 233, 319, 323, 442, 457
Turner-Jones, A., 34
Tursch, B., 250, 303
Tyler, J. E., 551

Ugi, I., 252
Uma, M., 396
Ungnade, H. E., 511, 536, 576
Utterback, E., 529

Vallance, D. G. M., 105
van Arkel, A. E., 263
Van Beek, L. K. H., 432
Vandenbelt, J. M., 409, 430, 480
Van der Linden, R., 210
van Gulick, N. M., 302
van Kamp, H., 230
Van Panthaleon Van Eck, C. L., 79
van Tamelen, E. E., 458
Van Vleck, J. H., 42, 72
Varech, D., 237
Vatsuro, K., 377
Vaughan, P., 342
Vaughan, W. R., 365
Vavon, G., 155
Veen, A. V., 263
Venkalaraghavan, R., 429
Verhoek, F. H., 81
Verkade, P. E., 263, 424
Verwey, E. J., 129, 135
Viervoll, H., 233
Visser, J., 230
Voigt, A. F., 95
Vosburgh, W. C., 565
Vosburgh, W. G., 149, 237, 541
Voter, R. C., 133, 154

Waack, R., 379
Waddington, G., 232, 319
Wagner, C. D., 454
Wagner, E. C., 139
Wagniere, 441, 503
Wahl, W. H., 432
Waight, E. S., 213, 512
Walborsky, H. M., 436
Walden, P., 356
Walia, J., 256
Walker, L. A., 158
Walker, S., 407
Wall, F. T., 142
Wall, L. A., 577
Wallace, D. J., 495
Wallace, W. J., 111
Walling, C., 120

Walls, W. S., 212
Walsh, A. D., 22, 40, 188, 201, 409, 542, 547
Walter, G. F., 518
Walz, H., 108, 252
Wang, S. M., 124
Wariyar, N. S., 503
Warner, C. M., 496
Waser, J., 451
Watanabe, K., 210, 401
Waugh, J. S., 490
Wawzonek, S., 433
Webb, R. L., 341, 454
Webster, D. E., 402
Wechter, W. J., 280
Weiher, J. F., 95
Weinberg, I., 491
Weinmayr, V., 94
Weinstein, J., 151, 424, 534
Weiss, J., 522
Weiss, N., 262
Weiss-Broday, M., 469
Weissberger, A., 196, 356, 461, 487, 542
Wells, A. J., 200
Weltner, Jr., W., 128, 141
Wender, I., 122
Wenzel, A., 482
Wepster, B. M., 263, 292, 332, 350, 403, 424, 454, 514, 515, 516, 546
Wertz, J. E., 486
Wesson, L. G., 201
West, R., 143, 536, 539, 540, 576, 579
West, R. W., 134
Westenberg, A. A., 59
Westheimer, F. H., 85, 148, 280, 283
Westmoreland, J. S., 424
Westrum, E. F., 133
Wetters, B. D. P., 165
Whatley, L. S., 536, 579
Wheeler, O. H., 456, 470
Wheland, G. W., 309, 310, 319, 336, 444, 447, 451, 454
Whetsel, K. B., 576
Whiffen, D. H., 464, 576
White, D. M., 171
White, E. H., 167
White, H. E., 6
White, T. R., 319
White, W. N., 118, 426
Whitear, B., 381
Whiteman, C., 130
Whiting, M. C., 89
Whitman, G. M., 93
Whitson, J., 359
Wiberg, K. B., 255, 543
Wick, G., 500
Wiegand, Ch., 275
Wilcox, Jr., C. F., 442, 472, 543
Wildi, B. S., 480
Wiley, D. W., 380
Wilkins, R. G., 77
Wilkinson, G., 71, 88, 89, 94, 95, 100
Wilkinson, P. G., 478

Wille, B., 503
Williams, A., 71
Williams, A. E., 63
Williams, E. F., 558
Williams, E. J., 432
Williams, F. V., 169, 291
Williams, G. A., 562
Williams, L. L., 472
Williams, R. J. P., 63, 79, 88
Williams, R. L., 180
Williamson, B., 518
Wilmshurst, J. K., 180, 188, 189
Wilputte-Steinert, L., 424
Wilson, A. M., 266
Wilson, C. L., 111
Wilson, Jr., E. B., 59, 200, 220, 327, 331, 342
Wilson, K. W., 66, 80
Wilson, M. K., 20
Wims, A. I., 191
Windgassen, Jr., R. J., 388, 449
Winkler, R. E., 442
Winmill, T. F., 126
Winstein, S., 240, 256, 269, 273, 424, 434, 436, 438, 439, 442, 486, 520, 525
Winston, A., 548

Witt, O. N., 482
Wittig, G., 62, 341
Wiswesser, W. J., 11
Wolfstirn, K. B., 120
Wolovsky, R., 390
Woods, W. G., 269
Woodward, L. A., 474
Woodward, R. B., 89, 99, 259
Wooley, H. W., 226
Woolfolk, E. O., 122
Wooster, C. B., 357
Wright, G. F., 207
Wulf, O. R., 470, 531
Wyman, G. M., 148, 151, 278, 534
Wynne-Jones, W. F. K., 148

Yabroff, D. L., 393, 412
Yager, B. J., 424
Yamada, H., 120, 471
Yamasaki, K., 67, 87
Yang, N. C., 366
Yankwich, P. E., 562
Yaroslavsky, S., 302
Yasuda, M., 87
Yates, P., 367, 472
Yi, P., 11
Yoe, J. H., 565

Yonezawa, T., 450
Yoshino, T., 237, 255
Young, R. L., 254
Young, W. G., 229, 301, 499, 563
Yukawa, Y., 417

Zagt, R., 394
Zahn, C. T., 223
Zartman, W. H., 296
Zavada, J., 244
Zbinden, R., 472
Zechmeister, L., 503
Zehrung, W. S., 146
Zeil, W., 37
Zeiss, H., 122
Zelinsky, N., 321
Zelokow, J., 321
Zenitz, B. L., 157
Ziegler, K., 356, 357, 360
Ziffer, H., 117, 262
Zimmerman, J. R., 491
Zimmermann, H., 319, 449
Zimmermann, M., 378
Zimmerschield, W. J., 169
Zingaro, R. A., 111
Zuffanti, S., 312
Zumwalt, L. R., 532

SUBJECT INDEX

Absorption of molecular energy, 49–53

Absorption spectra, 460–580; and bond characteristics, 546–547; and electronegativity, 541–544; and hydrogen bonding, 527–541; and intermolecular environment, 510–527; and polarizability, 545–546; and resonance, 493–510; study questions on, 573–580

Accidental discoveries, 88–89

Acetylene, bonding in, 28

Acid dissociation constants: of cyclohexanedicarboxylic acids, 265; and hydrogen bonding, 146–148; and resonance, 350–352

Acid strengths: of halophenols, 397; and solvation effects, 292–294; and steric effects, 292–294

Acrylonitrily, infrared spectrum, 467

Addition reactions: and resonance, 366–368; and steric effects, 296

Adsorption and hydrogen bonding, 150

Alicyclic compounds, spectra of, 519–527

Alicyclic systems, 230–274

Alkylbenzenes: bonding in, 401–412; ionization potentials of, 408; nuclear magnetic resonance shielding parameters for, 411; polarization in, 401ff.; ultraviolet spectra of, 408–411

Alkyl groups: polarizability of, table, 406; polar substituent constants for, 406

Alternant molecules, 392

Amide resonance, 334

Anchimetric assistance, 434

Angles of rotation in benzene derivatives, 284

Angular momentum, 16

Aniline, direction of dipole moment, 206

[18] Annulene, 390ff.

Anthracene, molecular diagrams for, 445, 447

Aromatic character: of [18] annulene, 390–391; of cyclic compounds, 379–392; definition, 379; of 2-π electron rings, 386–387; of 6-π electron rings, 380–386; of 10-π electron rings, 387–390; of 18-π electron rings, 390–391; of ferrocene rings, 90–91; and magnetic susceptibility, 387ff.; of pyrrole rings, 382

Aromatic halogenation, 114

Aromatic substitution, steric effects in, 297–299

Aryl halides: ionization potentials of, 401; ultraviolet spectra of, 399–400

Association: and boiling points, 137–139; of carboxylic acids, 140–143; dipole-dipole, 159–160; of D_2O, 156; through hydrogen bonding, 126

Association constants from spectral measurements, 566–567

Atomic electronegativities, 172–182; by Gordy's covalent boundary potential method, 177; by Mulliken's electroaffinity method, 177; by Pauling's thermochemical method, 174–177; by Rochow's electrostatic method, 178; by Sanderson's stability ratio method, 178–180; table, 179

Atomic energy levels, table, 18

Atomic orbitals, 6–18; $(n + l)$ rule, 11–12; relative energies of, 10–18; s character and electronegativity, 542; shapes, 6–10; study questions on, 58–60

Atoms, excited, 16

Auxochromes, 482

A values of equatorial and axial conformers, 240, 257

Axial haloketone rule, 262

Azulene: electron density in, 450; molecular diagram for, 449; reactivity of, 383

Azumuthal quantum number, 9, 16

Badger's rule, 476

Baeyer strain, 230

Baker-Nathan effect, 321, 402ff.

Barton molecular models, 219

Base dissociation constants: of anilines, table, 355; and B strain, 285ff.; and F strain, 285–291; of haloanilines, 397–398; and resonance, 351ff.

Basicity of ligands and chelate stability, 79–81

Beer-Lambert law, 463

Beer's law, 463

Benzene: bonding in, 30; Dewar structures, 29; molecular orbitals, 30

Benzenoid resonance in chelates, 81–82

Benzophenones, spectral characteristics, Table, 503

Benzyne, 334

Bergmann, 2

Berzelius, 2, 3

Bicyclo [2.2.1] heptanes, 253

Biphenyl: C—C bond dissociation energy, 46; isomerism, 274–278; spectra of derivatives, 511–513

Biphenylene, 451–452

Biradicals, 363–366

Bis-(indenyl)-iron, 98

Bohr magneton, definition, 57

Boiling points of associated and nonassociated compounds, table, 137

Bond angle strain, 230ff.

Bond angles, 20–26; and bond-type, 25; expansion of, 25; measurement of, 32ff.; and molecular orbitals, 20; for ortho substituents, 214

Bond characteristics: and absorption spectra, 546–547; of C—H bonds, 201

Bond contraction, 36–39, 330, 331ff.; in anilines, 332; and resonance 331ff.

Bond deformations in biphenyls, 280–283

Bond dipoles, 199–201; table, 200

Bond dissociation energies, table, 46

Bond distance (see also Bond lengths), 31ff.; and bond order, 336; of C—H bonds in substituted methands, 59; of C-halogen bonds, 400; delocalization effects on, 36; effect of electronegativity on, 36; experimental values, 38; and hybridization, 36–39, 329–330; in hydrogen bonds, 132; and hyperconjugation 326–330; and ligand field theory, 77–78; measurement of, 32ff.; from microwave spectra, 474; study questions on, 58–60; table, 34

Bond energies, 39ff.; bond length–bond energy relationships, 48–49; definition, 40; study questions on, 58–60; table, 48

Bond force constants: and infrared absorption frequencies, 468, 470, 471; from Raman spectra, 475; table, 476; use, 476

Bond length–bond energy relationships, 48–49

Bond lengths (see also Bond distances): in biphenylene, table, 452; and electron delocalization, 329–330; and orbital hybridization, 329–330

Bond moments, 199–201; and carbon hybridization, 202; table, 200

Bond number, 446

Bond order, 335–336, 443–447

Bond strengths: measurement of, 42ff.; from spectroscopy, 42–43

Bond type and bond angle, 25

Bonding: in alkylbenzenes, 401–412; in chelates, 67–86; in cyanogen chloride, 398–399; in halobenzenes, 393–401; historical development, 2–6

Bonds: in chelates, 67–86; chemical, 2; covalent, 6ff.; ion-dipole, 57–58; ionic, 57; polar, 57–58
Borazole, 386
Boron trichloride, bond angles in, 23
Boron trihalides, resonance of, 398
Bouguer-Beer law, 463; for molecular weight determination, 572
Bredt's rule, 270–271
Brode models, 219
Bromotriptycene, 270
B-strain, 285ff.
Butadiene: barrier to internal rotations in, 227; bonding in, 29; molecular diagram for, 447; molecular orbitals in, 29; nonplanar conformations and optical activity, 263
Butlerov, 4
Buttressing effect, 283–284, 513
t-Butyl alcohol, infrared spectrum, 530

Calculated conformer ratios, 264–265
Camphoric acid anhydrides, 271
Camphorquinone, dipole moment of, 206
Canonical set, 444
Carbenes, 366
Carbon: covalent radii, 39; electron distribution 14; energy levels of, 18; ionization potential of, 14; spectroscopic term symbol for, 17; tetrahedral, 5
Carbon dioxide vibrations, 466
Carbonium ions, stabilized by hyperconjugation, 328
Carbonyl compounds: some infrared absorption frequencies, table, 542, 543; spectra, 518–525, table, 525; spectral characteristics, table, 501
Carboxylic acids, hydrogen bonding in, 140–143
Chain induction, 183–186
Charge densities, calculated, 443–452
Charge density and chelate stability, 78–79
Charge distributions and molecular properties, 306–452
Charge-separation in resonance structures, 313
Charge-transfer complexes, 103–125; of aryl halides, 401; in biological systems, 124; bonding in, 103, 105, 106–108; diffraction studies of, 106; dipole moments of, 108; equilibrium with sigma complexes, 111–112; experimental study of, 105–108; of halogens, 112, 114; infrared study of, 106–107; magnetic susceptibility of, 108; of paracyclophanes, 107; physiological action

Charge-transfer complexes (cont.): of, 124–125; relative stability of, table, 114; study questions on, 125; table, 104; ultraviolet spectra and ionization potentials of, 116; ultraviolet study of, 107; uses, 122–125
Chelate stability: and cross conjugation, 83; and electronegativity, 79; and entropy effects, 85; and half-wave redox potentials, 85; and ionization potentials, 79–80; and resonance, 81–84; and steric requirements, 81, 86–88
Chelates, 62–88; bonding in, 67–86; general features, 62–64; infrared spectral characteristics, 548; ionization potentials and stability, 80; methods of study, 64; spectra of, 78; stability of 78–88; study questions on, 102ff.; titration curve for, 66; uses, 62–63, 88
Chelation, by hydrogen bonding, 126, 153
Chemical bonds, 2ff.; coordinate covalent, 60ff.; covalent, 6–58; definition of, 39; ion-dipole, 57–58; ionic, 57; polar, 57–58
Chemical equilibria: and resonance, 349–379; and steric effects, 284–294
Chemical properties: affected by hydrogen bonding, 153–155; and conformational analysis, 266–274; and steric requirements, 294–300
Chlorocamphene, 270
Chloronorbornane, 269
Choleic acids, 162ff.
Cholestanols, 273–274
Cholesterol, 577
Chromate oxidations of cyclohexanols, 273–274
Chromium, spectroscopic term symbol, 17
Chromophores, 482; spectral characteristics, table, 502
Clathrates, 160–171; hydrates, 165ff.
Clathration, 169–170
Cobaltocene, 94, 95
Complexes, spectroscopic study, 564–567
Compression energies and resonance, 315
Concept of resonance, 308–310
Conformation, definition, 217
Conformational analysis: and chemical properties, 266–274; definition, 217; from dipole moments, 258; by electron diffraction, 258; and elimination reactions, 266–269; and esterification, 272; and infrared spectra, 254–255; by infrared spectro-

Conformational analysis (cont.): scopy, 495; from Kerr constants, 265; from melting points, 265; from microwave spectra, 255; from nuclear magnetic resonance spectra, 255–257, 569–570; by the octant rule, 259–263; by optical rotatory dispersion, 259–264; and physical properties, 254–266; from Raman spectra, 255; and rates of solvolysis, 269–271; and reduction of cyclanones, 272–273; by spectroscopy, 569–570; by theoretical calculations, 264–265; from thermochemical measurements, 259; from ultraviolet spectra, 255; by X-ray diffraction, 257
Conformational compositions by physical methods, table, 264
Conformational ratios: in cyclohexanones, 241; and dipole moments, 265
Conformational rule, 265
Conformations: descriptive terms, 218–219; of 1,3-diketones, 219; energy differences, 222ff.; energy differences, table, 224; gauche, 227; s-cis and s-trans, 227
Conjugated systems, linear, 503–505
Conjugation and spectra, 493–519
Coordinate covalent bonds, 60
Coordination number, 24
Cotton effect of butadiene systems, 263; and conformational analysis, 259–263; definition, 259
Coulombic forces in charge-transfer complexes, 103
Couper, 4
Coupled infrared frequencies, 543
Courtauld atomic models, 219
Covalent bonds, 6–58; dissociation energy of, 39; force constants, 39; length-energy relationships for, 48–49; molecular orbitals and, 19; multiple, 26ff; study questions on, 58–60; table of bond distances, 34
Covalent molecules, ionic character of, 191–208
Covalent radii, 31ff.; additivity of, 35; effects of electronegativity on, 36; effects of hybridization on, 37–39; table, 35
Cross conjugation: and chelate stability, 83; and spectra, 502, 505–508
Crystal field splitting of d orbitals, 73
Crystal field stabilization energy, definition, 72
Crystal field theory, 72
Cyanogen chloride, 398–399
Cyclanols, oxidation of, 273–274
Cyclanones; infrared carbonyl

Cyclanones (*cont.*):
  frequencies, *table,* 543; reduction of, 272–273
Cycloalkenes, infrared frequencies, *table,* 543
Cycl[3.2.2]azine, 388–389; molecular diagram for, 449
Cyclobutadiene, 391
Cyclobutane, puckering of ring, 243
Cyclodecane, ring structure, 257–258
Cyclodextrins, 162ff.
Cycloheptatriene, metallocene derivatives of, 100, 101
Cyclohexane: conformational analysis by nuclear, magnetic resonance, 569–570; conformations of, 232ff.; ring strain, 231
Cyclohexanediol acetonide, 238
Cyclohexanediols, 233; bond distance and infrared frequency relationships, 238–239; hydrogen bonding in, 237
Cyclohexanols: conformations of, 259; oxidation of, 273–274
Cyclohexanones: conformations of, 241; and the Cotton effect, 263; reduction of, 272–273; ultraviolet spectra of *e* and *a* conformers, 255
Cyclohexene, oxidation of, 244
Cyclohexyl conformers, infrared frequencies of, 254
Cyclooctatetraene: metallocene derivatives of, 100; structure, 332
Cyclooctene oxide, solvolysis of, 245–247
Cyclopentadiene: covalent derivatives of, 89; Diels-Alder reaction, 90; Grignard reagent, 89; ionic salts of, 89; resonance of its anion, 90, 380ff.
Cyclopentane: conformations of, 232; puckering of ring, 231, 238; ring strain, 231
Cyclopropane, bonding in, 320
Cyclopropenium salts, 387
Cyclopropyl group, hyperconjugation of, 325–326

Dative bond, 61
Decalin, conformations of, 252
Dehalogenation, 228
Dehydro-isoestradiols, 552; infrared spectra, 551
Dehydro-isoestrones, 552; infrared spectra, 550
Delocalization effects: on bond distances, 36, 330–336; in hydrogen bonds, 130–135
Delta bonds, 70
Derived group radii, *table,* 277
Desoxycholic acid, 162
Dewar structures, 29
Diamagnetic susceptibility, study questions on, 59

Diamagnetism, 53
1,3-Diaxial repulsion, 236
Dibenzenechromium, 92
o-Di-t-butylbenzene, 298–299
2,6-Di-t-butylphenols, 299–300; acid strengths, 293–294; alkylation of, 293; free radicals of, 363–366; infrared spectral characteristics, 555ff.
1,2-Dichloroethane: conformations of, 33, 217, 221; energy difference of its conformers, *table,* 223; potential energy diagram, 220
Dielectric constants, 197–198
Diels-Alder reaction, 367
Dienes, ultraviolet spectral characteristics, 556ff.
Diffraction methods, 32ff.
α-Diketones, 373
5,5-Dimethylcyclopentadiene, 89
m-Dinitrobenzene, 333
4,4'-Dinitrobiphenyl inclusion compounds, 164
1,2-Diols, hydrogen bonding in, 139
1,1'-Diphenylazoferrocene, 94
Diphenylbutadiene, spectral characteristics, 513
Diphenylpolyenes, color and ultraviolet bands, *table,* 499
Dipole association, 159–160
Dipole moment: of lone-pair electrons, 207; magnitude, 196
Dipole moments: of some aldehydes, 324; of alkyl and phenyl halides, *table,* 396; of alkylbenzenes, *table,* 406; of aniline compounds, *table,* 348; application of, 208; of benzene derivatives, 205; of charge-transfer complexes, 108; and conformational analysis, 258; of durene compounds, *table,* 347; of halobenzenes, 395–397; of halogen compounds, *table,* 337; and hyperconjugation, 324–326; from infrared spectra, 571; of mesitylene compounds, *table,* 347; of monosubstituted benzenes, *table* 431; of nitriles, *table,* 342; and resonance, 336–344; and structure, 204; study questions on, 208–210; and substituent constants, 432; of substituted alkylbenzenes, *table,* 407; vector addition of, 199–208
Dispersion forces in hydrogen bonds, 135
Dissociation constants: of benzoic acid, 91; and electronegativity, 184–186; of ferrocenedicarboxylic acid, 91
Dissociation energies: of covalent bonds, 40; *table,* 46
Donor character: of ferrocenyl

Donor character (*cont.*):
  groups, 95–96; and hydrogen bond strength, 131
d Orbitals, crystal field splitting, 73
Double-bond character of boron-halogen bonds, 398
Double-bond distances, 34
Dreiding models, 219
Dualistic theory, 3
Dumas, 3
Durene derivatives, dipole moments of, *table,* 347

EDTA, 64–66
Electrical effects in substituted benzenes, 411–434; *table,* 431
Electric dipole moments, 172–208; and hyperconjugation, 324–326
Electromagnetic spectrum, 462–464; *table,* 462
Electron-cloud, 7
Electron configurations, *table,* 12–13
Electron delocalization and bond distances, 329–330
Electron diffraction, 32ff.; and conformational analysis, 258; and conformers of 1,2-dichloroethane, 33
Electron distributions (*see also* Charge distributions) of elements, 14; and ionization potentials, 14; and ligand field stabilization, 76; in metallocenes, 96, 97; study questions on, 58–60
Electronegativities, 172–196; atomic: by Gordy's covalent boundary potential method, 177, by Mulliken's electroaffinity method, 177; by Pauling's thermochemical method, 174–177; by Rochow's electrostatic method, 178; by Sanderson's stability ratio method, 178–180; *table,* 179; group, 182–191; miscellaneous scales of, 180–181; *table,* 179
Electronegativity, 172–196; alternation of, 176ff., 181; of atomic orbitals, 542; and chelate stability, 79; and dissociation constants, 184–186; effects on bond distances, 36; and infrared frequencies, 542ff.; and nuclear magnetic resonance, chemical shifts, 554; and spectra, 541–544; structural effects on, 181; study questions on, 208–210; units of, 182
Electron impact measurements, 43
2-π Electron rings, 386–387
6-π Electron rings, aromatic character of, 380–386
10-π Electron rings, 387–390
18-π Electron rings, 390–391
Electron shielding, 18

Electron shifts and resonance structures, 311
Electron spin, 9, 16
Electronic transitions, 477–479, 484
Electrophilic nitration of monosubstituted benzenes, *table,* 431
Electrophilic substituent constants, 416; *table,* 415
Electrophilic substitution: in chelates, 82; in ferrocene, 92; in ferrocenyl groups, 95; in halobenzenes, 393–394
Electrostatic forces in hydrogen bonds, 129–130
Electrostatic repulsion and conformational ratios, 265
Elements: electron configuration, *table,* 12; energy levels of, *table,* 18; ionization potentials of, 14–15
Elimination reactions and conformational analysis, 266–269
Empirical formulas, spectroscopic determination of, 565–567
Energies: bond dissociation, *table,* 46; bond, *table,* 48; of hydrogen bonds, *table,* 128
Energy: conversion chart, 51, 52; diagram for *d* orbitals in crystal field, 73; diagram for molecules, 50; diagram for octahedral ligand field, 74; ligand field stabilization chart, 76; molecular absorption of, 49–53; quantized, 49; units, 52
Energy barrier: to chair-chair transformations of cyclohexane, 234; to internal rotations, 221, 223, 569, *table,* 226; in *s-cis* and *s-trans* isomers, 227
Energy difference: of cyclohexane conformers, 233; of 1,2-dichloroethane conformers, 223
Energy levels, 11; atomic, *table,* 18; of elements, 16
Energy states, diagram, 50
Enol content: of acetoacetic esters, *table,* 371, 375; of aroylacetates, *table,* 376; of cyclanones, 378, 379; of 1,3-diketones, *table,* 375; of simple ketones, 378
Enol-imines, 374
Enol-ketone equilibrium (*see also* Keto-enol equilibrium), 368ff.
Enols: of α-diketones, 373; of β-diketones, 369ff.; infrared absorption frequencies, *table,* 533
α,β-Enones, ultraviolet characteristics, 556ff.
Enthalpy differences of *e* and *a* conformations, 240
Enthalpy values of *e* and *a* conformers, 257
Entropy effects: on chelate stability, 85; on keto-enol equilibrium, 376ff.
Erythro isomers, definition, 224–225

Ester group resonance, 334
Esterification: and conformational analysis, 272; and steric requirements, 294–296
Ethyl acetoacetyl boronite, 86
Ethyl alcohol, nuclear magnetic resonance spectrum of, 491
Ethylchlorobenzenes, infrared spectra of, 549
Ethylene: bonding in, 26; reduction, 367
Ethylene glycol, conformations of, 228
Experimental methods: to study association of carboxylic acids, 142; to study charge-transfer complexes, 119

Fajan's rule, 195–196
Ferricinium ions, 92
Ferrocene: aromatic character, 90–91; bonding in, 91; derivatives, chart of, 93, 94; discovery, 89; properties of, 90
Ferrocenedicarboxylic acids, 91
Ferrocenyl ruthenocenyl ketone, 93
Ferromagnetism, 55
Force constants, 40; of C—H bonds in substituted methands, 59; in cyanogen halides, 399
Formal charges, definition, 61; in resonance structures, 314
Formation constants of chelates, 65–67
Frankland, 4
Free radicals: measurement of, 356–357; relative stabilities of, 362; resonance stabilization of, 355–366; steric effects on stability, 363, 366
Free rotation, 217
Free valence, 443–449
F-Strain, 285–291
Fulvalene, 89

Geometric isomerism of metallocenes, 99
1,2-Glycols, infrared frequency-O···H distance relationships, 238–239
Gmelin, 3
Group electronegativities, 182–191; from acid dissociation constants, 183–186; from cleavage of mercurials, 182; from dipole moments, 183; from infrared absorption frequencies, 188–189; from infrared absorption intensities, 187–188; from nuclear magnetic resonance shielding parameters, 190–191; from polar substituent constants, 186; and properties, 191; *table,* 192–193

Hakala's empirical rule, 12–13
Half-chair conformation of cyclopentane, 232

Half-wave redox potentials: and chelate stability, 85; for halobenzenes, 395
Haloanilines, base strengths, 397–398
Halobenzenes: bonding in, 393–401; chemical reactivity, 393–394; dipole moments of, 395–397; half-wave reduction potentials of, 395; ultraviolet spectral characteristics, *table,* 545
Halogens, polarizability of, *table,* 400
Halophenols: acid strengths, 397; *cis-trans* isomerism, 532; hydrogen bonding in, 147; infrared frequencies, 532
Hammett equation, 412–434
Hammett sigma constants: in halobenzenes, 394; and oxidation potentials of ferrocene derivatives, 98; and stability of charge-transfer complexes, 116; *table,* 415
Hammett-type equations: applications, 424–428; study questions on, 453–458
Harmonic overtones, 469ff.; *table,* 470
Heat of atomization, 41–42
Heats of combustion, 45–47, 49, 50; of methane, 46; and resonance energies, 317–319; and ring strain, 230–231; *table,* for cycloalkanes, 231
Heats of formation, 47; of charge-transfer complexes, 120–121; *table,* 48
Heats of hydrogenation: and hyperconjugation, 322ff.; and resonance energies, 317–318; *table,* 318; *table,* 323
Heptafulvene, 379–380
Heptalene, 392
Hexaarylethanes, 358ff.
Hexamethylacetylacetone, 88
Hexaphenylethane, C—C bond dissociation energy of, 46
Hindered phenols, infrared spectral characteristics, 555ff.
Hindered rotations: and isomerism, 274–284; and optical activity, 279
Hirschfelder-Taylor models, 219
Historical development of structural and electronic theories, 2–6
Homoallylic systems, 435
Homoaromatic, 439ff.
Homoconjugation, 434–442; and spectra, 519ff.
Hückel rule, 380ff.
Hybrid orbitals, 22ff.; directional character, 22, 24
Hybridization, 21–26; and bond distances, 329–330; and bond

Hybridization (*cont.*):
moments, 202; of bond orbitals, 21; and covalent radii, 37; effect on bond distances, 36–39

Hydrogen bonding: and acid dissociation constants, 146–148; and adsorption, 150; and base strengths, 291–292; and boiling points, 137–139; in cyclohexanediols, 237; and dyeing, 150; effect on ultraviolet spectra, 527–528; and keto-enol equilibria, 369ff.; and melting points, 139; and physical properties, *table,* 154; and spectra, 527–541; and stereoisomerism, 148–150; and sublimation, 139, 145; and water solubility, 143–146; and wet-melting points, 145–146; in vapors, 140–143

Hydrogen bonds: bifurcated, 135; in biological systems, 155; and chemical properties, 153–155; contributions to energy of, *table,* 136; and dispersion forces, 135; distances, 132; effect on infrared spectra, 528–541; energies, *table,* 128; energy and acid strengths, 142; general description, 125–127; historical development, 127; infrared frequency shifts and acid strengths, 540; infrared frequency shifts and base strengths, 539ff.; nature of the bonding forces, 127–136; and physical properties, 136–153; in proteins, 149; and repulsive forces, 135–136; strength and infrared frequencies, 538ff.; study questions on, 156–158; symmetrical, 133

Hydrogen sulfide bond angles, 20, 21

Hydrolysis of alkyl halides, 289–290

Hyperconjugation, 320–330; in alkylbenzenes, 401–412; and bond distances, 326–330; and carbonium ion stability, 328; and C—C bonds, 328; and dipole moments, 324–326; and heats of hydrogenation, 322ff.; and ionization potentials, 323–324; and spectra, 498, 501

Inclusion compounds, 160–171; dimensional requirements, 161–167; general properties, 167–168; uses, 168–171

Index of refraction, 198

Induced dipole moments, 196ff.

Induced dipoles, 197

Induced magnetism, 55

Induction, chain, 183–186

Infrared absorption bands and charge-transfer complexes, 471

Infrared absorption frequencies: (*see also* Infrared frequencies), alternation with position, 473; alternation with ring size, 543; and bond force constants, 468, 470–471; for carbon dioxide, 466, doublets, 471–472; and group electronegativities, 188–189; harmonic overtones, 469ff.; mechanical analog, 464–466, 472; for methyl chloride, 467; of methylene groups, 466; of some carbonyl compounds, *table,* 542, 543; *table,* 465

Infrared absorption intensities and group electronegativities, 187–188

Infrared frequencies: (*see also* Infrared absorption frequencies) and acid strengths, 496; of *cis-trans* isomers, 573; and electronegativity, 542ff.; and hydrogen bond strengths, 538ff.; isotope effect, 469; and resonance, 493–495; of some carbonyl compounds, *table,* 496; of some enols, *table,* 533; of some hydrogen bonds, *table,* 529; of some phenols, *table,* 496, 497; of substituted acetic acids, *table,* 538; *table,* 494

Infrared frequency shifts: and basicity, 539ff.; and bond characteristics, 541; and hydrogen bonding, 529ff., 535ff.; and solvent effects, 535ff.

Infrared spectra, 464–474; and conformational analysis, 254–255; correlation with substituent constants, 429–430; effects of hydrogen bonding, 528–541; of ethylchlorobenzenes, 549; near infrared region, 470; of the penicillins, 558–560; solvent effect, 535ff.; steric effects, 536ff.; and steric hindrance, 525–526

Infrared spectral characteristics of chelates, 548; of 2,6-di-t-butylphenols, 555ff.

Infrared spectroscopy: and conformational analysis, 495; determination of charge-transfer equilibrium constants, 120; distinction of inter- and intramolecular hydrogen bonding, 534ff.; study questions on, 573–580

Induction in alkylbenzenes, 401ff.

Induction and resonance moments, 343ff.

Induction substituent constants, 418–422; and nuclear magnetic resonance chemical shifts, 430; *table,* 415, 420

Inductive effect: in halobenzenes, 393–401; on keto-enol equilibria, 375ff.

Inner orbital bonding, 70

Interaction resonance, 344ff.

Interaction resonance moments, *table,* 345

Intermolecular coordinate covalent bonds, 88, 91

Internal energy, 49–52

Internal rotations: study by nuclear magnetic resonance spectroscopy, 255–257; thermodynamic method of study, 221

Intramolecular environment and spectra, 510–527

Intramolecular forces, 212–304; van der Waals, 212–215

Intramolecular hydrogen bonds: in aliphatic amines, 134; in dicarboxylic acids, 133

Ionic bonds, 57

Ionic character: of covalent molecules, 191–208; and electronegativities, 194; and melting points, 348–349; and polarization, 195–196; and resonance, 336–349

Ionic radius and chelate formation, 87

Ionization constants from spectroscopic measurements, 566–567

Ionization of triphenylmethyl chlorides, 403

Ionization potentials, 14–15, 18; of alkylbenzenes, 408; of aryl halides, 401; and charge-transfer stability, 115; and chelate stability, 80; and electron distributions, 14; and hyperconjugation, 323–324; measurement from spectra of charge-transfer complexes, 116; *table,* 14, 80; of transition metals, 80

Ion-radicals, 121

Isomerism: and hindered rotations, 274–284; spectroscopic study, 569–570

Isotope effect of infrared frequencies, 469

Isotopic exchange in sigma complexes, 110–111

Isovalent resonance, 314–315; in aniline, 332

Kehrmann, 5

Kekule, 4

Kekule structures, 29ff.; of benzene, 308

Kerr constants and conformational analysis, 265

Ketamines, 374

Ketimines, 374

Keto-enol equilibrium, 368ff.; effect of resonance on, 369ff.; and hydrogen bonding, 369ff.; infrared spectral analysis, 552ff.; nuclear magnetic resonance, spectral analysis, 553–554

Ketyls, 362

Klyne-Prelog conformational terms, 219

Kolbe, 3

Lavoisier, 2

LeBel, 5

Liebig, 3

Ligand field stabilization energies, chart, 76

Ligand field theory, 5, 72–78

Ligands, basicity of, and chelate stability, 79–81

Linearly conjugated systems, spectra of, 503–505

Localization energy, 450ff.

Localization theory, 450

Logarithmic method of spectral analysis, 566ff.

Magnetic quantum number, 9, 16

Magnetic susceptibility, 53–57; and aromatic character, 387ff.; of charge-transfer complexes, 108; of cyclic compounds, *table*, 387; experimental measurements, 55–56; Pascal's constants, 54

Medium-size rings and ring strain, 251

Melting points: and conformational analysis, 265; and ionic character, 348–349

Menthene, 267

Menthol, 236, 272

Menthone, 272

Menthyl chloride, 267

Mesitylene derivatives and dipole moments, *table*, 347

Mesomerism, 308

Metacyclophanes, 249; nuclear magnetic resonance spectra, 527

Metal hydride reductions and conformational analysis, 272–273

Metallocenes, 88–102; aromatic character of, 90–91, 95; bonding in, 96–97; free rotation in, 99; geometric isomerism, 99; ionic, 94; study questions on, 102

Method of continuous variations of spectral analysis, 565ff.

Methyl chloride infrared frequencies, *table*, 467

Methylene, 366

Methylene group vibrations, 466

Methylphosphines, relative base strengths, 289

Meyer, Victor, 5

Microwave spectra, 473–474; and conformational analysis, 255

Mobile bond orders, 444

Mobile electrons, 27

Modern structural theory of organic chemistry, 306–308

Molar ratio of spectral analysis, 565ff.

Molecular absorption of energy, 49–53

Molar absorptivities of some sterically hindered compounds, *table*, 514

Molecular addition compounds (*see also* Charge-transfer compounds), 103

Molecular bonds, 88–125; in charge-transfer complexes, 103; in metallocenes, 88ff.

Molecular diagrams, 445, 447ff.

Molecular models, 218–219

Molecular orbital method, 445ff.

Molecular orbitals, 19ff.; antibonding, 27; in benzene, 30; dicentric, 28; polycentric, 28; study questions on, 58–60

Molecular orbital theory of bonding in chelates, 71

Molecular parameters from spectral measurements, 570–572

Molecular properties and charge distributions, 306–452

Molecular sieves, 167

Molecular weight determinations by ultraviolet spectroscopy, 122–123, 572

Moment of inertia and microwave spectroscopy, 473–474

Multiplicity, 17; and resonance, 312

Multiple bonds, energies, 48

Naphthalene, molecular diagrams of, 445, 447

Near infrared region of the spectrum, 470

Neighboring group participation, 269

Neomenthyl chloride, 267

Newman projection formulas, 218; of cyclohexane, 235

Nickel acetylacetone, 69

Nickel bis-(α,α'-dipyridyl) ion, 69

Nickel(II) cyanide ion, 69

Nickel ethylenediamine ion, 70

Nickelocene, 94

Nickel tetracarbonyl, 70

Nitrobenzene, molecular diagram, 448

($n + l$) rule, 11–12

Nobel, Alfred, 88

Nobel award winners, 4

Nodal plane, 26

Nonalternant molecules, 392

Nonbonding intermolecular forces, 158–171

Nonbonding repulsion, 25, 214

Nonclassical carbonium ions, 434ff.

Nonclassical resonance, 434–442

Nuclear magnetic resonance chemical shifts: of e and a protons, 256; and electronegativity, 544; of functional groups, *table*, 561; for monosubstituted benzenes, *table*, 431

Nuclear magnetic resonance coupling constants for C—H bonds, *table*, 544

Nuclear magnetic resonance shielding parameters, 488ff.; in alkylbenzenes, 411; and group electronegativities, 190–191; for halobenzenes, 394

Nuclear magnetic resonance spectra, 486–493; anisotropic effects, 489ff.; of aryl protons, 526–527; chemical shifts, 488ff.; and conformational analysis, 255–257; correlation with substituent constants, 430–432; and induction substituent constants, *table*, 420; spin-spin interactions, 490ff.

Nuclear magnetic resonance spectral characterization, 560ff.

Nuclear magnetic resonance spectroscopy and conformational analysis of cyclohexanes, 569–570; study questions on, 573–580

Nucleophilic substituent constants, 416–417, *table*, 415

Octalins, 247

Octant rule and conformational analysis, 259–263

Octet rule, 312

Optical activity: of biphenyls, 276–284; and hindered rotation, 279

Optical rotation and conformational analysis, 259–264

Optical rotatory dispersion and conformational analysis, 259ff.

Orbital, antibonding, 19, 27

Orbital hybridization and bond distances, 329–330

Orbitals: atomic, 6–18; available, and chelate stability, 79; bonding, 19; d type, 8; degenerate, 7; hybrid, 22ff.; molecular, 19; p type, 7; pi type, 19; s type, 7; sigma, 19; sp hybrid, 23ff.; sp^2 hybrid, 23ff., 26; sp^3 hybrid, 21

Organic chemistry: definition, 3; historical development, 2–6

Orthocyclophanes, nuclear magnetic resonance spectra, 527

Ortho effects in aromatic substitution, 297–299

Ortho substituents and bond angles, 214–215

Oscillator strength, 484

Outer orbital bonding, 70

π-Overlap and spectra, 519ff.

Oxidation: of benzidines, 278; of cyclanols, 273–274; of 2,6-di-t-butylphenols, 299–300

Oxine, 66, 87

Paracyclophanes, 107, 250, 518; nuclear magnetic resonance spectra, 527

Paramagnetism, 55; of charge-transfer complexes, 121

Para-ortho conversion of hydrogen, 365

Partial rate factors for halobenzenes, 394

Partition functions, 570

Pascal's constants, *table*, 54

Pauli exclusion principle, 9

Penicillins, spectral characterization, 558–560

Pentalene, 388

Pentalenyl anion, 388

Pentaphenyl phosphorus, 62, 340

Per cent double-bond character, 336–337, *table*, 337

Permanent dipole moments, 196–208

Peterson models, 219

Phosphorus ylenes, 340–341, 385

Photodesmotic band, 520ff.

Physical properties: and conformational analysis, 254–266; correlation with substituent constants, 428–434

Pi bonding, 27, in chelates, 71, 84

Pi bonds, 26, in chelates, 71

Pi complexes, 103

Picrates, 117

Picryl iodide, 334

Pi electrons, 26–27; and hydrogen bonds, 134

Pinenes, infrared spectra, 551

Pi orbitals, 26

Pitzer strain, 231ff., in cyclobutane rings, 243

Polar bonds, 57–58

Polar character of various classes of compounds, 159

Polar forces: in cyclohexane derivatives, 237; in cyclohexanones, 241

Polarizabilities, *table*, 199

Polarizability: of alkyl groups, *table*, 406; and charge-transfer complex stability, 115; electric, 197; of halogens, *table*, 400; and spectra, 545–546

Polarization: in alkylbenzenes, 401–412; of anions, 195; effect on ultraviolet spectra, 481ff.

Polarographic reduction of halobenzenes, 395

Polar substituent constants, 423ff.; for alkyl groups, 406; and group electronegativities, 186–187; *table*, 415

Polymerization in inclusion compounds, 171

Porphyrin ring, 84, 391

Potential energy, definition, 49

Potential energy diagram, 468

Process control by spectroscopy, 572–573

Product development control, 272

Pseudo-aromatic molecules, 392

Pyridine oxide, molecular diagram, 448

Pyrolysis of cyclic quarternary ammonium salts, 251

Pyrolytic eliminations and conformational analysis, 268

Pyrrole, molecular diagram, 448

Qualitative analysis by spectroscopy, 547ff.

Quantitative analysis by spectroscopy, 547–554; of multicomponent systems, 549–550

Quantum mechanics, 25, for charge-transfer complexes, 108–109

Quantum numbers, 9–10, 16

Quantum symbols, 16

Quinols, 165ff.

Racemization of biphenyls, 277–284

Raman spectra, 474–477; and conformational analysis, 255

Rare gas electron structures in metallocenes, 96

Rates of racemization, 277–283

Rates of reactions of diastereoisomers, 229

Reaction intermediates, spectroscopic detection, 567–568

Reaction kinetics, spectroscopic measurement, 567–568

Reaction mechanisms and substituent constants, 424ff.

Reactivity of alkyl benzenes, 405, *table*, 402

Redox potentials and substituent constants, 433

Reduction of cyclanones and conformational analysis, 272–273

Reduction potentials of conformers, 266

Relative acid strengths by infrared frequency shifts, 540

Relative base strengths: of amines and ammonia, 288ff.; by infrared frequency shifts, 539ff.; of pyridine derivatives, 286ff.; and solvation effects, 290–292

Relative stability: of *cis-trans* cycloolefins, 251; of cyclic geometric isomers, 236; of *e* and *a* isomers, 240ff.

Repulsive forces, 214, in hydrogen bonds, 135–136

Resolution of mixtures: by charge-transfer complexation, 123–124; by inclusion compound formation, 169–170

Resolution of racemates by charge-transfer complexation, 123

Resonance, 25, 308–453; and acid dissociation constants, 350–352; and addition reactions, 366–368; analogies, 309–310; and base strengths, 351ff.; and bond contraction, 331ff.; of boron trihalides, 398; in charge-transfer complexes, 103, 109; and chelate stability, 81–84; and chemical equilibria, 349–379; and coplanarity, 331ff.; of cyanogen chloride, 398; of cyclooctatetraene, 332; of cyclopentadienyl anion, 90; and dipole moments, 336–344; energies, 317–319, *table*, 319; and free radical formation, 355–366; in halobenzenes, 393–401; in hydrogen bond model, 130; and infrared frequencies,

Resonance (*cont.*):

493–495; and ionic character, 336–349; and the keto-enol equilibrium, 369ff.; moments, 341; in polyenes, 503; in sigma complexes, 116–117; and spatial configuration, 330–336; and spectra, 493–510; study questions on, 453–458; and ultraviolet spectra, 497–510

Resonance hybrid, definition, 308

Resonance moments, 341, 343ff.; for halogens, 395; *table*, 343

Resonance structures, 310–316

Resonance substituent constants, 418–422; and nuclear magnetic resonance chemical shifts, 430; *table*, 415

Resonance vs tautomerism, 310

Ring size, definition of terms, 230

Ring strain, 230ff.; in C$_{10}$ rings, 243–244; in cyclodecanes, 257–258; and hydride shifts, 244–247, 248; in medium-size rings, 251–252; and transannular electrophilic substitution, 247–249; and transannular nucleophilic substitution, 249–251

Rules on resonance, 310–316

Sandwich compounds, 88, 90, 103ff.

Schrödinger, 7

Semi-ionic bond, 61

Semipolar bond, 61

Sigma complexes, 109–125; color of, 110; difference between, and charge-transfer complexes, 110; electrical conductivity of, 110; isotopic exchange in, 110–111; *table* of relative stabilities, 114

Simmons' empirical rule, 12–13

Single bond: distances, 34, 36, 37, 38; energies, 48

Slope ratio method of spectroscopic analysis, 565

Solvation: and acid strengths, 292–294; and relative base strengths, 290–292

Solvation effects on reactivity of alkylbenzenes, 406ff.

Solvent effect: on ultraviolet absorption spectra, 485–486; and keto-enol equilibria, 374ff., *table*, 375

Solvolysis: and conformational analysis, 269–271; of norbornenyl compounds, 436ff.

Spatial configuration and resonance, 330–336

Spectra: and chelate stability, 78; conversion of units, 52; origin, 464; regions of, 51; types, 52

Spectra-structure relationships, 493–547; bond characteristics and spectra, 546–547; electronegativity and spectra, 541–544; hydrogen bonding and spectra, 527–541; intramolecular environ-